About the author

Philip José Farmer's revolutionary impact on
the science fiction scene was felt with the
appearance of his early novella *The Lovers*.
Since then Mr Farmer's work has been noted
for its open-minded thought, its humane
compassion and its superb craftmanship. With
such stories as the *Carmody* and *Riverworld*
series, with such extraordinary novels as
Flesh, with his Hugo Award-winning short
novel *Riders of the Purple Wage*, and with this
trilogy *The World of the Tiers* – which
includes *Maker of Universes*, *The Gates of
Creation* and *A Private Cosmos* – Philip José
Farmer has shown a talent of the very first
rank in science fiction and fantasy.
Mr Farmer was born in Peoria, Illinois, lived
for many years in Los Angeles, and has
recently returned with his wife to Illinois.

*Also by Philip José Farmer and available
from Sphere books*

THE GATES OF CREATION

A PRIVATE COSMOS

THE ALLEY GOD

BEHIND THE WALLS OF TERRA

THE MAKER OF UNIVERSES

The Maker of Universes

PHILIP JOSÉ FARMER

SPHERE BOOKS LIMITED
30/32 Gray's Inn Road, London WC1X 8JL

First published in Great Britain
by Sphere Books Ltd 1970
Reprinted December 1973
Reprinted February 1975
Copyright © Philip José Farmer 1965

Set in Linotype Times

Printed in Great Britain by
Hazell Watson & Viney Ltd
Aylesbury, Bucks

ISBN 0 7221 3444 4

CHAPTER ONE

The ghost of a trumpet call wailed from the other side of the doors. The seven notes were faint and far off, ectoplasmic issue of a phantom of silver, if sound could be the stuff from which shades are formed.

Robert Wolff knew that there could be no horn or man blowing upon it behind the sliding doors. A minute ago, he had looked inside the closet. Nothing except the cement floor, the white plasterboard walls, the clothes rod and hooks, a shelf and a lightbulb was there.

Yet he had heard the trumpet notes, feeble as if singing from the other wall of the world itself. He was alone, so that he had no one with whom to check the reality of what he knew could not be real. The room in which he stood entranced was an unlikely place in which to have such an experience. But he might not be an unlikely person to have it. Lately, weird dreams had been troubling his sleep. During the day, strange thoughts and flashes of images passed through his mind, fleeting but vivid and even startling. They were unwanted, unexpected, and unresistable.

He was worried. To be ready to retire and then to suffer a mental breakdown seemed unfair. However, it could happen to him as it had to others, so the thing to do was to be examined by a doctor. But he could not bring himself to act as reason demanded. He kept waiting, and he did not say anything to anybody, least of all to his wife.

Now he stood in the recreation room of a new house in the Hohokam Homes development and stared at the closet doors. If the horn bugled again, he would slide a door back and see for himself that nothing was there. Then, knowing that his own diseased mind was generating the notes, he would forget about buying this house. He would ignore his wife's hysterical protests, and he would see a medical doctor first and then a psychotherapist.

His wife called: "Robert! Haven't you been down there long enough? Come up here. I want to talk to you and Mr. Bresson!"

"Just a minute, dear," he said.

She called again, so close this time that he turned around. Brenda Wolff stood at the top of the steps that led down to the recreation room. She was his age, sixty-six. What beauty she had once had was now buried under fat, under heavily rouged and powdered wrinkles, thick spectacles, and steel-blue

7

hair. He winced on seeing her, as he winced every time he looked into the mirror and saw his own bald head, deep lines from nose to mouth, and stars of grooved skin radiating from the reddened eyes. Was this his trouble? Was he unable to adjust to that which came to all men, like it or not? Or was what he disliked in his wife and himself not the physical deterioration but the knowledge that neither he nor Brenda had realized their youthful dreams? There was no way to avoid the rasps and files of time on the flesh, but time had been gracious to him in allowing him to live this long. He could not plead short duration as an excuse for not shaping his psyche into beauty. The world could not be blamed for what he was. He and he alone was responsible; at least he was strong enough to face that. He did not reproach the universe or that part of it that was his wife. He did not scream, snarl, and whine as Brenda did.

There had been times when it would have been easy to whine or weep. How many men could remember nothing before the age of twenty? He thought it was twenty, for the Wolffs, who had adopted him, had said that he'd looked that age. He had been discovered wandering in the hills of Kentucky, near the Indiana border, by old man Wolff. He had not known who he was or how he had come there. Kentucky or even the United States of America had been meaningless to him, as had all the English tongue.

The Wolffs had taken him in and notified the sheriff. An investigation by the authorities had failed to identify him. At another time, his story might have attracted nationwide attention; however, the nation had been at war with the Kaiser and had had more important things to think about. Robert, named after the Wolff's dead son, had helped work on the farm. He had also gone to school, for he had lost all memory of his education.

Worse than his lack of formal knowledge had been his ignorance of how to behave. Time and again he had embarrassed or offended others. He had suffered from the scornful or sometimes savage reaction of the hill-folk, but had learned swiftly – and his willingness to work hard, plus his great strength in defending himself, had gained respect.

In an amazingly quick time, as if he had been relearning, he had studied and passed through grade and high school. Although he had lacked by many years the full time of attendance required, he had taken and passed the entrance examinations to the university with no trouble. There he'd begun his lifelong love affair with the classical languages. Most of all he loved Greek, for it struck a chord within him; he felt at home with it.

After getting his Ph.D. at the University of Chicago, he had

8

taught at various Eastern and Midwestern universities. He had married Brenda, a beautiful girl with a lovely soul. Or so he had thought at first. Later, he had been disillusioned, but still he was fairly happy.

Always, however, the mystery of his amnesia and his origin had troubled him. For a long time it had not disturbed him, but then, on retiring . . .

"Robert," Brenda said loudly, "come up here right now! Mr. Bresson is a busy man."

"I'm certain that Mr. Bresson has had plenty of clients who like to make a leisurely surveillance," he replied mildly. "Or perhaps you've made up your mind you don't want the house?"

Brenda glared at him, then waddled indignantly off. He sighed because he knew that, later, she would accuse him of deliberately making her look foolish before the real estate agent.

He turned to the closet doors again. Did he dare open them? It was absurd to freeze there, like someone in shock or in a psychotic state of indecision. But he could not move, except to give a start as the bugle again vented the seven notes, crying from behind a thick barricade but stronger in volume.

His heart thudded like an inward fist against his breast bone. He forced himself to step up to the doors and to place his hand within the brass-covered indentation at waist-level and shove the door to one side. The little rumble of the rollers drowned out the horn as the door moved to one side.

The white plaster boards of the wall had disappeared. They had become an entrance to a scene he could not possibly have imagined, although it must have originated in his mind.

Sunlight flooded in through the opening, which was large enough for him to walk through if he stooped. Vegetation that looked something like trees – but no trees of Earth – blocked part of his view. Through the branches and fronds he could see a bright green sky. He lowered his eyes to take in the scene on the ground beneath the trees. Six or seven nightmare creatures were gathered at the base of a giant boulder. It was of red, quartz-impregnated rock and shaped roughly like a toadstool. Most of the things had their black furry, misshapen bodies turned away from him, but one presented its profile against the green sky. Its head was brutal, subhuman, and its expression was malevolent. There were knobs on its body and on its face and head, clots of flesh which gave it a half-formed appearance, as if its Maker had forgotten to smooth it out. The two short legs were like a dog's hind legs. It was stretching its long arms up toward the young man who stood on the flat top of the boulder.

This man was clothed only in a buckskin breechcloth and

9

moccasins. He was tall, muscular, and broad-shouldered; his skin was sun-browned; his long thick hair was a reddish bronze; his face was strong and craggy with a long upper lip. He held the instrument which must have made the notes Wolff had heard.

The man kicked one of the misshapen things back down from its hold on the boulder as it crawled up toward him. He lifted the silver horn to his lips to blow again, then saw Wolff standing beyond the opening. He grinned widely, flashing white teeth. He called, "So you finally came!"

Wolff did not move or reply. He could only think, *Now I have gone crazy! Not just auditory hallucinations, but visual! What next? Should I run screaming, or just calmly walk away and tell Brenda that I have to see a doctor now? Now! No waiting, no explanations. Shut up, Brenda, I'm going.*

He stepped back. The opening was beginning to close, the white walls were reasserting their solidity. Or rather, he was beginning to get a fresh hold on reality.

"Here!" the youth on top of the boulder shouted. "Catch!"

He threw the horn. Turning over and over, bouncing sunlight off the silver as the light fell through the leaves, it flew straight toward the opening. Just before the walls closed in on themselves, the horn passed through the opening and struck Wolff on his knees.

He exclaimed in pain, for there was nothing ectoplasmic about the sharp impact. Through the narrow opening he could see the red-haired man holding up one hand, his thumb and index forming an O. The youth grinned and cried out, 'Good luck! Hope I see you soon! I am Kickaha!'"

Like an eye slowly closing in sleep, the opening in the wall contracted. The light dimmed, and the objects began to blur. But he could see well enough to get a final glimpse, and it was then that the girl stuck her head around the trunk of a tree.

She had unhumanly large eyes, as big in proportion to her face as those of a cat. Her lips were full and crimson, her skin golden-brown. The thick wavy hair hanging loose along the side of her face was tiger-striped: slightly zigzag bands of black almost touched the ground as she leaned around the tree.

Then the walls became white as the rolled-up eye of a corpse. All was as before except for the pain in his knees and the hardness of the horn lying against his ankle.

He picked it up and turned to look at it in the light from the recreation room. Although stunned, he no longer believed that he was insane. He had seen through into another universe and something from it had been delivered to him—why or how, he did not know.

The horn was a little less than two and a half feet long and

10

weighed less than a quarter of a pound. It was shaped like an African buffalo's horn except at the mouth, where it flared out broadly. The tip was fitted with a mouthpiece of some soft golden material; the horn itself was of silver or silver-plated metal. There were no valves, but on turning it over he saw seven little buttons in a row. A half-inch inside the mouth was a web of silvery threads. When the horn was held at an angle to the light from the bulbs overhead, the web looked as if it went deep into the horn.

It was then the light also struck the body of the horn so that he saw what he had missed during his first examination: a hieroglyph was lightly inscribed halfway down the length. It looked like nothing he had seen before, and he was an expert on all types of alphabetic writing, ideographs, and pictographs.

"Robert!" his wife said.

"Be right up, dear!" He placed the horn in the right-hand front corner of the closet and closed the door. There was nothing else he could do except to run out of the house with the horn. If he appeared with it, he would be questioned by both his wife and Bresson. Since he had not come into the house with the horn, he could not claim it was his. Bresson would want to take the instrument into his custody, since it would have been discovered on property of his agency.

Wolff was in an agony of uncertainty. How could he get the horn out of the house? What was to prevent Bresson from bringing around other clients, perhaps today, who would see the horn as soon as they opened the closet door? A client might call it to Bresson's attention.

He walked up the steps and into the large living room. Brenda was still glaring. Bresson, a chubby, spectacled man of about thirty-five, looked uncomfortable, although he was smiling.

"Well, how do you like it?" he asked.

"Great," Wolff replied. "It reminds me of the type of house we have back home."

"I like it," Bresson said. "I'm from the Midwest myself. I can appreciate that you might not want to live in a ranch-type home. Not that I'm knocking them. I live in one myself."

Wolff walked to the window and looked out. The midafternoon May sun shone brightly from the blue Arizona skies. The lawn was covered with the fresh Bermuda grass, planted three weeks before, new as the houses in this just-built development of Hohokam Homes.

"Almost all the houses are ground level," Bresson was saying. "Excavating in this hard caliche costs a great deal, but these houses aren't expensive. Not for what you get."

Wolff thought, *If the caliche hadn't been dug away to make*

11

room for the recreation room, what would the man on the other side have seen when the opening appeared? Would he have seen only earth and thus been denied the chance to get rid of that horn? Undoubtedly.

"You may have read why we had to delay opening this development," Bresson said. "While we were digging, we uncovered a former town of the Hohokam."

"Hohokam?" Mrs. Wolff said. "Who were they?"

"Lots of people who come into Arizona have never heard of them," Bresson replied. "But you can't live long in the Phoenix area without running across references to them. They were the Indians who lived a long time ago in the Valley of the Sun; they may have come here at least 1200 years ago. They dug irrigation canals, built towns here, had a swinging civilization. But something happened to them, no one knows what. They just up and disappeared several hundred years ago. Some archeologists claim the Papago and Pima Indians are their descendants."

Mrs. Wolff sniffed and said, "I've seen them. They don't look like they could build anything except those rundown adobe shacks on the reservation."

Wolff turned and said, almost savagely, "The modern Maya don't look as if they could ever have built their temples or invented the concept of zero, either. But they did."

Brenda gasped. Mr. Bresson smiled even more mechanically. "Anyway, we had to suspend digging until the archeologists were through. Held up operations about three months, but we couldn't do a thing because the state tied our hands.

"However, this may be a lucky thing for you. If we hadn't been held up, these homes might all be sold now. So everything turns out for the best, eh?"

He smiled brightly and looked from one to the other.

Wolff paused, took a deep breath, knowing what was coming from Brenda, and said, "We'll take it. We'll sign the papers right now."

"Robert!" Mrs. Wolff shrilled. "You didn't even ask me!"

"I'm sorry, my dear, but I've made up my mind."

"Well, I haven't!"

"Now, now, folks, no need to rush things," Bresson said. His smile was desperate. "Take your time, talk it over. Even if somebody should come along and buy this particular house—and it might happen before the day's over; they're selling like hotcakes—well, there're plenty more just like this."

"I want *this* house."

"Robert, are you out of your mind?" Brenda wailed. "I've never seen you act like this before."

"I've given in to you on almost everything," he said. "I

12

wanted you to be happy. So, now, give in to me on this. It's not much to ask. Besides, you said this morning that you wanted this type of house, and Hohokam Homes are the only ones like this that we can afford.

"Let's sign the preliminary papers now. I can make out a check as an earnest."

"I won't sign, Robert."

"Why don't you two go home and discuss this?" Bresson said. "I'll be available when you've reached a decision."

"Isn't my signature good enough?" Wolff replied.

Still holding his strained smile, Bresson said, "I'm sorry, Mrs. Wolff will have to sign, too."

Brenda smiled triumphantly.

"Promise me you won't show it to anybody else," Wolff said. "Not until tomorrow, anyway. If you're afraid of losing a sale, I'll make out an earnest."

"Oh, that won't be necessary." Bresson started toward the door with a haste that betrayed his wish to get out of an embarrassing situation. "I won't show it to anyone until I hear from you in the morning."

On the way back to their rooms in the Sands Motel in Tempe, neither spoke. Brenda sat rigidly and stared straight ahead through the windshield. Wolff glanced over at her now and then, noting that her nose seemed to be getting sharper and her lips thinner; if she continued, she would look exactly like a fat parrot.

And when she finally did burst loose, talking, she would sound like a fat parrot. The same old tired yet energetic torrent of reproaches and threats would issue. She would upbraid him because of his neglect of her all these years, remind him for the latest in God-knew-how-many-times that he kept his nose buried in his books or else was practicing archery or fencing, or climbing mountains, sports she could not share with him because of her arthritis. She would unreel the years of unhappiness, or claimed unhappiness, and end by weeping violently and bitterly.

Why had he stuck with her? He did not know except that he had loved her very much when they were young and also because her accusations were not entirely untrue. Moreover, he found the thought of separation painful, even more painful than the thought of staying with her.

Yet he was entitled to reap the harvests of his labors as a professor of English and classical languages. Now that he had enough money and leisure time, he could pursue studies that his duties had denied him. With this Arizona home as a base, he could even travel. Or could he? Brenda would not refuse to go with him—in fact, she would insist on accompanying him.

13

But she would be so bored that his own life would be miserable. He could not blame her for that, for she did not have the same interests as he. But should he give up the things that made life rich for him just to make her happy? Especially since she was not going to be happy anyway?

As he expected, her silent tongue became quite active after supper. He listened, tried to remonstrate quietly with her and point out her lack of logic and the injustice and baselessness of her recriminations. It was no use. She ended as always, weeping and threatening to leave him or to kill herself.

This time, he did not give in.

"I want that house, and I want to enjoy life as I've planned to," he said firmly. "That's that."

He put on his coat and strode to the door. "I'll be back later. Maybe."

She screamed and threw an ashtray at him. He ducked; the tray bounced off the door, gouging out a piece of the wood. Fortunately, she did not follow him and make a scene outside, as she had on previous occasions.

It was night now, the moon was not yet up, and the only lights came from the windows of the motel, the lamps along the streets, and numerous headlights of the cars along Apache Boulevard. He drove his car out onto the boulevard and went east, then turned south. Within a few minutes he was on the road to the Hohokam Homes. The thought of what he meant to do made his heart beat fast and turned his skin cold. This was the first time in his life that he had seriously considered committing a criminal act.

The Hohokam Homes were ablaze with lights and noisy with music over a PA system and the voices of children playing out in the street while their parents looked at the houses.

He drove on, went through Mesa, turned around and came back through Tempe and down Van Buren and into the heart of Phoenix. He cut north, then east, until he was in the town of Scottsdale. Here he stopped off for an hour and a half at a small tavern. After the luxury of four shots of *Vat 69*, he quit. He wanted no more—rather, feared to take more, because he did not care to be fuddled when he began his project.

When he returned to Hohokam Homes, the lights were out and silence had returned to the desert. He parked his car behind the house in which he had been that afternoon. With his gloved right fist, he smashed the window which gave him access to the recreation room.

By the time he was within the room, he was panting and his heart beat as if he had run several blocks. Though frightened, he had to smile at himself. A man who lived much in his imagination, he had often conceived of himself as a burglar—

14

not the ordinary kind, of course, but a Raffles. Now he knew that his respect for law was too much for him ever to become a great criminal or even a minor one. His conscience was hurting him because of this small act, one that he had thought he was fully justified in carrying out. Moreover, the idea of being caught almost made him give up the horn. After living a quiet, decent and respectable life, he would be ruined if he were to be detected. Was it worth it?

He decided it was. Should he retreat now, he would wonder the rest of his life what he had missed. The greatest of all adventures waited for him, one such as no other man had experienced. If he became a coward now, he might as well shoot himself, for he would not be able to endure the loss of the horn or the self-recriminations for his lack of courage.

It was so dark in the recreation room that he had to feel his way to the closet with his fingertips. Locating the sliding doors, he moved the left-hand one, which he had pushed aside that afternoon. He nudged it slowly to avoid noise, and he stopped to listen for sounds outside the house.

Once the door was fully opened, he retreated a few steps. He placed the mouthpiece of the horn to his lips and blew softly. The blast that issued from it startled him so much that he dropped it. Groping, he finally located it in the corner of the room.

The second time, he blew hard. There was another loud note, no louder than the first. Some device in the horn, perhaps the slivery web inside its mouth, regulated the decible level. For several minutes he stood poised with the horn raised and almost to his mouth. He was trying to reconstruct in his mind the exact sequence of the seven notes he had heard. Obviously the seven little buttons on the underside determined the various harmonics. But he could not find out which was which without experimenting and drawing attention.

He shrugged and murmured, "What the hell."

Again he blew, but now he pressed the buttons, operating the one closest to him first. Seven loud notes soared forth. Their values were as he remembered them, but not in the sequence he recalled.

As the final blast died out, a shout came from a distance. Wolff almost panicked. He swore, lifted the horn back to his lips, and pressed the buttons in an order which he hoped would reproduce the open sesame, the musical key, to the other world.

At the same time, a flashlight beam played across the broken window of the room, then passed by. Wolff blew again. The light returned to the window. More shouts arose. Desperate, Wolff tried different combinations of buttons. The third attempt seemed to be the duplicate of that which the youth on top of the toadstool-shaped boulder had produced.

The flashlight was thrust through the broken window. A deep voice growled, "Come on out, you in there! Come out, or I'll start shooting!"

Simultaneously, a greenish light appeared on the wall, broke through, and melted a hole. Moonlight shone through. The trees and the boulder were visible only as silhouettes against a green-silver radiating from a great globe of which the rim alone was visible.

He did not delay. He might have hesitated if he had been unnoticed, but now he knew he had to run. The other world offered uncertainty and danger, but this one had a definite, inescapable ignominy and shame. Even as the watchman repeated his demands, Wolff left him and his world behind. He had to stoop and to step high to get through the shrinking hole. When he had turned around on the other side to get a final glimpse, he saw through an opening no larger than a ship's porthole. In a few seconds, it was gone.

CHAPTER TWO

Wolff sat down on the grass to rest until he quit breathing so hard. He thought of how ironic it would be if the excitement were to be too much for his sixty-six year old heart. Dead on arrival, DOA. They—whoever "they" were—would have to bury him and put above his grave: THE UNKNOWN EARTHMAN.

He felt better then. He even chuckled while rising to his feet. With some courage and confidence, he looked around. The air was comfortable enough, about seventy degrees, he estimated. It bore strange and very pleasant, almost fruity, perfumes. Bird calls—he hoped they were only those—came from all around him. Somewhere far off, a low growl sounded, but he was not frightened. He was certain, with no rational ground for certainty, that it was the distance-muted crash of surf. The moon was full and enormous, two and a half times as large as Earth's.

The sky had lost the bright green it had had during the day and had become except for the moon's radiance, as black as the night-time sky of the world he had left. A multitude of large stars moved with a speed and in directions that made him dizzy with fright and confusion. One of the stars fell toward him, became bigger and bigger, brighter and brighter, until it swooped a few feet overhead. By the orange-yellow glow from its rear, he could see four great elliptoid wings and dangling skinny legs and, briefly, the silhouette of an antennaed head. It was a firefly of some sort with a wingspread of at least ten feet.

Wolff watched the shifting and expanding and contracting of the living constellations until he became used to them. He wondered which direction to take, and the sound of the surf finally decided him. A shoreline would give a definite point of departure, wherever he went after that. His progress was slow and cautious, with frequent stops to listen and to examine the shadows.

Something with a deep chest grunted nearby. He flattened himself on the grass under the shadow of a thick bush and tried to breathe slowly. There was a rustling noise. A twig crackled. Wolff lifted his head high enough to look out into the moonlit clearing before him. A great bulk, erect, biped, dark and hairy, shambled by only a few yards from him.

It stopped suddenly, and Wolff's heart skipped a beat. Its head moved back and forth, permitting Wolff to get a full view of a gorrilloid profile. However, it was not a gorilla – not a Terrestrial one, anyway. Its fur was not a solid black. Alternate stripes of broad black and narrow white zigzagged across its body and legs. Its arms were much shorter than those of its counterpart on Earth, and its legs were not only longer but straighter. Moreover, the forehead, although shelved with bone above the eyes, was high.

It muttered something, not an animal cry or moan but a sequence of clearly modulated syllables. The gorilla was not alone. The greenish moon exposed a patch of bare skin on the side away from Wolff. It belonged to a woman who walked by the beast's side and whose shoulders were hidden by his huge right arm.

Wolff could not see her face, but he caught enough of long slim legs, curving buttocks, a shapely arm, and long black hair to wonder if she were as beautiful from the front.

She spoke to the gorilla in a voice like the sound of silver bells. The gorilla answered her. Then the two had walked out of the green moon and into the darkness of the jungle.

Wolff did not get up at once, for he was too shaken.

Finally, he rose to his feet and pushed on through the undergrowth, which was not as thick as that of an Earth jungle. Indeed, the bushes were widely separated. If the environment had not been so exotic, he would not have thought of the flora as a jungle. It was more like a park, including the soft grass, which was so short it could have been freshly mown.

Only a few paces further on, he was startled when an animal snorted and then ran in front of him. He got a glimpse of red-

17

dish antlers, a whitish nose, huge pale eyes, and a polka-dot body. It crashed by him and disappeared, but a few seconds later he heard steps behind him. He turned to see the same cervine several feet away. When it saw that it was detected, it stepped forward slowly and thrust a wet nose into his outstretched hand. Thereafter, it purred and tried to rub its flank against him. Since it weighed perhaps a quarter of a ton, it tended to push him away from it.

He leaned into it, rubbed it behind its large cup-shaped ears, scratched its nose, and lightly slapped its ribs. The cervine licked him several times with a long wet tongue that rasped as roughly as that of a lion. His hopes that it would tire of its affections were soon realized. It left him with a bound as sudden as that which had brought it within his ken.

After it was gone, he felt less endangered. Would an animal be so friendly to a complete stranger if it had carnivores or hunters to fear?

The roar of the surf became louder. Within ten minutes he was at the edge of the beach. There he crouched beneath a broad and towering frond and examined the moon-brushed scene. The beach itself was white and, as his outstretched hand verified, made of very fine sand. It ran on both sides for as far as he could see, and the breadth of it, between forest and sea, was about two hundred yards. On both sides, at a distance, were fires around which capered the silhouettes of men and women. Their shouts and laughter, though muted by the distance, reinforced his impression that they must be human.

Then his gaze swept back to the beach near him. At an angle, about three hundred yards away and almost in the water, were two beings. The sight of them snatched his breath away.

It was not what they were doing that shocked him but the construction of their bodies. From the waist up the man and woman were as human as he, but at the point where their legs should have begun the body of each tapered into fins.

He was unable to restrain his curiosity. After caching the horn in a bed of feathery grasses, he crept along the edge of the jungle; when he was opposite the two, he stopped to watch. Since the male and female were now lying side by side and talking, their position allowed him to study them in more detail. He became convinced they could not pursue him with any speed on land and had no weapons. He would approach them. They might even be friendly.

When he was about twenty yards from them, he stopped to examine them again. If they were mermen, they certainly were not half-piscine. The fins at the end of their long tails were on a

18

horizontal plane, unlike those of fish, which are vertical. And the tail did not seem to have scales. Smooth brown skin covered their hybrid bodies from top to bottom.

He coughed. They looked up, and the male shouted and the female screamed. In a motion so swift he could not comprehend the particulars but saw it as a blur, they had risen on the ends of their tails and flipped themselves upward and out into the waves. The moon flashed on a dark head rising briefly from the waves and a tail darting upward.

The surf rolled and crashed upon the white sands. The moon shone hugely and greenly. A breeze from the sea patted his sweating face and passed on to cool the jungle. A few weird cries issued from the darkness behind him, and from down the beach came the sound of human revelry.

For awhile he was webbed in thought. The speech of the two merpeople had had something familiar about it, as had that of the zebrilla (his coinage for the gorilla) and the woman. He had not recognized any individual words, but the sounds and the asssociated pitches had stirred something in his memory. But what? They certainly spoke no language he had ever heard before. Was it similar to one of the living languages of Earth and had he heard it on a recording or perhaps in a movie?

A hand closed on his shoulder, lifted him and whirled him around. The Gothic snout and caverned eyes of a zebrilla were thrust in his face, and an alcoholic breath struck his own nostrils. It spoke, and the woman stepped out from the bushes. She walked slowly toward him, and at any other time he would have caught his breath at the magnificent body and beautiful face. Unfortunately, he was having a hard time breathing now for a different cause. The giant ape could hurl him into the sea with even more ease and speed than that which the merpeople had shown when they had dived away. Or the huge hand could close on him and meet on crushed flesh and shattered bone.

The woman said something, and the zebrilla replied. It was then that Wolff understood several words. Their language was akin to pre-Homeric Greek, to Mycenaean.

He did not immediately burst into speech to reassure them that he was harmless and his intentions good. For one thing, he was too stunned to think clearly enough. Also, his knowledge of the Greek of that period was necessarily limited, even if it was close to the Aeolic-Ionic of the blind bard.

Finally, he managed to utter a few inappropriate phrases, but he was not so concerned with the sense as to let them know he meant no harm. Hearing him, the zebrilla grunted, said something to the girl, and lowered Wolff to the sand. He sighed

19

with relief, but he grimaced at the pain in his shoulder. The huge hand of the monster was enormously powerful. Aside from the magnitude and hairiness, the hand was quite human.

The woman tugged at his shirt. She had a mild distaste on her face; only later was he to discover that he repulsed her. She had never seen a fat old man before. Moreover, the clothes puzzled her. She continued pulling at his shirt. Rather than have her request the zebrilla to remove it from him, he pulled it off himself. She looked at it curiously, smelled it, said, "Ugh!" and then made some gesture.

Although he would have preferred not to understand her and was even less reluctant to obey, he decided he might as well. There was no reason to frustrate her and perhaps anger the zebrilla. He shed his clothes and waited for more orders. The woman laughed shrilly; the zebrilla barked and pounded his thigh with his huge hand so that it sounded as if an axe were chopping wood. He and the woman put their arms around each other and, laughing hysterically, staggered off down the beach.

Infuriated, humiliated, ashamed, but also thankful that he had escaped without injury, Wolff put his pants back on. Picking up his underwear, socks, and shoes, he trudged through the sand and back into the jungle. After taking the horn from its hiding place, he sat for a long while, wondering what to do. Finally, he fell asleep.

He awoke in the morning, muscle-sore, hungry, and thirsty.

The beach was alive. In addition to the mermen and merwomen he had seen the night before, several large seals with bright orange coats flopped back and forth over the sand in pursuit of amber balls flung by the merpeople and a man with ram's horns projecting from his forehead, furry legs and a short goatish tail chased a woman who looked much like the one who had been with the zebrilla. She, however, had yellow hair. She ran until the horned man leaped upon her and bore her, laughing, to the sand. What happened thereafter showed him that these beings were as innocent of a sense of sin, and of inhibitions, as Adam and Eve must have been.

This was more than interesting, but the sight of a mermaid eating aroused him in other and more demanding directions. She held a large oval yellow fruit in one hand and a hemisphere that looked like a coconut shell in the other. The female counterpart of the man with ram's horns squatted by a fire only a few yards from him and fried a fish on the end of a stick. The odor made his mouth water and his belly rumble.

First he had to have a drink. Since the only water in sight

was the ocean, he strode out upon the beach and toward the surf.

His reception was what he had expected: surprise, withdrawal, apprehension to some degree. All stopped their activities, no matter how absorbing, to stare at him. When he approached some of them he was greeted with wide eyes, open mouths, and retreat. Some of the males stood their ground, but they looked as if they were ready to run if he said boo. Not that he felt like challenging them, since the smallest had muscles that could easily overpower his tired old body.

He walked into the surf up to his waist and tasted the water. He had seen others drink from it, so he hoped that he would find it acceptable. It was pure and fresh and had a tang that he had never experienced before. After drinking his fill, he felt as if he had had a transfusion of young blood. He walked out of the ocean and back across the beach and into the jungle. The others had resumed their eating and recreations, and though they watched him with a bold direct stare they said nothing to him. He gave them a smile, but quit when it seemed to startle them. In the jungle, he searched for and found fruit and nuts such as the merwoman had been eating. The yellow fruit had a peach pie taste, and the meat inside the pseudococonut tasted like very tender beef mixed with small pieces of walnut.

Afterward he felt very satisfied, except for one thing: he craved his pipe. But tobacco was one thing that seemed to be missing in this paradise.

The next few days he haunted the jungle or else spent some time in or near the ocean. By then, the beach crowd had grown used to him and even began to laugh when he made his morning appearances. One day, some of the men and women jumped him and, laughing uproariously, removed his clothes. He ran after the woman with the pants, but she sped away into the jungle. When she reappeared she was emptyhanded. By now he could speak well enough to be understood if he uttered the phrases slowly. His years of teaching and study had given him a very large Greek vocabulary, and he had only to master the tones and a number of words that were not in his Autenreith.

"Why did you do that?" he asked the beautiful black-eyed nymph.

"I wanted to see what you were hiding beneath those ugly rags. Naked, you are ugly, but those things on you made you look even uglier."

"Obscene?" he said, but she did not understand the word.

He shrugged and thought, *When in Rome* . . . Only this was more like the Garden of Eden. The temperature by day or night was comfortable and varied about seven degrees. There was no problem getting a variety of food, no work demanded, no rent, no politics, no tension except an easily relieved sexual tension, no national or racial animosities. There were no bills to pay. Or were there? That you did not get something for nothing was the basic principle of the universe of Earth. Was it the same here? Somebody should have to foot the bill.

At night he slept on a pile of grass in a large hollow in a tree. This was only one of thousands of such hollows, for a particular type of tree offered this natural accommodation. Wolff did not stay in bed in the mornings, however. For some days he got up just before dawn and watched the sun arrive. Arrive was a better word than rise, for the sun certainly did not rise. On the other side of the sea was an enormous mountain range, so extensive that he could see neither end. The sun always came around the mountain and was high when it came. It proceeded straight across the green sky and did not sink but disappeared only when it went around the other end of the mountain range.

An hour later, the moon appeared. It, too, came around the mountain, sailed at the same level across the skies, and slipped around the other side of the mountain. Every other night it rained hard for an hour. Wolff usually awoke then, for the air did get a little chillier. He would snuggle down in the leaves and shiver and try to get back to sleep.

He was finding it increasingly more difficult to do so with each succeeding night. He would think of his own world, the friends and the work and the fun he had there—and of his wife. What was Brenda doing now? Doubtlessly she was grieving for him. Bitter and nasty and whining though she had been too many times, she loved him. His disappearance would be a shock and a loss. However, she would be well taken care of. She had always insisted on his carrying more insurance than he could afford; this had been a quarrel between them more than once. Then it occurred to him that she would not get a cent of insurance for a long time, for proof of his death would have to be forthcoming. Still, if she had to wait until he was legally declared dead, she could survive on social security. It would mean a drastic lowering of her living standards, but it would be enough to support her.

Certainly he had no intention of going back. He was regaining his youth. Though he ate well, he was losing weight, and his muscles were getting stronger and harder. He had a spring in his legs and a sense of joy lost sometime during his early twenties. The seventh morning, he had rubbed his scalp and discovered that it was covered with little bristles. The tenth morning, he woke up with pain in his gums. He rubbed the swollen flesh and wondered if he were going to be sick. He had forgotten that there was such a thing as disease, for he had been extremely well and none of the beach crowd, as he called them, ever seemed ill.

His gums continued to hurt him for a week, after which he took to drinking the naturally fermented liquor in the "punch-nut". This grew in great clusters high at the top of a slender tree with short, fragile, mauve branches and tobacco-pipe-shaped yellow leaves. When its leathery rind was cut open with a sharp stone, it exuded an odor as of fruity punch. It tasted like a gin tonic with a dash of cherry bitters and had a kick like a slug of tequila. It worked well in killing both the pain in his gums and the irritation the pain had generated in him.

Nine days after he first experienced the trouble with his gums, ten tiny, white, hard teeth began to shove through the flesh. Moveover, the gold fillings in the others were being pushed out by the return of the natural material. And a thick black growth covered his formerly bald pate.

This was not all. The swimming, running, and climbing had melted off the fat. The prominent veins of old age had sunk back into smooth firm flesh. He could run for long stretches without being winded or feel as if his heart would burst. All this he delighted in, but not without wondering why and how it had come about.

He asked several among the beach-crowd about their seemingly universal youth. They had one reply: "It's the Lord's will."

At first he thought they were speaking of the Creator, which seemed strange to him. As far as he could tell, they had no religion. Certainly they did not have one with any organized approach, rituals, or sacraments.

"Who is the Lord?" he asked. He thought that perhaps he had mistranslated their word *wanaks*, that it might have a slightly different meaning than that found in Homer.

Ipsewas, the zebrilla, the most intelligent of all he had so far met, answered, "He lives on top of the world, beyond Okeanos." Ipsewas pointed up and over the sea, toward the mountain range at its other side. "The Lord lives in a beautiful and impregnable palace on top of the world. He it was who made this world and who made us. He used to come down often to make merry with us. We do as the Lord says and play with him. But we are always frightened. If he becomes angry or is displeased, he is likely to kill us. Or worse."

Wolff smiled and nodded his head. So Ipsewas and the others had no more rational explanation of the origins or workings of their world than the people of his. But the beach-crowd did have one thing lacking on Earth. They had uniformity of opinion. Everyone he asked gave him the same answer as the zebrilla.

"It is the will of the Lord. He made the world, he made us."

"How do you know?" Wolff asked. He did not expect any more than he had gotten on Earth when he asked that question. But he was surprised.

"Oh," replied a mermaid, Paiawa, "the Lord told us so. Besides, my mother told me, too. She ought to know. The Lord made her body; she remembers when he did it, although that was so long, long ago."

"Indeed?" Wolff said, wondering whether or not she were pulling his leg, and thinking also that it would be difficult to retaliate by doing the same to her. "And where is your mother? I'd like to talk to her."

Paiawa waved a hand toward the west. "Somewhere along there."

"Somewhere" could be thousands of miles away, for he had no idea how far the beach extended.

"I haven't seen her for a long time," Paiawa added.

"How long?" Wolff said.

Paiawa wrinkled her lovely brow and pursed her lips. Very kissable, Wolff thought. And that body! The return of his youth was bringing back a strong awareness of sex.

Paiawa smiled at him and said, "You *are* showing some interest in me, aren't you?"

He flushed and would have walked away, but he wanted an answer to his question. "How many years since you saw your mother?" he asked again.

Paiawa could not answer. The word for "year" was not in her vocabulary.

He shrugged and walked swiftly away, to disappear behind the savagely colored foliage by the beach. She called after him, archly at first, then angrily when it became evident he was not going to turn back. She made a few disparaging remarks about him as compared to the other males. He did not argue with her —it would have been beneath his dignity, and besides, what she said was true. Even though his body was rapidly regaining its youth and strength, it still suffered in comparison with the near-perfect specimens all around him.

He dropped this line of thought, and considered Paiawa's story. If he could locate her mother or one of her mother's contemporaries in age, he might be able to find out more about the Lord. He did not discredit Paiawa's story, which would have been incredible on Earth. These people just did not lie. Fiction was a stranger to them. Such truthfulness had its advantages, but it also meant that they were decidedly limited in imagination and had little humor or wit. They laughed often enough, but it was over rather obvious and petty things. Slapstick was as high as their comedy went—and crude practical jokes.

24

He cursed because he was having difficulty in staying on his intended track of thought. His trouble with concentration seemed to get stronger every day. Now, what had he been thinking about when he'd strayed off to his unhappiness over his maladjustment with the local society? Oh, yes, Paiawa's mother! Some of the oldsters might be able to enlighten him— if he could locate any. How could he identify any when all adults looked the same age? There were only a very few youngsters, perhaps three in the several hundred beings he had encountered so far. Moreover, among the many animals and birds here (some rather weird ones, too), only a half-dozen had not been adults.

If there were few births, the scale was balanced by the absence of death. He had seen three dead animals, two killed by accident and the third during a battle with another over a female. Even that had been an accident, for the defeated male, a lemon-colored antelope with four horns curved into figure-eights, had turned to run away and broken his neck while jumping over a log.

The flesh of the dead animal had not had a chance to rot and stink. Several omnipresent creatures that looked like small bipedal foxes with white noses, floppy basset-hound ears, and monkey paws had eaten the corpse within a matter of an hour. The foxes scoured the jungle and scavenged everything—fruit, nuts, berries, corpses. They had a taste for the rotten; they would ignore fresh fruits for bruised. But they were not sour notes in the symphony of beauty and life. Even in the Garden of Eden, garbage collectors were necessary.

At times Wolff would look across the blue, white-capped Okeanos at the mountain range, called Thayaphayawoed. Perhaps the Lord did live up there. It might be worthwhile to cross the sea and climb up the formidable steeps on the chance that some of the mystery of this universe would be revealed. But the more he tried to estimate the height of Thayaphayawoed, the less he thought of the idea. The black cliffs soared up and up and up until the eye wearied and the mind staggered. No man could live on its top, because there would be no air to breathe.

CHAPTER THREE

One day Robert Wolff removed the silver horn from its hiding place in the hollow of a tree. Setting off through the forest, he walked toward the boulder from which the man who called himself Kickaha had thrown the horn. Kickaha and the bumpy creatures had dropped out of sight as if they never existed and no one to whom he had talked had ever seen or heard of them. He would re-enter his native world and give it another chance. If he thought its advantages outweighed those of the Garden planet, he would remain there. Or, perhaps, he could travel back and forth and so get the best of both. When tired of one, he would vacation in the other.

On the way, he stopped for a moment at an invitation from Elikopis to have a drink and to talk. Elikopis, whose name meant "Bright-eyed," was a beautiful, magnificently rounded dryad. She was closer to being "normal" than anyone he had so far met. If her hair had not been a deep purple, she would, properly clothed, have attracted no more attention on Earth than was usually bestowed on a woman of surpassing fairness.

In addition, she was one of the very few who could carry on a worthwhile conversation. She did not think that conversation consisted of chattering away or laughing loudly without cause and ignoring the words of those who were supposed to be communicating with her. Wolff had been disgusted and depressed to find that most of the beach-crowd or the forest-crowd were monologists, however intensely they seemed to be speaking or however gregarious they were.

Elikopis was different, perhaps because she was not a member of any "crowd," although it was more likely that the reverse was the cause. In this world along the sea, the natives, lacking even the technology of the Australian aborigine (and not needing even that) had developed an extremely complex social relationship. Each group had definite beach and forest territories with internal prestige levels. Each was able to recite in detail (and loved to) his/her horizontal/vertical position in comparison with each person of the group, which usually numbered about thirty. They could and would recite the arguments, reconciliations, character faults and virtues, athletic prowess or lack thereof, skill in their many childish games, and evaluate the sexual ability of each.

Elikopis had a sense of humor as bright as her eyes, but she also had some sensitivity. Today, she had an extra attraction, a mirror of glass set in a golden circle encrusted with diamonds. It was one of the few artifacts he had seen.

"Where did you get that?" he asked.

"Oh, the Lord gave it to me," Elikopis replied. "Once, a long-time ago, I was one of his favorites. Whenever he came down from the top of the world to visit here, he would spend much time with me. Chryseis and I were the ones he loved the most. Would you believe it, the others still hate us for that? That's why I'm so lonely—not that being with the others is much help.'

"And what did the Lord look like?"

She laughed and said, "From the neck down, he looked much like any tall, well-built man such as you."

She put her arm around his neck and began kissing him on his cheek, her lips slowly traveling toward his ear.

"His face?" Wolff said.

"I do not know. I could feel it, but I could not see it. A radiance from it blinded me. When he got close to me, I had to close my eyes, it was so bright."

She shut his mouth with her kisses, and presently he forgot his questions. But when she was lying half-asleep on the soft grass by his side, he picked up the mirror and looked into it. His heart opened with delight. He looked like he had when he had been twenty-five. This he had known but had not been able to fully realize until now.

"And if I return to Earth, will I age as swiftly as I have regained my youth?"

He rose and stood for awhile in thought. Then he said, "Who do I think I'm kidding? I'm not going back."

"If you're leaving me now," Elikopis said drowsily, "look for Chryseis. Something has happened to her; she runs away every time anybody gets close. Even I, her only friend, can't approach her. Something dreadful has occurred, something she won't talk about. You'll love her. She's not like the others; she's like me."

"All right," Wolff replied absently. "I will."

He walked until he was alone. Even if he did not intend to use the gate through which he had come, he did want to experiment with the horn. Perhaps there were other gates. It was possible that at any place where the horn was blown, a gate would open.

The tree under which he had stopped was one of the numerous cornucopias. It was two hundred feet tall, thirty feet thick, had a smooth, almost oily, azure bark, and branches as thick as his thigh and about sixty feet long. The branches were twigless and leafless. At the end of each was a hard-shelled flower, eight feet long and shaped exactly like a cornucopia.

Out of the cornucopias intermittent trickles of chocolatey stuff fell to the ground. The product tasted like honey with a very slight flavor of tobacco—a curious mixture, yet one he liked. Every creature of the forest ate it.

Under the cornucopia tree, he blew the horn. No "gate" appeared. He tried again a hundred yards away but without success. So, he decided, the horn worked only in certain areas, perhaps only in that place by the toadstool-shaped boulder.

Then he glimpsed the head of the girl who had come from around the tree that first time the gate had opened. She had the same heart-shaped face, enormous eyes, full crimson lips, and long tiger-stripes of black and auburn hair.

He greeted her, but she fled. Her body was beautiful; her legs were the longest, in proportion to her body, that he had ever seen in a woman. Moreover, she was slimmer than the other too-curved and great-busted females of this world.

Wolff ran after her. The girl cast a look over her shoulder, gave a cry of despair, and continued to run. He almost stopped then, for he had not gotten such a reaction from any of the natives. An initial withdrawal, yes, but not sheer panic and utter fright.

The girl ran until she could go no more. Sobbing for breath, she leaned against a moss-covered boulder near a small cataract. Ankle-high yellow flowers in the form of question-marks surrounded her. An owl-eyed bird with corkscrew feathers and long forward-bending legs stood on top of the boulder and blinked down at them. It uttered soft *wee-wee-wee!* cries.

Approaching slowly and smiling, Wolff said, "Don't be afraid of me. I won't harm you. I just want to talk to you."

The girl pointed a shaking finger at the horn. In a quavery voice she said, "Where did you get that?"

"I got it from a man who called himself Kickaha. You saw him. Do you know him?"

The girl's huge eyes were dark green; he thought them the most beautiful he had ever seen. This despite, or maybe because of, the catlike pupils.

She shook her head. "No. I did not know him. I first saw him when those"—she swallowed and turned pale and looked as if she were going to vomit—"things chased him to the boulder. And I saw them drag him off the boulder and take him away."

"Then he wasn't ended?" Wolff asked. He did not say *killed* or *slain* or *dead*, for these were taboo words.

"No. Perhaps those things meant to do something even worse than . . . ending him?"

"Why run from me?" Wolff said. "I am not one of those things."

"I . . . I can't talk about it."

Wolff considered her reluctance to speak of unpleasantness. These people had so few repulsive or dangerous phenomena in their lives, yet they could not face even these. They were overly conditioned to the easy and the beautiful.

"I don't care whether or not you want to talk about it," he said. "You must. It's very important."

She turned her face away. "I won't."

"Which way did they go?"

"Who?"

"Those monsters. And Kickaha."

"I heard him call them *gworl*," she said. "I never heard that word before. They . . . the gworl . . . must come from somewhere else." She pointed seawards and up. "They must come from the mountain. Up there, somewhere."

Suddenly she turned to him and came close to him. Her huge eyes were raised to his, and even at this moment he could not help thinking how exquisite her features were and how smooth and creamy her skin was.

"Let's get away from here!" she cried. "Far away! Those things are still here. Some of them may have taken Kickaha away, but all of them didn't leave! I saw a couple a few days ago. They were hiding in the hollow of a tree. Their eyes shone like those of animals, and they have a horrible odor, like rotten fungus-covered fruit!"

She put her hand on the horn. "I think they want this!"

Wolff said, "And I blew the horn. If they're anywhere near, they must have heard it!"

He looked around through the trees. Something glittered behind a bush about a hundred yards away.

He kept his eyes on the bush, and presently he saw the bush tremble and the flash of sunlight again. He took the girl's slender hand in his and said, "Let's get going. But walk as if we'd seen nothing. Be nonchalant."

She pulled back on his hand and said, "What's wrong?"

"Don't get hysterical. I think I saw something behind a bush. It might be nothing, then again it could be the gworl. Don't look over there! You'll give us away!"

He spoke too late, for she had jerked her head around. She gasped and moved close to him. "They . . . they!"

He looked in the direction of her pointing finger and saw two dark, squat figures shamble from behind the bush. Each carried a long, wide, curved blade of steel in its hand. They waved the knives and shouted something in a hoarse rasping voice. They wore no clothes over their dark furry bodies, but a broad belt around their waists supported scabbards from which protruded knife-handles.

Wolff said, "Don't panic. I don't think they can run very fast on those short bent legs. Where's a good place to get away from them, someplace they can't follow us?"

"Across the sea," she said in a shaking voice. "I don't think they could find us if we got far enough ahead of them. We can go on a *histoikhthys*."

She was referring to one of the huge molluscs that abounded in the sea. These had bodies covered with paper-thin but tough shells shaped like a racing yacht's hull. A slender but strong rod of cartilage projected vertically from the back of each, and

29

a triangular sail of flesh, so thin it was transparent, grew from the cartilage mast. The angle of the sail was controlled by muscular movement, and the force of the wind on the sail, plus expulsion of a jet of water, enabled the creature to move swiftly in a wind or a calm. The merpeople and the sentients who lived on the beach often hitched rides on these creatures, steering them by pressure on exposed nerve centers.

"You think the gworl will have to use a boat?" he said. "If so, they'll be out of luck unless they make one. I've never seen any kind of sea craft here."

Wolff looked behind him frequently. The gworl were coming at a faster pace, their bodies rolling like those of drunken sailors at every step. Wolff and the girl came to a stream which was about seventy feet broad and, at the deepest, rose to their waists. The water was cool but not chilling, clear, with slivery fish darting back and forth in it. When they reached the other side, they hid behind a large cornucopia tree. The girl urged him to continue, but he said, "They'll be at a disadvantage when they're in the middle of the stream."

"What do you mean?" she asked.

He did not reply. After placing the horn behind the tree, he looked around until he found a stone. It was half the size of his head, round, and rough enough to be held firmly in his hand. He hefted one of the fallen cornucopias. Though huge, it was hollow and weighed no more than twenty pounds. By then, the two gworl were on the bank of the opposite side of the stream. It was then that he discovered a weakness of the hideous creatures. They walked back and forth along the bank, shook their knives in fury, and growled so loudly in their throaty language that he could hear them from his hiding place. Finally, one of them stuck a broad splayed foot in the water. He withdrew it almost immediately, shook it as a cat shakes a wet paw, and said something to the other gworl. That one rasped back, then screamed at him.

The gworl with the wet foot shouted back, but he stepped into the water and reluctantly waded through it. Wolff watched him and also noted that the other was going to hang back until his companion had safely made the trip. Wolff waited until the creature had passed the middle of the stream; then he picked up the cornucopia in one hand, the stone in the other, and ran toward the stream. Behind him, the girl screamed. Wolff cursed because it gave the gworl notice that he was coming.

The gworl paused, the water up to its waist, yelled at Wolff and brandished the knife. Wolff reserved his breath, for he did not want to waste his wind. He sped toward the edge of the water, while the gworl resumed his progress to the same bank.

The gworl on the opposite edge had frozen at Wolff's appearance; now he had plunged into the stream to help the other. This action fell in with Wolff's plans. He only hoped that he could deal with the first before the second reached the middle.

The nearest gworl flipped his knife; Wolff lifted the cornucopia before him. The knife thudded into its thin but tough shell with a force that almost tore it from his grasp. The gworl began to draw another knife from its scabbard. Wolff did not stop to pull the first knife from the cornucopia; he kept on running. Just as the gworl raised the knife to slash at Wolff, Wolff dropped the stone, lifted the great bell-shape high, and slammed it over the gworl.

A muffled squawk came from within the shell. The cornucopia tilted over, the gworl with it, and both began floating downstream. Wolff ran into the water, picked up the stone, and grabbed the gworl by one of its thrashing feet. He took a hurried glance at the other and saw it was raising its knife for a throw. Wolff grabbed the handle of the knife that was sticking in the shell, tore it out, and then threw himself down behind the shelter of the bell-shape. He was forced to release his hold on the gworl's hairy foot, but he escaped the knife. It flew over the rim of the shell and buried itself to the hilt in the mud of the bank.

At the same time, the gworl within the cornucopia slid out, sputtering. Wolff stabbed at its side; the knife slid off one of the cartilaginous bumps. The gworl screamed and turned toward him. Wolff rose and thrust with all his strength at its belly. The knife went in to the hilt. The gworl grabbed at it; Wolff stepped back; the gworl fell into the water. The cornucopia floated away, leaving Wolff exposed, the knife gone, and only the stone in his hand. The remaining gworl was advancing on him, holding its knife across its breast. Evidently it did not intend to try for a second throw. It meant to close in on Wolff.

Wolff forced himself to delay until the thing was only ten feet from him. Meanwhile, he crouched down so that the water came to his chest and hid the stone, which he had shifted from his left to his right hand. Now he could see the gworl's face clearly. It had a very low forehead, a double ridge of bone above the eyes, thick mossy eyebrows, close-set lemon-yellow eyes, a flat, single-nostriled nose, thin black animal lips, a prognathous jaw which curved far out and gave the mouth a froglike appearance, no chin, and the sharp, widely separated teeth of a carnivore. The head, face, and body were covered with long, thick, dark fur. The neck was very thick, and the shoulders were stooped. Its wet fur stank like rotten fungus-diseased fruit.

Wolff was scared at the thing's hideousness, but he held his

31

ground. If he broke and ran, he would go down with a knife in his back.

When the gworl, alternately hissing and rasping in its ugly speech, had come within six feet, Wolff stood up. He raised his stone, and the gworl, seeing his intention, raised his knife to throw it. The stone flew straight and thudded into a bump on the forehead. The creature staggered backward, dropped the knife, and fell on its back in the water. Wolff waded toward it, groped in the water for the stone, found it, and came up from the water in time to face the gworl. Although it had a dazed expression and its eyes were slightly crossed, it was not out of the fight. And it held another knife.

Wolff raised the stone high and brought it down on top of the skull. There was a loud crack. The gworl fell back again, disappeared in the water, and appeared several yards away floating on its face.

Reaction took him. His heart was hammering so hard he thought it would rupture, he was shaking all over, and he was sick. But he remembered the knife stuck in the mud and retrieved it.

The girl was still behind the tree. She looked too horror-struck to speak. Wolff picked up the horn, took the girl's arm with one hand, and shook her roughly.

"Snap out of it! Think how lucky you are! You could be dead instead of them!"

She burst into a long wailing, then began weeping. He waited until she seemed to have no more grief in her before speaking. "I don't even know your name."

Her enormous eyes were reddened, and her face looked older. Even so, he thought, he had not seen an Earthwoman who could compare with her. Her beauty made the terror of the fight thin away.

"I'm Chryseis," she said. As if she were proud of it but at the same time shy of her proudness, she said, "I'm the only woman here who is allowed that name. The Lord forbade others to take it."

He growled, "The Lord again. Always the Lord. Who in hell is the Lord?"

"You really don't know?" she replied as if she could not believe him.

"No, I don't." He was silent for a moment, then said her name as if he were tasting it. "Chryseis, heh? It's not unknown on Earth, although I fear that the university at which I was teaching is full of illiterates who've never heard the name. They know that Homer composed the Iliad, and that's about it.

"Chryseis, the daughter of Chryses, a priest of Apollo. She was captured by the Greeks during the siege of Troy and

32

given to Agamemnon. But Agamemnon was forced to restore her to her father because of the pestilence sent by Apollo."

Chryseis was silent for so long that Wolff became impatient. He decided that they should move away from this area, but he was not certain which direction to take or how far to go.

Chryseis, frowning, said, "That was a long time ago. I can barely remember it. It's all so vague now."

"What are you talking about?"

"Me. My father. Agamemnon. The war."

"Well, what about it?" He was thinking that he would like to go to the base of the mountains. There, he could get some idea of what a climb entailed.

"I am Chryseis," she said. "The one you were talking about. You sound as if you had just come from Earth. Oh, tell me, is it true?"

He sighed. These people did not lie, but there was nothing to keep them from believing that their stories were true. He had heard enough incredible things to know that they were not only badly misinformed but likely to reconstruct the past to suit themselves. They did so in all sincerity, of course.

"I don't want to shatter your little dream-world," he said, "but this Chryseis, if she ever existed, died at least 3000 years ago. Moreover, she was a human being. She did not have tiger-striped hair and eyes with feline pupils."

"Nor did I . . . then. It was the Lord who abducted me, brought me to this universe, and changed my body. Just as it was he who abducted the others, changed them, or else inserted their brains in bodies he created."

She gestured seaward and upward. "He lives up there now, and we don't see him very often. Some say that he disappeared a long time ago, and a new Lord has taken his place."

"Let's get away from here," he said. "We can talk about this later."

They had gone only a quarter of a mile when Chryseis gestured at him to hide with her behind a thick purple-branched, gold-leaved bush. He crouched by her and, parting the branches a little, saw what had disturbed her. Several yards away was a hairy-legged man with heavy ram's horns on top of his head. Sitting on a low branch at a level with the man's eyes was a giant raven. It was as large as a golden eagle and had a high forehead. The skull looked as if it could house a brain the size of a fox terrier's.

Wolff was not surprised at the bulk of the raven, for he had seen some rather enormous creatures. But he was shocked to find the bird and the man carrying on a conversation.

"The Eye of the Lord," Chryseis whispered. She stabbed a finger at the raven in answer to his puzzled look. "That's one of

33

the Lord's spies. They fly over the world and see what's going on and then carry the news back to the Lord."

Wolff thought of Chryseis' apparently sincere remark about the insertion of brains into bodies by the Lord. To his question, she replied, "Yes, but I do not know if he put human brains into the ravens' heads. He may have grown small brains with the larger human brains as models, then educated the ravens. Or he could have used just part of a human brain."

Unfortunately, though they strained their ears, they could only catch a few words here and there. Several minutes passed. The raven, loudly croaking a goodbye in distorted but understandable Greek, launched himself from the branch. He dropped heavily, but his great wings beat fast, and they carried him upward before he touched ground. In a minute he was lost behind the heavy foliage of the trees. A little later, Wolff caught a glimpse of him through a break in the vegetation. The giant black bird was gaining altitude slowly, his point of flight the mountain across the sea.

He noticed that Chryseis was trembling. He said, "What could the raven tell the Lord that would scare you so?"

"I am not frightened so much for myself as I am for you. If the Lord discovers you are here, he will want to kill you. He does not like uninvited guests in his world."

She placed her hand on the horn and shivered again. "I know that it was Kickaha who gave you this, and that you can't help it that you have it. But the Lord might not know it isn't your fault. Or, even if he did, he might not care. He would be terribly angry if he thought you'd had anything to do with stealing it. He would do awful things to you; you would be better off if you ended yourself now rather than have the Lord get his hands on you."

"Kickaha stole the horn? How do you know?"

"Oh, believe me, I know. It is the Lord's. And Kickaha must have stolen it, for the Lord would never give it to anyone."

"I'm confused," Wolff said. "But maybe we can straighten it all out someday. The thing that bothers me right now is, where's Kickaha?"

Chryseis pointed toward the mountain and said, "The gworl took him there. But before they did . . ."

She covered her face with her hands; tears seeped through the fingers.

"They did something to him?" Wolff said.

She shook her head. "No. They did something to . . . to . . ."

Wolff took her hands from her face. "If you can't talk about it, would you show it to me?"

"I can't. It's . . . too horrible. I get sick."

"Show me anyway."

34

"I'll take you near there. But don't ask me to look at . . . her . . . again."

She began walking, and he followed her. Every now and then she would stop, but he would gently urge her on. After a zig-zag course of over half a mile, she stopped. Ahead of them was a small forest of bushes twice as high as Wolff's head. The leaves of the branches of one bush interlaced with those of its neighbors. The leaves were broad and elephant-ear-shaped, light green with broad red veins, and tipped with a rusty fleur-de-lys.

"She's in there," Chryseis said. "I saw the gworl . . . catch her and drag her into the bushes. I followed . . . I . . ." She could talk no more.

Wolff, knife in one hand, pushed the branches of the bushes aside. He found himself in a natural clearing. In the middle, on the short green grass, lay the scattered bones of a human female. The bones were gray and devoid of flesh, and bore little toothmarks, by which he knew that the bipedal vulpine scavengers had gotten to her.

He was not horrified, but he could imagine how Chryseis must have felt. She must have seen part of what had taken place, probably a rape, then murder in some gruesome fashion. She would have reacted like the other dwellers in the Garden. Death was something so horrible that the word for it had long ago become taboo and then dropped out of the language. Here, nothing but pleasant thoughts and acts were to be contemplated, and anything else was to be shut out.

He returned to Chryseis, who looked with her enormous eyes at him as if she wanted him to tell her that there was nothing within the clearing. He said, "She's only bones now, and far past any suffering."

"The gworl will pay for this!" she said savagely. "The Lord does not allow his creatures to be hurt! This Garden is his, and any intruders are punished!"

"Good for you," he said. "I was beginning to think that you may have become frozen by the shock. Hate the gworl all you want; they deserve it. And you need to break loose."

She screamed and leaped at him and beat on his chest with her fists. Then she began weeping, and presently he took her in his arms. He raised her face and kissed her. She kissed him back passionately, though the tears were still flowing.

Afterward, she said, "I ran to the beach to tell my people what I'd seen. But they wouldn't listen. They turned their backs on me and pretended they hadn't heard me. I kept trying to make them listen, but Owisandros"—the ram-horned man who had been talking with the raven—"Owisandros hit me with his fist and told me to go away. After that, none of them would

35

have anything to do with me. And I . . . I needed friends and love."

"You don't get friends or love by telling people what they don't want to hear," he said. "Here or on Earth. But you have me, Chryseis, and I have you. I think I'm beginning to fall in love with you, although I may just be reacting to loneliness and to the most strange beauty I've ever seen. And to my new youth."

He sat up and gestured at the mountain. "If the gworl are intruders here, where did they come from? Why were they after the horn? Why did they take Kickaha with them? And who is Kickaha?"

"He comes from up there, too. But I think he's an Earthman."

"What do you mean, Earthman? You say you're from Earth."

"I mean he's a newcomer. I don't know. I just had a feeling he was."

He stood up and lifted her up by hands. "Let's go after him."

Chryseis sucked in her breath and, one hand on her breast, backed away from him. "No!"

"Chryseis, I could stay here with you and be very happy. For awhile. But I'd always be wondering what all this is about the Lord and what happened to Kickaha. I only saw him for a few seconds, but I think I'd like him very much. Besides, he didn't throw the horn to me just because I happened to be there. I have a hunch that he did it for a good reason, and that I should find out why. And I can't rest while he's in the hands of those things, the gworl."

He took her hand from her breast and kissed the hand. "It's about time you left this Paradise that is no Paradise. You can't stay here forever, a child forever."

She shook her head. "I wouldn't be any help to you. I'd just get in your way. And . . . leaving . . . leaving I'd, well, I'd just end."

"You're going to have to learn a new vocabulary," he said. "Death will be just one of the many new words you'll be able to speak without a second thought or a shiver. You will be a better woman for it. Refusing to say it doesn't stop it from happening, you know. Your friend's bones are there whether or not you can talk about them."

"That's horrible!"

"The truth often is."

He turned away from her and started toward the beach. After a hundred yards, he stopped to look back. She had just started running after him. He waited for her, took her in his arms, kissed her, and said, "You may find it hard going, Chry-

36

seis, but you won't be bored, won't have to drink yourself into a stupor to endure life."

"I hope so," she said in a low voice. "But I'm scared."

"So am I, but we're going."

CHAPTER FOUR

He took her hand in his as they walked side by side toward the roar of the surf. They had traveled not more than a hundred yards when Wolff saw the first gworl. It stepped out from behind a tree and seemed to be as surprised as they. It shouted, snatched its knife out, then turned to yell at others behind it. In a few seconds, a party of seven had formed, each gworl with a long curved knife.

Wolff and Chryseis had a fifty-yard headstart. Still holding Chryseis' hand, the horn in his other hand, Robert Wolff ran as fast as he could.

"I don't know!" she answered despairingly. "We could hide in a tree hollow, but we'd be trapped if they found us."

They ran on. Now and then he looked back: the brush was thick hereabouts and hid some of the gworl, but there was always one or two in evidence.

"The boulder!" he said. "It's just ahead. We'll take that way out!"

Suddenly he knew how much he did not want to return to his native world. Even if it meant a route of escape and a temporary hiding place, he did not want to go back. The prospect of being trapped there and being unable to return here was so appalling that he almost decided not to blow the horn. But he had to do so. Where else could he go?

The decision was taken away from him a few seconds later. As he and Chryseis sped toward the boulder, he saw several dark figures hunched at its base. These rose and became gworl with flashing knives and long white canines.

Wolff and the girl angled away while the three at the boulder joined the chase. These were nearer than the others, only twenty yards behind the fugitives.

"Don't you know any place?" he panted.

"Over the edge," she said. "That's the only place they might not follow us. I've been down the face of the rim; there're caves there. But it's dangerous."

He did not reply, saving his breath for the run. His legs felt heavy and his lungs and throat burned. Chryseis seemed to be in better shape than he: she ran easily, her long legs pumping, breathing deeply but not agonizingly.

37

"Another two minutes, we'll be there," she said.

The two minutes seemed much longer, but every time he felt he had to stop, he took another look behind him and renewed his strength. The gworl, although even further behind, were in sight. They rolled along on their short, crooked legs, their bumpy faces set with determination.

"Maybe if you gave them the horn," Chryseis said, "they'd go away. I think they want the horn, not us."

"I'll do it if I have to," he gasped. "But only as a last resort."

Suddenly, they were going up a steep slope. Now his legs did feel burdened, but he had caught his second wind and thought that he could go awhile longer. Then they were on top of the hill and at the edge of a cliff.

Chryseis stopped him from walking on. She advanced ahead of him to the edge, halted, looked over, and beckoned him. When he was by her side, he, too, gazed down. His stomach clenched like a fist.

Composed of hard black shiny rock, the cliff went straight down for several miles. Then, nothing.

Nothing but the green sky.

"So . . . it is the edge . . . of the world!" he said.

Chryseis did not answer him. She trotted ahead of him, looking over the side of the cliff, halting briefly now and then to examine the rim.

"About sixty yards more," she said. "Beyond those trees that grow right up to the edge."

She started running swiftly with him closely behind her. At the same time, a gworl burst out of the bushes growing on the inner edge of the hill. He turned once to yell, obviously notifying his fellows that he had found the quarry. Then he attacked without waiting for them.

Wolff ran toward the gworl. When he saw the creature lift its knife to throw, he hurled the horn at it. This took the gworl by surprise—or perhaps the turning horn reflected sunlight into his eyes. Whatever the cause, his hesitation was enough for Wolff to get the advantage. He sped in as the gworl both ducked and reached a hand out for the horn. The huge hairy fingers curled around the horn, a cry of grating delight came from the creature, and Wolff was on him. He thrust at the protruding belly; the gworl brought his own knife up; the two blades clanged.

Having missed the first stroke, Wolff wanted to run again. This thing was undoubtedly skilled at knife-fighting. Wolff knew fencing quite well and had never given up its practice. But there was a big difference between dueling with the rapier and dirty in-close knivery, and he knew it. Yet he could not leave. In the first place, the gworl would down him with a

38

thrown blade in his back before he could take four steps. Also, there was the horn, clenched in the gnarled left fist of the gworl. Wolff could not leave that.

The gworl, realizing that Wolff was in a very bad situation, grinned. His upper canines shone long and wet and yellow and sharp. With those, thought Wolff, the thing did not need a knife.

Something goldenbrown, trailing long black-and-auburn-striped hair, flashed by Wolff. The gworl's eyes opened, and he started to turn to his left. The butt end of a pole, a long stick stripped of its leaves and part of its bark, drove into the gworl's chest. At the other end was Chryseis. She had run at top speed with the dead branch held like a vaulter's pole, but just before impact she had lowered it and it hit the creature with enough speed and weight behind it to bowl him over backward. The horn dropped from his fist, but the knife remained in the other.

Wolff jumped forward and thrust the end of his blade between two cartilaginous bosses and into the gworl's thick neck. The muscles were thick and tough there, but not enough to stop the blade. Only when the steel severed the windpipe did it halt.

Wolff handed Chryseis the gworl's knife. "Here, take it!"

She accepted it, but she seemed to be in shock. Wolff slapped her savagely until the glaze went from her eyes. "You did fine!" he said. "Which would you rather see dead, me or him?"

He removed the belt from the corpse and fastened it on himself. Now he had three knives. He scabbarded the bloody weapon, took the horn in one hand, Chryseis' hand in the other, and began running again. Behind them, a howl arose as the first of the gworl came over the edge of the hill. However, Wolff and Chryseis had about thirty yards' start, which they maintained until they reached the group of trees growing on the rim. Chryseis took the lead. She let herself face down on the rim and rolled over. Wolff looked over once before blindly following and saw a small ledge about six feet down from the rim. She had already let herself down the ledge and now was hanging by her hands. She dropped again, this time to a much more narrow ledge. But it did not end; it ran at a forty-five degree angle down the face of the cliff. They could use it if they faced inward against the stone cliff-wall and moved sideways, their hands spread to gain friction against the wall.

Wolff used both hands also; he had stuck the horn through the belt.

There was a howl from above. He looked up to see the first of the gworl dropping onto the first ledge. Then he glanced back at Chryseis and almost fell off from shock. She was gone.

Slowly, he turned his head to see over his shoulder and down

39

below. He fully expected to find her falling down the face of the cliff, if not already past it and plunging into the green abyss.

"Wolff!" she said. Her head was sticking out from the cliff itself. "There's a cave here. Hurry."

Trembling, sweating, he inched along the ledge to her and presently was inside an opening. The ceiling of the cave was several feet higher than his head; he could almost touch the walls on both sides when he stretched out his arms; the interior ran into the darkness.

"How far back does it go?"

"Not very far. But there's a natural shaft, a fault in the rock, that leads down. It opens on the bottom of the world; there's nothing below, nothing but air and sky."

"This can't be," he said slowly. "But it is. A universe founded on physical principles completely different than those of my universe. A flat planet with edges. But I don't understand how gravity works here. Where is its center?"

She shrugged and said, "The Lord may have told me a long time ago. But I've forgotten. I'd even forgotten he told me that Earth was round."

Wolff took the leather belt off, slid the scabbards off it, and picked up an oval black rock weighing about ten pounds. He slipped the belt through the buckle and then placed the stone within the loop. After piercing a hole near the buckle with the point of his knife, he tightened the loop. He had only to buckle the belt, and he was armed with a thong at the end of which was a heavy stone.

"You get behind and to one side of me," he said. "If I miss any, if one gets in past me, you push while he's off-balance. But don't go over yourself. Do you think you can do it?"

She nodded her head but evidently did not trust herself to speak.

"This is asking a lot of you. I'd understand if you cracked up completely. But, basically, you're made of sturdy ancient-Hellenic stock. They were a pretty tough lot in those days; you can't have lost your strength, even in this deadening pseudo-Paradise."

"I wasn't Achaean," she said. "I was Sminthean. But you are, in a way, right. I don't feel as badly as I thought I would. Only . . ."

"Only it takes getting used to." he said. He was encouraged, for he had expected a different reaction. If she could keep it up, the two of them might make it through this. But if she fell apart and he had a hysterical woman to control, both might fall under the attack of the gworl.

"Speaking of which," he muttered as he saw black, hairy,

40

gnarled fingers slide around the corner of the cave. He swung the belt hard so that the stone at its end smashed the hand. There was a bellow of surprise and pain, then a long ululating scream as the gworl fell. Wolff did not wait for the next one to appear. He got as close to the lip of the cave ledge as he dared and swung the stone again. It whipped around the corner and thudded against something soft. Another scream came, and it, too, faded away into the nothingness of the green sky.

"Three down, seven to go! Provided that no more have joined them."

He said to Chryseis, "They may not be able to get in here. But they can starve us out."

"The horn?"

He laughed. "They wouldn't let us go now even if I did hand them the horn. And I don't intend for them to get it. I'll throw the horn into the sky rather than do that."

A figure was silhouetted against the mouth of the cave as it dropped from above. The gworl, swinging in, landed on his feet and teetered for a second. But he threw himself forward, rolled in a hairy ball, and was up on his feet again. Wolff was so surprised that he failed to react immediately. He had not expected them to be able to climb above the cave and let themselves down, for the rock above the cave had looked smooth. Somehow, one had done it, and now he was inside, on his feet, a knife in hand.

Wolff whirled the stone at the belt-end and loosed it at the gworl. The creature flipped its knife at him; Wolff dodged but spoiled his aim of the stone. It flew over the furry bumpy head; the thrown knife brushed him lightly on his shoulder. He jumped for his own knife on the floor of the cave, saw another dark shape drop into the cave from above, and a third come around the corner of the mouth.

Something hit his head. His vision blurred, his senses grew dim, his knees buckled.

When he awoke, a pain in the side of his head, he had a frightening sensation. He seemed to be upside down and floating above a vast polished black disc. A rope was tied around his neck, and his hands were tied behind his back. He was hanging with his feet up in the empty air, yet there was only a slight tension of rope around his neck.

Bending his head back, he could see that the rope led upward into a shaft in the disc and that at the far end of the shaft was a pale light.

He groaned and closed his eyes, but opened them again. The world seemed to spin. Suddenly, he was reoriented. Now he knew that he was not suspended upside down against all the laws of gravity. He was hanging by a rope from the bottom underside of the planet. The green below him was the sky.

He thought, *I should have strangled before now. But there is no gravity pulling me downward.*

He kicked his feet, and the reaction drove him upward. The mouth of the shaft came closer. His head entered it, but something resisted him. His motion slowed, stopped, and, as if there were an invisible and compressed spring against his head, he began to move back down. Not until the rope tightened again did he stop his flight.

The gworl had done this to him. After knocking him out, they had let him down the shaft, or more probably, had carried him down. The shaft was narrow enough for a man to get down it with his back to one wall and his feet braced against the other. The descent would scrape the skin off a man, but the hairy hide of the gworl had looked tough enough to withstand descent and ascent without injury. Then a rope had been lowered, placed around his neck, and he had been dropped through the hole in the bottom of the world.

There was no way of getting himself back up. He would starve to death. His body would dangle in the winds of space until the rope rotted. He would not then fall, but would drift about in the shadow cast by the disc. The gworl he had knocked off the ledge had fallen, but their acceleration had kept them going.

Though despairing because of his situation, he could not help speculating about the gravitational configuration of the flat planet. The center must be at the very bottom; all attraction was upward through the mass of the planet. On this side, there was none.

What had the gworl done to Chryseis? Had they killed her as they had her friend?

He knew then that however they had dealt with her, they had purposely not hung her with him. They had planned that part of his agony would be that of not knowing her fate. As long as he could live at the end of this rope, he would wonder what had happened to her. He would conjure a multitude of possibilities, all horrible.

For a long time he hung suspended at a slight degree from the perpendicular, since the wind held him steady. Here, where there was no gravity, he could not swing like a pendulum.

Although he remained in the shadow of the black disc, he could see the progress of the sun. The sun itself was invisible, hidden by the disc, but the light from it fell on the rim of the great curve and slowly marched along it. The green sky beneath the sun glowed brightly, while the unlit portions before and after became dark. Then a paler lighting along the edge of the disc came into his sight, and he knew that the moon was following the sun.

It must be midnight, he thought. *If the gworl are taking her someplace, they could be some distance out on the sea. If they've been torturing her, she could be dead. If they've hurt her, I hope she's dead.*

Abruptly, while he hung in the gloom beneath the bottom of the world, he felt the rope at his neck jerk. The noose tightened, although not enough to choke him, and he was being drawn upward toward the shaft. He craned his neck to see who was hauling him up, but he could not penetrate the darkness of the mouth of the shaft. Then his head broke through the web of gravity—like surface tension on water, he thought—and he was hoisted clear of the abyss. Great strong hands and arms came around him to hug him against a hard, warm, furry chest. An alcoholic breath blew into his face. A leathery mouth scraped his cheek as the creature hugged him closer and began inching up the shaft with Wolff in its arms. Fur scraped on rock as the thing pushed with its legs. There was a jerk as the legs came up suddenly and took a new hold, followed by another scrape and lunge upward.

"Ipsewas?" Wolff said.

The zebrilla replied, "Ipsewas. Don't talk now. I have to save my wind. This isn't easy."

Wolff obeyed, although he had a difficult time in not asking about Chryseis. When they reached the top of the shaft, Ipsewas removed the rope from his neck and tossed him onto the floor of the cave.

Now at last he dared to speak. "Where is Chryseis?"

Ipsewas landed on the cave floor softly, turned Wolff over, and began to untie the knots around his wrists. He was breathing heavily from the trip up the shaft, but he said, "The gworl took her with them to a big dugout and began to sail across the sea toward the mountain. She shouted at me, begged me to help her. Then a gworl hit her, knocked her unconscious, I suppose. I was sitting there, drunk as the Lord, half-unconscious myself with nut juice, having a good time with Autonoe —you know, the *akowile* with the big mouth.

"Before Chryseis was knocked out, she screamed something about you hanging from the Hole in the Bottom of the World. I didn't know what she was talking about, because it's been a long time since I was here. How long ago I hate to say. Matter of fact, I don't really know. Everything's pretty much of a haze any more, you know."

"No, I don't," Wolff said. He rose and rubbed his wrists.

43

"But I'm afraid that if I stay here much longer, I might end up in an alcoholic fog, too."

"I was thinking about going after her," Ipsewas said. "But the gworl flashed those long knives at me and said they'd kill me. I watched them drag their boat out of the bushes, and about then I decided, what the hell, if they killed me, so what? I wasn't going to let them get away with threatening me or taking poor little Chryseis off to only the Lord knows what. Chryseis and I were friends in the old days, in the Troad, you know, although we haven't had too much to do with each other here for some time. I think it's been a long time. Anyway, I suddenly craved some real adventure, some genuine excitement—and I loathed those monstrous bumpy creatures.

"I ran after them, but by then they'd launched the boat, with Chryseis in it. I looked around for a *histoikhthys*, thinking I could ram their boat with it. Once I had them in the water, they'd be mine, knives or not. The way they acted in the boat showed me that they felt far from confident on the sea. I doubt they can even swim."

"I doubt it, too," Wolff said.

"But there wasn't a *histoikhthys* in reaching distance. And the wind was taking the boat away; it had a large lateen sail. I went back to Autonoe and took another drink. I might have forgotten about you, just as I was trying to forget about Chryseis. I was sure she was going to get hurt, and I couldn't bear to think about it, so I wanted to drink myself into oblivion. But Autonoe, bless her poor boozed-up brain, reminded me of what Chryseis had said about you.

"I took off fast, and looked around for awhile, because I couldn't remember just where the ledges were that led to the cave. I almost gave up and started drinking again. But something kept me going. Maybe I wanted to do just one good thing in this eternity of doing nothing, good or evil."

"If you hadn't come, I'd have hung there until I died of thirst. Now, Chryseis has a chance, if I can find her. I'm going after her. Do you want to come along?"

Wolff expected Ipsewas to say yes, but he did not think that Ipsewas would stick to his determination once the trip across the sea faced him. He was surprised, however.

The zebrilla swam out, seized a projection of shell as a *histoikhthys* sailed by, and swung himself upon the back of the creature. He guided it back to the beach by pressing upon the great nerve spots, dark purple blotches visible on the exposed skin just back of the cone-shaped shell that formed the prow of the creature.

Wolff, under Ipsewas' guidance, maintained pressure on a spot to hold the sailfish (for that was the literal translation of

44

histoikhthys) on the beach. The zebrilla gathered several arm-loads of fruit and nuts and a large collection of the punchnuts.

"We have to eat and drink, especially drink," Ipsewas muttered. "It may be a long way across Okeanos to the foot of the mountain. I don't remember."

A few minutes after the supplies had been stored in one of the natural receptacles on the sailfish's shell, they left. The wind caught the thin cartilage sail, and the great mollusc gulped in water through its mouth and ejected it through a fleshy valve in its rear.

"The gworl have a headstart," Ipsewas said, "but they can't match our speed. They won't get to the other side long before we do." He broke open a punchnut and offered Wolff a drink. Wolff accepted. He was exhausted but nervestrung. He needed something to knock him out and let him sleep. A curve of the shell afforded a cavelike ledge for him to crawl within. He lay hugged against the bare skin of the sailfish, which was warm. In a short time he was asleep, but his last glimpse was of the shouldering bulk of Ipsewas, his stripes blurred in the moon-light, crouching by the nerve spots. Ipsewas was lifting another punchnut above his head and pouring the liquid contents into his outthrust gorilloid lips.

When Wolff awoke, he found the sun was just coming around the curve of the mountain. The full moon (it was always full, for the shadow of the planet never fell on it) was just slipping around the other side of the mountain.

Refreshed but hungry, he ate some of the fruit and the protein-rich nuts. Ipsewas showed him how he could vary his diet with the "bloodberries". These were shiny maroon balls that grew in clusters at the tips of fleshy stalks that sprouted out of the shell. Each was large as a baseball and had a thin, easily torn skin that exuded a liquid that looked and tasted like blood. The meat within tasted like raw beef with a soup-con of shrimp.

"They fall off when they're ripe, and the fish get most of them," Ipsewas said. "But some float in to the beach. They're best when you get them right off the stalk."

Wolff crouched down by Ipsewas. Between mouthfuls, he said, "The *histoikhthys* is handy. They seem almost too much of a good thing."

"The Lord designed and made them for our pleasure and his," Ipsewas replied.

"The Lord made this universe?" Wolff said, no longer sure that the story was a myth.

"You better believe it," Ipsewas replied, and took another drink. "Because if you don't, the Lord will end you. As it is,

45

I doubt that he'll let you continue, anyway. He doesn't like uninvited guests."

Ipsewas lifted the nut and said, "Here's to your escaping his notice. And a sudden end and damnation to the Lord."

He dropped the nut and leaped at Wolff. Wolff was so taken by surprise he had no chance to defend himself. He went sprawling into the hollow of shell in which he had slept, with Ipsewas' bulk on him.

"Quiet!" Ipsewas said. "Stay curled up inside here until I tell you it's all right. It's an Eye of the Lord."

Wolff shrank back against the hard shell and tried to make himself one with the shadow of the interior. However, he did look out with one eye and thus he saw the ragged shadow of the raven scud across, followed by the creature itself. The dour bird flashed over once, wheeled, and began to glide in for a landing on the stern of the sailfish.

"Damn him! He can't help seeing me," Wolff muttered to himself.

"Don't panic," Ipsewas called. "Ahhh!"

There was a thud, a splash, and a scream that made Wolff start up and bump his head hard against the shell above him. Through the flashes of light and darkness, he saw the raven hanging limply within two giant claws. If the raven was eagle-sized, the killer that had dropped like a bolt from the green sky seemed, in that first second of shock, to be as huge as a roc. Wolff's vision straightened and cleared, and he saw an eagle with a light-green body, a pale red head, and a pale yellow beak. It was six times the bulk of the raven, and its wings, each at least thirty feet long, were flapping heavily as it strove to lift higher from the sea into which its missile thrust had carried both it and its prey. With each powerful downpush, it rose a few inches higher. Presently it began climbing higher, but before it got too far away, it turned its head and allowed Wolff to see its eyes. They were black shields mirroring the flames of death. Wolff shuddered; he had never seen such naked lust for killing.

"Well may you shudder," Ipsewas said. His grinning head was thrust into the cave of the shell. "That was one of Podarge's pets. Podarge hates the Lord and would attack him herself if she got the chance, even if she knew it would be her end. Which it would. She knows she can't get near the Lord, but she can tell her pets to eat up the Eyes of the Lord. Which they do, as you have seen."

Wolff left the cavern of the shell and stood for awhile, watching the shrinking figure of the eagle and its kill.

"Who is Podarge?"

"She is, like me, one of the Lord's monsters. She, too, once

46

lived on the shores of the Aegean; she was a beautiful young girl. That was when the great king Priamos and the godlike Akhilleus and crafty Odysseus lived. I knew them all; they would spit on the Kretan Ipsewas, the once-brave sailor and spear-fighter, if they could see me now. But I was talking of Podarge. The Lord took her to this world and fashioned a monstrous body and placed her brain within it.

"She lives up there someplace, in a cave on the very face of the mountain. She hates the Lord; she also hates every normal human being and will eat them, if her pets don't get them first. But most of all she hates the Lord."

That seemed to be all that Ipsewas knew about her, except that Podarge had not been her name before the Lord had taken her. Also, he remembered having been well acquainted with her. Wolff questioned him further, for he was interested in what Ipsewas could tell him about Agamemnon and Achilles and Odysseus and the other heroes of Homer's epic. He told the zebrilla that Agamemnon was supposed to be a historical character. But what about Achilles and Odysseus? Had they really existed?

"Of course they did," Ipsewas said. He grunted, then continued, "I suppose you're curious about those days. But there is little I can tell you. It's been too long ago. Too many idle days. Days?—centuries, millenia!—the Lord alone knows. Too much alcohol, too."

During the rest of the day and part of the night, Wolff tried to pump Ipsewas, but he got little for his trouble. Ipsewas, bored, drank half his supply of nuts and finally passed out snoring. Dawn came green and golden around the mountain. Wolff stared down into the waters, so clear that he could see the hundreds of thousands of fish, of fantastic configurations and splendors of colors. A bright-orange seal rose from the depths, a creature like a living diamond in its mouth. A purple-veined octopus, shooting backward, jetted by the seal. Far, far down, something enormous and white appeared for a second, then dived back toward the bottom.

Presently the roar of surf came to him, and a thin white line frothed at the base of Thayaphayawoed. The mountain, so smooth at a distance, was now broken by fissures, by juts and spires, by rearing scarps and frozen fountains of stone. Thayaphayawoed went up and up and up; it seemed to hang over the world.

Wolff shook Ipsewas until, moaning and muttering, the zebrilla rose to his feet. He blinked reddened eyes, scratched, coughed, then reached for another punchnut. Finally, at Wolff's urging, he steered the sailfish so that its course paralleled the base of the mountain.

"I used to be familiar with this area," he said. "Once I thought about climbing the mountain, finding the Lord, and trying to . . ." He paused, scratched his head, winced, and said, "Kill him! There! I knew I could remember the word. But it was no use. I didn't have the guts to try it alone."

"You're with me now," Wolff said.

Ipsewas shook his head and took another drink. "Now isn't then. If you'd been with me then . . . Well, what's the use of talking? You weren't even born then. Your great-great-great-great-grandfather wasn't born then. No, it's too late."

He was silent while he busied himself with guiding the sail-fish through an opening in the mountain. The great creature abruptly swerved; the cartilage sail folded up against the mast of stiff bone-braced cartilage; the body rose on a huge wave. And then they were within the calm waters of a narrow, steep, and dark fjord.

Ipsewas pointed at a series of rough ledges.

"Take that. You can get far. How far I don't know. I got tired and scared and I went back to the Garden. Never to return, I thought."

Wolff pleaded with Ipsewas. He said that he needed Ipsewas' strength very much and that Chryseis needed him. But the zebrilla shook his massive somber head.

"I'll give you my blessing, for what it's worth."

"And I thank you for what you've done," Wolff said. "If you hadn't cared enough to come after me, I'd still be swinging at the end of a rope. Maybe I'll see you again. With Chryseis."

"The Lord is too powerful," Ipsewas replied. "Do you think you have a chance against a being who can create his own private universe?"

"I have a chance," Wolff said. "As long as I fight and use my wits and have some luck, I have a chance."

He jumped off the decklike shell and almost slipped on the wet rock. Ipsewas called, "A bad omen, my friend!"

Wolff turned and smiled at him and shouted, "I don't believe in omens, my superstitious Greek friend! So long!"

CHAPTER FIVE

He began climbing and did not stop to look down until about an hour had passed. The great white body of the *histoikhthys* was a slim, pale thread by then, and Ipsewas was only a black dot on its axis. Although he knew he could not be seen, he waved at Ipsewas and resumed climbing.

Another hour's scrambling and clinging on the rocks brought him out of the fjord and onto a broad ledge on the face of the cliff. Here it was bright sunshine again. The mountain seemed as high as ever, and the way was as hard. On the other hand, it seemed no more difficult, although that was nothing over which to exult. His hands and knees were bleeding, and the ascent had made him tired. At first he was going to spend the night there, but he changed his mind. As long as the light lasted, he should take advantage of it.

Again he wondered if Ipsewas was correct about the gworl probably having taken just this route. Ipsewas claimed that there were other passages along the mountain where the sea rammed against it, but these were far away. He had looked for signs that the gworl had come this way and had found none. This did not mean that they had taken another path—if you could call this ragged verticality a path.

A few minutes later he came to one of the many trees that grew out of the rock itself. Beneath its twisted gray branches and mottled brown and green leaves were broken and empty nutshells and the cores of fruit. They were fresh. Somebody had paused for lunch not too long ago. The sight gave him new strength. Also, there was enough meat left in the nut shells for him to half-satisfy the pangs in his belly. The remnants of the fruits gave him moisture to put in his dry mouth.

Six days he climbed, and six nights rested. There was life on the face of the perpendicular, small trees and large bushes grew on the ledges, from the caves, and from the cracks. Birds of all sorts abounded, and many little animals. These fed off the berries and nuts or on each other. He killed birds with stones and ate their flesh raw. He discovered flint and chipped out a crude but sharp knife. With this, he made a short spear with a wooden shaft and another flint for the tip. He grew lean and hard with thick callouses on his hands and feet and knees. His beard lengthened.

On the morning of the seventh day, he looked out from a ledge and estimated that he must be at least twelve thousand feet above the sea. Yet the air was no thinner or colder than when he had begun climbing. The sea, which must have been at least two hundred miles across, looked like a broad river. Beyond was the rim of the world's edge, the Garden from which he had set out in pursuit of Chryseis and the gworl. It was as narrow as a cat's whisker. Beyond it, only the green sky.

A midnoon on the eighth day, he came across a snake feeding upon a dead gworl. Forty feet long, it was covered with black diamond spots and crimson seals of Solomon. The feet

49

that arrayed both sides grew out of the body without blessing of legs and were distressingly human-shaped. Its jaws were lined with three rows of sharkish teeth.

Wolff attacked it boldly, because he saw that a knife was sticking from its middle part and fresh blood was still oozing out. The snake hissed, uncoiled, and began to back away. Wolff stabbed at it a few times, and it lunged at him. Wolff drove the point of the flint into one of the large dull-green eyes. The snake hissed loudly and reared, its two-score of five-toed feet kicking. Wolff tore the spear loose from the bloodied eye and thrust it into the dead white area just below the snake's jaw. The flint went in deeply; the snake jerked so violently that it tore the shaft loose from Wolff's grip. But the creature fell over on its side, breathing deeply, and after awhile it died.

There was a scream above him, followed by a shadow. Wolff had heard that scream before, when he had been on the sailfish. He dived to one side and rolled across the ledge. Coming to a fissure, he crawled within it and turned to see what had threatened him. It was one of the enormous wide-winged, green-bodied, red-headed, yellow-beaked eagles. It was crouched on the snake and tearing out gobbets with a beak as sharp as the teeth in the snake's jaws. Between gulps it glared at Wolff, who tried to shrink even further within the protection of the fissure.

Wolff had to stay within his crevice until the bird had filled its crop. Since this took all of the rest of the day and the eagle did not leave the two corpses that night, Wolff became hungry, thirsty, and more than uncomfortable. By morning, he was also getting angry. The eagle was sitting by the two corpses, its wings folded around its body and its head drooping. Wolff thought that, if it were asleep, now would be the time to make a break. He stepped out of the crevice, wincing with the pain of stiff muscles. As he did so, the eagle jerked its head up, half-spread its wings, and screamed at him. Wolff retreated to the crevice.

By noon, the eagle still showed no intention of leaving. It ate little and seemed to be fighting drowsiness. Occasionally it belched. The sun beat down upon the bird and the two corpses. All three stank. Wolff began to despair. For all he knew, the eagle would remain until it had picked both reptile and gworl bare to the bone. By that time, he, Wolff, would be half-dead of starvation and thirst.

He left the fissure and picked up the spear. This had fallen out when the bird had ripped out the flesh around it. He jabbed threateningly at the eagle, which glared, hissed, and then screamed at him. Wolff shouted back and slowly backed away from the bird. It advanced with short slow steps, rolling slightly. Wolff stopped, yelled again, and jumped at the eagle. Startled, it leaped back and screamed again.

Wolff resumed his cautious retreat, but this time the eagle did not go after him. Only when the curve of the mountain took the predator out of view did Wolff resume climbing. He made sure that there was always a place to dodge into if the bird should come after him. However, no shadow fell on him. Apparently the eagle had wanted only to protect its food.

The middle of the next morning, he came across another gworl. This one had a smashed leg and was sitting with its back against the trunk of a small tree. It brandished a knife at a dozen red and rangy hoglike beasts with hooves like those of mountain goats. These paced back and forth before the crippled gworl and grunted in their throats. Now and then one made a short charge, but stopped a few feet away from the waving knife.

Wolff climbed a boulder and began throwing rocks at the hooved carnivores. A minute later, he wished he had not drawn attention to himself. The beasts clambered up the steep boulder as if stairs had been built for them. Only by rapid thrusting with the spear did he manage to push them back down on the ledge below. The flint tip dug into their tough hides a little but not enough to seriously hurt them.

Squealing, they landed on the rock below, only to scramble back up toward him. Their boar-tusks slashed close to him; a pair almost snipped one of his feet. He was busy trying to keep them from swarming over him when a moment came when all were on the ledge and none on the boulder. He dropped his spear, lifted a rock twice the size of his head, and hurled it down on the back of a boar. The beast screamed and tried to crawl away on its two undamaged front legs. The pack closed in on his paralyzed rear legs and began eating them. When the wounded beast turned to defend himself, he was seized by the throat. In a moment he was dead and being torn apart.

Wolff picked up his spear, climbed down the other side of the rock, and walked to the gworl. He kept an eye upon the feeders, but they did no more than raise their heads briefly to check on him before resuming their tearing at the carcass.

The gworl snarled at Wolff and held its knife ready. Wolff stopped far enough away so that he could dodge if the knife were thrown. A splinter of bone stuck out from the ravaged leg below the knee. The eyes of the gworl, sunk under the pads of cartilage on its low forehead, looked glassy.

Wolff had an unexpected reaction. He had thought that he would at once and savagely kill any gworl he came across. But now he wanted to talk to him. So lonely had he become during

51

the days and nights of climbing that he was glad to speak even to this loathsome creature.

He said, in Greek, "Is there any way in which I can help you?"

The gworl spoke in the back-of-the-throat syllables of its kind and raised the knife. Wolff started walking toward it, then hurled himself to one side as the knife whished by his head. He retrieved the knife, then walked up to the gworl and spoke to him again. The thing grated back, but in a weaker voice. Wolff, bending over to repeat his question, was struck in the face with a mass of saliva.

That triggered off his hate and fear. He rammed the knife into the thick neck; the gworl kicked violently several times and died. Wolff wiped the knife on the dark fur and looked through the leather bag attached to the gworl's belt. It contained dried meat, dried fruit, some dark, hard bread, and a canteen with a fiery liquor. Wolff was not sure about where the meat came from, but he told himself that he was too hungry to be picky. Biting into the bread was an experience; it was almost as hard as stone but, when softened with saliva, tasted like graham crackers.

Wolff kept on climbing. The days and nights passed with no more signs of the gworl. The air was as thick and warm as at sea level, yet he estimated that he must be at least 30,000 feet up. The sea below was a thin silver girdle around the waist of the world.

That night he awakened to feel dozens of small furry hands on his body. He struggled, only to find that the many hands were too strong. They gripped him fast while others tied his hands and feet together with a rope that had a grassy texture. Presently he was lifted high and carried out onto the stone apron before the small cave in which he had slept. The moonlight showed several score bipeds, each about two and a half feet high. They were covered with sleek gray fur, mouselike, but had a white ruff around their necks. The faces were black and pushed in and resembled a bat's. Their ears were enormous and pointed.

Silently, they rushed him over the apron and into another fissure. This opened to reveal a large chamber about thirty feet wide and twenty high. Moonlight bored through a crack in the ceiling and revealed what his nose had already detected, a pile of bones with some rotting flesh. He was set down near the bones while his captors retreated to one corner of the cave. They began talking, or at least twittering, among themselves. One walked over to Wolff, looked at him a moment, and sank onto his knees by Wolff's throat. A second later, he was gnawing at the throat with tiny but very sharp teeth. Others followed him; teeth began chewing all over his body.

It was all done in a literally deadly silence. Even Wolff made no noise beyond his harsh breathing as he struggled. The sharp little pains of the teeth quickly passed, as if some mild anaesthetic were being released into his blood.

He began to feel drowsy. Despite himself, he quit fighting. A pleasant numbness spread through him. It did not seem worthwhile to battle for his life; why not go out pleasantly? At least his death would not be useless. There was something noble in giving his body so that these little beings could fill their bellies and be well-fed and happy for a few days.

A light burst into the cave. Through the warm haze, he saw the batfaces leap away from him and run to the extreme end of the cave, where they cowered together. The light became stronger and was revealed as a torch of burning pine. An old man's face followed the light and bent over him. He had a long white beard, a sunken mouth, a curved sharp nose, and huge supraorbital ridges with bristling eyebrows. A dirty white robe covered his shrunken body. His big-veined hand held a staff on the end of which was a sapphire, large as Wolff's fist, carved in the image of a harpy.

Wolff tried to speak but could only mutter a tangled speech, as if he were coming up out of ether after an operation. The old man gestured with the staff, and several of the batfaces detached themselves from the mass of fur. They scurried sideways across the floor, their slanted eyes turned fearfully toward the old man. Quickly, they untied Wolff. He managed to rise to his feet, but he was so wobbly that the old man had to support him out of the cave.

The ancient spoke in Mycenaean Greek. "You'll feel better soon. The venom does not last long."

"Who are you? Where are you taking me?"

"Out of this danger," the old man said. Wolff pondered the enigmatic answer. By the time that his mind and body were functioning well again, they had come to another entrance to a cave. They went through a complex of chambers that gradually led them upward. When they had covered about two miles, the old man stopped before a cave with a large iron door. He handed the torch to Wolff, pulled the door open, and waved him on in. Wolff entered into a large cavern bright with torches. The door clanged behind him, succeeded by the thud of a bolt shooting fast.

The first thing that struck him was the choking odor. The next, the two green red-headed eagles that closed in on him. One spoke in a voice like a giant parrot's and ordered him to march on ahead. He did so, noting at the same time that the batfaces must have removed his knife. The weapon would not have done him much good. The cave was thronged with the birds, each of which towered above him.

Against one wall were two cages made of thin iron bars. In one was a group of six gworl. In the other was a tall well-built youth wearing a deerskin breech-cloth. He grinned at Wolff and said, "So you made it! How you've changed!"

Only then did the reddish-bronze hair, long upper lip, and craggy but merry face become familiar. Wolff recognized the man who had thrown the horn from the gworl-besieged boulder and who called himself Kickaha.

CHAPTER SIX

Wolff did not have time to reply, for the cage door was opened by one of the eagles, who used his foot as effectively as a hand. A powerful head and hard beak shoved him into the cage; the door ground shut behind him.

"So, here you are," Kickaha said in a rich baritone voice. "The question is, what do we do now? Our stay here may be short and unpleasant."

Wolff, looking through the bars, saw a throne carved out of rock, and on it a woman. A half-woman, rather, for she had wings instead of arms and the lower part of her body was that of a bird. The legs, however, were much thicker in proportion than those of a normal-sized Earth eagle. They had to support more weight, Wolff thought, and he knew that here was another of the Lord's laboratory-produced monsters. She must be the Podarge of whom Ipsewas had spoken.

From the waist up she was such a woman as few men are privileged to see. Her skin was white as a milky opal, her breasts superb, the throat a column of beauty. The hair was long and black and straight and fell on both sides of a face that was even more beautiful than Chryseis', an admission that he had not thought it possible to evoke from him.

However, there was something horrible in the beauty: a madness. The eyes were fierce as those of a caged falcon teased beyond endurance.

Wolff tore his eyes from hers and looked about the cave. "Where is Chryseis?" he whispered.

"Who?" Kickaha whispered back.

With a few quick sentences, Wolff described her and what had happened to him.

Kickaha shook his head. "I've never seen her."

"But the gworl?"

54

"There were two bands of them. The other must have Chryseis and the horn. Don't worry about them. If we don't talk our way out of this, we're done for. And in a very hideous way."

Wolff asked about the old man. Kickaha replied that he had once been Podarge's lover. He was an aborigine, one of those who had been brought into this universe shortly after the Lord had fashioned it. The harpy now kept him to do the menial work which required human hands. The old man had come at Podarge's order to rescue Wolff from the batfaces, undoubtedly because she had long ago heard from her pets of Wolff's presence in her domain.

Podarge stirred restlessly on her throne and unfolded her wings. They came together before her with a splitting noise like distant lightning.

"You two there!" she shouted. "Quit your whispering! Kickaha, what more do you have to say for yourself before I loose my pets?"

"I can only repeat, at the risk of seeming tiresome, what I said before!" Kickaha replied loudly. "I am as much the enemy of the Lord as you, and he hates me, he would kill me! He knows I stole his horn and that I'm a danger to him. His Eyes rove the four levels of the world and fly up and down the mountains to find me. And . . ."

"Where is this horn you said you stole from the Lord? Why don't you have it now? I think you are lying to save your worthless carcass!"

"I told you that I opened a gate to the next world and that I threw it to a man who appeared at the gate. He stands before you now."

Podarge turned her head as an eagle swivels hers, and she glared at Wolff. "I see no horn. I see only some tough stringy meat behind a black beard!"

"He says that another band of gworl stole it from him," Kickaha replied. "He was chasing after them to get it back when the batfaces captured him and you so magnanimously rescued him. Release us, gracious and beautiful Podarge, and we will get the horn back. With it, we will be in a position to fight the Lord. He can be beaten! He may be the powerful Lord, but he is not all-powerful! If he were, he would have found us and the horn long ago!"

Podarge stood up, preened her wings, and walked down the steps from the throne and across the floor to the cage. She did not bob as a bird does when walking, but strode stiff-legged.

"I wish that I could believe you," she said in a lower but just as intense voice. "If only I could! I have waited through the years and the centuries and the millenia, oh, so long that

55

my heart aches to think of the time! If I thought that the weapons for striking back at him had finally come within my hands ..."

She stared at them, held her wings out before her, and said, "See! 'My hands,' I said. But I do not have hands, nor the body that once was mine. That ..." And she burst into a raging invective that made Wolff shrink. It was not the words but the fury, bordering on divinity or mindlessness, that made him grow cold.

"If the Lord can be overthrown—and I believe he can—you will be given back your human body," Kickaha said when she had finished.

She panted with a clench of her anger and stared at them with the lust of murder. Wolff felt that all was lost, but her next words showed that the passion was not for them.

"The old Lord has been gone for a long time, so the rumor says. I sent one of my pets to investigate, and she came back with a strange tale. She said that there is a new Lord there, but she did not know whether or not it was the same Lord in a new body. I sent her back to the Lord, who refused my pleas to be given my rightful body again. So it does not matter whether or not there is another Lord. He is just as evil and hateful as the old one, if he is indeed not the old one. But I must know!

"First, whoever now is the Lord must die. Then I will find out if he had a new body or not. If the old Lord has left this universe, I will track him through the worlds and find him!"

"You can't do that without the horn," Kickaha said. "It and it alone opens the gate without a counter-device in the other world."

"What have I to lose?" Podarge said. "If you are lying and betray me, I will have you in the end, and the hunt might be fun. If you mean what you say, then we will see what happens."

She spoke to the eagle beside her, and it opened the gate. Kickaha and Wolff followed the harpy across the cave to a great table with chairs around it. Only then did Wolff see that the chamber was a treasure house; the loot of a world was piled up in it. There were large open chests crammed with gleaming jewels, pearl necklaces, and golden and silver cups of exquisite shape. There were small figurines of ivory and of some shining hard-grained black wood. There were magnificent paintings. Armor and weapons of all kinds, except firearms, were piled carelessly at various places.

Podarge commanded them to sit down in ornately wrought chairs with carved lion's feet. She beckoned with a wing, and out of the shadows stepped a young man. He carried a heavy golden tray on which were three finely chiseled cups of crystal-quartz. These were fashioned as leaping fish with wide open mouths; the mouths were filled with a rich dark red wine.

"One of her lovers," Kickaha whispered in answer to Wolff's curious stare at the handsome blond youth. "Carried by her eagles from the level known as Dracheland or Teutonia. Poor fellow! But it's better than being eaten alive by her pets, and he always has the hope of escaping to make his life bearable."

Kickaha drank and breathed out satisfaction at the heavy but blood-brightening taste. Wolff felt the wine writhe as if alive. Podarge gripped the cup between the tips of her two wings and lifted it to her lips.

"To the death and damnation of the Lord. Therefore, to your success!"

The two drank again. Podarge put her cup down and flicked Wolff lightly across the face with the ends of the feathers of one wing. "Tell me your story."

Wolff talked for a long while. He ate from slices of a roast goat-pig, a light brown bread, and fruit, and he drank the wine. His head began reeling, but he talked on and on, stopping only when Podarge questioned him about something. Fresh torches replaced the old and still he talked.

Abruptly, he awoke. Sunshine was coming in from another cave, lighting the empty cup and the table on which his head had lain while he had slept. Kickaha, grinning, stood by him.

"Let's go," he said. "Podarge wants us to get started early. She's eager for revenge. And I want to get out before she changes her mind. You don't know how lucky we are. We're the only prisoners she's ever given freedom."

Wolff sat up and groaned with the ache in his shoulders and neck. His head felt fuzzy and a little heavy, but he had had worse hangovers.

"What did you do after I fell asleep?" he said.

Kickaha smiled broadly. "I paid the final price. But it wasn't bad, not bad at all. Rather peculiar at first, but I'm an adaptable fellow."

They walked out of the cave into the next one and from thence onto the wide lip of stone jutting from the cliff. Wolff turned for one last look and saw several eagles, green monoliths, standing by the entrance to the inner cave. There was a flash of white skin and black wings as Podarge crossed stiff-legged before the giant birds.

"Come on," Kickaha said. "Podarge and her pets are hungry. You didn't see her try to get the gworl to plead for mercy. I'll say one thing for them, they didn't whine or cry. They spat at her."

Wolff jumped as a ripsaw scream came from the cave mouth.

Kickaha took Wolff's arm and urged him into a fast walk. More jagged cries tore from eagle beaks, mingled with the ululations from beings in fear and pain of death.

"That'd be us, too," Kickaha said, "if we hadn't had something to trade for our lives."

They began climbing and by nightfall were three thousand feet higher. Kickaha untied the knapsack of leather from his back and produced various articles. Among these was a box of matches, with one of which he started a fire. Meat and bread and a small bottle of the Rhadamanthean wine followed. The bag and the contents were gifts from Podarge.

"We've got about four days of climbing before we get to the next level," the youth said. "Then, the fabulous world of Amerindia.'

Wolff started to ask questions, but Kickaha said, that he ought to explain the physical structure of the planet. Wolff listened patiently, and when he had heard Kickaha out, he did not scoff. Moreover, Kickaha's explanation corresponded with what he had so far seen. Wolff's intentions to ask how Kickaha, obviously a native of Earth, had come here were frustrated. The youth, complaining that he had not slept for a long time and had had an especially exhausting night, fell asleep.

Wolff stared for awhile into the flames of the dying fire. He had seen and experienced much in a short time, but he had much more to go through. That is, he would if he lived. A whooping cry rose from the depths, and a great green eagle screamed somewhere in the air along the mountain-face.

He wondered where Chryseis was tonight. Was she alive, and if so, how was she faring? And where was the horn? Kickaha had said that they had to find the horn if they were to have any success at all. Without it, they would inevitably lose.

So thinking, he too fell asleep.

Four days later, when the sun was in the midpoint of its course around the planet, they pulled themselves over the rim. Before them was a plain that rolled for at least 160 miles before the horizon dropped it out of sight. To both sides, perhaps a hundred miles away, were mountain ranges. These might be large enough to cause comparison with the Himalayas. But they were mice beside the monolith, Abharhploonta, that dominated this section of the multilevel planet. Abharhploonta was, so Kickaha claimed, fifteen hundred miles from the rim, yet it looked no more than fifty miles away. It towered fully as high as the mountain up which they had just climbed.

58

"Now you get the idea," Kickaha said. "This world is not pear-shaped. It's a planetary Tower of Babylon. A series of staggered columns, each smaller than the one beneath it. On the very apex of this Earth-sized tower is the palace of the Lord. As you can see, we have a long way to go.

"But it's a great life while it lasts! I've had a wild and wonderful time! If the Lord struck me at this moment, I couldn't complain. Although, of course, I would, being human and therefore bitter about being cut off in my prime! And believe me, my friend, I'm prime!"

Wolff could not help smiling at the youth. He looked so gay and buoyant, like a bronze statue suddenly touched into animation and overflowingly joyous because he was alive.

"Okay!" Kickaha cried. "The first thing we have to do is get some fitting clothes for you! Nakedness is chic in the level below, but not on this one. You have to wear at least a breech-cloth and a feather in your hair; otherwise the natives will have contempt for you. And contempt here means slavery or death for the contemptible."

He began walking along the rim, Wolff with him.

"Observe how green and lush the grass is and how it is as high as our knees, Bob. It affords pasture for browsers and grazers. But it is also high enough to conceal the beasts that feed on the grass-eaters. So beware! The plains puma and the dire wolf and the striped hunting dog and the giant weasel prowl through the grasses. Then there is Felis Atrox, whom I call the atrocious lion. He once roamed the plains of the North American Southwest, became extinct there about 10,000 years ago. He's very much alive here, one-third larger than the African lion and twice as nasty.

"Hey, look there! Mammoths!"

Wolff wanted to stop to watch the huge gray beasts, which were about a quarter of a mile away. But Kickaha urged him on. "There're plenty more around, and there'll be times when you wish there weren't. Spend your time watching the grass. If it moves contrary to the wind, tell me."

They walked swiftly for two miles. During this time, they came close to a band of wild horses. The stallions whickered and raced up to investigate them, then stood their ground, pawing and snorting, until the two had passed. They were magnificent animals, tall, sleek, and black or glossy red or spotted white and black.

"Nothing of your Indian pony there," Kickaha said. "I think the Lord imported nothing but the best stock."

Presently, Kickaha stopped by a pile of rocks. "My marker," he said. He walked straight inward across the plain from the cairn. After a mile they came to a tall tree. The youth leaped

59

up, grabbed the lowest branch, and began climbing. Half-way up, he reached a hollow and brought out a large bag. On returning, Kickaha took out of the bag two bows, two quivers of arrows, a deerskin breechcloth, and a belt with a skin scabbard in which was a long steel knife.

Wolff put on the loincloth and belt and took the bow and quiver.

"You know how to use these?" Kickaha said.

"I've practised all my life."

"Good. You'll get more than one chance to put your skill to the test. Let's go. We've many a mile to cover."

They began wolf-trotting: run a hundred steps, walk a hundred steps. Kickaha pointed to the range of mountains to their right.

"There is where my tribe, the Hrowakas, the Bear People, live. Eighty miles away. Once we get there, we can take it easy for awhile, and make preparations for the long journey ahead of us."

"You don't look like an Indian," Wolff said.

"And you, my friend, don't look like a sixty-six-year old man, either. But here we are. Okay. I've put off telling my story because I wanted to hear yours first. Tonight I'll talk."

They did not speak much more that day. Wolff exclaimed now and then at the animals he saw. There were great herds of bison, dark, shaggy, bearded, and far larger than their cousins of Earth. There were other herds of horses and a creature that looked like the prototype of the camel. More mammoths and then a family of steppe mastodons. A pack of six dire wolves raced alongside the two for awhile at a distance of a hundred yards. These stood almost as high as Wolff's shoulder.

Kickaha, seeing Wolff's alarm, laughed and said, "They won't attack us unless they're hungry. That isn't very likely with all the game around here. They're just curious."

Presently, the giant wolves curved away, their speed increasing as they flushed some striped antelopes out of a grove of trees.

"This is North America as it was a long time before the white man," Kickaha said. "Fresh, spacious, with a multitude of animals and a few tribes roaming around."

A flock of a hundred ducks flew overhead, honking. Out of the green sky, a hawk fell, struck with a thud, and the flock was minus one comrade. "The Happy Hunting Ground!" Kickaha cried. "Only it's not so happy sometimes!"

Several hours before the sun went around the mountain, they stopped by a small lake. Kickaha found the tree in which he had built a platform.

"We'll sleep here tonight, taking turns on watch. About the only animal that might attack us in the tree is the giant weasel, but he's enough to worry about. Besides, and worse, there could be war parties."

Kickaha left with his bow in hand and returned in fifteen minutes with a large buck rabbit. Wolff had started a small fire with little smoke; over this they roasted the rabbit. While they ate, Kickaha explained the topography of the country.

"Whatever else you can say about the Lord, you can't deny he did a good job of designing this world. You take this level, Amerindia. It's not really flat. It has a series of slight curves each about 160 miles long. These allow the water to run off, creeks and rivers and lakes to form. There's no snow anywhere on the planet—can't be, with no seasons and a fairly uniform climate. But it rains every day—the clouds come in from space somewhere."

They finished eating the rabbit and covered the fire. Wolff took first watch. Kickaha talked all through Wolff's turn at guard. And Wolff stayed awake through Kickaha's watch to listen.

In the beginning, a long time ago, more than 20,000 years, the Lords had dwelt in a universe parallel to Earth's. They were not known as the Lords then. There were not very many of them at that time, for they were the survivors of a millenia-long struggle with another species. They numbered perhaps ten thousand in all.

"But what they lacked in quantity they more than possessed in quality," Kickaha said. "They had a science and technology that makes ours, Earth's, look like the wisdom of Tasmanian aborigines. They were able to construct these private universes. And they did.

"At first each universe was a sort of playground, a microcosmic country club for small groups. Then, as was inevitable, since these people were human beings no matter how godlike in their powers, they quarreled. The feeling of property was, is, as strong in them as in us. There was a struggle among them. I suppose there were also deaths from accident and suicide. Also, the isolation and loneliness of the Lords made them megalomaniacs, natural when you consider that each played the part of a little god and came to believe in his role.

"To compress an eons-long story into a few words, the Lord who built this particular universe eventually found himself alone. Jadawin, was his name, and he did not even have a mate of his own kind. He did not want one. Why should he share this world with an equal, when he could be a Zeus with a million Europas, with the loveliest of Ledas?

"He had populated this world with beings abducted from

other universes, mainly Earth's, or created in the laboratories in the palace on top of the highest tier. He had created divine beauties and exotic monsters as he wished.

"The only trouble was, the Lords were not content to rule over just one universe. They began to covet the worlds of the others. And so the struggle was continued. They erected nearly impregnable defenses and conceived almost invincible offenses. The battle became a deadly game. This fatal play was inevitable, when you consider that boredom and ennui were enemies the Lords could not keep away. When you are near-omnipotent, and your creatures are too lowly and weak to interest you forever, what thrill is there besides risking your immortality against another immortal?"

"But how did you come into this?" Wolff said.

"I? My name on Earth was Paul Janus Finnegan. My middle name was my mother's family name. As you know, it also happens to be that of the Latin god of gates and of the old and new year, the god with two faces, one looking ahead and one looking behind."

Kickaha grinned and said, "Janus is very appropriate, don't you think? I am a man of two worlds, and I came through the gate between. Not that I have ever returned to Earth or want to. I've had adventures and I've gained a stature here I never could have had on that grimy old globe. Kickaha isn't my only name, and I'm a chief on this tier and a big shot of sorts on other tiers. As you will find out."

Wolff was beginning to wonder about him. He had been so evasive that Wolff suspected Kickaha had another identity about which he did not intend to talk.

"I know what you're thinking, but don't you believe it," Kickaha said. "I'm a trickster, but I'm leveling with you. By the way, did you know how I came by my name among the Bear People? In their language, a *kickaha* is a mythological character, a semidivine trickster. Something like the Old Man Coyote of the Plains Indians or Nanabozho of the Ojibway or Wakdjunkaga of the Winnebago. Some day I'll tell you how I earned that name and how I became a councilor of the Hrowakas. But I've more important things to tell you now."

CHAPTER SEVEN

In 1941, at the age of twenty-three Paul Finnegan had volunteered for the U.S. Cavalry because he loved horses. A short time later, he found himself driving a tank. He was with the Eighth Army and so eventually crossed the Rhine. One day, after having helped take a small town, he discovered an extra-ordinary object in the ruins of the local museum. It was a crescent of silvery metal, so hard that hammer blows did not dent it nor an acetylene torch melt it.

"I asked some of the citizens about it. All they knew was that it had been in the museum a long time. A professor of chemistry, after making some tests on it, had tried to interest the University of Munich in it but had failed.

"I took it home with me after the war, along with other souvenirs. Then I went back to the University of Indiana. My father had left me enough money to see me through for a few years, so I had a nice little apartment, a sports car, and so on.

"A friend of mine was a newspaper reporter. I told him about the crescent and its peculiar properties and unknown composition. He wrote a story about it which was printed in Bloomington, and the story was picked up by a syndicate. It didn't create much interest among scientists—in fact, they wanted nothing to do with it.

"Three days later, a man calling himself Mr. Vannax appeared at my apartment. I thought he was Dutch because of his name and his foreign accent. He wanted to see the crescent. I obliged. He got very excited, although he tried to appear calm. He said he'd like to buy it from me. I asked how much he'd pay, and he said he'd give ten thousand dollars, but no more.

"'Sure you can go higher,' I said," Kickaha continued. "'Because if you don't, you'll get nowhere.'

"'Twenty thousand?' Vannax said.

"'Let's pump it up a bit,' I said.

"'Thirty thousand?'"

Finnegan decided to plunge. He asked Vannax if he would pay $100,000. Vannax became even redder in the face and swelled up "like a hoppy toad", as Finnegan-Kickaha said. But he replied that he would have the sum in twenty-four hours.

"Then I knew I really had something," Kickaha said to Wolff. "The question was, what? Also, why did this Vannax character so desperately want it? And what kind of a nut was he? No one with good sense, no normal human being, would rise so fast to the bait. He'd be cagier."

"What did Vannax look like?" Wolff asked.

"Oh, he was a big guy, a well-preserved sixty-five. He had an eagle beak and eagle eyes. He was dressed in expensive conservative clothes. He had a powerful personality, but he was trying to restrain it, to be real nice. And having a hell of a time doing it. He seemed to be a man who wasn't used to being balked in any thing."

63

" 'Make it $300,000, and it's yours' I said. I never dreamed he'd say yes. I thought he'd get made and take off. Because I wasn't going to sell the crescent, not if he offered me a million."

Vannax, although furious, said that he would pay $300,000 but Finnegan would have to give him an additional twenty-four hours.

" 'You have to tell me why you want the crescent and what good it is first,' I said.

" 'Nothing doing!' he shouted. 'It is enough for you to rob me, you pig of a merchant, you, you earth . . . worm!'

" 'Get out before I throw you out. Or before I call the police,' I said."

Vannax began shouting in a foreign tongue. Finnegan went into his bedroom and came out with a .45 automatic. Vannax did not know it was not loaded. He left, although he was cursing and talking to himself all the way to his 1940 Rolls-Royce.

That night Finnegan had trouble getting to sleep. It was after 2:00 P.M. before he succeeded, and even then he kept waking up. During one of his rousings he heard a noise in the front room. Quietly, he rolled out of bed and took the .45, now loaded, from under his pillow. On the way to the bedroom door he picked up his flashlight from the bureau.

Its beam caught Vannax stooping over in the middle of the living room. The silvery crescent was in his hand.

"Then I saw the second crescent on the floor. Vannax had brought another with him. I'd caught him in the act of placing the two together to form a complete circle. I didn't know why he was doing it, but I found out a moment later.

"I told him to put his hands up. He did so, but he lifted his foot to step into the circle. I told him not to move even a trifle, or I'd shoot. He put one foot inside the circle, anyway. So I fired. I shot over his head, and the slug went into a corner of the room. I just wanted to scare him, figuring if he got shaken up enough he might start talking. He was scared all right; he jumped back.

"I walked across the room while he backed up toward the door. He was babbling like a maniac, threatening me in one breath and offering me half a million in the next. I thought I'd back him up against the door and jam the .45 in his belly. He'd really talk then, spill his guts out about the crescent.

"But as I followed him across the room I stepped into the circle formed by the two crescents. He saw what I was doing and screamed at me not to. Too late then. He and the apartment disappeared, and I found myself still in the circle—only it wasn't quite the same—and in this world. In the palace of the Lord, on top of the world."

Kickaha said he might have gone into shock then. But he had avidly read fantasy and science-fiction since the fourth grade of grammar school. The idea of parallel universes and devices for transition between them was familiar. He had been conditioned to accept such concepts. In fact, he half-believed in them. Thus he was flexible-minded enough to bend without breaking and then bounce back. Although frightened, he was at the same time excited and curious.

"I figured out why Vannax hadn't followed me through the gate. The two crescents, placed together, formed a 'circuit'. But they weren't activated until a living being stepped within whatever sort of 'field' they radiated. Then one semicircle remained behind on Earth while the other was gated through to this universe, where it latched onto a semicircle waiting for it. In other words, it takes three crescents to make a circuit. One in the world to which you're going, and two in the one you're leaving. You step in; one crescent transfers over to the single one in the next universe, leaving only one crescent in the world you just left.

"Vannax must have come to Earth by means of these crescents. And he would not, could not, do so unless there had been a crescent already on Earth. Somehow, maybe we'll never know, he lost one of them on Earth. Maybe it was stolen by someone who didn't know its true value. Anyway, he must've been searching for it, and when that news story went out about the one I had found in Germany, he knew what it was. After talking to me, he concluded I might not sell it. So he got into my apartment with the crescent he did have. He was just about to complete the circle and pass on over when I stopped him.

"He must be stranded on Earth and unable to get here unless he finds another crescent. For all I know, there may be others on Earth. The one I got in Germany might not even be the one he lost."

Finnegan wandered about the "palace" for a long while. It was immense, staggeringly beautiful and exotic and filled with treasure, jewels and artifacts. There were also laboratories, or perhaps bioprocess chambers was a better title. In these, Finnegan saw strange creatures slowly forming within huge transparent cylinders. There were many consoles with many operating devices, but he had no idea what they did. The symbols beneath the buttons and levers were unfamiliar.

"I was lucky. The palace is filled with traps to snare or kill the uninvited. But they were not set—why, I don't know, any more than I knew then why the place was untenanted. But it was a break for me."

Finnegan left the palace for awhile to go through the exquisite garden that surrounded it. He came to the edge of the monolith on which the palace and garden were.

"You've seen enough to imagine how I felt when I looked over the edge. The monolith must be at least thirty thousand feet high. Below it is the tier that the Lord named Atlantis. I don't know whether the Earth myth of Atlantis was founded on this Atlantis or whether the Lord got the name from the myth.

"Below Atlantis is the tier called Dracheland. Then, Amerindia. One sweep of my eye took it in, just as you can see one side of the Earth from a rocket. No details, of course, just big clouds, large lakes, seas, and outlines of continents. And a good part of each successively lower tier was obscured by the one just above it.

"But I could make out the Tower of Babylon structure of this world, even though I didn't, at that time, understand what I was seeing. It was just too unexpected and alien for me to apprehend any sort of *gestalt*. It didn't mean anything."

Finnegan could, however, understand that he was in a desperate situation. He had no means of leaving the top of this world except by trying to return to Earth through the crescents. Unlike the sides of the other monoliths, the face of this one was smooth as a bearing ball. Nor was he going to use the crescents again, not with Vannax undoubtedly waiting for him.

Although he was in no danger of starving—there was food and water enough to last for years—he could not and did not want to stay there. He dreaded the return of the owner, for he might have a very nasty temper. There were some things in the palace which made Kickaha feel uneasy.

"But the gworl came," Kickaha said. "I suppose—I know —they came from another universe through a gate similar to that which had opened the way for me. At the time, I had no way of knowing how or why they were in the palace. But I was glad I'd gotten there first. If I'd fallen into their hands. . . ! Later, I figured out they were agents for another Lord. He's sent them to steal the horn. Now, I'd seen the horn during my wandering about the palace, and had even blown it. But I didn't know how to press the combinations of buttons on it to make it work. As a matter of fact, I didn't know its real purpose.

"The gworl came into the palace. A hundred or so of them. Fortunately, I saw them first. Right away, they let their lust for murder get them into trouble. They tried to kill some of the Eyes of the Lord, the eagle-sized ravens in the garden. These hadn't bothered me, perhaps because they thought I was a guest or didn't look dangerous.

"The gworl tried to slit a raven's throat, and the ravens attacked them. The gworl retreated into the palace, where the big birds followed them. There were blood and feathers and pieces of bumpy hairy hide and a few corpses of both sides all over that end of the palace. During the battle, I noticed a gworl coming out of a room with the horn. He went through the corridors as if looking for something."

Finnegan followed the gworl into another room, about the size of two dirigible hangars. This held a swimming pool and a number of interesting but enigmatic devices. On a marble pedestal was a large golden model of the planet. On each of its levels were several jewels. As Finnegan was to discover, the diamonds, rubies, and sapphires were arranged to form symbols. These indicated various points of resonance.

"Points of resonance?"

"Yes. The symbols were coded mnemonics of the combination of notes required to open gates at certain places. Some gates open to other universes, but others are simply gates between the tiers on this world. These enabled the Lord to travel instantaneously from one level to the next. Associated with the symbols were tiny models of outstanding characteristics of the resonant points on the various tiers."

The gworl with the horn must have been told by the Lord how to read the symbols. Apparently, he was testing for the Lord to make sure he had the correct horn. He blew seven notes toward the pool, and the waters parted to reveal a piece of dry land with scarlet trees around it and a green sky beyond.

"It was the conceit of the original Lord to enter into the Atlantean tier through the pool itself. I didn't know at that time where the gate led to. But I saw my only chance to escape from the trap of the palace, and I took it. Coming up from behind the gworl, I snatched the horn from his hand and pushed him sideways into the pool—not into the gate, but into the water.

"You never heard such squawks and screams and such thrashings around. All the fear they don't have for other things is packed into a dread of water. This gworl went down, came up sputtering and yelling, and then managed to grab hold of the side of the gate. A gate has definite edges, you know, tangible if changing.

"I heard roars and shouts behind me. A dozen gworl with big and bloody knives were entering the room. I dived into the hole, which had started shrinking. It was so small I scraped the skin off my knees going through. But I got through, and the hole closed. It took off both the arms of the gworl who was trying to get out of the water and follow me. I had the horn in my hand, and I was out of their reach for the time being."

Kickaha grinned as if relishing the memory. Wolff said,

"The Lord who sent the gworl ahead is the present Lord, right? Who is he?"

"Arwoor. The Lord who's missing was known as Jadawin. He must be the man who called himself Vannax. Arwoor moved in, and ever since he's been trying to find me and the horn."

Kickaha outlined what had happened to him since he had found himself on the Atlantean tier. During the twenty years (of Earth time), he had been living on one tier or another, always in disguise. The gworl and the ravens, now serving the new Lord Arwoor, had never stopped looking for him. But there were long periods of time, sometimes two or three years on end, when Kickaha had not been disturbed.

"Wait a minute," Wolff said. "If the gates between the tiers were closed, how did the gworl get down off the monolith to chase you?"

Kickaha had not been able to understand that either. However, when captured by the gworl in the Garden level, he had questioned them. Although surly, they had given him some answers. They had been lowered to the Atlantean tier by cords.

"Thirty thousand feet?" Wolff said.

"Sure, why not? The palace is a fabulous many-chambered storehouse. If I'd had a chance to look long enough, I'd have found the cords myself. Anyway, the gworl told me they were charged by the Lord Arwoor not to kill me. Even if it meant having to let me escape at the time. He wants me to enjoy a series of exquisite tortures. The gworl said that Arwoor had been working on new and subtle techniques, plus refining some of the well established methods. You can imagine how I was sweating it out on the journey back."

After his capture in the Garden, Kickaha was taken across Okeanos to the base of the monolith. While they were climbing up it, a raven Eye stopped them. He had carried the news of Kickaha's capture to the Lord, who sent him back with orders. The gworl were to split into two bands. One was to continue with Kickaha. The other was to return to the Garden rim. If the man who now had the horn were to return through the gate with it, he was to be captured. The horn would be brought back to the Lord.

Kickaha said, "I imagine Arwoor wanted you brought back, too. He probably forgot to relay such an order to the gworl through the raven. Or else he assumed you'd be taken to him, forgetting that the gworl are very literal-minded and unimaginative.

"I don't know why the gworl captured Chryseis. Perhaps they intend to use her as a peace-offering to the Lord. The gworl know he is displeased with them because I've led them such a long and sometimes even merry chase. They may mean to placate him with the former Lord's most beautiful master-piece."

Wolff said, "Then the present Lord can't travel between tiers via the resonance points?"

"Not without the horn. And I'll bet he's in a hot-and-cold running sweat right now. There's nothing to prevent the gworl from using the horn to go to another universe and present it to another Lord. Nothing except their ignorance of where the resonance points are. If they should find one ... However, they didn't use it by the boulder, so I imagine they won't try it else-where. They're vicious but not bright."

Wolff said, "If the Lords are such masters of super-science, why doesn't Arwoor use aircraft to travel?"

Kickaha laughed for a long time. Then he said, "That's the joker. The Lords are heirs to a science and power far surpass-ing Earth's. But the scientists and technicians of their people are dead. The ones now living know how to operate their devices, but they are incapable of explaining the principles behind them or of repairing them.

"The millenia-long power struggle killed off all but a few. These few, despite their vast powers, are ignoramuses. They're sybarites, megalomaniacs, paranoiacs, you name it. Anything but scientists.

"It's possible that Arwoor may be a dispossessed Lord. He had to run for his life, and it was only because Jadawin was gone for some reason from this world that Arwoor was able to gain possession of it. He came empty-handed into the palace; he has no access to any powers except those in the palace, many of which he may not know how to control. He's one up in this Lordly game of musical universes, but he's still handi-capped."

Kickaha fell asleep. Wolff stared into the night, for he was on first watch. He did not find the story incredible, but he did think that there were holes in it. Kickaha had much more explaining to do. Then there was Chryseis. He thought of an achingly beautiful face with delicate bone structure and great cat-pupiled eyes. Where was Chryseis, how was she faring, and would he ever see her again?

CHAPTER EIGHT

During Wolff's second watch, something black and long and swift slipped through the moonlight between two bushes. Wolff sent an arrow into the predator, which gave a whistling scream and reared up on its hind legs, towering twice as high as a horse. Wolff fitted another arrow to the string and fired it into the white belly. Still the animal did not die, but went whistling and crashing away through the brush.

By then Kickaha, knife in hand, was beside him. "You were lucky," he said. "You don't always see them, and then, pffft! They go for the throat."

"I could have used an elephant gun," Wolff said, "and I'm not sure that would have stopped it. By the way, why don't the gworl—or the Indians, from what you've told me—use firearms?"

"It's strictly forbidden by the Lord. You see, the Lord doesn't like some things. He wants to keep his people at a certain population level, at a certain technological level, and within certain social structures. The Lord runs a tight planet.

"For instance, he likes cleanliness. You may have noticed that the folk of Okeanos are a lazy, happy-go-lucky lot. Yet they always clean up their messes. No litter anywhere. The same goes on this level, on every level. The Amerindians are also personally clean, and so are the Drachelanders and Atlanteans. The Lord wants it that way, and the penalty for disobedience is death."

"How does he enforce his rules?" Wolff asked.

"Mostly by having implanted them in the mores of the inhabitants. Originally, he had a close contact with the priests and medicine men, and by using religion—with himself as the deity—he formed and hardened the ways of the populace. He liked neatness, disliked firearms or any form of advanced technology. Maybe he was a romantic; I don't know. But the various societies on this world are mainly conformist and static."

"So there's no progress?"

"So what? Is progress necessarily desirable or a static society undesirable? Personally, though I detest the Lord's arrogance, his cruelty and lack of humanity, I approve of some of the things he's done. With some exceptions, I like this world, far prefer it to Earth."

"You're a romantic, too!"

"Maybe. This world is real and grim enough, as you already know. But it's free of grit and grime, of diseases of any kind, of flies and mosquitoes and lice. Youth lasts as long as you live. All in all, it's not such a bad place to live in. Not for me, anyway."

Wolff was on the last watch when the sun rounded the corner of the world. The starflies paled, and the sky was green wine. The air passed cool fingers over the two men and washed their lungs with invigorating currents. They stretched and then went

70

down from the platform to hunt for breakfast. Later, full of roast rabbit and juicy berries, they renewed their journey.

The evening of the third day after, while the sun was a hand's breadth from slipping around the monolith, they were out on the plain. Ahead of them was a tall hill beyond which, so Kickaha said, was a small woods. One of the high trees there would give them refuge for the night.

Suddenly a party of about forty men rode around the hill. They were dark-skinned and wore their hair in two long braids. Their faces were painted with white and red streaks and black X's. Their lower arms bore small round shields, and they held lances or bows in their hands. Some wore bear-heads as helmets; others had feathers stuck into caps or wore bonnets with sweeping bird feathers.

Seeing the two men on foot before them, the riders yelled and urged their horses into a gallop. Lances tipped with steel points were leveled. Bows were fitted with arrows, and heavy steel axes or blade-studded clubs were lifted.

"Stand firm!" Kickaha said. He was grinning. "They are the Hrowakas, the Bear People. My people."

He stepped forward and lifted his bow above him with both hands. He shouted at the charging men in their own tongue, a speech with many glottalized stops, nasalized vowels, and a swift-rising but slow-descending intonation.

Recognizing him, they shouted, "AngKungawas TreKickaha!" They galloped by, their spears stabbing as closely as possible without touching him, the clubs and axes whistling across his face or above his head, and arrows plunging near his feet or even between them.

Wolff was given the same treatment, which he bore without flinching. Like Kickaha, he showed a smile, but he did not think that it was as relaxed.

The Hrowakas wheeled their horses and charged back. This time they pulled their beasts up short, rearing, kicking, and whinnying. Kickaha leaped up and dragged a feather-bonneted youth from his animal. Laughing and panting, the two wrestled on the ground until Kickaha had pinned the Hrowakas. Then Kickaha arose and introduced the loser to Wolff.

"NgashuTangis, one of my brothers-in-law."

Two Amerinds dismounted and greeted Kickaha with much embracing and excited speech. Kickaha waited until they were calmed down and then began to speak long and earnestly. He frequently jabbed his finger toward Wolff. After a fifteen-minute discourse, interrupted now and then by a brief question, he turned smiling to Wolff.

"We're in luck. They're on their way to raid the Tsenakwa, who live fairly close to the Trees of Many Shadows. I explained what we were doing here, though not all of it by any means. They don't know we're bucking the Lord himself, and I'm not about to tell them. But they do know we're on the trail of Chryseis and the gworl and that you're a friend of mine. They also know that Podarge is helping us. They've got a great respect for her and her eagles and would like to do her a favor if they could.

"They've got plenty of spare horses, so take your choice. Only thing I hate about this is that you won't get to visit the lodges of the Bear People and I'll miss seeing my two wives, Giushowei and Angwanat. But you can't have everything."

The warparty rode hard that day and the next, changing horses every half-hour. Wolff became saddle-sore—blanket-sore, rather. By the third morning he was in as good a shape as any of the Bear People and could stay on a horse all day without feeling that he had lockjaw in every muscle of his body and even in some of the bones.

The fourth day, the party was held up for eight hours. A herd of the giant bearded bison marched across their path; the beasts formed a column two miles across and ten miles long, a barrier that no one, man or animal, could cross. Wolff chafed, but the others were not too unhappy, because rider and horse alike needed a rest. Then, at the end of the column, a hundred Shanikotsa hunters rode by, intent on driving their lances and arrows into the bison on the fringes. The Hrowakas wanted to swoop down upon them and slay the entire group and only an impassioned speech by Kickaha kept them back. Afterwards, Kickaha told Wolff that the Bear People thought one of them was equal to ten of any other tribe.

"They're great fighters, but a little bit overconfident and arrogant. If you knew how many times I've had to talk them out of getting into situations where they would have been wiped out!"

They rode on, but were halted at the end of an hour by NgashuTangis, one of the scouts for that day. He charged in yelling and gesturing. Kickaha questioned him, then said to Wolff, "One of Podarge's pets is a couple of miles from here. She landed in a tree and requested NgashuTangis to bring me to her. She can't make it herself; she's been ripped up by a flock of ravens and is in a bad way. Hurry!"

The eagle was sitting on the lowest branch of a lone tree, her talons clutched about the narrow limb, which bent under her weight. Dried red-black blood covered her green feathers, and one eye had been torn out. With the other, she glared at the Bear People, who kept a respectful distance. She spoke in Mycenaean to Kickaha and Wolff.

72

"I am Aglaia. I know you of old, Kickaha—Kickaha the trickster. And I saw you, O Wolff, when you were a guest of great-winged Podarge, my sister and queen. She it was who sent many of us out to search for the dryad Chryseis and the gworl and the horn of the Lord. But I, I alone, saw them enter the Trees of Many Shadows on the other side of the plain.

"I swooped down on them, hoping to surprise them and seize the horn. But they saw me and formed a wall of knives against which I could only impale myself. So I flew back up, so high they could not see me. But I, far-sighted treader of the skies, could see them."

"They're arrogant, even while dying," Kickaha said softly in English to Wolff. "Rightly so."

The eagle drank water offered by Kickaha, and continued. "When night fell, they camped at the edge of a copse of trees. I landed on the tree below which the dryad slept under a deer-skin robe. It had dried blood on it, I suppose from the man who had been killed by the gworl. They were butchering him, getting ready to cook him over their fires.

"I came down to the ground on the opposite side of the tree. I had hoped to talk to the dryad, perhaps even enable her to escape. But a gworl sitting near her heard the flutter of my wings. He looked around the tree, and that was his mistake, for my claws took him in his eyes. He dropped his knife and tried to tear me loose from his face. And so he did, but much of his face and both eyes came along with my talons. I told the dryad to run then, but she stood up and the robe fell off. I could see then that her hands and her legs were bound.

"I went into the brush, leaving the gworl to wail for his eyes. For his death, too, because his fellows would not be burdened with a blind warrior. I escaped through the woods and back to the plains. There I was able to fly off again. I flew toward the nest of the Bear People to tell you, O Kickaha and O Wolff, beloved of the dryad. I flew all night and on into the day.

"But a hunting pack of the Eyes of the Lord saw me first. They were above and ahead of me, in the glare of the sun. They plummeted down, those play-hawks, and took me by surprise. I fell, driven by their impact and by the weight of a dozen with their talons clamped upon me. I fell, turning over and over and bleeding under the thrusts of flint-sharp beaks.

"Then I, Aglaia, sister to Podarge, righted myself and also gathered my senses. I seized the shrieking ravens and bit their heads off or tore their wings or legs off. I killed the dozen on me, only to be attacked by the rest of the pack. These I fought, and the story was the same. They died, but in their dying they caused my death. Only because they were so many."

There was a silence. She glared at them with her remaining

73

eye, but the life was swiftly unraveling from it to reveal the blank spool of death. The Bear People had fallen quiet; even the horses had ceased snorting. The wind whispering in from the skies was the loudest noise.

Abruptly, Aglaia spoke in a weak but still arrogantly harsh voice.

"Tell Podarge she need not be ashamed of me. And promise me, O Kickaha—no trickster words to me—promise me that Podarge will be told."

"I promise, O Aglaia," Kickaha said. "Your sisters will come here and carry your body far out from the rims of the tiers, out in the green skies, and you will be launched to float through the abyss, free in death as in life, until you fall into the sun or find your resting place upon the moon."

"I hold you to it, manling," she said.

Her head drooped, and she fell forward. But the iron talons were locked in on the branch so that she swung back and forth, upside down. The wings sagged and spread out, the tips brushing the ends of the grass.

Kickaha exploded into orders. Two men were dispatched to look for eagles to be informed of Aglaia's report and of her death. He said nothing, of course, about the horn, and he had to spend some time in teaching the two a short speech in Mycenaean. After being satisfied that they had memorized it satisfactorily, he sent them on their way. Then the party was delayed further in getting Aglaia's body to a higher position in the tree, where she would be beyond the reach of any carnivore except the puma and the carrion birds.

It was necessary to chop off the limb to which she clung and to hoist the heavy body up to another limb. Here she was tied with rawhide to the trunk and in an upright position.

"There!" Kickaha said when the work was done. "No creature will come near her as long as she seems to be alive. All fear the eagles of Podarge."

The afternoon of the sixth day after Aglaia the party made a long stop at a waterhole. The horses were given a chance to rest and to fill their bellies with the long green grass. Kickaha and Wolff squatted side by side on top of a small hill and chewed on an antelope steak. Wolff was gazing interestedly at a small herd of mastodons only four hundred yards away. Near them, crouched in the grass, was a striped male lion, a 900-pound specimen of Felix Atrox. The lion had some slight hopes of getting a chance at one of the calves.

Kickaha said, "The gworl were damn lucky to make the forest in one piece, especially since they're on foot. Between

74

here and the Trees of Many Shadows are the Tsenakwa and other tribes. And the KhingGatawriT."

"The Half-Horses?" Wolff said. In the few days with the Hrowakas, he had picked up an amazing amount of vocabulary items and was even beginning to grasp some of the complicated syntax.

"The Half-Horses. *Hoi Kentauroi*. Centaurs. The Lord made them, just as he's made the other monsters of this world. There are many tribes of them on the Amerindian plains. Some are Scythian or Sarmatian speakers, since the Lord snatched part of his centaur material from those ancient steppe-dwellers. But others have adopted the tongues of their human neighbors. All have adopted the Plains tribal culture—with some variations."

The warparty came to the Great Trade Path. This was distinguishable from the rest of the plain only by posts driven into the ground at mile-intervals and topped by carved ebony images of the Tishquetmoac god of commerce, Ishquettlammu. Kickaha urged the party into a gallop as they came near it and it did not slow until the Path was far behind.

"If the Great Trade Path ran to the forest, instead of parallel with it," he told Wolff, "we'd have it made. As long as we stayed on it, we'd be undisturbed. The Path is sacrosanct; even the wild Half-Horses respect it. All the tribes get their steel weapons, cloth blankets, jewelry, chocolate, fine tobacco, and so on from the Tishquetmoac, the only civilized people on this tier. I hurried us across the Path because I wouldn't be able to stop the Hrowakas from tarrying for a few days' trade if we came across a merchant caravan. You'll notice our braves have more furs than they need on their horses. That's just in case. But we're okay now."

Six days went by with no sign of enemy tribes except the black-and-red striped tepees of the Irennussoik at a distance. No warriors rode out to challenge them, but Kickaha did not relax until many miles had fallen behind them. The next day the plain began to change: the knee-high and bright green grass was interspersed with a bluish grass only several inches high. Soon the party was riding over a rolling land of blue.

"The stamping ground of the Half-Horse," Kickaha said. He sent the scouts to a greater distance from the main party.

"Don't let yourself be taken alive," he reminded Wolff.

"Especially by the Half-Horse. A human plains tribe might decide to adopt you instead of killing you if you had guts enough to sing merrily and spit in their faces while they roasted you over a low fire. But the Half-Horses don't even have human slaves. They'd keep you alive and screaming for weeks."

75

On the fourth day after Kickaha's warning, they topped a rise and saw a black band ahead.

"Trees growing along the Winnkaknaw River," Kickaha said. "We're almost halfway to the Trees of Many Shadows. Let's push the horses until we get to the river. I've got a hunch we've eaten up most of our luck."

He fell silent as he and the others saw a flash of sun on white several miles to their right. Then the white horse of Wicked Knife, a scout, disappeared into a shallow between rises. A few seconds later, a dark mass appeared on the rise behind him.

"The Half-Horse!" Kickaha yelled. "Let's go! Make for the river! We can make a stand in the trees along it, if we can get there!"

CHAPTER NINE

With a single lurch, the entire warparty broke into a gallop. Wolff crouched over his horse, a magnificent roan stallion, urging it on although it needed no encouragement. The plain sped by as the roan stretched his heart to drive his legs. Despite his intensity on speed, Wolff kept glancing to his right. Wicked Knife's white mare was visible now and then as she came over a swell of the plain. The scout was directing her at an angle toward his people. Less than a quarter of a mile behind, and gaining, was the horde of Half-Horse. They numbered at least a hundred and fifty, maybe more.

Kickaha brought his stallion, a golden animal with a pale silvery mane and tail, alongside Wolff. "When they catch up with us—which they will—stay by my side! I'm organizing a column of twos, a classic maneuver, tried and true! That way, each man can guard the other's side!"

He dropped back to give orders to the rest. Wolff guided his roan to follow in line behind Wolverine Paws and Sleeps Standing Up. Behind him, White Nose Bear and Big Blanket were trying to maintain an even distance from him. The rest of the party was strung out in a disorder which Kickaha and a councillor, Spider Legs, were trying to break up.

Presently, the forty were arranged in a ragged column. Kickaha rode up beside Wolff and shouted above the pound of hooves and whistling of wind: "They're stupid as porcupines! They wanted to turn and charge the centaurs! But I talked some sense into them!"

Two more scouts, Drunken Bear and Too Many Wives, were riding in from the left to join them. Kickaha gestured at them to fall in at the rear. Instead, the two continued their 90-degree approach and rode on past the tail of the column.

"The fools are going to rescue Wicked Knife—they think!"

The two scouts and Wicked Knife approached toward a converging point. Wicked Knife was only four hundred yards away from the Hrowakas with the Half-Horses several hundred yards behind him. They were lessening the gap with every second, traveling at a speed no horse burdened with a rider could match. As they came closer, they could be seen in enough detail for Wolff to understand just what they were.

They were indeed centaurs, although not quite as the painters of Earth had depicted. This was not surprising. The Lord, when forming them in his biolabs, had had to make certain concessions to reality. The main adjustment had been regulated by the need for oxygen. The large animal part of a centaur had to breathe, a fact ignored by the conventional Terrestrial representations. Air had to be supplied not only to the upper and human torso but to the lower and theriomorphic body. The relatively small lungs of the upper part could not handle the air requirements.

Moreover, the belly of the human trunk would have stopped all supply of nourishment to the large body beneath it. Or, if the small belly was attached to the greater equine digestive organs to transmit the food, diet was still a problem. Human teeth would quickly wear out under the abrasion of grass.

Thus the hybrid beings coming so swiftly and threateningly toward the men did not quite match the mythical creatures that had served as their models. The mouths and necks were proportionately large to allow intake of enough oxygen. In place of the human lungs was a bellows-like organ which drove the air through a throat-like opening and thence into the great lungs of the hippoid body. These lungs were larger than a horse's, for the vertical part increased the oxygen demands. Space for the bigger lungs was made by removal of the larger herbivore digestive organs and substitution of a smaller carnivore stomach. The centaur ate meat, including the flesh of his Amerind victims.

The equine part was about the size of an Indian pony of Earth. The hides were red, black, white, palomino, and pinto. The horsehair covered all but the face. This was almost twice as large as a normal-sized man's and was broad, high-cheekboned, and big-nosed. They were, on a larger scale, the features of the Plains Indians of Earth, the faces of Roman Nose, Sitting Bull, and Crazy Horse. Warpaint streaked their features and feathered bonnets and helmets of buffalo hides with projecting horns were on their heads.

Their weapons were the same as those of the Hrowakas, except for one item. This was the bola: two round stones, each secured to the end of a strip of rawhide. Even as Wolff won-

77

dered what he would do if a bola were cast at him, he saw them put into action. Wicked Knife and Drunken Bear and Too Many Wives had met and were racing beside each other about twenty yards ahead of their pursuers. Drunken Bear turned and shot an arrow. The missile plunged into the swelling bellows-organ beneath the human-chest of a Half-Horse. The Half-Horse went down and turned over and over and then lay still. The upper torso was bent at an angle that could result only from a broken spine. This despite the fact that a universal joint of bone and cartilage at the juncture of the human and equine permitted extreme flexibility of the upper torso.

Drunken Bear shouted and waved his bow. He had made the first kill, and his exploit would be sung for many years in the Hrowakas Council House.

If there's anybody left to tell about it, Wolff thought.

A number of bolas, whirled around and around till the stones were barely visible, were released. Rotating like airplane propellors that had spun off from their shafts, the bolas flew through the air. The stone at the end of one struck Drunken Bear on the neck and hurled him from his horse, cutting off his victory chant in the middle. Another bola wrapped itself around the hind leg of his horse to send it crashing into the ground.

Wolff, at the same time as some of the Hrowakas, released an arrow. He could not tell if it went home, for it was difficult to get a good aim and release from a position on a galloping horse. But four arrows did strike, and four Half-Horses fell. Wolff at once drew another arrow from the quiver on his back, noting at the same time that Too Many Wives and his horse were on the ground. Too Many Wives had an arrow sticking from his back.

Now, Wicked Knife was overtaken. Instead of spearing him, the Half-Horses split up to come in on either side of him.

"No!" Wolff cried. "Don't let them do it!"

Wicked knife, however, had not earned his public name for no good reason. If the Half-Horse passed up the chance to kill him so they could take him alive for torture, they would have to pay for their mistake. He flipped his long Tishquetmoac knife through the air into the equine body of the Half-Horse closest to him. The centaur cart-wheeled. Wicked Knife drew another blade from his scabbard and, even as a spear was driven into his horse, he launched himself onto the centaur who had thrust the spear.

Wolff caught a glimpse of him through the massed bodies. He had landed on the back of the centaur, which almost collapsed at the impact of his weight but managed to recover and

78

bear him along. Wicked Knife drove his knife into the back of the human torso. Hooves flashed; the centaur's tail rose into the air above the mob, followed by the rump and the hindlegs.

Wolff thought that Wicked Knife was finished. But no, there he was, miraculously on his feet and then, suddenly, on the horse-barrel of another centaur. This time Wicked Knife held the edge of his blade against his enemy's throat. Apparently he was threatening to cut the jugular vein if the Half-Horse did not carry him out and away from the others.

But a lance, thrust from behind, plunged into Wicked Knife's back. Not, however, before he had carried out his threat and slashed open the neck of the Half-Horse he rode.

"I saw that!" Kickaha shouted. "What a man, that Wicked Knife! After what he did, not even the savage Half-Horse would dare mutilate his body! They honor a foe who gives them a great fight, although they'll eat him, of course."

Now the KhingGatawriT came up closely behind the end of the Hrowakas train. They split up into parts and increased their speed to overtake them on both sides. Kickaha told Wolff that the Half-Horses would not, at first, close in on the Hrowakas in a mass charge. They would try to have some fun with their enemies and would also give their untried young warriors a chance to show their skill and courage.

A black-and-white-spotted Half-Horse, wearing a single hawk's feather in a band around his head, detached himself from the main group on the left. Whirling a bola in his right hand, holding a feathered lance in his left, he charged at an angle toward Kickaha. The stones at the rawhide ends circled to become a blur, then darted from his hand. Their path of flight was downward, toward the legs of his enemy's horse.

Kickaha leaned out and deftly stuck the tip of his lance at the bola. The lancehead was so timed that it met the rawhide in the middle. Kickaha raised the lance, the bola whirled around and around it, and wrapped itself shut. A good part of the energy of the bola was absorbed by the length of the lance. Also, the lance was brought over in an arc to Kickaha's right side nearly striking Wolff, who had to duck. Even so, Kickaha almost lost the lance, for it slid from his hand, carried by the inertia of the bola. But he kept his grip and shook the lance with the bola at its upper end.

The frustrated Half-Horse shook his fist in fury and would have charged Kickaha with his lance. A roar of acclamation and admiration arose from the two columns of centaurs. A chief raced out to forestall the youngster. He spoke a few words to send him in shame back to the main body. The chief was a large roan with a many-feathered bonnet and a number of black chevrons, crossed with a bar, painted on his equine ribs.

"Charging Lion!" Kickaha shouted in English. "He thinks I'm worthy of his attention!"

He yelled something in the chief's language and then whooped with laughter as the dark skin became even darker. Charging Lion shouted back and spurted forward to bring him even with his insulter. The lance in his right hand stabbed at Kickaha, who countered with his own. The two shafts bounced off each other. Kickaha immediately detached his small mammoth-hide shield from his left arm. He blocked another thrust from the centaur's lance with his lance, then spun the shield like a disc. It sailed out and struck Charging Lion's right foreleg.

The centaur slipped and fell on his front legs and skidded upright through the grass. When he attempted to rise, he found that his right front leg was lamed. A yell broke loose from his group; a dozen bonneted chiefs ran with leveled lances at Charging Lion. He bore himself bravely and waited for his death with folded arms as a great, but now defeated and crippled, Half-Horse should.

"Pass the word along to slow down!" Kickaha said. "The horses can't keep this pace up much longer; their lungs are foaming out now. Maybe we can spare them and gain some time if the Half-Horses want to blood some more of their untrieds. If they don't, well, what's the difference?"

"It's been fun," Wolff said. "If we don't make it, we can at least say we weren't bored."

Kickaha rode close enough to clap Wolff on the shoulder. "You're a man after my own heart! I'm happy to have known you. Oh oh! Here comes an unblooded now! But he's going to pick on Wolverine Paws!"

Wolverine Paws, one of Kickaha's fathers-in-law, was at the head of the Hrowakas column and just in front of Wolff. He screamed insults at the Half-Horse charging in with circling bola, and then threw his lance. The Half-Horse, seeing the weapon flying toward him, loosed the bola before he had intended. The lance pierced his shoulder; the bola went true anyway and wrapped itself around Wolverine Paws. Unconscious from a blow by one of the stones, he fell off his horse.

The horses of both Wolff and Kickaha leaped over his body, which was lying before them. Kickaha leaned down to his right and stabbed Wolverine Paws with his lance.

"They won't take delight in torturing you, Wolverine Paws!" Kickaha said. "And you have made them pay for a life with a life."

80

A period of individual combat followed. Again and again a young untried charged out of the main group to challenge one of the human beings. Sometimes the man won, sometimes the centaur. At the end of a nightmare thirty minutes, the forty Hrowakas had become twenty-eight. Wolff's turn was with a large warrior armed with a club tipped with steel points. He also carried a small round shield with which he tried to duplicate Kickaha's trick. It did not work, for Wolff deflected the shield with the point of his lance. However, his guard was open for a moment, during which the centaur took his advantage. He galloped in so close that Wolff could not turn to draw far back enough to use the lance.

The club was raised high; the sun glittered on the sharp tips of its spike. The huge broad painted face was split with a grin of triumph. Wolff had no time to dodge and if he tried to grab the club he would end with a smashed and mangled hand. Without thinking, he did a thing that surprised both himself and the centaur. Perhaps he was inspired by Wicked Knife's feat. He launched himself from his horse, came in under the club, and grappled the Half-Horse around the neck. His foe squawked with dismay. Then they went down to the ground with a shock that knocked the wind from both.

Wolff leaped up, hoping that Kickaha had grabbed his horse so he could remount. Kickaha was holding it, but he was making no move to bring it back. Indeed, both the Hrowakas and Half-Horse had stopped.

"Rules of war!" Kickaha shouted. "Whoever gets the club first should win!"

Wolff and the centaur, now on his hooves, made a dash for the club, which was about thirty feet behind them. Four-legged speed was too much for two-legged. The centaur reached the club ten feet ahead of him. Without checking his pace, the centaur leaned his human trunk down and scooped up the club. Then he slowed and whirled, so swiftly that he had to rear up on his hind legs.

Wolff had not stopped running. He came in and then up at the Half-Horse even as it reared. A hoof flashed out at him, but he was by it, though the leg brushed against him. He crashed into the upper part, carried it back a little with him, and both fell again.

Despite the impact, Wolff kept his right arm around the centaur's neck. He hung on while the creature struggled to his hooves. The centaur had lost the club and now strove to overcome the human with sheer strength. Again he grinned, for he outweighed Wolff by at least seven hundred pounds. His torso, chest, and arms were also far bulkier than Wolff's.

Wolff braced his feet against the shoving weight of the centaur and would not move back. The grip around the huge neck tightened, and suddenly the Half-Horse could not breathe.

Then the Half-Horse tried to get his knife out, but Wolff grabbed the wrist with his other hand and twisted. The centaur screamed with the pain and dropped the knife.

A roar of surprise came from the watching Half-Horses. They had never seen such power in a mere man before.

Wolff strained, jerked, and brought the struggling warrior to his foreknees. His left fist punched into the heaving bellows beneath the ribs and sank in. The Half-Horse gave a loud whoosh. Wolff released his hold, stepped back, and used his right fist against the thick jaw of the half-unconscious centaur. The head snapped back, and the centaur fell over. Before he could regain consciousness, his skull was smashed by his own club.

Wolff remounted, and the three columns rode on at a canter. For awhile, the Half-Horse made no move against their enemies. Their chiefs seemed to be discussing something. Whatever it was they intended to do, they lost their chance a moment later.

The cavalcades went over a slight rise and down into a broad hollow. This was just deep enough to conceal from them the pride of lions that had been lying there. Apparently the twenty or so of Felis Atrox had fed off a protocamel the night before and had been too drowsy to pay any attention to the noise of the approaching hooves. But now that the intruders were suddenly among them, the great cats sprang into action. Their fury was aggravated even more by their desire to protect the cubs among them.

Wolff and Kickaha were lucky. Although there were huge shapes bounding on every side, none came at them. But Wolff did get close enough to a male to view every awe-inspiring detail, and that was as close as he ever cared to be. The cat was almost as large as a horse and, though he lacked the mane of the African lion, he did not lack for majesty and ferocity. He bounded by Wolff and hurled himself upon the nearest centaur, which went down screaming. The jaws closed on the centaur's throat, and it was dead. Instead of worrying the corpse, as he might normally have done, the male sprang upon another Half-Horse, and this one went down as easily.

All was a chaos of roaring cats and screaming horses, men, and Half-Horse. It was everyone for himself; to hell with the battle that had been going on.

It took only thirty seconds for Wolff and Kickaha and those Hrowakas who had been fortunate enough not to be attacked to ride out of the hollow. They did not need to urge their horses

82

to speed, but they did have trouble keeping them from running themselves to death.

Behind them, but at a distance now, the centaurs who had evaded the lions streamed out of the hollow. Instead of pursuing the Hrowakas at once, they rode to a safe distance from the lions and then paused to evaluate their losses. Actually, they had not suffered more than a dozen casualties, but they had been severely shaken up.

"A break for us!" Kickaha shouted. "However, unless we can get to the woods before they catch up again, we're done for! They aren't going to continue the individual combats anymore. They'll make a concerted charge!"

The woods that they longed for still looked as far off as ever. Wolff did not think that his horse, magnificent beast though it was, could make it. Its coat was dark with sweat, and it was breathing heavily. Yet it pounded on, an engine of finely tempered flesh and spirit that would run until its heart ruptured.

Now the Half-Horse were in full gallop and slowly catching up with them. In a few minutes they were within arrow range. A few shafts came flying by the pursued and plunged into the grass. Thereafter, the centaurs held their fire, for they saw that bows were too inaccurate with the speed and unevenness at which both archer and target were traveling.

Suddenly Kickaha gave a whoop of delight. "Keep going!" he shouted at them all. "May the Spirit of Akjaw-Dimis favor you!"

Wolff did not understand him until he looked at where Kickaha's finger was pointing. Before them, half-hidden by the tall grass, were thousands of little mounds of earth. Before these sat creatures that looked like striped prairie dogs.

The next moment, the Hrowakas had ridden into the colony with the Half-Horse immediately behind them. Shouts and screams arose as horses and centaurs, stepping into holes, went crashing down. The beasts and the Half-Horses that had fallen down, kicked and screamed with the pain of broken legs. The centaurs just behind the first wave reared to halt themselves, and those following rammed into them. For a minute, a pile of tangled and kicking four-legged bodies was spread across the border of the prairie-dog field. The Half-Horses lucky enough to be far enough behind halted and watched their stricken comrades. Then they trotted cautiously, intent on where they placed their hooves. They cut the throats of those with broken legs and arms.

The Hrowakas, though aware of what was taking place behind them, had not stayed to watch. They pushed on but at a reduced pace. Now, they had ten horses and twelve men; Hums Like A Bee and Tall Grass were riding double with two whose horses had not broken their legs.

Kickaha, looking at them, shook his head. Wolff knew what he was thinking. He would have to order Hums Like A Bee and Tall Grass to get off and go on foot. Otherwise, not only they but the men who had picked them up would inevitably be overtaken. Then Kickaha, saying, "To hell with it, I won't abandon them!" dropped back. He spoke briefly to the tandem riders and brought his horse back up alongside Wolff. "If they go, we all go," he said. "But you don't have to stay with us, Bob. Your loyalty lies elsewhere. No reason for you to sacrifice yourself for us and lose Chryseis and the horn."

"I'll stay," Wolff said.

Kickaha grinned and slapped him on the shoulder. "I'd hoped we could get to the woods, but we won't make it. Almost but not quite. By the time we get to that big hill just half a mile ahead, we'll be caught up with. Too bad. The woods are only another half-mile away."

The prairie-dog colony was as suddenly behind them as it had been before them. The Hrowakas urged their beasts to a gallop. A minute later, the centaurs had passed safely through the field, and they, too, were at full speed. Up the hill went the pursued and at the top they halted to form a circle.

Wolff pointed down the side of the hill and across the plain at a small river. There were woods along it, but it was not that which caused his excitement. At the river's edge, partially blocked by the trees, white tepees shone.

Kickaha looked long before saying, "The Tsenakwa. The mortal enemy of the Bear People, as who isn't?"

"Here they come," Wolff said. "They must have been notified by sentinels."

He gestured at a disorganized body of horsemen riding out of the woods, the sun striking off white horses, white shields, and white feathers and sparking the tips of lance.

One of the Hrowakas, seeing them, began a high-pitched wailing song. Kickaha shouted at him, and Wolff understood enough to know that Kickaha was telling him to shut up. Now was no time for a death-song; they would cheat the Half-Horse and the Tsenakwa yet.

"I was going to order our last stand here," Kickaha said. "But not now. We'll ride toward the Tsenakwa, then cut away from them and toward the woods along the river. How we come out depends on whether or not both our enemies decide to fight. If one refuses, the other will get us. If not ... Let's go!"

Haiyeeing, they pounded their heels against the ribs of their

84

beasts. Down the hill, straight toward the Tsenakwa, they rode. Wolff glanced back over his shoulder and saw that the Half-Horse were speeding down the side of the hill after them. Kickaha yelled, "I didn't think they'd pass this up. There'll be a lot of women wailing in the lodges tonight, but it won't be only among the Bear People!"

Now the Hrowakas were close enough to discern the devices on the shields of the Tsenakwa. These were black swastikas, a symbol Wolff was not surprised to see. The crooked cross was ancient and widespread on Earth; it was known by the Trojans, Cretans, Romans, Celts, Norse, Indian Buddhists and Brahmans, the Chinese, and throughout pre-Columbian North America. Nor was he surprised to see that the oncoming Indians were red-haired. Kickaha had told him that the Tsenakwa dyed their black locks.

Still in an unordered mass but now bunched more closely together, the Tsenakwa leveled their lances and gave their charge-cry, an imitation of the scream of a hawk. Kickaha, in the lead, raised his hand, held it for a moment, then chopped it downward. His horse veered to the left and away, the line of the Bear people following him, he the head and the others the body of the snake.

Kickaha had cut it close, but he had used correct and exact timing. As the Half-Horse and Tsenakwa plunged with a crash and flurry into each other and were embroiled in a melee, the Hrowakas pulled away. They gained the woods, slowed to go through the trees and underbrush, and then were crossing the river. Even so, Kickaha had to argue with several of the braves. These wanted to sneak back across the river and raid the tepees of the Tsenakwa while their warriors were occupied with the Half-Horse.

"Makes sense to me," Wolff said, "if we stay there only long enough to pick up some horses. Hums Like A Bee and Tall Grass can't keep on riding double."

Kickaha shrugged and gave the order. The raid took five minutes. The Hrowakas recrossed the river and burst from the trees and among the tepees with wild shouts. The women and children screamed and took refuge in the trees or lodges. Some of the Hrowakas wanted not only the horses but loot. Kickaha said that he would kill the first man he caught stealing anything besides bows and arrows. But he did reach down off his horse and give a pretty but battling woman a long kiss.

"Tell your men I would have taken you to bed and made you forever after dissatisfied with the puny ones of your tribe!" Kickaha said to her. "But we have more important things to do!" Laughing, he released the woman, who ran into her lodge. He did pause long enough to make water into the big cooking pot in the middle of the camp, a deadly insult, and then he ordered the party to ride off.

CHAPTER TEN

They rode on for two weeks and then were at the edge of the Trees of Many Shadows. Here Kickaha took a long farewell of the Hrowakas. These also each came to Wolff and, laying their hands upon his shoulders, made a farewell speech. He was one of them now. When he returned, he should take a house and wife among them and ride out on hunts and war with them. He was *KwashingDa,* the Strong One; he had made his kill side by side with them; he had outwrestled a Half-Horse; he would be given a bear cub to raise as his own; he would be blessed by the Lord and have sons and daughters, and so forth and so on.

Gravely, Wolff replied that he could think of no greater honor than to be accepted by the Bear People. He meant it.

Many days later, they had passed through the Many Shadows. They lost both horses one night to something that left footprints ten times as large as a man's, and four-toed. Wolff was both saddened and enraged, for he had a great affection for his animal. He wanted to pursue the WaGanassit and take vengeance. Kickaha threw his hands up in horror at the suggestion.

"Be happy you weren't carried off, too!" he said. "The WaGanassit is covered with scales that are half-silicon. Your arrows would bounce off. Forget about the horses. We can come back someday and hunt it down. They can be trapped and then roasted in a fire, which I'd like to do, but we have to be practical. Let's go."

On the other side of the Many Shadows, they built a canoe and went down a broad river that passed through many large and small lakes. The country was hilly here, with steep cliffs at many places. It reminded Wolff of the dells of Wisconsin.

"Beautiful land, but the Chacopewachi and the Enwaddit live here."

Thirteen days later, during which they had had to paddle furiously three times to escape pursuing canoes of warriors, they left the canoe. Having crossed a broad and high range of hills, mostly at night, they came to a great lake. Again they built a canoe and set out across the waters. Five days of paddling brought them to the base of the monolith, Abharhploonta. They began their slow ascent, as dangerous as that up the first monolith. By the time they reached the top, they had expended their supply of arrows and were suffering several nasty wounds.

"You can see why traffic between the tiers is limited," Kickaha said. "In the first place, the Lord has forbidden it. However, that doesn't keep the irreverent and adventurous, nor the trader, from attempting it.

"Between the rim and Dracheland is several thousand miles of jungle with large plateaus interspersed here and there. The Guzirit River is only a hundred miles away. We'll go there and look for passage on a riverboat."

They prepared flint tips and shafts for arrows. Wolff killed a tapirlike animal. Its flesh was a little rank, but it filled their bellies with strength. He wanted then to push on, finding Kickaha's reluctance aggravating.

Kickaha looked up into the green sky and said, "I was hoping one of Podarge's pets would find us and have news for us. After all, we don't know which direction the gworl are taking. They have to go toward the mountain, but they could take two paths. They could go all the way through the jungle, a route not recommended for safety. Or they could take a boat down the Guzirit. That has its dangers, too, especially for rather outstanding creatures like the gworl. And Chryseis would bring a high price in the slave market."

"We can't wait forever for an eagle," Wolff said.

"No, nor will we have to," Kickaha said. He pointed up, and Wolff, following the direction of his fingertip, saw a flash of yellow. It disappeared, only to come into view a moment later. The eagle was dropping swiftly, wings folded. Shortly, it checked its drop and glided in.

Phthie introduced herself and immediately thereafter said that she carried good news. She had spotted the gworl and the woman, Chryseis, only four hundred miles ahead of them. They had taken passage on a merchant boat and were traveling down the Guzirit toward the Land of Armored Men.

"Did you see the horn?" Kickaha asked.

"No," Phthie replied. "But they doubtless have it concealed in one of the skin bags they are carrying. I snatched one of the bags away from a gworl on the chance it might contain the horn. For my troubles, I got a bag full of junk and almost received an arrow through my wing."

"The gworl have bows?" Wolff asked, surprised.

"No. The rivermen shot at me."

Wolff, asking about the ravens, was told that there were many. Apparently the Lord must have ordered a number to keep watch on the gworl.

"That's bad," Kickaha said. "If they spot us, we're in real trouble."

87

"They don't know what you look like," Phthie said. "I've eavesdropped on the ravens when they were talking, hiding when I longed to seize them and tear them apart. But I have orders from my mistress, and I obey. The gworl have tried to describe you to the Eyes of the Lord. The ravens are looking for two traveling together, both tall, one black-haired, the other bronze-haired. But that is all they know, and many men conform to that description. The ravens, however, will be watching for two men on the trail of the gworl."

"I'll dye my beard, and we'll get Khamshem clothes," Kickaha said.

Phthie said that she must be getting on. She had been on her way to report to Podarge, having left another sister to continue the surveillance of the gworl, when she had spied the two. Kickaha thanked her and made sure that she would carry his regards to Podarge. After the giant bird had launched herself from the rim of the monolith, the men went into the jungle.

"Walk softly, speak quietly," Kickaha said. "Here be tigers. In fact, the jungle's lousy with them. Here also be the great axebeak. It's a wingless bird so big and fierce even one of Podarge's pets would skedaddle away from it. I saw no tigers and an axebeak tangle once, and the tigers didn't hang around long before they caught on it'd be a good idea to take off fast."

Despite Kickaha's warnings, they saw very little life except for a vast number of manycolored birds, monkeys, and mouse-sized antlered beetles. For the beetles, Kickaha had one word: "poisonous". Thereafter, Wolff took care before bedding down that none were about.

Before reaching their immediate destination, Kickaha looked for a plant, the *ghubharash*. Locating a group after a half-day's search, he pounded the fibers, cooked them, and extracted a blackish liquid. With this he stained his hair, beard, and his skin from top to bottom.

"I'll explain my green eyes with a tale of having a slave-mother from Teutonia," he said. "Here. Use some yourself. You could stand being a little darker."

They came to a half-ruined city of stone and wide-mouthed squatting idols. The citizens were a short, thin, and dark people who dressed in maroon capes, and black loincloths. Men and women wore their hair long and plastered with butter, which they derived from the milk of piebald goats that leaped from ruin to ruin and fed on the grasses between the cracks in the stone. These people, the Kaidushang, kept cobras in little cages and often took their pets out to fondle. They chewed dhiz, a plant which turned their teeth black and gave their eyes a smoldering look and their motions a slowness.

Kickaha, using H'vaizhum, the pidgin rivertalk, bartered

with the elders. He traded a leg of a hippopotamus-like beast he and Wolff had killed for Khamshem garments. The two donned the red and green turbans adorned with *kigglibash* feathers, sleeveless white shirts, baggy pantaloons of purple, sashes that wound around and around their waists many times, and the black, curling toed slippers.

Despite their dhiz-stupored minds, the elders were shrewd in their trading. Not until Kickaha brought a very small sapphire from his bag—one of the jewels given him by Podarge—would they sell the pearl-encrusted scabbards and the scimitars in their hidden stock.

"I hope a boat comes along soon," Kickaha said. "Now that they know I have stones, they might try to slit our throats. Sorry, Bob, but we're going to have to keep watch at night. They also like to send in their snakes to do their dirty work for them."

That very day, a merchantman sailed around the bend of the river. At sight of the two standing on the rotting pier and waving long white handkerchiefs, the captain ordered the anchor dropped and sails lowered.

Wolff and Kickaha got into the small boat lowered for them and were rowed out to the *Khrillquz*. This was about forty feet long, low amidships but with towering decks fore and aft, and one fore-and-aft sail and jib. The sailors were mainly of that branch of Khamshem folk called the Shibacub. They spoke a tongue the phonology and structure of which had been described by Kickaha to Wolff. He was sure that it was an archaic form of Semitic influenced by the aboriginal tongues.

The captain, Arkhyurel, greeted them politely on the poopdeck. He sat cross-legged on a pile of cushions and rich rugs and sipped on a tiny cup of thick wine.

Kickaha, calling himself Ishnaqrubel, gave his carefully prepared story. He and his companion, a man under a vow not to speak again until he returned to his wife in the far off land of Shiashtu, had been in the jungle for several years. They had been searching for the fabled lost city of Ziqooant.

The captain's black and tangled eyebrows rose, and he stroked the dark-brown beard that fell to his waist. He asked them to sit down and to accept a cup of the Akhashtum wine while they told their tale. Kickaha's eyes shone and he grinned as he plunged into his narration. Wolff did not understand him, yet he was sure that his friend was in raptures with his long, richly detailed, and adventurous lies. He only hoped Kickaha would not get too carried away and arouse the captain's incredulity.

The hours passed while the caravel sailed down the river. A

89

sailor clad only in a scarlet loincloth, bangs hanging down below his eyes, played softly on a flute on the foredeck. Food was carried to them on silver and gold platters: roasted monkey, stuffed bird, a black hard bread, and a tart jelly. Wolff found the meat too highly spiced, but he ate.

The sun neared its nightly turn around the mountain, and the captain arose. He led them to a little shrine behind the wheel; here was an idol of green jade, Tartartar. The captain chanted a prayer, the prime prayer to the Lord. Then Arkhyurel got down on his knees before the minor god of his own nation and made obeisance. A sailor sprinkled a little incense on the tiny fire glowing in the hollow in Tartartar's lap. While the fumes spread over the ship, those of the captain's faith prayed also. Later, the mariners of other gods made their private devotions.

That night, the two lay on the mid-deck on a pile of furs which the captain had furnished them.

"I don't know about this guy Arkhyurel," Kickaha said. "I told him we failed to locate the city of Ziqooant but that we did find a small treasure cache. Nothing to brag about but enough to let us live modestly without worry when we return to Shiashtu. He didn't ask to see the jewels, even though I said I'd give him a big ruby for our passage. These people take their time in their dealings; it's an insult to rush business. But his greed may overrule his sense of hospitality and business ethics if he thinks he can get a big haul just by cutting our throats and dumping our bodies into the river."

He stopped for a moment. Cries of many birds came from the branches along the river; now and then a great saurian bellowed from the bank or from the river itself.

"If he's going to do anything dishonorable, he'll do it in the next thousand miles. This is a lonely stretch of river; after that, the towns and cities begin to get more numerous."

The next afternoon, sitting under a canopy erected for their comfort, Kickaha presented the captain with the ruby, enormous and beautifully cut. With it, Kickaha could have purchased the boat itself and the crew from the captain. He hoped that Arkhyurel would be more than satisfied with it; the captain himself could retire on its sale if he wished. Kickaha then did what he had wanted to avoid but knew that he could not. He brought out the rest of the jewels: diamonds, sapphires, rubies, garnets, tourmalines and topazes. Arkhyurel smiled and licked his lips and fondled the stones for three hours. Finally he forced himself to give them back.

That night, while lying on their beds on the deck, Kickaha brought out a parchment map which he had borrowed from the captain. He indicated a great bend of the river and tapped a circle marked with the curlicue syllabary symbols of Khamshem writing.

"The city of Khotsiqsh. Abandoned by the people who built it, like the one from which we boarded this boat, and inhabited by a half-savage tribe, the Weezwart. We'll quietly leave ship the night we drop anchor there and cut across the thin neck of land to the river. We may be able to pick up enough time to intercept the boat that's carrying the gworl. If we don't, we'll still be way ahead of this boat. We'll take another merchant. Or, if none is available, we'll hire a Weezwart dugout and crew."

Twelve days later the Khrillquz tied up alongside a massive but cracked pier. The Weezwart crowded the stone tongue and shouted at the sailors and showed them jars of dhiz, and of laburnum, singing birds in wooden cages, monkeys and servals on the end of leashes, artifacts from hidden and ruined cities in the jungle, bags and purses made from the pebbly hides of the river saurians, and cloaks from tigers and leopards. They even had a baby axeback, which they knew the captain would pay a good price for and would sell to the Bashishub, the king, of Shibacub. Their main wares, however, were their women. These, clad from head to foot in cheap cotton robes of scarlet and green, paraded back and forth on the pier. They would flash open their robes and then quickly close them, all the while screaming the price of a night's rent to the women-starved sailors. The men, wearing only white turbans and fantastic codpieces, stood to one side, chewed dhiz, and grinned. All carried six-foot long blow-guns and long, thin, crooked knives stuck into the tangled knots of hair on top of their heads.

During the trading between the captain and Weezwart, Kickaha and Wolff prowled through the cyclopean stands and falls of the city. Abruptly, Wolff said, "You have the jewels with you. Why don't we get a Weezwart guide and take off now? Why wait until nightfall?"

"I like your style, friend," Kickaha said. "Okay. Let's go."

They found a tall thin man, Wiwhin, who eagerly accepted their offer when Kickaha showed him a topaz. At their insistence, he did not tell his wife where he was going but straightway led them into the jungle. He knew the paths well and, as promised, delivered them to the city of Qirruqshak within two days. Here he demanded another jewel, saying that he would not tell anybody at all about them if he was given a bonus.

"I did not promise you a bonus," Kickaha said. "But I like the fine spirit of free enterprise you show, my friend. So here's another. But if you try for a third, I shall kill you."

Wiwhin smiled and bowed and took the second topaz and

91

trotted off into the jungle. Kickaha, staring after him, said, "Maybe I should've killed him anyway. The Weezwart don't even have the word *honor* in their vocabulary."

They walked into the ruins. After a half-hour of climbing and threading their way between collapsed buildings and piles of dirt, they found themselves on the river-side of the city. Here were gathered the Dholinz, a folk of the same language family as the Weezwart. But the men had long, drooping mousstaches and the women painted their upper lips black and wore nose-rings. With them was a group of merchants from the land which had given all the Khamshem-speakers their name. There was no river-caravel by the pier. Kickaha, seeing this, halted and started to turn back into the ruins. He was too late, for the Khamshem saw him and called out to them.

"Might as well brave it out," Kickaha muttered to Wolff. "If I holler, run like hell! Those birds are slave-dealers."

There were about thirty of the Khamshem, all armed with scimitars and daggers. In addition, they had about fifty soldiers, tall broad-shouldered men, lighter than the Khamshem, with swirling patterns tattooed on their faces and shoulders. These, Kickaha said, were the Sholkin mercenaries often used by the Khamshem. They were famous spearmen, mountain people, herders of goats, scorners of women as good for nothing but housework, fieldwork, and bearers of children.

"Don't let them take you alive," was Kickaha's final warning before he smiled and greeted the leader of the Khamshem. This was a very tall and thickly muscled man named Abiru. He had a face that would have been handsome if his nose had not been a little too large and curved like a scimitar. He answered Kickaha politely enough, but his large black eyes weighed them as if they were so many pounds of merchandisable flesh.

Kickaha gave him the story he had told Arkhyurel but shortened it considerably and left out the jewels. He said that they would wait until a merchant boat came along and would take it back to Shiashtu. And how was the great Abiru doing?

(By now, Wolff's quickness at picking up languages enabled him to understand the Khamshem tongue when it was on a simple conversational basis.)

Abiru replied that, thanks to the Lord and Tartartar, this business venture had been very rewarding. Besides the usual type of slave-material picked up, he had captured a group of very strange creatures. Also, a woman of surpassing beauty, the like of which had never been seen before. Not, at least, on this tier.

Wolff's heart began to beat hard. Was it possible?

Abiru asked if they would care to take a peek at his captives.

Kickaha flicked a look of warning at Wolff but replied that he would very much like to see both the curious beings and the fabulously beautiful woman. Abiru beckoned to the captain of the mercenaries and ordered him and ten of his men to come along. Then Wolff scented the danger of which Kickaha had been aware from the beginning. He knew that they should run, though this was not likely to be successful. The Sholkin seemed accustomed to bringing down fugitives with their spears. But he wanted desperately to see Chryseis again. Since Kickaha made no move, Wolff decided not to do so on his own. Kickaha, having more experience, presumably knew how best to act.

Abiru, chatting pleasantly of the attractions of the capital city of Khamshem, led them down the underbrush-grown street and to a great stepped building with broken statues on the levels. He halted before an entrance by which stood ten more Sholkin. Even before they went in, Wolff knew that the gworl were there. Riding over the stink of unwashed human bodies was the rotten-fruit odor of the bumpy people.

The chamber within was huge and cool and twilighty. Against the far wall, squatting on the dirt piled on the stone floor, was a line of about a hundred men and women and thirty gworl. All were connected by long, thin iron chains around iron collars about their necks.

Wolff looked for Chryseis. She was not there.

Abiru, answering the unspoken question, said, "I keep the cat-eyed one apart. She has a woman attendant and a special guard. She gets all the attention and care that a precious jewel should."

Wolff could not restrain himself. He said, "I would like to see her."

Abiru stared and said, "You have a strange accent. Didn't companion say you were from the land of Shiashtu, also?"

He waved a hand at the soldiers, who moved forward, their spears leveled. "Never mind. If you see the woman, you will see her from the end of a chain."

Kickaha sputtered indignantly. "We are subjects of the king of Khamshem and free men! You cannot do this to us! It will cost you your head, after certain legal tortures, of course!"

Abiru smiled. "I do not intend to take you back to Khamshem, friend. We are going to Teutonia, where you will bring a good price, being a strong man, albeit too talkative. However, we can take care of that by slicing off your tongue."

The scimitars of the two were removed along with the bag.

Herded by the spears, they moved to the end of the line, immediately behind the gworl, and were secured with iron collars. Abiru, dumping the contents of the bag on the floor, swore as he saw the pile of jewels.

"So, you did find something in the lost cities? How fortunate for us. I'm almost—but not quite—tempted to release you for having enriched me so."

"How corny can you get?" Kickaha muttered in English. "He talks like a grade-B movie villain. Damn him! If I get the chance, I'll cut out more than his tongue."

Abiru, happy with his riches, left. Wolff examined the chain attached to the collar. It was made of small links. He might be able to break it if the iron was not too high a quality. On Earth, he had amused himself, secretly of course, by snapping just such chains. But he could not try until nightfall.

Behind Wolff, Kickaha whispered, "The gworl won't recognize us in this getup, so let's leave it that way."

"What about the horn?" Wolff said.

Kickaha, speaking the early Middle High German form of Teutonic, tried to engage the gworl in conversation. After narrowly missing getting hit in the face with a gob of saliva, he quit. He did manage to talk to one of the Sholkin soldiers and some of the human slaves. From them he gleaned much information.

The gworl had been passengers on the *Qaqiirzhub*, captained by one Rakhhamen. Putting in at this city, the captain had met Abiru and invited him aboard for a cup of wine. That night—in fact, the night before Wolff had entered the city—Abiru and his men had seized the boat. During the struggle, the captain and several of his sailors had been slain. The rest were now in the chain-line. The boat had been sent on down the river and up a tributary with a crew to be sold to a river-pirate of whom Abiru had heard.

As for the horn, none of the crew of the *Qaqiirzhub* had heard of it. Nor would the soldier supply any news. Kickaha told Wolff that he did not think that Abiru was likely to let anybody else learn about it. He must recognize it, for everybody had heard of the horn of the Lord. It was part of the universal religion and described in the various sacred literatures.

Night came. Soldiers entered with torches and food for the slaves. After meal time, two Sholkin remained within the chamber and an unknown number stood guard outside. The sanitary arrangements were abominable; the odor became stifling. Apparently Abiru did not care about observing the proprieties as laid down by the Lord. However, some of the more religious Sholkin must have complained, for several Dholinz entered and cleaned up. Water in buckets was dashed over each slave, and several buckets were left for drinking. The gworl howled when the water struck them and complained and cursed for a long time afterwards. Kickaha added to Wolff's store of information by telling him that the gworl, like the kangaroo rat and other desert animals of Earth, did not have to drink water. They had a biological device, similar to the arid-dwellers, which oxidized their fat into the hydrogen oxide required.

The moon came up. The slaves lay on the floor or leaned against the wall and slept. Kickaha and Wolff pretended to do likewise. When the moon had come around into position so that it could be seen through the doorway, Wolff said, "I'm going to try to break the chains. If I don't have time to break yours, we'll have to do a Siamese twin act."

"Let's go," Kickaha whispered back.

The length of the chain between each collar was about six feet. Wolff slowly inched his way toward the nearest gworl to give himself enough slack. Kickaha crept along with him. The journey took about fifteen minutes, for they did not want the two sentinels in the chamber to become aware of their progress. Then Wolff, his back turned to the guards, took the chain in his two hands. He pulled and felt the links hold fast. Slow tension would not do the job. So, a quick jerk. The links broke with a noise.

The two Sholkin, who had been talking loudly and laughing to keep each other awake, stopped. Wolff did not dare to turn over to look at them. He waited while the Sholkin discussed the possible origin of the sound. Apparently it did not occur to them that it could be the chain parting. They spent some time holding the torches high and peering up toward the ceiling. One made a joke, the other laughed, and they resumed their conversation.

"Want to try for two?" Kickaha said.

"I hate to, but we'll be handicapped if I don't," Wolff said.

He had to wait awhile, for the gworl to whom he had been attached had been awakened by the breaking. He lifted his head and muttered something in his file-against-steel speech. Wolff began sweating even more heavily. If the gworl sat up or tried to stand up, his motion would reveal the damage.

After a heart-piercing minute, the gworl settled back down and soon was snoring again. Wolff relaxed a little. He even grinned tightly, for the gworl's actions had given him an idea.

"Crawl up toward me as if you wanted to warm yourself against me," Wolff said softly.

"You kidding?" Kickaha whispered back. "I feel as if I'm in a steam bath. But okay. Here goes."

He inched forward until his head was opposite Wolff's knees.

"When I snap the chain, don't go into action," Wolff said.

"I have an idea for bringing the guards over here without alarming those outside."

"I hope they don't change guards just as we're starting to operate," Kickaha said.

"Pray to the Lord," Wolff replied. "Earth's."

"He helps him who helps himself," Kickaha said.

Wolff jerked with all his strength; the links parted with a noise. This time, the guards stopped talking and the gworl rose up abruptly. Wolff bit down hard on the toe of the gworl. The creature did not cry out but grunted and started to rise. One of the guards ordered him to remain seated, and both started toward him. The gworl did not understand the language. He did understand the tone of voice, and the spear waved at him. He lifted his foot and began to rub it, meanwhile grating curses at Wolff.

The torches became brighter as the feet of the guards scraped against the stone exposed beneath the loose dirt. Wolff said, "Now!"

He and Kickaha arose simultaneously, whirled, and were facing the surprised Sholkin. A spearhead was within Wolff's reach. His hand slid along it, grasped the shaft just behind the point, and jerked. The guard opened his mouth to yell, but it snapped shut as the lifted butt of the spear cracked against his jaw.

Kickaha had not been so fortunate. The Sholkin stepped back and raised his spear to throw it. Kickaha went at him as a tackler after the man with the ball; he came in low, rolled, and the spear clanged against the wall.

By then, the silence was gone. One guard started to yell. The gworl picked up the weapon that had fallen by his side and threw it. The head drove into the exposed neck of the guard, and the point came out through the back of the neck.

Kickaha jerked the spearhead loose, drew the dead guard's knife from his scabbard, and flipped it. The first Sholkin to enter from outside received it to the hilt in his solar plexus. Seeing him go down, others who had been so eager to follow him withdrew. Wolff took the knife from the other corpse, shoved it into his sash, and said, "Where do we go from here?"

Kickaha slid the knife from the solar plexus and wiped it on the corpse's hair. "Not through that door. Too many."

Wolff pointed at a doorway at the far end and started to run toward it. On the way, he scooped up the torch dropped by the guard. Kickaha did the same. The doorway was partly choked up by dirt, forcing them to get down on their hands and knees and crawl through. Presently they were at the place through

96

which the dirt had dropped. The moon revealed an empty place in the stone slabs of the ceiling.

"They must know about this," Wolff said. "They can't be that careless. We'd better go further back in."

They had scarcely moved past the point below the break in the roof when torches flared above. The two scuttled ahead as fast as they could while Sholkin voices came excitedly through the opening. A second later, a spear slammed into the dirt, narrowly missing Wolff's leg.

"They'll be coming in after us, now that they know we've left the main chamber," Kickaha said.

They went on, taking branches which seemed to offer access to the rear. Suddenly the floor sank beneath Kickaha. He tried to scramble on across before the stone on which he was would drop, but he did not make it. One side of a large slab came up, and that side which had dropped propelled Kickaha into a hole. Kickaha yelled, at the same time releasing the hold on his torch. Both fell.

Wolff was left staring at the tipped slab and the gape beside it. No light came from the hole, so the torch had either gone out or the hole was so deep that the flare was out of sight. Moaning in his anxiety, he crawled forward and held the torch over the edge while he looked below. The shaft was at least ten feet wide and fifty deep. It had been dug out of the dirt and at various places down it large pieces had fallen off. The bottom was a heap of dirt. But there was no Kickaha nor even a depression to indicate where he had landed.

Wolff called his name, at the same time hearing the shouts of the Sholkin as they crawled through the corridors in pursuit.

Receiving no answer, he extended his body as far as he dared over the lip of the shaft and examined the depth more closely. All his waving about of the torch to illuminate the dark places showed nothing but the fallen extinguished torch.

Some of the edges of the bottom remained black as if there were holes in the sides. He could only conclude that Kickaha had gone into one of these.

Now the sound of voices became louder and the first flickerings of a torch came from around the corner at the end of the hall. He could do nothing but continue. He rose as far as possible, threw his torch ahead of him to the other side, and leaped with all the strength of his legs. He shot in an almost horizontal position, hit the lip, which was wet soft earth, and slid forward on his face. He was safe, although his legs were sticking out over the edge.

Picking up the torch, which was still burning, he crawled on. At the end of the corridor he found one branch completely blocked by fallen earth. The other was partially stopped up by a great slab of smoothly cut stone lying at a forty-five degree angle to horizontal. By the sacrifice of some skin on his chest and back, he squeezed through between the earth and the stone. Beyond was an enormous chamber, even larger than the one in which the slaves had been kept.

There was a series of rough terraces formed by slippage of stone at the opposite end. He made his way up these toward the corner of the ceiling and the wall. A patch of moonlight shone through this, his only means of exit. He put his torch out. If the Sholkin were roaming around the top of the building, they would see the light from it coming through the small hole. At the cavity, he crouched for awhile on the narrow ledge beneath it and listened carefully. If his torch had been seen, he would be caught as he slid out of the hole, helpless to defend himself. Finally, hearing only distant shouts, and knowing that he must use this only exit, he pulled himself through it.

He was near the top of the mound of dirt which covered the rear part of the building. Below him were torches. Abiru was standing in their light, shaking his fist at a soldier and yelling.

Wolff looked down at the earth beneath his feet, imagined the stone and the hollows they contained, and the shaft down which Kickaha had hurtled to his death.

He raised his spear and murmured, "Ave atque vale, Kickaha!"

He wished he could take some more Sholkin lives—especially that of Abiru—in payment for Kickaha's. But he had to be practical. There was Chryseis, and there was the horn. But he felt empty and weak, as if part of his soul had left him.

CHAPTER ELEVEN

That night he hid in the branches of a tall tree some distance from the city. His plan was to follow the slavers and rescue Chryseis and the horn at the first chance. The slavers would have to take the trail near which he waited; it was the only one leading inward to Teutonia. Dawn came while he waited, hungry and thirsty. By noon he became impatient. Surely they would not still be looking for him. At evening, he decided that he had to have at least a drink of water. He climbed down and headed for a nearby stream. A growl sent him up another tree. Presently a family of leopards slipped through the bush and lapped at the water. By the time they were through and had slid back into the bush, the sun was close to the corner of the monolith.

He returned to the trail, confident that he had been too close to it for a large train of human beings to walk by unheard. Yet no one came. That night he sneaked into the ruins and close to the building from which he had escaped. No one was in evidence. Sure now that they had left, he prowled through the bush-grown lanes and streets until he came upon a man sitting against a tree. The man was half-conscious from dhiz, but Wolff woke him by slapping him hard against his cheeks. Holding his knife against his throat, he questioned him. Despite his limited Khamshem and the Dholinz's even lesser mastery, they managed to communicate. Abiru and his party had left that morning on three large war-canoes with hired Dholinz paddlers.

Wolff knocked the man unconscious and went down to the pier. It was deserted, thus giving him a choice of any craft there he wanted. He took a narrow light boat with a sail and set off down the river.

Two thousand miles later, he was on the borders of Teutonia and the civilized Khamshem. The trail had led him down the Guzirit River for three hundred miles, then across country. Although he should have caught up with the slow-moving train long before, he had lost them three times and been detained at other times by tigers and axebeaks.

Gradually the land sloped upward. Suddenly a plateau rose from the jungle. A climb of a mere six thousand feet was nothing to a man who had twice scaled thirty thousand. Once over the rim, he found himself in a different country. Though the air was no cooler, it bred oak, sycamore, yew, box, elder, walnut, cottonwood and linden. However, the animals differed. He had walked no more than two miles through the twilight of an oak forest before he was forced to hide.

A dragon slowly paced by him, looked at him once, hissed, and went on. It resembled the conventional Western representations, was about forty feet long, ten feet high, and was covered with large scaly plates. It did not breathe fire. In fact, it stopped a hundred feet from Wolff's tree-branch refuge and began to eat upon a tall patch of grass. So, Wolff thought, there was more than one type of dragon. Wondering how he would be able to tell the carnivorous type from the herbivorous without first assuring a safe observation post, Wolff climbed down from the tree. The dragon continued to munch while its belly, or bellies, emitted a weak thunder of digestion.

More cautiously than before, Wolff passed beneath the giant limbs of the trees and the moss, cataracts of green, that hung from the limbs. Dawn of the next day found him leaving the edge of the forest. Before him the land dipped gently. He could see for many miles. To his right, at the bottom of a valley, was a

99

river. On the opposite side, topping a column of shaggy rock, was a tiny castle. At the foot of the rock was a minute village. Smoke rose from the chimneys to bring a lump in his throat. It seemed to him that he would like nothing better than to sit down at a breakfast table over a cup of coffee with friends, after a good night's sleep in a soft bed, and chatter away about nothing in particular. God! How he missed the faces and the voices of genuine human beings, of a place where every hand was not against him!

A few tears trickled down his cheek. He dried them and went on his way. He had made his choice and must take the bad with the good, just as he would have in the Earth he had renounced. And this world, at this moment, anyway, was not so bad. It was fresh and green with no telephone lines, billboards, paper and cans strewn along the countryside, no smog or threat of bomb. There was much to be said for it, no matter how bad his present situation might be. And he had that for which many men would have sold their souls: youth combined with the experience of age.

Only an hour later, he wondered if he would be able to retain the gift. He had come to a narrow dirt road and was striding along it when a knight rode around the bend in the road, followed by two men-at-arms. His horse was huge and black and accoutered partly in armor. The knight was clad in black plate-and-mail armor which, to Wolff, looked like the type worn in Germany of the thirteenth century. His visor was up, revealing a grim hawk's face with bright blue eyes.

The knight reined in his horse. He called to Wolff in the Middle High German speech with which Wolff had become acquainted through Kickaha and also through his studies on Earth. The language had, of course, changed somewhat and was loaded with Khamshem and aboriginal loanwords. But Wolff could make out most of what his accoster said.

"Stand still, oaf!" the man cried. "What are you doing with a bow?"

"May it please your august self," Wolff replied sarcastically, "I am a hunter and so bear the king's license to carry a bow."

"You are a liar! I know every lawful hunter for miles hereabouts. You look like a Saracen to me or even a Yidshe, you are so dark. Throw down your bow and surrender, or I will cut you down like the swine you are!"

"Come and take it," Wolff said, his rage swelling.

The knight couched his lance, and his steed broke into a gallop.

Wolff resisted the impulse to hurl himself to either side or back from the glittering tip of the lance. At what he hoped was the exact split-second, he threw himself forward. The lance

100

dipped to run him through, slid less than an inch over him, and then drove into the ground. Like a pole-vaulter, the knight rose from the saddle and, still clutching the lance, described an arc. His helmet struck the ground first at the end of the arc, the impact of which must have knocked him out or broken his neck or back, for he did not move.

Wolff did not waste his time. He removed the scabbarded sword of the knight and placed the belt around his waist. The dead man's horse, a magnificent roan, had come back to stand by his ex-master. Wolff mounted him and rode off.

Teutonia was so named because of its conquest by a group of The Teutonic Order or Teutonic Knights of St Mary's Hospital at Jerusalem. This order originated during the Third Crusade but later deviated from its original purpose. In 1229 *der Deutsche Orden* began the conquest of Prussia to convert the Baltic pagans and to prepare for colonization by Germans. A group had entered the Lord's planet on this tier, either through accident, which did not seem likely, or because the Lord had deliberately opened a gate for them or forcibly caused them to enter.

Whatever the cause, the Ritters of the Teutonic Knights had conquered the aborigines and established a society based on that which they had left on Earth. This, of course, had changed both because of natural evolution and the Lord's desire to model it to his own wishes. The original single kingdom or Grand Marshalry had degenerated into a number of independent kingdoms. These, in turn, consisted of loosely bound baronetcies and a host of outlaw or robber baronetcies.

Another aspect of the plateau was the state of Yidshe. The founders of this had entered through a gate coevally with the Teutonic Knights. Again, whether they had entered accidentally or through design of the Lord was unknown. But a number of Yiddish-speaking Germans had established themselves at the eastern end of the plateau. Though originally merchants, they had become masters of the native population. Also, they had adopted the feudal-chivalry setup of the Teutonic Order—probably had had to do so to survive. It was this state that the first knight had referred to when he had accused Wolff of being a Yidshe.

Thinking of this, Wolff had to chuckle. Again, it might have been accident that the Germans had entered into a level where the archaic-Semitic Khamshem already existed and where their contemporaries were the despised Jews. But Wolff thought he could see the ironic face of the Lord smiling behind the situation.

Actually, there were not any Christians or Jews in Drache-land. Although the two faiths still used their original titles, both had become perverted. The Lord had taken the place of Yahweh and Gott, but he was addressed by these names. Other changes in theology had followed: ceremonies, rituals, sacraments, and the literature had subtly become twisted. The parent faiths of both would have rejected their descendants in this world as heretics.

Wolff made his way toward von Elgers'. He could not do so as swiftly as he wished, because he had to avoid the roads and the villages along the way. After being forced to kill the knight, he did not even dare cut through the baronetcy of von Laurentius, as he had at first planned. The entire country would be searching for him; men and dogs would be everywhere. The rough hills marking the boundary were his most immediate form of passage, which he took.

Two days later, he came to a point where he could descend without being within the suzerainty of von Laurentius. As he was clambering down a steep but not especially difficult hill, he came around a corner. Below him was a broad meadow by a riverlet. Two camps were pitched at opposite ends. Around the brave flag-and-pennon draped pavilions in the center of each were a number of smaller tents, cooking fires, and horses. Most of the men were in two groups. They were watching their champion and his antagonist, who were charging each other with couched lances. Even as Wolff saw them, they met together in the middle of the field with a fearful clang. One knight went sailing backward with the lance of the other jammed into his shield. The other, however, lost his balance and fell with a clang several seconds later.

Wolff studied the tableau. It was no ordinary jousting tourney. The peasants and the townspeople who should have thronged the sides and the jerrybuilt stadium with its flowerbed of brilliantly dressed nobility and ladies were absent. This was a lonely place beside the road where champions had pitched their tents and were taking on all qualified passersby.

Wolff worked his way down the hill. Although exposed to the sight of those below, he did not think that they would take much interest in a lone traveler at this time. He was right. No one hastened from either camp to question him. He was able to walk up to the edge of the meadow and make a leisurely inspection.

The flag above the pavilion to his left bore a yellow field with a Solomon's seal. By this he knew that a Yidshe champion had pitched his tent here. Below the national flag was a green banner with a silver fish and hawk. The other camp had several state and personal pennons. One of them leaped out into Wolff's gaze and caused him to cry out with surprise. On a white field was a red ass's head with a hand below it, all fingers

102

clenched but the middle. Kickaha had once told him of it, and Wolff had gotten a big laugh out of it. It was just like Kickaha to pick such a coat of arms.

Wolff sobered then, knowing that, more likely, it was borne by the man who took care of Kickaha's territory while he was gone.

He changed his decision to pass on by the field. He had to determine for himself that the man using that banner was not Kickaha, even though he knew that his friend's bones must be rotting under a pile of dirt at the bottom of a shaft in a ruined city of the jungle.

Unchallenged, he made his way across the field and into the camp at the western end. Men-at-arms and retainers stared, only to turn away from his glare. Somebody muttered, "Yidshe dog!" but none owned to the comment when he turned. He went on around a line of horses tethered to a post and up to the knight who was his goal. This one was clad in shining red armor, visor down, and held a huge lance upright while he waited his turn. The lance bore near its tip a pennon on which were the red ass's head and human hand.

Wolff placed himself near the prancing horse, making it even more nervous. He cried out in German, "Baron von Horstmann?"

There was a muffled exclamation, a pause, and the knight's hand raised his visor. Wolff almost wept with joy. The merry long-lipped face of Finnegan-Kickaha-von Horstmann was inside the helmet.

"Don't say anything," Kickaha cautioned. "I don't know how in hell you found me, but I'm sure happy about it. I'll see you in a moment. That is, if I come back alive. This funem Laksfalk is one tough hombre."

CHAPTER TWELVE

Trumpets fared, Kickaha rode out to a spot indicated by the marshals. A shaven-headed, long-robed priest blessed him while, at the other end of the field, a rabbi was saying something to Baron funem Laksfalk. The Yidshe champion was a large man in a silver armor, his helmet shaped like a fish's head. His steed was a huge powerful black. The trumpets blew again. The two contenders dipped their lances in salute. Kickaha briefly gripped his lance with his left hand while he crossed himself with his right. (He was a stickler for observing the religious rules of the people among whom he happened to be at the moment.)

103

Another blast of long-shafted, big-mouthed trumpets was followed by the thunder of the hooves of the knights' horses and the cheers of the onlookers. The two met exactly in the middle of the field, as did the lance of each in the middle of the other's shield. Both fell with a clangor that startled the birds from the nearby trees, as they had been startled many times that day. The horses rolled on the ground.

The men of each knight ran out onto the field to pick up their chief and to drag away the horses, both of which had broken their necks. For a moment, Wolff thought that the Yidshe and Kickaha were also dead, for neither stirred. After being carried back, however, Kickaha came to. He grinned feebly and said, "You ought to see the other guy."

"He's okay," Wolff said after a glance at the other camp.

"Too bad," Kickaha replied. "I was hoping he wouldn't give us any more trouble. He's held me up too long as it is."

Kickaha ordered all but Wolff to leave the tent. His men seemed reluctant to leave him but they obeyed, though not without warning looks at Wolff. Kickaha said, "I was on my way from my castle to von Elgers' when I passed funem Laksfalk's pavilion. If I'd been alone, I would have thumbed my nose at his challenge and ridden on. But there were also Teutoniacs there, and I had my own men to consider. I couldn't afford to get a reputation of cowardice; my own men would've pelted me with rotten cabbage and I'd have had to fight every knight in the land to prove my courage. I figured that it wouldn't take me long to straighten out the Yidshe on who the best man was, and then I could take off.

"It didn't work out that way. The marshals had me listed in the Number Three position. That meant I had to joust with three men for three days before I'd get to the big time. I protested; no use. So I swore to myself and sweated it out. You saw my second encounter with funem Laksfalk. We both knocked each other off the saddle the first time, too. Even so, that's more than the others have done. They're burned up because a Yidshe has defeated every Teuton except me. Besides, he's killed two already and crippled another for life."

While listening to Kickaha, Wolff had been taking the armor off. Kickaha sat up suddenly, groaning and wincing, and said, "Hey, how in hell did you get here?"

"I walked mostly. But I thought you were dead."

"The report wasn't too grossly exaggerated. When I fell down that shaft I landed halfway up on a ledge of dirt. It broke off and started a little cave-in that buried me after I landed on the bottom. But I wasn't knocked out long, and the dirt only lightly covered my face, so I wasn't asphyxiated. I lay quiet for a while because the Sholkin were looking down

104

the hole then. They even threw a spear down, but it missed me by a mole's hair.

"After a couple of hours, I dug myself out. I had a time getting out, I can tell you. The dirt kept breaking off, and I kept falling back. It must've taken me ten hours, but I was lucky at that. Now, how did *you* get here, you big lunk?"

Wolff told him. Kickaha frowned and said, "So I was right in figuring that Abiru would come to von Elgers' on his way. Listen, we got to get out of here and fast. How would you like to take a swing at the big Yid?"

Wolff protested that he knew nothing of the fine points of jousting, that it took a lifetime to learn. Kickaha said, "If you were going to break a lance with him, you'd be right. But we'll challenge him to a contest with swords, no shields. Broad-swording isn't exactly duelling with a rapier or saber; it's main strength and that's what you've got!"

"I'm not a knight. The others saw me enter as a common vagrant."

"Nonsense! You think these chevaliers don't go around in disguise all the time? I'll tell them you're a Saracen, a pagan Khamshem, but you're a real good friend of mine, I rescued you from a dragon or some cock-and-bull story like that. They'll eat it up. I got it! You're the Saracen Wolf—there's a famous knight by that name. You've been journeying in disguise, hoping to find me and pay me back for saving you from the dragon. I'm too hurt to break another lance with funem Laksfalk—that's no lie; I'm so stiff and sore I can hardly move—and you're taking up the gauntlet for me."

Wolff asked what excuse he would give for not using the lance.

Kickaha said, "I'll give them some story. Say a thieving knight stole your lance and you've sworn never to use one until you get the stolen one back. They'll accept that. They're always making some goofy vow or other. They act just like a bunch of knights from King Arthur's Round Table. No such knights ever existed on Earth, but it must have pleased the Lord to make these act as if they just rode out of Camelot. He was a romantic, whatever else you can say about him."

Wolff said he was reluctant, but if it would help speed them to von Elgers', he would do anything. Kickaha's own armor was not large enough for Wolff, so the armor of a Yid-she knight Kickaha had killed the day before was brought in. The retainers clad him in blue plates and chain-mail and then led him out to his horse. This was a beautiful palomino mare that had also belonged to the knight Kickaha had slain, the Ritter oyf Roytfeldz. With only a little difficulty, Wolff mounted the charger. He had expected that the armor would be so heavy a crane would have to lift him upon the saddle. Kick-aha told him that that might have once been true here, but the knights had long since gone back to lighter plates and more chain-mail.

The Yidshe go-between came to announce that funem Laks-falk had accepted the challenge despite the Saracen Wolf's lack of credentials. If the valiant and honorable robber Baron Horst von Horstmann vouched for the Wolf, that was good enough for funem Laksfalk. The speech was a formality. The Yidshe champion would not for one moment have thought of turning down a challenge.

"Face is the big thing here," Kickaha said to Wolff. Having managed to limp out of his tent, he was giving his friend last-minute instructions. "Man, am I glad you came along. I couldn't have taken one more fall, and I didn't dare back out."

Again, the trumpets flourished. The palomino and the black broke into a headlong gallop. They passed each other going at full speed, during which time both men swung their swords. They clanged together; a paralyzing shock ran down Wolff's hand and arm. However, when he turned his charger, he saw that his antagonist's sword was on the ground. The Yidshe was dismounting swiftly to get to the blade before Wolff. He was in such a hurry he slipped and fell headlong onto the ground.

Wolff rode his horse up slowly and took his time dismounting to allow the other to recover. At this chivalrous move, both camps broke into cheers. By the rules, Wolff could have stayed in the saddle and cut funem Laksfalk down without permitting him to pick up his weapon.

On the ground, they faced each other. The Yidshe knight raised his visor, revealing a handsome face. He had a thick moustache and pale blue eyes. He said, "I pray you let me see your face, noble one. You are a true knight for not striking me down while helpless."

Wolff lifted his visor for a few seconds. Both then advanced and brought their blades together again. Once more, Wolff's stroke was so powerful that it tore the blade of the other from his grip.

Funem Laksfalk raised his visor, this time with his left arm. He said, "I cannot use my right arm. If you will permit me to use my left?"

Wolff saluted and stepped back. His opponent gripped the long hilt of his sword and, stepping close, brought it around from the side with all his force. Once more, the shock of Wolff's stroke broke the Yidshe's grasp.

Funem Laksfalk lifted his visor for the third time. "You are

106

such a champion as I have never met. I am loath to admit it, but you have defeated me. And that is something I have never said nor thought to say. You have the strength of the Lord himself."

"You may keep your life, your honor, and your armor and horse," Wolff replied. "I want only that my friend von Horstmann and I be allowed to go on without further challenges. We have an appointment."

The Yidshe answered that it would be so. Wolff returned to his camp, there to be greeted joyously, even by those who had thought of him as a Khamshem dog.

Chortling, Kickaha ordered camp struck. Wolff asked him if he did not think they could make far better time unencumbered with a train.

"Sure, but it's not done very often," Kickaha replied. "Oh, well, you're right. I'll send them on home. And we'll get these damn locomotive plates off."

They had not ridden far before they heard the drum of hooves. Coming up the road behind them was funem Laksfalk, also minus his armor. They halted until he had overtaken them.

"Noble knights," he said, smiling, "I know that you are on a quest. Would it be too much for me to ask to join? I would feel honored. I also feel that only by assisting you can I redeem my defeat."

Kickaha looked at Wolff and said, "It's up to you. But I like his style."

"Would you bind yourself to aid us in whatever we do? As long as it is not dishonorable, of course. You may release yourself from your oath at any time, but you must swear by all that's holy that you will never aid our enemies."

"By God's blood and the beard of Moses, I swear."

That night, while they made camp in a brake alongside a brook, Kickaha said, "There's one problem that having funem Laksfalk along might complicate. We have to get the stain off your skin, and that beard has to go, too. Otherwise, if we run into Abiru, he might identify you."

"One lie always leads to another," Wolff said. "Well, tell him that I'm the younger son of a baron who kicked me out because my jealous brother falsely accused me. I've been traveling around since then, disguised as a Saracen. But I intend to return to my father's castle—he's dead now—and challenge my brother to a duel."

"Fabulous! You're a second Kickaha! But what about when he learns of Chryseis and the horn?"

"We'll think of something. Maybe the truth. He can always back out when he finds he's bucking the Lord."

The next morning they rode until they came to the village of

Etzelbrand. Here Kickaha purchased some chemicals from the local white-wizard and made a preparation to remove the stain. Once past the village, they stopped off at the brook. Funem Laksfalk watched with interest, then amazement, then suspicion as the beard came off, followed by the stain.

"God's eyes! You were a Khamshem, now you could be a Yidshe!"

Kickaha thereupon launched into a three-hour, much-detailed story in which Wolff was the bastard son of a Yidshe maiden lady and a Teutoniac knight on a quest. The knight, a Robert von Wolfram, had stayed at a Yidshe castle after covering himself with glory during a tournament. He and the maiden had fallen in love, too much so. When the knight had ridden out, vowing to return after completing his quest, he had left Rivke pregnant. But von Wolfram had been killed and the girl had had to bear young Robert in shame. Her father had kicked her out and sent her to a little village in Khamshem to live there forever. The girl had died when giving birth to Robert, but a faithful old servant had revealed the secret of his birth to Robert. The young bastard had sworn that when he gained manhood, he would go to the castle of his father's people and claim his rightful inheritance. Rivke's father was dead now but his brother, a wicked old man, held the castle. Robert intended to wrest the baronetcy from him if he would not give it up.

Funem Laksfalk had tears in his eyes at the end of the story. He said, "I will ride with you, Robert, and help you against your wicked uncle. Thus may I redeem my defeat."

Later, Wolff reproached Kickaha for making up such a fantastic story, so detailed that he might easily be tripped up. Moreover, he did not like to deceive such a man as the Yidshe knight.

"Nonsense! You couldn't tell him the whole truth, and it's easier to make up a whole lie than a half-truth! Besides, look at how much he enjoyed his little cry! And, I am Kickaha, the *kickaha*, the tricky one, the maker of fantasies and of realities. I am the man whom boundaries cannot hold. I slip from one to another, in-again-out-again Finnegan. I seem to be killed, yet I pop up again, alive, grinning, and kicking! I am quicker than men who are stronger than me, and stronger than those who are quicker! I have few loyalties, but those are unshakable! I am the ladies' darling wherever I go, and many are the tears shed after I slip through the night like a red-headed ghost! But tears cannot hold me any more than chains! Off I go, and where I will appear or what my name will be, few know! I am the Lord's gadfly; he cannot sleep at nights because I elude his Eyes, the ravens, and his hunters, the gworl!"

Kickaha stopped and began laughing uproariously. Wolff had to grin back. Kickaha's manner made it plain that he was poking fun at himself. However, he did half-believe it, and why should he not? What he said was not actually exaggeration.

This thought opened the way to a train of speculation that brought a frown to Wolff. Was it possible that Kickaha was the Lord himself in disguise? He could be amusing himself by running with hare and hound both. What better entertainment for a Lord, a man who had to look far and deep for something new with which to stave off ennui? There were many unexplained things about him.

Wolff, searching Kickaha's face for some clue to the mystery, felt his doubts evaporate. Surely that merry face was not the mask for a hideously cold being who toyed with lives. And then there was Kickaha's undeniably Hoosier accent and idioms. Could a Lord master these?

Well, why not? Kickaha had evidently mastered other languages and dialects as well.

So it went in Wolff's mind that long afternoon as they rode. But dinner and drink and good fellowship dispelled them so that, at bedtime, he had forgotten his doubts. The three had stopped at a tavern in the village of Gnazelschist and eaten heartily. Wolff and Kickaha devoured a roast suckling pig between them. Funem Laksfalk, although he shaved and had other liberal views of his religion, refused the taboo pork. He ate beef—although he knew it had not been slaughtered à la kosher. All three downed many steins of the excellent local dark beer, and during the drink-conversation Wolff told funem Laksfalk a somewhat edited story about their search for Chryseis—a noble quest indeed, they agreed, and then they all staggered off to bed.

In the morning, they took a shortcut through the hills which would save them three days' time—if they got through. The road was rarely traveled, and with good reason, for outlaws and dragons frequented the area. They made good speed, saw no men-of-the-woods and only one dragon. The scaly monster scrambled up from a ditch a hundred yards ahead of them. It snorted and disappeared into the trees on the other side of the road, as eager as they to avoid a fight.

Coming down out of the hills to the main highway, Wolff said, "A raven's following us."

"Yeah, I know it, but don't get your neck hot. They're all over the place. I doubt that it knows who we are. I sincerely hope it doesn't."

At noon of the following day, they entered the territory of the Komtur of Tregyln. More than twenty-four hours later, they arrived within sight of the castle of Tregyln, the Baron von Elgers' seat of power. This was the largest castle Wolff had so far seen. It was built of black stone and was situated on top of a high hill a mile from the town of Tregyln.

In full armor, pennoned lances held upright, the three rode boldly to the moat that surrounded the castle. A warder came out of a small blockhouse by the moat and politely inquired of them their business.

"Take word to the noble lord that three knights of good fame would be his guests," Kickaha said. "The Barons von Horstmann and von Wolfram and the far-famed Yidshe baron, funem Laksfalk. We look for a noble to hire us for fighting or to send us on a quest."

The sergeant shouted at a corporal, who ran off across the drawbridge. A few minutes afterwards, one of von Elgers' sons, a youth splendidly dressed, rode out to welcome them. Inside the huge courtyard, Wolff saw something that disturbed him. Several Khamshem and Sholkin were lounging around or playing dice.

"They won't recognize either one of us," Kickaha said. "Cheer up. If they're here, then so are Chryseis and the horn."

After making sure that their horses were well taken care of, the three went to the quarters given them. They bathed and put on the brilliantly colored new clothes sent up to them by von Elgers. Wolff observed that these differed little from the garments worn during the thirteenth century. The only innovations, Kickaha said, were traceable to aboriginal influence.

By the time they entered the vast dining-hall, the supper was in full blast. Blast was the right word, for the uproar was deafening. Half the guests were reeling, and the others did not move much because they had passed the reeling stage. Von Elgers managed to rise to greet his guests. Graciously, he apologized for being found in such a condition at such an early hour.

"We have been entertaining our Khamshem guest for several days. He has brought unexpected wealth to us, and we've been spending a little of it on a celebration."

He turned to introduce Abiru, did so too swiftly, and almost fell. Abiru rose to return their bow. His black eyes flickered like a sword point over them; his smile was broad but mechanical. Unlike the others, he appeared sober. The three took their seats, which were close to the Khamshem because the previous occupants had passed out under the table. Abiru seemed eager to talk to them.

"If you are looking for service, you have found your man. I am paying the baron to conduct me to the hinterland, but I can always use more swords. The road to my destination is long and hard and beset with many perils."

110

"And where is your destination?" Kickaha asked. No one looking at him would have thought him any more than idly interested in Abiru for he was hotly scanning the blonde beauty across the table from him.

"There is no secret about that," Abiru said. "The lord of Kranzelkracht is said to be a very strange man, but it is also said that he has more wealth even than the Grand Marshal of Teutonia."

"I know that for a fact," Kickaha replied. "I have been there, and I have seen his treasures. Many years ago, so it is said, he dared the displeasure of the Lord and climbed the great mountain to the tier of Atlantis. He robbed the treasure house of the Rhadamanthus himself and got away with a bagful of jewels. Since then, von Kranzelkracht has increased his wealth by conquering the states around his. It is said that the Grand Marshal is worried by this and is thinking of organizing a crusade against him. The Marshal claims that the man is a heretic. But if he were, would not the Lord have blasted him with lightning long ago?"

Abiru bowed his head and touched his forehead with his fingertips.

"The Lord works in mysterious ways. Besides, who but the Lord knows the truth? In any event, I am taking my slaves and certain possessions to Kranzelkracht. I expect to make an enormous profit from my venture, and those knights bold enough to share it will gain much gold—not to mention fame."

Abiru paused to drink from a glass of wine. Kickaha, aside to Wolff, said, "The man's as big a liar as I am. He intends to use us to get him as far as Kranzelkracht, which is near the foot of the monolith. Then he will take Chryseis and the horn up to Atlantis, where he should be paid with a houseful of jewels and gold for the two.

"That is, unless his game is even deeper than I think at this moment."

He lifted his stein and drank for a long time, or appeared to. Setting the stein down with a crash, he said, "I'll be damned if there isn't something familiar about Abiru! I had a funny feeling the first time I saw him, but I was too busy thereafter to think much about it. Now, I know I've seen him before."

Wolff replied that that was not amazing. How many faces had he seen during his twenty-year wanderings?

"Maybe you're right," Kickaha muttered. "But I don't think it was any slight acquaintance I had with him. I'd sure like to scrape off his beard."

Abiru arose and excused himself, saying that it was the hour of prayer to the Lord and his personal deity, Tartartar. He would be back after his devotions. At this, von Elgers beckoned

111

to two men-at-arms and ordered them to accompany him to his quarters and make sure that he was safe. Abiru bowed and thanked him for his consideration. Wolff did not miss the intent behind the baron's polite words. He did not trust the Khamshem, and Abiru knew it. Von Elgers, despite his drunkenness, was aware of what was going on and would detect anything out of the way.

"Yeah, you're right about him," Kickaha said. "He didn't get to where he is by turning his back on his enemies. And try to conceal your impatience, Bob. We've got a long wait ahead of us. Act drunk, make a few passes at the ladies—they'll think you're queer if you don't. But don't go off with any. We got to keep each other in sight so we can take off together when the right time comes."

CHAPTER THIRTEEN

Wolff drank enough to loosen the wires that seemed to be wound around him. He even began to talk with the Lady Alison, wife of the baron of the Wenzelbricht March. A dark-haired and blue-eyed woman of statuesque beauty, she wore a clinging white samite gown. It was so low cut that she should have been satisfied with its exhilarating effect on the men, but she kept dropping her fan and picking it up herself. At any time other than this, Wolff would have been happy to break his woman-fast with her. It was obvious he would have no trouble doing so, for she was flattered that the great von Wolfram was interested in her. She had heard of his victory over von Laksberg. But he could think only of Chryseis, who must be somewhere in the castle. Nobody had mentioned her, and he dared not. Yet he was aching to do so and several times found that he had to bite the question off the tip of his tongue.

Presently, and just at the right time for him—since he could not any longer refuse the Lady Alison's bold hints without offending her—Kickaha was at his side. Kickaha had brought Alison's husband along to give Wolff a reasonable excuse for leaving. Later, Kickaha revealed that he had dragged von Wenzelbricht away from another woman on the pretext that his wife demanded he come to her. Both Kickaha and Wolff walked away, leaving the beer-stupored baron to explain just what he wanted of her. Since neither he nor his wife knew, they must have had an interesting, if mystifying, conversation.

Wolff gestured at funem Laksfalk to join them. Together, the three pretended to stagger off to the toilet. Once out of sight of those in the dining-hall, they hurried down a hall away

112

from their supposed destination. Unhindered, they climbed four flights of steps. They were armed only with daggers, for it would have been an insult to wear armor or swords to dinner. Wolff, however, had managed to untie a long cord from the draperies in his apartment. He wore this coiled around his waist under his shirt.

The Yidshe knight said, "I overheard Abiru talk with his lieutenant, Rhamnish. They spoke in the trade language of H'vaizhum, little knowing that I have traveled on the Guzirit River in the jungle area. Abiru asked Rhamnish if he had found out yet where von Elgers had taken Chryseis. Rhamnish said that he had spent some gold and time in talking to servants and guards. All he could find out was that she is on the east side of the castle. The gworl, by the way, are in the dungeon."

"Why should von Elgers keep Chryseis from Abiru?" Wolff said. "Isn't she Abiru's property?"

"Maybe the baron has some designs on her," Kickaha said. "If she's as extraordinary and beautiful as you say . . ."

"We've got to find her!"

"Don't get your neck hot. We will. Oh, oh, there's a guard at the end of the hall. Keep walking toward him—stagger a little more."

The guard raised his spear as they reeled in front of him. In a polite but firm voice, he told them they must go back. The baron had forbidden anybody, under pain of death, to proceed further.

"All right," Wolff said, slurring the words. He started to turn, then suddenly leaped and grabbed the spear. Before the startled sentry could loose the yell from his open mouth, he was slammed against the door and the shaft of the spear was brought up hard against his throat. Wolff continued to press it. The sentry's eyes goggled, his face became red, then blue. A minute later, he slumped forward, dead.

The Yidshe dragged the body down the hall and into a side-room. When he returned, he reported that he had hidden the corpse behind a large chest.

"Too bad," Kickaha said cheerfully. "He may have been a nice kid. But if we have to fight our way out, we'll have one less in our way."

However, the dead man had had no key to unlock the door.

"Von Elgers is probably the only man who has one, and we'd play hell getting it off him," Kickaha said. "Okay. We'll go around."

He led them back down the hall to another room. They climbed through its tall pointed window. Beyond its ledge was a series of projections, stones carved in the shape of dragon heads, fiends, boars. The adornments had not been spaced to provide for easy climbing, but a brave or desperate man could ascend them. Fifty feet below them, the surface of the moat glittered dully in the light of torches on the drawbridge. Fortunately, thick black clouds covered the moon and would prevent those below from seeing the climbers.

Kickaha looked down at Wolff, who was clinging to a stone gargoyle, one foot on a snake-head. "Hey, did I forget to tell you that the baron keeps the moat stocked with water-dragons? They're not very big, only about twenty feet long, and they don't have any legs. But they're usually underfed."

"There are times when I find your humor in bad taste," Wolff said fiercely. "Get going."

Kickaha gave a low laugh and continued climbing. Wolff followed, after glancing down to make sure that the Yidshe was doing all right. Kickaha stopped and said. "There's a window here, but it's barred. I don't think there's anyone inside. It's dark."

Kickaha continued climbing. Wolff paused to look inside the window. It was black as the inside of a cave fish's eye. He reached through the bars and groped around until his fingers closed on a candle. Lifting it carefully so that it would come out of its holder, he passed it through the bars. With one arm hooked around a steel rod, he hung while he fished a match from the little bag on his belt with the other hand.

From above, Kickaha said, "What are you doing?"

Wolff told him, and Kickaha said, "I spoke Chryseis' name a couple of times. There's no one in there. Quit wasting time."

"I want to make sure."

"You're too thorough; you pay too much attention to detail. You got to take big cuts if you want to chop down a tree. Come on."

Not bothering to reply, Wolff struck the match. It flared up and almost went out in the breeze, but he managed to stick it inside the window quickly enough. The flare of light showed a bedroom with no occupant.

"You satisfied?" Kickaha's voice came, weaker because he was climbing upward. "We got one more chance, the bartizan. If there's no one ... Anyway, I don't know how—*ugh!*"

Afterwards, Wolff was thankful that he had been so reluctant to give up his hopes that Chryseis would be in the room. He had let the match burn out until it threatened his fingers and only then let go of it. Immediately after that and Kickaha's muffled exclamation, he was struck by a falling body. The impact felt as if it had almost torn his arm loose from its socket. He gave a grunt that echoed the one from above and hung on with one arm. Kickaha clung to him for several seconds, shivered, then breathed deeply and resumed his climb. Neither said a word about it, but both knew that if it had not been for Wolff's stubbornness, Kickaha's fall would also have knocked Wolff from a precarious hold on a gargoyle. Possibly funem Laksfalk would have been dislodged also, for he was directly below Wolff.

The bartizan was a large one. It was about one third of the way up the wall, projected far outward from the wall, and a light fell from its cross-shaped window. The wall a little distance above it was bare of decoration.

An uproar broke loose below and a fainter one within the castle. Wolff stopped to look down toward the drawbridge, thinking that they must have been seen. However, although there were a number of men-at-arms and guests on the drawbridge and the grounds outside, many with torches, not a single one was looking up toward the climbers. They seemed to be searching for someone in the bushes and trees.

He thought that their absence and the body of the guard had been noted. They would have to fight their way out. But let them find Chryseis first and get her loose; then would be time to think of battle.

Kickaha, ahead of him, said, "Come on, Bob!" His voice was so excited that Wolff knew he must have located Chryseis. He climbed swiftly, more swiftly than good sense permitted. It was necessary to climb to one side of the projection, for its underside angled outward. Kickaha was lying on the flat top of the bartizan and just in the act of pulling himself back from its edge. "You have to hang upside down to look in the window, Bob. She's there, and she's alone. But the window's too narrow for either of you to go through."

Wolff slid out over the edge of the projection while Kickaha grabbed his legs. He went out and over, the black moat below, and bent down until he would have fallen if his legs had not been held. The slit in the stone showed him the face of Chryseis, inverted. She was smiling but tears were rolling down her cheeks.

Afterward, he did not exactly remember what they said to each other, for he was in a fever of exaltation, succeeded by a chill of frustration and despair, then followed by another fever. He felt as if he could talk forever, and he reached his hand out to touch hers. She strained against the opening in the rock in vain to reach him.

"Never mind, Chryseis," he said. "You know we're here. We're not going to leave until we take you away, I swear it."

"Ask her where the horn is!" Kickaha said.

Hearing him, Chryseis said, "I do not know, but I think that von Elgers has it."

115

"Has he bothered you?" Wolff asked savagely.

"Not so far, but I do not know how long it will be before he takes me to bed," she replied. "He's restrained himself only because he does not want to lower the price he'll get for me. He says he's never seen a woman like me."

Wolff swore, then laughed. It was like her to talk thus frankly, for in the Garden world self-admiration was an accepted attitude.

"Cut out the unnecessary chatter," Kickaha said. "There'll be time for that if we get her out."

Chryseis answered Wolff's questions as concisely and clearly as possible. She described the route to this room. She did not know how many guards were stationed outside her door or on the way up.

"I do know one thing that the baron does not," she said. "He thinks that Abiru is taking me to von Kranzelkracht. I know better. Abiru means to ascend the Doozvillnava to Atlantis. There he will sell me to the Rhadamanthus."

"He won't sell you to anybody, because I'm going to kill him," Wolff said. "I have to go now, Chryseis, but I'll be back as soon as possible. And I won't be coming this way. Until then, I love you."

Chryseis cried, "I have not heard a man tell me that for a thousand years! Oh, Robert Wolff, I love you! But I am afraid! I . . ."

"You don't have to be afraid of anything," he said. "Not while I am alive, and I don't intend to die."

He gave the word for Kickaha to drag him back onto the rooftop of the bartizan. He rose and almost fell over from dizziness, for his head was gorged with blood.

"The Yidshe has already started down," Kickaha said. "I sent him to find out if we can get back the way we came and also to see what's causing the uproar."

"Us?"

"I don't think so. The first thing they'd do, they'd check on Chryseis. Which they haven't done."

The descent was even slower and more dangerous than the climb up, but they made it without mishap. Funem Laksfalk was waiting for them by the window which had given them access to the outside.

"They've found the guard you killed," he said. "But they don't think we had anything to do with it. The gworl broke loose from the dungeon and killed a number of men. They also seized their own weapons. Some got outside, but not all."

The three left the room and merged quickly with the searchers. They had no chance to go up the flight of steps at the end

116

of which was the room where Chryseis was imprisoned. Without a doubt, Von Elgers would have made sure that the guards were increased.

They wandered around the castle for several hours, acquainting themselves with its layout. They noted that, though the shock of the gworl's escape had sobered the Teutons somewhat, they were still very drunk. Wolff suggested that they go to their room, and talk about possible plans. Perhaps they could think of something reasonably workable.

Their room was on the fifth story and by a window at an angle below the window of Chryseis' bartizan. To get to it, they had to pass many men and women, all stinking of beer and wine, reeling, babbling away, and accomplishing very little. Their room could not have been entered and searched, for only they and the chief warder had the keys. He had been too busy elsewhere to get to their room. Besides, how could the gworl enter through a locked door?

The moment Wolff stepped into his room, he knew that they had somehow entered. The musty rotten-fruit stench hit him in the nostrils. He pulled the other two inside and swiftly shut and locked the door behind them. Then he turned with his dagger in his hand. Kickaha also, his nostrils dilating and his eyes stabbing, had his blade out. Only funem Laksfalk was unaware that anything was wrong except for an unpleasant odor.

Wolff whispered to him; the Yidshe walked toward the wall to get their swords, then stopped. The racks were empty.

Silently and slowly, Wolff went into the other room. Kickaha, behind him, held a torch. The flame flickered and cast humped shadows that made Wolff start. He had been sure that they were the gworl.

The light advanced; the shadows fled or changed into harmless shapes.

"They're here," Wolff said softly. "Or they've just left. But where could they go?"

Kickaha pointed at the high drapes that were drawn over the window. Wolff strode up to them and began thrusting through the red-purple velvet cloth. His blade met only air and the stone of the wall. Kickaha pulled the drapes back to reveal what the dagger had told him. There were no gworl.

"They came in through the window," the Yidshe said. "But why?"

Wolff lifted his eyes at that moment, and he swore. He stepped back to warn his friends, but they were already looking upward. There, hanging upside down by their knees from the heavy iron drapery rod, were two gworl. Both had long, bloody knives in their hands. One, in addition, clutched the silver horn.

117

The two creatures stiffened their legs the second they realized they were discovered. Both managed to flip over and come down heads-up. The one to the right kicked out with his feet. Wolff rolled and then was up, but Kickaha had missed with his knife and the gworl had not. It slid from his palm through a short distance into Kickaha's arm.

The other threw his knife at funem Laksfalk. It struck the Yidshe in the solar plexus with a force that made him bend over and stagger back. A few seconds later, he straightened up to reveal why the knife had failed to enter his flesh. Through the tear in his shirt gleamed the steel of light chain-mail.

By then, the gworl with the horn had gone through the window. The others could not rush to the window because the gworl left behind was putting up a savage battle. He knocked down Wolff again, but with his fist this time. He threw himself like a whirlwind at Kickaha, his fists flailing, and drove him back. The Yidshe, his knife in hand, jumped at him and thrust for his belly, only to have his wrist seized and turned until he cried out with pain and the knife fell from his fist.

Kickaha, lying on the floor, raised one leg and then drove the heel of his foot against the gworl's ankle. He fell, although he did not hit the floor because Wolff seized him. Around and around, their arms locked around each other, they circled. Each was trying to break the other's back and also trying to trip the other. Wolff succeeded in throwing him over. They toppled against the wall with the gworl receiving the most damage when the back of his head struck the wall.

For a flicker of an eyelid he was stunned. This gave Wolff enough time to pull the stinking, hairy, bumpy creature hard against him and pull with all his strength against the gworl's spine. Too heavily muscled and too heavily boned, the gworl resisted the spine-snapping. By then, the other two men were upon him with their knives. They thrust several times and would have continued to try for a fatal spot in the tough cartilage-roughened hide had Wolff not told them to stop.

Stepping back, he released the gworl, who fell bleeding and glaze-eyed to the floor. Wolff ignored him for a moment to look out the window after the gworl who had escaped with the horn. A party of horsemen, holding torches, was thundering over the drawbridge and out into the country. The light showed only the smooth black waters of the moat; there was no gworl climbing down the wall. Wolff turned back to the gworl who had remained behind.

"His name is Diskibibol, and the other is Smeel," Kickaha said.

"Smeel must have drowned," Wolff said. "Even if he could

118

swim, the water-dragons might have gotten him. But he can't swim."

Wolff thought of the horn lying in the muck at the bottom of the moat. "Apparently no one saw Smeel fall. So the horn's safe there, for the time being."

The gworl spoke. Although he used German, he could not master the sounds accurately. His words grated deep in the back of his throat. "You will die, humans. The Lord will win; Arwoor is the Lord; he cannot be defeated by filth such as you. But before you die, you will suffer the most . . . the . . . the most . . ."

He began coughing, threw up blood, and continued to do so until he was dead.

"We'd better get rid of his body," Wolff said. "We might have a hard time explaining what he was doing here. And von Elgers might connect the missing horn with their presence here."

A look out of the window showed him that the search party was far down the trail road leading to the town. For the moment, at least, no one was on the bridge. He lifted the heavy corpse up and shoved it out the window. After Kickaha's wound was bandaged, Wolff and the Yidshe wiped up the evidences of the struggle.

Only after they were through did funem Laksfalk speak. His face was pale and grim. "That was the horn of the Lord. I insist that you tell me how it got here and what your part is in this . . . this seeming blasphemy."

"Now's the time for the whole truth," Kickaha said. "You tell him, Bob. For once, I don't feel like hogging the conversation."

Wolff was concerned for Kickaha, for his face, too, was pale, and the blood was oozing out through the thick bandages. Nevertheless, he told the Yidshe what he could as swiftly as possible.

The knight listened well, although he could not help interjecting questions frequently or swearing when Wolff told him something particularly amazing.

"By God," he said when Wolff seemed to be finished, "this tale of another world would make me call you a liar if the rabbis had not already told me that my ancestors, and those of the Teutons, had come from just such a place. Then there is the Book of the Second Exodus, which says the same thing and also claims that the Lord came from a different world.

"Still, I had always thought these tales the stuff that holy men, who are a trifle mad, dream up. I would never have dreamed of saying so aloud, of course, for I did not want to be stoned for heresy. Also, there's always the doubt that these could be true. And the Lord punishes those who deny him; there's no doubt of that.

"Now, you put me in a situation no man could envy. I know you two for the most redoubtable knights it has ever been my fortune to encounter. You are such men as would not lie; I would stake my life on that. And your story rings true as the armor of the great dragon-slayer, fun Zilberbergl. Yet, I do not know."

He shook his head. "To seek to enter the citadel of the Lord himself, to strike again the Lord! That frightens me. For the first time in my life, I, Leyb fumen Laksfalk, admit that I am afraid."

Wolff said, "You gave your oath to us. We release you but ask that you do as you swore. That is, you tell no one of us or our quest."

Angrily, the Yidshe said, "I did not say I would quit you! I will not, at least not yet. There is this that makes me think you might be telling the truth. The Lord is omnipotent, yet his holy horn has been in your hands and those of the gworl, and the Lord has done nothing. Perhaps . . ."

Wolff replied that he did not have time to wait for him to make up his mind. The horn must be recovered now, while there was the opportunity. And Chryseis must be freed at the first chance. He led them from the room and into another, unoccupied at the moment. There they took three swords to replace theirs, which the gworl must have cast out of the window into the moat. Within a few minutes, they were outside the castle and pretending to search through the woods for the gworl.

By then most of the Teutons outside had returned to the castle. The three waited until the stragglers decided that no gworl were around. When the last of these had gone across the drawbridge, Wolff and his friends put out their torches. Two sentries remained at the guardhouse by the end of the bridge. These, however, were a hundred yards distant and could not see into the shadows where the three crouched. Moreover, they were too busy discussing the events of the night and looking into the darkness of the woods. They were not the original sentries, for these had been killed by the gworl when they had made their dash for freedom across the bridge.

"The point just below our window should be where the horn is," Wolff said. "Only . . ."

"The water-dragons," Kickaha said. "They'll have dragged off Smeel and Diskibibol's bodies to their lairs, wherever those are. But there might be some others cruising around. I'd go, but this wound of mine would draw them at once."

120

"I was just talking to myself," Wolff said. He began to take off his clothes. "How deep's the moat?"

"You'll find out," Kickaha said.

Wolff saw something gleam redly in the reflected light from the distant bridge torches. An animal's eyes, he thought. The next moment, he and the others were caught within something sticky and binding. The stuff, whatever it was, covered his eyes and blinded him.

He fought savagely but silently. Though he did not know who his assailants were, he did not intend to arouse the castle people. However the struggle came out, the issue did not concern them; he knew that.

The more he thrashed, the tighter the webs clung to him and bound him. Eventually, raging, breathing hard, he was helpless. Only then did a voice speak, low and rasping. A knife cut the web to leave his face exposed. In the dim light of the distant torches, he could see two other figures wrapped in the stuff and a dozen crooked shapes. The rotten-fruit stench was powerful.

"I am Ghaghrill, the Zdrrikh'agh of Abbkmung. You are Robert Wolff and our great enemy Kickaha, and the third one I do not know."

"The Baron funem Laksfalk!" the Yidshe said. "Release me, and you will soon find out whether I am a good man to know or not, you stinking swine!"

"Quiet! We know you have somehow slain two of my best killers, Smeel and Diskibibol, though they could not have been so fierce if they allowed themselves to be defeated by such as you. We saw Diskibibol fall from where we hid in the woods. And we saw Smeel jump with the horn."

Ghagrill paused, then said, "You, Wolff, will go after the horn into the waters and bring it back to us. If you do, I swear by the honor of the Lord that we will release all three of you. The Lord wants Kickaha, too, but not as badly as the horn, and he said that we were not to kill him, even if we had to let him go to keep from killing him. We obey the Lord, for he is the greatest killer of all."

"And if I refuse?" Wolff said. "It is almost certain death for me with the water-dragons in the moat."

"It will be certain death for you if you don't."

Wolff considered. He was the logical choice, he had to admit. The quality and relationship of the Yidshe was unknown to the gworl, so they could not let him go after the horn; he might fail to return. Kickaha was a prize second only to the horn. Besides, he was wounded, and the blood from the wound would attract the water-monsters. Wolff, if he cared for Kickaha, would return. They could not, of course, be sure of the depth of his feelings for Kickaha. That was a chance they would have to take.

One thing was certain. No gworl was about to venture into such deep water if he had someone else to do it for him.

"Very well," Wolff said. "Let me loose, and I will go after the horn. But at least give me a knife to defend myself against the dragons."

"No," Ghaghrill said.

Wolff shrugged. After he was cut loose of the web-net, he removed all of his clothes except his shirt. This covered the cord wound around his waist.

"Don't do it, Bob," Kickaha said. "You can't trust a gworl any more than his master. They will take the horn from you and then do to us what they wish. And laugh at us for being their tools."

"I don't have any choice," Wolff said. "If I find the horn, I'll be back. If I don't return, you'll know I died trying."

"You'll die anyway," Kickaha replied. There was a smack of a fist against flesh. Kickaha cursed but did so softly.

"Speak any more, Kickaha," Ghaghrill said, "and I will cut out your tongue. The Lord did not forbid that."

CHAPTER FOURTEEN

Wolff looked up at the window, from which a torch-light still shone. He walked into the water, which was chilly but not cold. His feet sank into thick gluey mud which evoked images of the many corpses whose rotting flesh must form part of this mud. And he could not keep from thinking of the saurians swimming out there. If he was lucky, they would not be in the immediate neighbourhood. If they had dragged off the bodies of Smeel and Diskibibol . . . Better quit dwelling on them and start swimming.

The moat was at least two hundred yards wide at this point. He even stopped at the midway point to tread water and turn around to look at the shore. From this distance he could see nothing of the group.

On the other hand, they could not see him either. And Ghaghrill had given him no time limit to return. However, he knew that if he were not back before dawn, he would not find them there.

At a spot immediately below the light from the window, he dived. Down he went, the water becoming colder almost with every stroke. His ears began to ache, then to hurt intensely. He blew some bubbles of air out to relieve the pressure, but he was not helped much by this. Just as it seemed that he could go no deeper without his ears bursting, his hand plunged into soft mud. Restraining the desire to turn at once and swim upwards for the blessed relief from pressure and the absolutely needed air, he groped around on the floor of the moat. He found nothing but mud and, once, a bone. He drove himself until he knew he had to have air.

Twice he rose to the surface and then dived again. By now, he knew that even if the horn were lying on the bottom, he might not ever find it. Blind in the murky waters, he could pass within an inch of the horn and never know it. Moreover, it was possible that Smeel had thrown the horn far away from him when he had fallen. Or a water-dragon could have carried it off with Smeel's corpse, even swallowed the horn.

The third time, he swam a few strokes to the right from his previous dives before plunging under. He dived down at what he hoped was a ninety-degree angle from the bottom. In the blackness, he had no way of determining direction. His hand plowed into the mud; he settled close to it to feel around, and his fingers closed upon cold metal. A quick slide of them along the object passed over seven little buttons.

When he reached the surface, he trod water and gasped for wind. Now to make the trip back, which he hoped he could do. The water-dragons could still show up.

Then he forgot the dragons, for he could see nothing. The torchlight from the drawbridge, the feeble moonglow through the clouds, the light from the window overhead, all these were gone.

Wolff forced himself to keep on treading water while he thought his situation through. For one thing, there was no breeze. The air was stale. Thus, he could only be in one place, and it was his fortune that such a place happened to be just where he had dived. Also, it was his luck that he had come up from the bottom at an oblique angle.

Still, he could not see which way was shoreward and which way castleward. To find out took only a few strokes. His hand contacted stone—stone bricks. He groped along it until it began to curve inward. Following the curve, he finally came to that which he had hoped for. It was a flight of stone steps that rose out of the water and led upward.

He climbed up it, slowly, his hand out for a sudden obstacle. His feet slid over each step, ready to pause if an opening appeared or a step seemed loose. After twenty steps upward, he came to their end. He was in a corridor cut out of stone.

Von Elgers, or whoever had built the castle, had constructed a means for secret entrance and exit. An opening below water level in the walls led to a chamber, a little port, and from thence into the castle. Now, Wolff had the horn and a way to get unnoticed into the castle. But he did not know what to do.

Should he return the horn to the gworl first? Afterward, he and the two others could return this way and search for Chryseis.

He doubted that Ghaghrill would keep his word. However, even if the gworl were to release their captives, if they swam to this place, Kickaha's wound would draw the saurians and all three would be lost. Chryseis would have no chance of getting free. Kickaha could not be left behind while the other two went back to the castle. He would be exposed as soon as dawn came. He could hide in the woods, but the chances were that another hunting party would be searching that area then. Especially after it was discovered that the three stranger knights were gone.

He decided to go on down the hall. This was too good a chance to pass up. He would do his best before daylight. If he failed, then he would go back with the horn.

The horn! No use taking that with him. Should he be captured without it, his knowledge of its location might help him.

He returned to where the steps came to an end below the water. He dived down to a depth of about ten feet and left the horn on the mud.

Back in the corridor, he shuffled until he came to more steps at its end. The flight led upward on a tight spiraling course. A count of steps led him to think that he had ascended at least five stories. At every estimated story he felt around the narrow walls for doors or releases to open doors. He found none.

At what could have been the seventh story, he saw a tiny beam of light from a hole in the wall. Bending down, he peered through it. By the far end of the room, seated at a table, a bottle of wine before him, was Baron von Elgers. The man seated across the table from the baron was Abiru.

The baron's face was flushed by more than drink. He snarled at Abiru, "That's all I intend to say, Khamshem! You will get the horn back from the gworl, or I'll have your head! Only first you'll be taken to the dungeon! I have some curious iron devices there that you will be interested in!"

Abiru rose. His face was as pale beneath its dark pigment as the baron's was crimson.

"Believe me, sire, if the horn has been taken by the gworl, it will be recovered. They can't have gone far with it—if they have it—and they can easily be tracked down. They can't pass themselves off as human beings, you know. Besides, they're stupid."

The baron roared, stood up, and crashed his fist against the top of the table.

"Stupid! They were clever enough to break out of my dun-

124

geon, and I would have sworn that no one could do that! And they found my room and took the horn! You call that stupid!"

"At least," Abiru said, "they didn't steal the girl, too. I'll get something out of this. She should fetch a fabulous price."

"She'll fetch nothing for you! She is mine!"

Abiru glared and said, "She is my property. I obtained her at great peril and brought her all this way at much expense. I am entitled to her. What are you, a man of honor or a thief?"

Von Elgers struck him and knocked him down. Abiru, rubbing his cheek, got to his feet at once. Looking steadily at the baron, his voice tight, he said, "And what about my jewels?"

"They are in my castle!" the baron shouted. "And what is in my castle is the von Elgers'!"

He strode away out of Wolff's sight but apparently opened a door. He bellowed for the guard, and when they had come they took Abiru away between them.

"You are fortunate I do not kill you!" the baron raged. "I am allowing you to keep your life, you miserable dog! You should get down on your knees and thank me for that! Now get out of the castle at once. If I hear that you are not making all possible speed to another state, I will have you hung on the nearest tree!"

Abiru did not reply. The door closed. The baron paced back and forth for awhile, then abruptly came toward the wall behind which Wolff was crouched. Wolff left the peephole and retreated far down the steps. He hoped he had chosen the right direction in which to go. If the baron came down the staircase, he could force Wolff into the water and perhaps back out into the moat. But he did not think the baron intended to come that way.

For a second the light was cut off. A section of wall swung out with the baron's finger thrust through the hole. The torch held by von Elgers lit the well. Wolff crouched down behind the shadow cast by a turn of the corkscrew case. Presently, the light became weaker as the baron carried it up the steps. Wolff followed.

He could not keep his eyes on von Elgers all the time, for he had to dodge down behind various turns to keep from being detected if the baron should look downward. So it was that he did not see von Elgers leave the stairs nor know it until the light suddenly went out.

He went swiftly after the baron, although he did pause by the peephole. He stuck his finger in it and lifted upward. A small section gave way, a click sounded, and a door swung open for him. The inner side of the door formed part of the wall of the baron's quarters. Wolff stepped into the room, chose a thin

125

eight-inch dagger from a rack in the wall, and went back out to the stairs. After shutting the door, he climbed upward.

This time he had no light from a hole to guide him. Nor was he even sure that he had stopped at the same place as the baron. He had made a rough estimate of the height from himself to the baron when the baron had disappeared. There was nothing else to do but feel around for the device which the baron must have used to open another door. When he placed his ear against the wall to listen for voices, he heard nothing.

His fingers slid over bricks and moisture-crumbled mortar until they met wood. That was all he could find: stone and a wooden frame in which a broad and high panel of wood was smoothly inset. There was nothing to indicate an open-sesame.

He climbed a few steps more and continued to probe. The bricks were innocent of any trigger or catch. He returned to the spot opposite the door and felt the wall there. Nothing.

Now he was frantic. He was sure that von Elgers had gone to Chryseis' room, and not just to talk. He went back down the steps and fingered the walls. Still nothing.

Again he tried the area around the door with no success. He pushed on one side of the door, only to find it would not budge. For a moment he thought of hammering on the wood and attracting von Elgers. If the baron were to come through to investigate, he would be helpless for a moment to an attack from above.

He rejected the idea. The baron was too canny to fall for such a trick. While he was unlikely to go for help, because he would not want to reveal the passageway to others, he could leave Chryseis' room through the regular door. The guard posted outside it might wonder where he came from, although he would probably think that the baron had been inside before the watch had been changed. In any case, the baron could permanently shut the mouth of a suspicious guard. Wolff pushed in on the other side of the door, and it swung inward. It had not been locked; all it needed was pressure on the correct side.

He groaned softly at missing the obvious so long and stepped through. It was dark beyond the door; he was in a small room, almost a closet. This was composed of mortared bricks, except at one side. Here a metal rod poked from the wooden wall. Before working it, Wolff placed his ear against the wall. Muffled voices came through, too faint for him to recognize.

The metal rod had to be pulled out to activate the release on the door. Dagger in hand, Wolff stepped through it. He was in a large chamber of great stone blocks. There was a large

126

bed with four ornately carved posters of glossy black wood and a bright-pink tasseled canopy. Beyond it was the narrow cross-shaped window through which he had looked earlier that night.

Von Elgers' back was to him. The baron had Chryseis in his arms and was forcing her toward the bed. Her eyes were closed, and her head was turned away to avoid von Elgers' kisses. Both of them were still fully clothed.

Wolff bounded across the room, seized the baron by the shoulder, and pulled him backward. The baron let loose of Chryseis to reach for the dagger in his scabbard, then remembered that he had brought none. Apparently he had not intended to give Chryseis a chance to stab him.

His face, so flaming before, was gray now. His mouth worked, the cry for help to the guards outside the door frozen by surprise and fear.

Wolff gave him no chance to summon help. He dropped the dagger to strike the baron on the chin with his fist. Von Elgers, unconscious, slumped. Wolff did not want to waste any time, so he brushed by Chryseis, huge-eyed and pale. He cut off two strips of cloth from the bedsheets. The smaller he placed inside the baron's mouth, the larger he used as a gag. Then he removed a piece of the cord around his waist and tied von Elgers' hands in front of him. Hoisting the limp body over his shoulder, he said to Chryseis, "Come on. We can talk later."

He did pause to give instructions to Chryseis to close the wall-door behind them. There was no sense in letting others find the passageway when they finally came to investigate the baron's long absence. Chryseis held the torch behind him as they went down the steps. When they had come to the water, Wolff told her what they must do to escape. First, he had to retrieve the horn. Having done so, he scooped up water with his hands and threw it on the baron's face. When he saw his eyes open, he informed him of what he must do.

Von Elgers shook his head no. Wolff said, "Either you go with us as hostage and take your chances with the water-dragons or you die right now. So which is it?"

The baron nodded. Wolff cut his bonds but attached the end of the cord to his ankle. All three went into the water. Immediately, von Elgers swam out to the wall and dived. The others followed under the wall, which only went about four feet below the surface. Coming up on the other side, Wolff saw that the clouds were beginning to break. The moon would soon be bearing down in all her green brightness.

As directed, the baron and Chryseis swam at an angle toward the other side of the moat. Wolff followed with the end of the cord in one hand. With its burden, they could not go

127

swiftly. In fifteen minutes the moon would be rounding the monolith, with the sun not far behind it at the other corner. There was not much time for Wolff to carry out his plan, but it was impossible to keep control of the baron unless they took their time.

Their point of arrival at the bank of the moat was a hundred yards beyond where the gworl and their captives waited. Within a few minutes they were around the curve of the castle and out of sight of the gworl and the guards on the bridge even if the moon became unclouded. This path was a necessary evil—evil because every second in the water meant more chance for the dragons to discover them.

When they were within twenty yards of their goal, Wolff felt rather than saw the roil of water. He turned to see the surface lift a little and a small wave coming toward him. He drew up his feet and kicked. They struck something hard and solid enough to allow him to spring away. He shot backward, dropping the end of the cord at the same time. The bulk passed between him and Chryseis, struck von Elgers, and was gone.

So was Wolff's hostage.

They abandoned any attempt to keep from making splashing noises. They swam as hard as they could. Only when they reached the bank and scrambled up onto it and ran to a tree did they stop. Sobbing for breath, they clung to the trunk.

Wolff did not wait until he had fully regained his breath. The sun would be around Doozvillnavava within a few minutes. He told Chryseis to wait for him. If he did not return shortly after sunaround, he would not be coming for a long time—if ever. She would have to leave and hide in the woods and then do whatever she could.

She begged him not to go, for she could not stand the idea of being all alone here.

"I have to," he said, handing her an extra dagger which he had stuck through his shirt and secured by knotting the shirttail about it.

"I will use it on myself if you are killed," she said.

He was in agony at the thought of her being so helpless, but there was nothing he could do about it.

"Kill me now before you leave me," she said. "I've gone through too much; I can't stand any more."

He kissed her lightly on the lips and said, "Sure you can. You're tougher than you used to be and always were tougher than you thought. Look at you now. You can say *kill* and *death* without so much as flinching."

He was gone, running crouched over toward the spot where he had left his friends and the gworl. When he estimated he was about twenty yards from them, he stopped to listen. He

128

heard nothing except the cry of a nightbird and a muffled shout from somewhere in the castle. On his hands and knees, the dagger in his teeth, he crawled toward the place opposite the light from the window of his quarters. At any moment he expected to smell the musty odor and to see a clump of blackness against the lesser dark.

But there was nobody there. Only the glimmer-gray remnants of the web-nets remained to show that the gworl had actually been there.

He prowled around the area. When it became evident that there was no clue and that the sun would shortly expose him to the bridge guards, he returned to Chryseis. She clung to him and cried a little.

"See! I'm here after all," he said. "But we have to get out of here now."

"We're going back to Okeanos?"

"No, we're going after my friends."

They trotted away, past the castle and toward the monolith. The absence of the baron would soon be noticed. For miles around, no ordinary hiding place would be safe. And the gworl, knowing this, must also be making speed toward Doozvillnavava. No matter how badly they wanted the horn, they could not hang around now. Moreover, they must think that Wolff had drowned or been taken by a dragon. To them, the horn might be out of reach just now, but they could return when it was safe to do so.

Wolff pushed hard. Except for brief rests, they did not stop until they had reached the thick forest of the Rauhwald. There they crawled beneath the tangled thorns and through the intertwined bushes until their knees bled and their joints ached. Chryseis collapsed. Wolff gathered many of the plentiful berries for them to feed upon. They slept all night, and in the morning resumed their all-fours progress. By the time they had reached the other side of the Rauhwald, they were covered with thorn-wounds. There was no one waiting for them on the other side, as he had feared there would be.

This and another thing made him happy. He had come across evidence that the gworl had also passed this way. There were bits of coarse gworl hair on thorns and pieces of cloth. No doubt Kickaha had managed to drop these to mark the way if Wolff should be following.

CHAPTER FIFTEEN

After a month, they finally arrived at the foot of the monolith, Doozvillnavava. They knew they were on the right trail, since they had heard rumors of the gworl and even talked with those who had sighted them from a distance.

"I don't know why they've gone so far from the horn," he said. "Perhaps they mean to hole up in a cave in the face of the mountain and will come back down after the cry for them has died out."

"Or it could be," Chryseis said, "that they have orders from the Lord to bring Kickaha back first. He has been like an insect on the Lord's eardrum so long that the Lord must be crazed even by the thought of him. Maybe he wants to make sure that Kickaha is out of the way before he sends the gworl again for the horn."

Wolff agreed that she could be right. It was even possible that the Lord was going to come down from the palace via the same cords by which he had lowered the gworl. That did not seem likely, however, for the Lord would not want to be stranded. Could he trust the gworl to hoist him back up?

Wolff looked at the eye-staggering heights of the continent-broad tower of Doozvillnavava. It was, according to Kickaha, at least twice as high as the monolith of Abharhploonta, which supported the tier of Dracheland. It soared 60,000 feet or more, and the creatures that lived on the ledges and recesses and in the caves were fully as dreadful and hungry as those on the other monoliths. Doozvillnavava was gnarled and scoured and slashed and bristly; its ravaged face had an enormous recession that gave it a dark and gaping mouth; the giant seemed ready to eat all who dared to annoy it.

Chryseis, also examining the savage cliffs and their incredible height, shivered. But she said nothing; she had quit voicing her fears some time ago.

It could be that she was no longer concerned with herself, Wolff thought, but was intent upon the life within her. She was sure that she was pregnant.

He put his arm around her, kissed her, and said, "I'd like to start at once, but we'll have to make preparations for several days. We can't attack that monster without resting or without enough food."

Three days later, dressed in tough buckskin garments and carrying ropes, weapons, climbing tools, and bags of food and water, they began the ascent. Wolff bore the horn in a soft leather bag tied to his back.

Ninety-one days later, they were at an estimated halfway point. And at least every other step had been a battle against smooth verticality, rotten and treacherous rock, or against the predators. These included the many-footed snake he had encountered on Thayaphayawoed, wolves with great rock-gripping paws, the boulder ape, ostrich-sized axebeaks, and the small but deadly downdropper.

When the two climbed over the edge of the top of Doozvillnavava, they had been 186 days on the journey. Neither was the same, physically or mentally, as at the start. Wolff weighed less but he had far more endurance and wiriness to his strength. He bore the scars of downdroppers, boulder apes, and axebeaks on his face and body. His hatred for the Lord was even more intense, for Chryseis had lost the foetus before they had gotten 10,000 feet up. Such was to be expected, but he could not forget that they would not have had to make the climb if it had not been for the Lord.

Chryseis had been toughened in body and spirit by her experiences before she had started up Doozvillnavava. Yet the things and situations on this monolith had been far worse than anything previously, and she might have broken. That she did not vindicated Wolff's original feeling that she was basically of strong fiber. The effects of the millenia of sapping life in the Garden had been sloughed off. The Chryseis who conquered this monolith was much like the woman who had been abducted from the savage and demanding life of the ancient Aegean. Only she was far wiser.

Wolff waited for several days to rest and hunt and repair the bows and make new arrows. He also kept a watch for an eagle. He had not been in contact with any since he had talked to Phthie in the ruined city by the river of Guzirit. No green-bodied yellow-headed bird appeared, so he reluctantly decided to enter the jungle. As on Dracheland, a thousand-mile thick belt of jungle circled the entire rim. Within the belt was the land of Atlantis. This, exclusive of the monolith in its center, covered an area the size of France and Germany combined.

Wolff had looked for the pillar on top of which was the Lord's palace, since Kickaha had said that it could be seen from the rim even though it was much more slender than any of the other monoliths. He could see only a vast and dark continent of clouds, jagged and coiled with lightning. Idaquizzoorhruz was hidden. Now, whenever Wolff ascended a high hill or climbed a tall tree, could he see it. A week later, the stormclouds continued to shroud the pillar of stone. This worried him, for he had not seen such a storm in the three and a half years that he had been on this planet.

Fifteen days passed. On the sixteenth, they found on the narrow green-fraught path a headless corpse. A yard away in the bush was the turbaned head of a Khamshem.

"Abiru could be trailing the gworl, too," he said. "Maybe the gworl took his jewels when they left von Elgers' castle. Or, more likely, he thinks they have the horn."

A mile and a half further on, they came across another Khamshem, his stomach ripped open and his entrails hanging out. Wolff tried to get information out of him until he found that the man was too far gone. Wolff put him out of his pain, noting that Chryseis did not even look away while he did so. Afterward, he put his knife in his belt and held the Khamshem's scimitar in his right hand. He felt that he would soon need it.

A half-hour later, he heard shouts and whoops down the trail. He and Chryseis concealed themselves in the foliage beside the path. Abiru and two Khamshem came running with death loping after them in the form of three squat Negroids with painted faces and long kinky scarlet-dyed beards. One threw his spear; it sailed through the air to end in the back of a Khamshem. He plunged forward without a sound and slid on the soft damp earth like a sailboat launched into eternity, the spear as the mast. The other two Khamshem turned to make a stand.

Wolff had to admire Abiru, who fought with great skill and courage. Although his companion went down with a spear in his solar plexus, Abiru continued to slash with his scimitar. Presently two of the savages were dead, and the third turned tail. After the Negroid had disappeared, Wolff came up silently behind Abiru. He struck with the edge of his palm to paralyze the man's arm and cause the scimitar to drop.

Abiru was so startled and scared he could not talk. On seeing Chryseis step out from the bushes, his eyes bulged even more. Wolff asked him what the situation was. After a struggle, Abiru regained his tongue and began to talk. As Wolff had guessed, he had pursued the gworl with his men and a number of Sholkin. Some miles from here, he had caught up with them. Rather, they had caught him. The ambush had been half-successful, for it had slain or incapacitated a good third of the Khamshem. All this had been done without loss to the gworl, who had cast knives from trees or from the bushes.

The Khamshem had broken away and fled, hoping to make a stand in a better place down the trail—if they could find one. Then both hunted and hunter had run into a horde of black savages.

132

"And there'll be more of them soon looking for you," Wolff said. "What about Kickaha and funem Laksfalk?"

"I do not know about Kickaha. He was not with the gworl. But the Yidshe knight was."

For a moment, Wolff thought of killing Abiru. However, he disliked doing it in cold blood and he also wanted to ask him more questions. He believed that there was more to him than he pretended to be. Shoving Abiru on ahead with the point of the scimitar, he went down the trail. Abiru protested that they would be killed; Wolff told him to shut up. In a few minutes they heard the shouts and screams of men in battle. They crossed a shallow stream and were at the bottom of a steep, high hill.

This was so rocky that comparatively little vegetation covered it. Along a line up the hill was the wake of the fight—dead and wounded gworl, Khamshem, Sholkin, and savages. Near the top of the hill, their backs against a V-shaped wall and under an overhang formed by two huge boulders, three held off the blacks. These were a gworl, a Khamshem, and the Yidshe baron. Even as Wolff and Chryseis started to go up, the Khamshem fell, pierced by several of the shovel-sized spearheads. Wolff told Chryseis to go back. For answer, she fitted an arrow to her bow and shot. A savage in the rear of the mob fell backward, the shaft sticking from his back.

Wolff smiled grimly and began to work his own bow. He and Chryseis chose only those at the extreme rear, hoping to shoot down a number before those at the front noticed. They were successful until the twelfth fell. A savage happened to glance back and see the man behind him crumple. He yelled and pulled at the arms of those nearest him. These immediately brandished their spears and began running down the hill toward the two, leaving most of their party to attack the gworl and the Yidshe. Before they had reached the bottom half of the hill, four more were down.

Three more tumbled headlong and rolled down with shafts in them. The remaining six lost their zeal to come at close quarters. Halting, they threw their spears, which were launched at such a distance that the archers had no trouble dodging them. Wolff and Chryseis, operating coolly and skilfully from much practice and experience, then shot four more. The two survivors, screaming, ran back up to their fellows. Neither made it, although one was only wounded in the leg.

By then, the gworl had fallen. Funem Laksfalk was left alone against forty. He did have a slight advantage, which was that they could get to him only two at a time. The walls of the boulders and the barricade of corpses prevented the others from swarming over him. Funem Laksfalk, his scimitar bloody and swinging, sang loudly some Yiddish fighting song.

Wolff and Chryseis took partial cover behind two boulders and renewed their rear attack. Five more fell, but the quivers of both were then empty. Wolff said, "Pull some from the corpses and use them again. I'm going to help him."

He picked up a spear and ran at an angle across and up the hill, hoping that the savages would be too occupied to see him. When he had come around the hill, he saw two savages crouched on top of the boulder. These were kept from jumping down upon the Yidshe's rear by the overhang of the roughly shaped boulders. But they were waiting for a moment when he would venture too far out from its protection.

Wolff hurled his spear and caught one in the buttocks. The savage cried out and pitched forward from the rock and, presumably, on his fellows below. The other stood up and whirled around in time to get Wolff's knife in his belly. He fell backward off the rock.

Wolff lifted a small boulder and heaved it on top of one of the great boulders and climbed up after it. Then he lifted the small boulder again, raised it above his head, and walked to the front of the great boulder. He yelled and threw it down into the crowd. They looked up in time to see the rock descending on them. It smashed at least three and rolled down the hill. At that, the survivors fled in a panic. Perhaps they thought that there must be others than Wolff. Or, because they were undisciplined savages, they had been unnerved by too many losses already. The sight of so many of their dead shot down behind them must also have added to their panic.

Wolff hoped they would not return. To add fuel to their fright, he leaped down and picked up the boulder again and sent it crashing down the hill after them. It leaped and bounded as if it were a wolf after a rabbit and actually struck one more before it reached bottom.

Chryseis, from behind her boulder, put two more arrows into the savages.

He turned to the baron and found him lying on the ground. His face was gray, and blood was welling from around the spearhead driven into his chest.

"You!" he said faintly. "The man from the other world. You saw me fight?"

Wolff stepped down by him to examine the wound. "I saw. You fought like one of Joshua's warriors, my friend. You fought as I have never seen any fight. You must have slain at least twenty."

Funem Laksfalk managed to smile a trifle. "It was twenty-five. I counted them."

Then he smiled broadly and said, "We are both stretching the truth a trifle, as our friend Kickaha would say. But not too much. It was a great fight. I only regret that I had to fight unfriended and unarmored and in a lonely place where none will ever know that a funem Laksfalk added honor to the name. Even if it was against a bunch of howling and naked savages."

"They will know," Wolff said. "I will tell them some day."

He did not give false words of comfort. He and the Yidshe both knew that death was around the corner, sniffing eagerly at the end of the track.

"Do you know what happened to Kickaha?" he said.

"Ah, that trickster! He slipped his chains one night. He tried to loosen mine, too, but he could not. Then he left, with the promise that he would return to free me. And so he will, but he will be too late."

Wolff looked down the hill. Chryseis was climbing toward him with several arrows which she had recovered from corpses. The blacks had regrouped at the foot and were talking animatedly among themselves. Others came out of the jungle to join them. The fresh ones swelled the number to forty. These were led by a man garbed in feathers and wearing a hideous wooden mask. He whirled a bull-roarer, leaped up and down, and seemed to be haranguing them.

The Yidshe asked Wolff what was happening. Wolff told him. The Yidshe spoke so weakly that Wolff had to put his ear close to the knight's mouth.

"It was my fondest dream, Baron Wolff, that I would some day fight by your side. Ah, what a noble pair of knights we would have made, in armor and swinging our . . . S'iz kalt."

The lips became silent and blue. Wolff rose to look down the hill again. The savages were moving up and also spreading out to prevent flight. Wolff set to work dragging bodies and piling them to form a rampart. The only hope, a weak one, was to permit passage for only one or two to attack at a time. If they lost enough men, they might get discouraged and leave. He did not really think so, for these savages showed a remarkable persistence despite what must be to them staggering losses. Also, they could always retreat just far enough to wait for Wolff and Chryseis to be driven from their refuge by thirst and hunger.

The savages stopped halfway up to give those who had gone around the hill time to establish their stations. Then, at a cry from the man in the wooden mask, they climbed up as swiftly as possible. The two defenders made no move until the thrown spears rattled against the sides of the boulders or plunged into the barricade of dead. Wolff shot twice, Chryseis three times. Not one arrow missed.

Wolff loosed his final shaft. It struck the mask of the leader and knocked him back down the hill. A moment later he threw off the mask. Although his face was bleeding, he led the second charge.

A weird ululation arose from the jungle. The savages stopped, spun, and became silent as they stared at the green around the hill. Again, the swelling-falling cry came from somewhere in the trees.

Abruptly, a bronze-haired man clad only in a leopard loin-cloth raced from the jungle. He carried a spear in one hand and a long knife in the other. Coiled around his shoulder was a lariat, and a quiver and bow were hung from a belt over the other shoulder. Behind him, a mass of hulking long-armed, mound-chested, and long-fanged apes poured from the trees.

At sight of these, the savages cried out aloud and tried to run around the hill. Other apes appeared from the other side; like hairy jaws, the two columns closed on the blacks.

There was a brief fight. Some apes fell with spears in their bellies, but most of the blacks threw down their weapons and tried to run or else crouched trembling and paralyzed. Only twelve escaped.

Wolff, smiling and laughing in his relief, said to the man in the leopard-skin, "And how are you named on this tier?"

Kickaha grinned back. "I'll give you one guess."

His smile died when he saw the baron. "Damn it! It took me too much time to find the apes and then to find you! He was a good man, the Yidshe; I liked his style. Damn it! Anyway, I promised him that if he died I'd take his bones back to his ancestral castle, and that's one promise I'll keep. Not just now, though. We have some business to attend to."

Kickaha called some of the apes to be introduced. "As you'll notice," he said to Wolff, "they're built more like your friend Ipsewas than true apes. Their legs are too long and their arms too short. Like Ipsewas and unlike the great apes of my favorite childhood author, they have the brains of men. They hate the Lord for what he has done to them; they not only want revenge, they want a chance to walk around in human bodies again."

Not until then did Wolff remember Abiru. He was nowhere to be seen. Apparently he had slipped off when Wolff had gone to funem Laksfalk's aid.

That night, around a fire and eating roast deer, Wolff and Chryseis heard about the cataclysm taking place in Atlantis. It had started with the new temple that the Rhadamanthus of Atlantis had started to build. Ostensibly the tower was for the greater glory of the Lord. It was to reach higher than any

building ever known on the planet. The Rhadamanthus recruited his entire state to erect the temple. He kept on adding
story to story until it looked as if he wanted to reach the sky
itself.

Men asked each other when there would be an end to the
work. All were slaves with but one purpose in mind: build.
Yet they dared not speak openly, for the soldiers of the Rhadamanthus killed all who objected or who failed to labor. Then it
became obvious that the Rhadamanthus had something else
besides a temple in his crazed mind. The Rhadamanthus intended to erect a means to storm the heavens themselves,
the palace of the Lord.

"A thirty-thousand-foot building?" said Wolff.

"Yeah. It couldn't be done, of course, not with the technology available in Atlantis. But the Rhadamanthus was mad;
he really thought he could do it. Maybe he was encouraged
because the Lord hadn't appeared for so many years, and he
thought that maybe the rumors were true that the Lord was
gone. Of course, the ravens must have told him different, but
he could have figured they were lying to protect themselves."

Kickaha said that the devastating phenomena now destroy-
ing Atlantis were proof of more than that the Lord was reveng-
ing himself against the hubris of Rhadamanthus. The Lord
must have finally unlocked the secrets of how to operate some
of the devices in the palace.

"The Lord who disappeared would have taken precautions
against a new occupant manipulating his powers. But the new
Lord has at last succeeded in learning where the controls of the
storm-makers are."

Proof: the gigantic hurricanes, tornados, and continual rain
sweeping the land. The Lord must be out to rid this tier of all
life.

Before reaching the edge of the jungle, they met the tidal
wave of refugees. These had stories of houses and great buildings blown down, of men picked up and carried off and
smashed by the winds, of the floods that were stripping the
earth of trees and all life and even washing away the hills.

By then, Kickaha's party had to lean to walk against the
wind. The clouds closed around them; rain struck them; lightning blinded and crashed on all sides.

Even so, there were periods when the rain and lightning
ceased. The energies loosed by Arwoor had to spend themselves, and new forces had to be built up before being released again. In these comparative lulls, the party made progress, although slowly. They crossed swollen rivers bearing
the wreck of a civilization: houses, trees, furniture, chariots,
the corpses of men, women, children, dogs, horses, birds and

wild animals. The forests were uprooted or smashed by the strokes of electrical bolts. Every valley was running with water; every depression was filled. And a choking stench filled the air.

When their journey was little more than half-completed, the clouds began to thin away. They were in the sunshine again, but in a land silent with death. Only the roar of water or the cry of a bird that had somehow survived broke the stone of quiet. Sometimes the howl of a demented human being sent chills through them, but these were few.

The last cloud was carried off. And the white monolith of Idaquizzoorhruz shone before them, three hundred miles away on the horizonless plain. The city of Atlantis—or what was left of it—was a hundred miles distant. It took them twenty days to reach its outskirts through flood and debris.

"Can the Lord see us now?" Wolff asked.

Kickaha said, "I suppose he could with some sort of telescope. I'm glad you asked, though, because we'd better start traveling by night. Even so, we'll be spotted by them."

He pointed at a raven flying over.

Passing through the ruins of the capital city, they came near the imperial zoo of Rhadamanthus. There were some strong cages left standing, and one of these contained an eagle. On the muddy bottom were a number of bones, feathers, and beaks. The caged eagles had evaded starvation by eating each other. The lone survivor sat emaciated, weak and miserable on the highest perch.

Wolff opened the cage, and he and Kickaha talked to the eagle, Armonide. At first, Armonide wanted nothing but to attack them, enfeebled though she was. Wolff threw her several pieces of meat, then the two men continued their story. Armonide said that they were liars and had some human, and therefore evil, purpose in mind. When she had heard Wolff's story through and his pointing out that they did not have to release her, she began to believe. When Wolff explained that he had a plan in mind to gain revenge upon the Lord, the dullness in her eyes was replaced by a sharp light. The idea of actually assaulting the Lord, perhaps successfully, was more food than meat itself. She stayed with them for three days, eating, gaining strength, and memorizing exactly what she was to tell Podarge.

"You will see the Lord's death yet, and new and youthful and lovely maiden bodies will be yours," Wolff said. "But only if Podarge does as I ask her."

Armonide launched herself from a cliff, swooped down, flapped her spreading wings, and began to climb. Presently the green feathers of her body were absorbed by the green

138

sky. Her red head became a black dot, and then it too was gone.

Wolff and his party remained in the tangle of fallen trees until night before going on. By now, through some subtle process, Wolff had become the nominal leader. Before, Kickaha had had the reins in his hands with the approval of all. Something had happened to give Wolff the power of decision-making. He did not know what, for Kickaha was as boisterous and vigorous as before. And the passing of captainship had not been caused by a deliberate effort on Wolff's part. It was as if Kickaha had been waiting until Wolff had learned all he could from him. Then Kickaha had handed over the baton.

They traveled strictly within the night-hours, during which time they saw very few ravens. Apparently there was no need for them in this area since it was under the close surveillance of the Lord himself. Besides, who would dare intrude here after the anger of the Lord had been so catastrophically wrought?

On arriving at the great tumbled mass of Rhadamanthus' tower, they took refuge within the ruins. There was more than enough metal for Wolff's plan. Their only two problems were getting enough food and trying to conceal the noise of their sawing and hammering and the glare of their little smithies. The first was solved when they discovered a storehouse of grain and dried meat. Much of the supplies had been destroyed by fire and then by water, but there was enough left to see them through several weeks. The second was dealt with by working deep within the underground chambers. The tunneling took five days, a period which did not concern Wolff because he knew that it would be some time before Armonide would reach Podarge—if she got to her destination at all. Many things could happen to her on the way, especially an attack by the ravens.

"What if she doesn't make it?" Chryseis asked.

"Then we'll have to think of something else," Wolff replied. He fondled the horn and pressed its seven buttons. "Kickaha knows the gate through which he came when he left the palace. We could go back through it. But it would be folly. The present Lord would not be so stupid as not to leave a heavy guard there."

Three weeks passed. The supply of food was so low that hunters would have to be sent out. This was dangerous even at night, for there was no telling when a raven might be around. Moreover, for all Wolff knew the Lord could have devices for seeing as easily at night as at day.

At the end of the fourth week, Wolff had to give up his dependence on Podarge. Either Armonide had not reached her or Podarge had refused to listen.

139

That very night, as he sat under cover of a huge plate of bent steel and stared at the moon, he heard the rustle of wings. He peered into the darkness. Suddenly, moonlight shone on something black and pale, and Podarge was before him. Behind her were many winged shapes and the gleam of moon on yellow beaks and redly shining eyes.

Wolff led them down through the tunnels and into a large chamber. By the small fires, he looked again into the tragically beautiful face of the harpy. But now that she thought she could strike back at the Lord, she actually looked happy. Her flock had carried food along, so, while all ate, Wolff explained his plan to her. Even as they were discussing the details, one of the apes, a guard, brought in a man he had caught skulking about the ruins. He was Abiru the Khamshem.

"This is unfortunate for you and a sorry thing for me," Wolff said. "I can't just tie you up and leave you here. If you escaped and contacted a raven, the Lord would be forewarned. So, you must die. Unless you can convince me otherwise."

Abiru looked about him and saw only death.

"Very well," he said. "I had not wanted to speak nor will I speak before everyone, if I can avoid it. Believe me, I must talk to you alone. It is as much for your life as for mine."

"There is nothing you can say that could not be said before all," Wolff replied. "Speak up."

Kickaha placed his mouth close to Wolff's ear and whispered, "Better do as he says."

Wolff was astonished. The doubts about Kickaha's true identity came back to him. Both requests were so strange and unexpected that he had a momentary feeling of disassociation. He seemed to be floating away from them all.

"If no one objects, I will hear him alone," he said. Podarge frowned and opened her mouth, but before she could say anything she was interrupted by Kickaha. "Great One, now is the time for trust. You must believe in us, have confidence. Would you lose your only chance for revenge and for getting your human body back? You must go along with us on this. If you interfere, all is lost."

Podarge said, "I do not know what this is all about, and I feel that I am somehow being betrayed. But I will do as you say, Kickaha, for I know of you and know that you are a bitter enemy of the Lord. But do not try my patience too far."

Then Kickaha whispered an even stranger thing to Wolff. "Now I recognize Abiru. That beard and the stain on his skin fooled me, plus not having heard his voice for twenty years."

Wolff's heart beat fast with an undefined apprehension. He took his scimitar and conducted Abiru, whose hands were bound behind him, into a small room. And here he listened.

140

CHAPTER SIXTEEN

An hour later, he returned to the others. He looked stunned.

"Abiru will go with us," he said. "He could be very valuable. We need every hand we can get and every man with knowledge."

"Would you care to explain that?" Podarge said. She was narrow-eyed, the mask of madness forming over her face.

"No, I will not and cannot," he replied. "But I feel more strongly than ever that we have a good chance for victory. Now, Podarge how strong are your eagles? Have they flown so far tonight that we must wait until tomorrow night for them to rest?"

Podarge answered that they were ready for the task ahead of them. She wanted to delay no longer.

Wolff gave his orders, which were relayed by Kickaha to the apes, since they obeyed only him. They carried out the large crossbars and the ropes to the outside, and the others followed them.

In the bright light of the moon, they lifted the thin but strong cross-bars. The human beings and the fifty apes then fitted themselves into the weblike cradles beneath the cross-bars and tied straps to secure themselves. Eagles gripped the ropes attached to each of the four ends of the bars and another gripped the rope tied to the center of the cross. Wolff gave the signal. Though there had been no chance to train, each bird jumped simultaneously into the air, flapped her wings and slowly rose upward. The ropes were paid out to over fifty feet to give the eagles a chance to gain altitude before the cross-bars and the human attached to each had to be lifted.

Wolff felt a sudden jerk, and he uncoiled his bent legs to give an extra push upward. The bar tilted to one side, almost swinging him over against one of the bars. Podarge, flying over the others, gave an order. The eagles pulled up more rope or released more length to adjust for balance. In a few seconds, the cross-bars were at the correct level.

On Earth this plan would not have been workable. A bird the size of the eagle probably could not have gotten into the air without launching herself from a high cliff. Even then, her flight would have been very slow, maybe too slow to keep from stalling or sinking back to Earth. However, the Lord had given the eagles muscles with strength to match their weight.

They rose up and up. The pale sides of the monolith, a mile away, glimmered in the moonlight. Wolff clutched the straps of his cradle and looked at the others. Chryseis and Kickaha waved back. Abiru was motionless. The shattered and prone wreck of Rhadamanthus' tower became smaller. No ravens flew by to be startled and to wing upward to warn the Lord. Those eagles not serving as carriers spread wide to forestall such a possibility. The air was filled with an armada; the beat of their wings drummed loudly in Wolff's ears, so loudly that he could not imagine the noise not traveling for miles.

The time came when this side of ravaged Atlantis was spread out in the moonlight for him to scan in one sweep of the eye. Then the rim appeared, and part of the tier below it. Dracheland became visible as a great half-disc of darkness. The hours crept by. The mass of Amerindia appeared, grew and was suddenly chopped off at the rim. The garden of Okeanos, so far below Amerindia and so narrow, could not be seen.

Both the moon and the sun were visible now because of the comparative slenderness of this monolith. Nevertheless, the eagles and their burdens were still in darkness, in the shadow of Idaquizzoorhruz. It would not last for long. Soon this side would be under the full glare of the daytime luminary. Any ravens would be able to see them from miles away. The party had, however, drifted close to the monolith, so that anyone on top would have to be on the edge to detect them.

At last, after over four hours, just as the sun touched them, they were level with the top. Beside them was the garden of the Lord, a place of flaming beauty. Beyond rose the towers and minarets and flying buttresses and spiderweb architectures of the palace of the Lord. It soared up for two hundred feet and covered, according to Kickaha, more than three hundred acres.

They did not have time to appreciate its wonder, for the ravens in the garden were screaming. Already the hundreds of Podarge's pets had swooped down upon them and were killing them. Others were winging toward the many windows to enter and seek out the Lord.

Wolff saw a number get inside before the traps of the Lord could be activated. Shortly thereafter, those attempting to climb in through the openings disappeared in a clap of thunder and a flash of lightning. Charred to the bone, they fell off the ledges and onto the ground below or on the rooftops or buttresses.

The human beings and the apes settled to the ground just outside a diamond-shaped door of rose stone set with rubies. The eagles released the ropes and gathered by Pordarge to wait for her orders.

142

Wolff untied the ropes from the metal rings on the cross-bars. Then he lifted the bars above his head. After running to a point just a few feet from the diamond-shaped doorway, he cast the steel cross into it. One bar went through the entrance; the two at right angles to it jammed against the sides of the door.

Flame exploded again and again. Thunder deafened him. Tongues of searing voltage leaped out at him. Suddenly, smoke poured from within the palace, and the lightning ceased. The ravaging device had either burned out from the load or was temporarily discharged.

Wolff took one glance around him. Other entrances were also spurting bursts of flame or else their defenses had burned out. Eagles had taken many of the cross-bars and were dropping them at an angle into the windows above. He leaped over the white-hot liquid of his cross-bar and through the door. Chryseis and Kickaha joined him from another entrance. Behind Kickaha came the horde of giant apes. Each carried a sword or battleaxe in his hand.

Kickaha asked, "Is it coming back to you?"

Wolff nodded. "Not all, but enough, I hope. Where's Abiru?"

"Podarge and a couple of the apes are keeping on eye on him. He could try something for his own purposes."

Wolff in the lead, they walked down a hall the walls of which were painted with murals that would have delighted and awed the most critical of Terrestrials. At the far end was a low gate of delicate and intricate tracery and of a shimmering bluish metal. They proceeded toward it but stopped as a raven, fleeing for its life, sped over them. Behind it came an eagle.

The raven passed over the gate, and as it did so it flew headlong into an invisible screen. Abruptly, the raven was a scatter of thin slices of flesh, bones and feathers. The pursuing eagle screamed as it saw this and tried to check her flight, but too late. She too was cut into strips.

Wolff pulled the left section of the gate toward him instead of pushing in on it as he would naturally have done. He said, "It should be okay now. But I'm glad the raven triggered the screen first. I hadn't remembered it."

Still, he stuck his sword forward to test, then it came back to him that only living matter activated the trap. There was nothing to do but to trust that he could remember correctly. He walked forward without feeling anything but the air, and the others followed.

"The Lord will be holed up in the center of the palace,

143

where the defense control room is," he said. "Some of the defenses are automatic, but there are others he can operate himself. That is, if he's found out how to operate them, and he's certainly had enough time to learn."

They padded through a mile of corridors and rooms, each one of which could have detained anyone with a sense of beauty for days. Every now and then a boom or a scream announced a trap set off somewhere in the palace.

A dozen times, they were halted by Wolff. He stood frowning for awhile until he suddenly smiled. Then he would move a picture at an angle or touch a spot on the murals: the eye of a painted man, the horn of a buffalo in a scene of the Amerindian plains, the hilt of a sword in the scabbard of a knight in a Teutoniac tableau. Then he would walk forward.

Finally, he summoned an eagle. "Go bring Podarge and the others," he said. "There is no use their sacrificing themselves any more. I will show the way."

He said to Kickaha, "The sense of *déjà vu* is getting stronger every minute. But I don't remember all. Just certain details."

"As long as they're the significant details, that's all that matters at this moment," Kickaha said. His grin was broad, and his face was lit with the delight of conflict. "Now you can see why I didn't dare to 'try re-entry by myself. I got the guts but I lack the knowledge."

Chryseis said, "I don't understand."

Wolff pulled her to him and squeezed her. "You will soon. That is, if we make it. I've much to tell you, and you have much to forgive."

A door ahead of them slid into the wall, and a man in armor clanked toward them. He held a huge axe in one hand, swinging it as if it were a feather.

"It's no man," Wolff said. "It's one of the Lord's taloses."

"A robot!" Kickaha said.

Wolff thought, *Not quite in the sense Kickaha means*. It was not all steel and plastic and electrical wires. Half of it was protein, formed in the biobanks of the Lord. It had a will for survival that no machine of all-inanimate parts could have. This was a strength and also a weakness.

He spoke to Kickaha, who ordered the apes behind him to obey Wolff. A dozen stepped forward, side by side, and hurled their axes simultaneously. The talos dodged but could not evade all. It was struck with a force and precision that would have chopped it apart if it had not been armor-plated. It fell backward and rolled, then rose to its feet. While it was down, Wolff ran at it. He struck at it with his scimitar at the junc-

144

ture of shoulder and neck. The blade broke without cutting into the metal. However, the force of the blow did knock the talos down again.

Wolff dropped his weapons, seized the talos around its waist, and lifted it. Silently, for it had no voice-chords, the armored thing kicked and reached down to grip Wolff. He hurled it against the wall, and it crashed down on the floor. As it began to get to its feet once more, Wolff drew his dagger and drove it into one of the eye-holes. There was a crack as the plastic over the eye gave way and was dislodged. The tip of the knife broke off, and Wolff was hurled back by a blow from the mailed fist. He came back quickly, grabbed the extended fist again, turned, and flopped it over his back. Before it could arise, it found itself gripped and hoisted high again. Wolff ran to the window and threw it headlong out.

It turned over and over and smashed against the ground four stories below. For a moment it lay as if broken, then it began to rise again. Wolff shouted at some eagles outside on a buttress. They launched themselves, soared down, and a pair grabbed the talos' arms. Up they rose, found it too heavy, and sank back. But they were able to keep it aloft a few inches from the ground. Over the surface, between buttresses and curiously carved columns, they flew. Their destination was the edge of the monolith, from which they would drop the talos. Not even its armor could withstand the force at the end of the 30,000-foot fall.

Wherever the Lord was hidden, he must have seen the fate of the single talos he had released. Now, a panel in the wall slid back, and twenty taloses came out, each with an axe in his hand. Wolff spoke to the apes. These hurled their axes again, knocking down many of the things. The gorilla-sized anthropoids charged in and several seized each talos. Although the mechanical strength of each android was more than that of a single ape, the talos was outmatched by two. While one ape wrestled with an android, the other gripped the helmet-head and twisted. Metal creaked under the strain; suddenly, neck-mechanisms broke with a snap. Helmets rolled on the floor with an ichorish liquid flowing out. Other taloses were lifted up and passed from hand to hand and dumped out of the window. Eagles carried each one off to the rim.

Even so, seven apes died, cut down by axes or with their own heads twisted off. The quick-to-learn protein brains of the semiautomatons imitated the actions of their antagonists, if it was to their advantage.

A little further on in the hall, thick sheets of metal slid down before and behind them to block off advance or retreat.

Wolff had forgotten this until just a second before the plates were lowered. They descended swiftly but not so swiftly that he did not have time to topple a marble stone pedestal with a statue on it. The end of the fallen column lay under the plate and prevented its complete closure. The forces driving the plate were, however, so strong that the edge of the plate began to drive through the stone. The party slid on their backs through the decreasing space. At the same time, water flooded into the area. If it had not been for the delay in closing the plate, they would have been drowned.

Sloshing ankle deep in the water, they went down the hall and up another flight of steps. Wolff stopped them by a window, through which he cast an axe. No thunder and lightning resulted, to he leaned out and called Podarge and her eagles in to him. Having been blocked off by the plates, they had gone outside to find another route.

"We are close to the heart of the palace, to the room in which the Lord must be," he said. "Every corridor from here on in has walls which hold dozens of laser beam-projectors. The beams can form a network through which no one could penetrate alive."

He paused, then said, "The Lord could sit in there forever. The fuel for his projectors will not give out, and he has food and drink enough to last for any siege. But there's an old military axiom which states that any defense, no matter how formidable, can be broken if the right offense is found."

He said to Kickaha, "When you took the gate through the Atlantean tier, you left the crescent behind you. Do you remember where?"

Kickaha grinned and said, "Yeah! I stuck it behind a statue in a room near the swimming pool. But what if it was found by the gworl?"

"Then I'll have to think of something else. Let's see if we can find the crescent."

"What's the idea?" Kickaha said in a low voice.

Wolff explained that Arwoor must have an escape route from the control room. As Wolff remembered it, there was a crescent set in the floor and several loose ones available. Each of these, when placed in contact with the immobile crescent, would open a gate to the universe for which the loose one had a resonance. None of them gave access to other levels of the planet in this universe. Only the horn could affect a gate between tiers.

"Sure," Kickaha said. "But what good will the crescent do us even if we find it? It has to be matched up against another, and where's the other? Anyway, anyone using it would only be taken through to Earth."

Wolff pointed over his back to indicate the long leather box slung there by a strap. "I have the horn."

They started down a corridor. Podarge strode after them. "What are you up to?" she asked fiercely.

Wolff answered that they were looking for means to get within the control room. Podarge should stay behind to handle any emergency. She refused, saying that she wanted them in her sight now that they were so close to the Lord. Besides, if they could get through to the Lord, they would have to take her along. She reminded Wolff of his promise that the Lord would be hers to do with as she wished. He shrugged and walked on.

They located the room in which was the statue behind which Kickaha had concealed the crescent. But it had been over-turned in the struggle between apes and gworl. Their bodies lay sprawled around the room. Wolff stopped in surprise. He had seen no gworl since entering the palace and had taken it for granted that all had perished during the fight with the savages. The Lord had not sent all of them after Kickaha.

Kickaha cried, "The crescent's gone!"

"Either it was found some time ago or someone just found it after the statue was knocked over," Wolff said. "I have an idea of who did take it. Have you seen Abiru?"

Neither of the others had seen him since shortly after the invasion of the palace had started. The harpy, who was sup-posed to keep an eye on him, had lost him.

Wolff ran toward the labs with Kickaha and Podarge, wings half-opened, behind him. By the time he had covered the 3000 feet to it, Wolff was winded. Breathing hard, he stopped at the entrance.

"Vannax may be gone already and within the control room," he said. "But if he's still in there working on the crescent, we'd better enter quietly and hope to surprise him."

"Vannax?" Podarge said.

Wolff swore mentally. He and Kickaha had not wanted to reveal the identity of Abiru until later. Podarge hated any Lord so much that she would have killed him at once. Wolff wanted to keep him alive because Vannax, if he did not try to betray them, could be valuable in the taking of the palace. Wolff had promised Vannax that he could go into another world to try his luck there if he helped them against Arwoor. And Vannax had explained how he had managed to get back to this universe. After Kickaha (born Finnegan) had accident-ally come here, taking a crescent with him, Vannax had con-tinued his search for another. He had been successful in, of all

147

places, a pawn shop in Peoria, Illinois. How it had gotten there and what Lord had lost it on Earth would never be known. Doubtless there were other crescents in obscure places on Earth. However, the crescent he had found had passed him through a gate located on the Amerindian tier. Vannax had climbed Thayaphayawoed to Khamshem, where he had been lucky enough to capture the gworl, Chryseis, and the horn. Thereafter, he had made his way toward the palace hoping to get within.

Wolff muttered, "The old saying goes that you can't trust a Lord."

"What did you say?" Podarge asked. "And I repeat, who is Vannax?"

Wolff was relieved that she did not know the name. He answered that Abiru had sometimes disguised himself under that name. Not wanting to reply to any more questions, and feeling that time was vital, he entered the laboratory. It was a room broad enough and high-ceilinged enough to house a dozen jet airliners. Cabinets and consoles and various apparatuses, however, gave it a crowded appearance. A hundred yards away, Vannax was bent over a huge console, working with the buttons and levers.

Silently, the three advanced on him. They were soon close enough to see that two crescents were locked down on the console. On the broad screen above Vannax was the ghostly image of a third semicircle. Wavy lines of light ran across it.

Vannax suddenly gave an *ah!* of delight as another crescent appeared by the first on the screen. He manipulated several dials to make the two images move toward each other and then merge into a single one again.

Wolff knew that the machine was sending out a frequency-tracer and had located that of the crescent set into the floor of the control room. Next, Vannax would subject the crescents clamped to the console to a treatment which would change their resonance to match that of the control room. Where Vannax had gotten the two semicircles was a mystery until Wolff thought of that crescent which must have accompanied him when he passed through the gate to the Amerindian tier. Somehow, during the time between his capture and the flight, he had gotten hold of this crescent. He must have hidden it in the ruins before the ape had captured him.

Vannax looked up from his work, saw the three, glanced at the screen, and snatched the two crescents from the spring-type clamps on the console. The three ran toward him as he placed one crescent on the floor and then the other. He laughed,

148

made an obscene gesture, and stepped into the circle, a dagger in his hand.

Wolff gave a cry of despair, for they were too far away to stop him. Then he stopped and threw a hand over his eyes, but too late to shut out the dazzling flash. He heard Kickaha and Podarge, also blinded, shouting. He heard Vannax's scream and smelled the burned flesh and clothes.

Sightlessly, he advanced until his feet touched the hot corpse.

"What the hell happened?" Kickaha said. "God, I hope we're not permanently blinded!"

"Vannax thought he was slipping in through Arwoor's gate in the control room," Wolff said. "But Arwoor had set a trap. He could have been satisfied with wrecking the matcher, but it must have amused him to kill the man who would try it."

He stood and waited, knowing that time was getting short and that he was not serving his cause or anyone else's by his patience with his blindness. But there was nothing else he could do. And, after what seemed like an unbearably long time, sight began to come back.

Vannax was lying on his back, charred and unrecognizable. The two crescents were still on the floor and undamaged. These were separated a moment later by Wolff with a scribe from a console.

"He was a traitor," Wolff said in a low voice to Kickaha. "But he did us a service. I meant to try the same trick, only I was going to use the horn to activate the crescent you hid after I'd changed its resonance."

Pretending to inspect other consoles for booby-traps, he managed to get Kickaha and himself out of ear-range of Podarge.

"I didn't want to do it," he whispered. "But I'm going to have to. The horn must be used if we're to drive Arwoor out of the control room or get him before he can use his crescents to escape."

"I don't get you," Kickaha said.

"When I had the palace built, I incorporated a thermitic substance in the plastic shell of the control room. It can be triggered only by a certain sequence of notes from the horn, combined with another little trick. I don't want to set the stuff off because the control room will then also be lost. And this place will be indefensible later against any other Lords."

"You better do it," Kickaha said. "Only thing is, what's to keep Arwoor from getting away through the crescents?"

Wolff smiled and pointed at the console. "Arwoor should have destroyed that instead of indulging his sadistic imagination. Like all weapons, it's two-edged."

He activated the controls, and, again, an image of the crescent shone on the screen. Curving lines of light ran across the plate. Wolff went to another console and opened a little door on the top to reveal a panel with unmarked controls. After flipping two, he pressed a button. The screen went blank.

"The resonance of his crescent has been changed," Wolff said. "When he goes to use it with any of the others he has, he'll get a hell of a shock. Not the kind Vannax got. He just won't have a gate through which to escape."

"You Lords are a mean, crafty, sneaky bunch," Kickaha said. "But I like your style, anyway."

He left the room. A moment later, his shouts came down the corridor. Podarge started to leave the room, then stopped to glare suspiciously at Wolff. He broke into a run. Podarge, satisfied he was coming, raced ahead. Wolff stopped and removed the horn from the case. He reached a finger into its mouth, hooked it through the only opening in the weblike structure therein large enough to accept his finger. A pull drew the web out. He turned it around and inserted it with its front now toward the inside of the horn. Then he put the horn back into the case and ran after the harpy.

She was with Kickaha, who was explaining that he thought he had seen a gworl but it was just a prowling eagle. Wolff said they must go back to the others. He did not explain that it was necessary that the horn be within a certain distance of the control room walls. When they had returned to the hall outside the control room, Wolff opened the case. Kickaha stood behind Podarge, ready to knock her unconscious if she started any trouble. What they could do with the eagles, besides sicking the apes on them, was another matter.

Podarge exclaimed when she saw the horn but made no hostile move. Wolff lifted the horn to his lips and hoped he could remember the correct sequence of notes. Much had come back to him since he had talked with Vannax; much was yet lost.

He had just placed the mouthpiece to his lips when a voice roared out. It seemed to come from ceiling and walls and floor, from everywhere. It spoke in the language of the Lords, for which Wolff was glad. Podarge would not know the tongue.

"Jadawin! I did not recognize you until I saw you with the horn! I thought you looked familiar—I should have known. But it's been such a long time! How long?"

"It's been many centuries, or millenia, depending upon the time scale. So, we two old enemies face each other again. But this time you have no way out. You will die as Vannax died."

"How so?" roared Arwoor's voice.

"I will cause the walls of your seemingly impregnable fortress to melt. You will either stay inside and roast or come out and die another way. I don't think you'll stay in."

Suddenly he was seized with a concern and a sense of injustice. If Podarge should kill Arwoor, she would not be killing the man who was responsible for her present state. It did not matter that Arwoor would have done the same thing if he had been the Lord of this world at that time.

On the other hand, he, Wolff, was not to blame, either. He was not the lord Jadawin who had constructed this universe and then manipulated it so foully for so many of its creatures and abducted Terrestrials. The attack of amnesia had been complete; it had wiped all of Jadawin from him and made him a blank page. Out of the blankness had emerged a new man, Wolff, one incapable of acting like Jadawin or any of the other lords.

And he was still Wolff, except that he remembered what he had been. The thought made him sick and contrite and eager to make amends as best he could. Was this the way to start, by allowing Arwoor to die horribly for a crime he had not commited?

"Jadawin!" boomed Arwoor. "You may think you have won this move! But I have topped you again! I have one more coin to put on the table, and its value is far more than what your horn will do to me!"

"And what is that?" Wolff asked. He had a black feeling that Arwoor was not bluffing.

"I've planted one of the bombs I brought with me when I was dispossessed of Chiffaenir. It's under the palace, and when I so desire, it will go off and blow the whole top of this monolith off. It's true I'll die, too, but I'll take my old enemy with me! And your woman and your friends will die, too! Think of them!"

Wolff was thinking of them. He was in an agony.

"What are your terms?" he asked. "I know that you don't want to die. You're so miserable you *should* want to die, but you've clung to your worthless life for ten thousand years."

"Enough of insults! Will you or won't you? My finger is an inch above the button." Arwoor chuckled and continued, "Even if I'm bluffing, which I'm not, you can't afford to take the chance."

Wolff spoke to the others, who had been listening without understanding but knew that something drastic had happened. He explained as much as he dared, omitting any connection of himself with the Lords.

151

Podarge, her face a study in combined frustration and madness, said, "Ask him what his terms are."

She added, "After this is all over, you have much to explain to me, O Wolff."

Arwoor replied, "You must give me the silver horn, the all-precious and unique work of the master, Ilmarwolkin. I will use it to open the gate in the pool and pass through to the Atlantean tier. That is all I want, except your promise that none will come after me until the gate is closed."

Wolff considered for a few seconds. Then he said, "Very well. You may come out now. I swear to you on my honor as Wolff and by the Hand of Detiuw that I will give you the horn and I will send no one after you until the gate is closed."

Arwoor laughed and said, "I'm coming out."

Wolff waited until the door at the end of the hall was swinging out. Knowing that he could not be overheard by Arwoor then, he said to Podarge, "Arwoor thinks he has us, and he may well be confident. He will emerge through the gate at a place forty miles from here, near Ikwekwa, a suburb of the city of Atlantis. He would still be at the mercy of you and your eagles if there were not another resonant point only ten miles from there. This point will open when the horn is blown and admit him to another universe. I will show you where it is after Arwoor goes through the pool."

Arwoor advanced confidently. He was a tall, broad-shouldered and good-looking man with wavy blond hair and blue eyes. He took the horn from Wolff, bowed ironically, and walked on down the hall. Podarge stared at him so madly that Wolff was afraid that she would leap upon him. But he had told her that he must keep his promises: the one to her and the one to Arwoor.

Arwoor strode past the silent and menacing files as if they were no more than statues of marble. Wolff did not wait for him to get to the pool, but went at once into the control room. A quick examination showed him that Arwoor had left a device which would depress the button to set off the bomb. Doubtless he had given himself plenty of time to get away. Nevertheless, Wolff sweated until he had removed the device. By then, Kickaha had returned from watching Arwoor go through the gate in the pool.

"He got away, all right," he said, "but it wasn't as easy as he had thought. The place of emergence was under water, caused by the flood he himself had created. He had to drop into the water and swim for it. He was still swimming when the gate closed."

Wolff took Podarge into a huge map room, and indicated the town near which the gate was. Then, in the visual-room, he showed her the gate at close range on a screen. Podarge studied the map and the screen for a minute. She gave an order to her eagles, and they trooped out after her. Even the apes were awed by the glare of death in their eyes.

Arwoor was forty miles from the monolith, but he had ten miles to travel. Moreover, Podarge and her pets were launching themselves from a point 30,000 feet up. They would descend at such an angle and for such a distance that they could build up great speed. It would be a close race between Podarge and her quarry.

While he waited before the screen, Wolff had time to do much thinking. Eventually, he would tell Chryseis who he was and how he had come to be Wolff. She would know that he had been to another universe to visit one of the rare friendly lords. The Vaernirn became lonely, despite their great powers, and wanted to socialize now and then with their peers. On his return to this universe, he had fallen into a trap set by Vannax, another dispossessed Lord. Jadawin had been hurled into the universe of Earth, but he had taken the surprised Vannax with him. Vannax had escaped with a crescent after the savage tussle on the hill slope. What had happened to the other crescent, Wolff did not know. But Vannax had not had it, that was sure.

Amnesia had struck then, and Jadawin had lost all memory —had become, in effect, a baby, a *tabula rasa*. Then the Wolffs had taken him in, and his education as an Earthman had begun.

Wolff did not know the reason for the amnesia. It might have been caused by a blow on the head during his struggle with Vannax. Or it might have resulted from the terror of being marooned and helpless on an alien planet. Lords had depended upon their inherited science so long that, stripped of them, they became less than men.

Or his loss of memory might have come from the long struggle with his conscience. For years before being thrust willynilly into another world, he had been dissatisfied with himself, disgusted with his ways and saddened by his loneliness and insecurity. No being was more powerful than a Lord, yet none was lonelier or more conscious that any minute might be his last. Other Lords were plotting against him; all had to be on guard every minute.

Whatever the reason, he had become Wolff. But, as Kickaha pointed out, there was an affinity between him and the horn and the points of resonance. It had been no accident that he

153

had happened to be in the basement of that house in Arizona when Kickaha had blown the horn. Kickaha had had his suspicions that Wolff was a dispossessed Lord deprived of his memory.

Wolff knew now why he had learned the languages here so extraordinarily quickly. He was remembering them. And he had had such a swift and powerful attraction to Chryseis because she had been his favorite of all the women of his domain. He had even been thinking of bringing her to the palace and making her his Lady.

She did not know who he was on meeting him as Wolff because she had never seen his face. That cheap trick of the dazzling radiance had concealed his features. As for his voice, he had used a device to magnify and distort it, merely to further awe his worshippers. Nor was his great strength natural, for he had used the bioprocesses to equip himself with superior muscles.

He would make such amends as he could for the cruelty and arrogance of Jadawin, a being now so little a part of him. He would make new human bodies in the biocylinders and insert in them the brains of Podarge and her sisters, Kickaha's apes, Ipsewas, and any others who so desired. He would allow the people of Atlantis to rebuild, and he would not be a tyrant. He was not going to interfere in the affairs of the world of tiers unless it was absolutely necessary.

Kickaha called him to the screen. Arwoor had somehow found a horse in that land of dead and was riding him furiously.

"The luck of the devil!" Kickaha said, and he groaned.

"I think the devil's after him," Wolff said. Arwoor had looked behind and above him and then begun to beat his horse with a stick.

"He's going to make it!" Kickaha said. "There's a Temple of the Lord only a half-mile ahead!"

Wolff looked at the great white stone structure on top of a high hill. Within it was the secret chamber which he himself had used when he had been Jadawin.

He shook his head and said, "No!"

Podarge swooped within the field of vision. She was coming at great speed, her wings flapping, her face thrust forward, white against the green sky. Behind her came her eagles.

Arwoor rode the horse as far up the hill as he could. Then the mare's legs gave out, and she collapsed. Arwoor hit the ground running. Podarge dived at him. Arwoor dodged like a rabbit fleeing from a hawk. The harpy followed him in his zigzags, guessed which way he would go during one of his sideleaps, and was on him. Her claws struck his back. He threw his hands in the air and his mouth became an O through which soared a scream, voiceless to the watchers of the screen.

Arwoor fell with Podarge upon him. The other eagles landed and gathered to watch.

Science Against Man

Edited by ANTHONY CHEETHAM

"A very good collection of 11 short stories taking the theme
that science has stopped being a good servant and is
becoming a hard master.

"THE LOST CONTINENT by Norman Spinrad . . . is
brilliant. So is HAROLD WILSON AT THE COSMIC
COCKTAIL PARTY . . . by Bob Shaw. Notable
contributions come from Harry Harrison, James Blish
and Robert Silverberg."
– Edmund Cooper, *The Sunday Times*

Other contributors include:

Brian Aldiss
Andrew Travers
John Brunner
Piers Anthony
Paul Ableman
Michael Moorcock

Sphere   30p

Out of the Mouth of the Dragon

MARK S. GESTON

Amon VanRoark heard the prophet speaking in the market place of the decayed city. He called men to the wars, to the fabled Meadows where the armies of Good would meet the forces of Evil, in one final Armageddon that would decide the fate of a world already doomed and dying.

VanRoark followed the prophet to the Meadows and there he witnessed the last cataclismic battle between humanity and the dark powers of Salasar.

Sphere   30p

The Year's Best Science Fiction No. 5

Edited by HARRY HARRISON
& BRIAN ALDISS

The best SF shorts of 1971

Including stories by

ROBERT SCHECKLEY

ARTHUR C. CLARKE

JAMES BLISH

DONALD BARTHELME

NORMAN SPINRAD

KINGSLEY AMIS

THOMAS M. DISCH

and 11 other writers whose stories
represent the finest sf of 1971

Sphere 35p

Science Fiction Hall of Fame

Edited by ROBERT SILVERBERG

This superb anthology contains the finest SF stories
published before 1965.

Volume 1 includes stories by Clifford Simak, Robert
Heinlein, Isaac Asimov, A. E. van Vogt.

Volume 2 includes such writers as Cordwainer Smith,
James Blish, Ray Bradbury, Anthony Boucher and
Arthur C. Clarke.

"Something for the connoisseur to gloat over, a magnificent
line-up" – *Evening Standard*

Sphere   40p each

About the Author

Born in Buenos Aires, Alejandro Fogel has excavated existence, both temporal and ephemeral for over 40 years. His work has taken the form of writing, paintings, installations, prints, videos, photographs and travel performances transforming mundane objects and materials into treasured possessions that document his encounters with the overlapings of time, geography, philosophy, physics, history and peoples. Through it all, he follows his father's journey in war-torn Europe and South America and how it intersects and diverges with his own journey.

As in life, much of his work is stored in sealed boxes waiting to be deteriorated by time and obsolete technologies. As the stories he tells are consumed by the passage of time, often losing relevance and disappearing, his material analog art works are also fading and becoming only memories. Some of his pieces quickly become blank as they are made with consumer products designed to rapidly self-destruct. Others fade slowly, darkened to obscurity. They all follow the same ultimate destination.

Fogel's work is an exploration of the interstices of modern and ancient structures and their metaphysical, cultural, and historical value to contemporary society; their transformation and final extinction.

Alejandro Fogel has received numerous awards and honors and exhibited his work around the world. He was a Fellow of the Institute of Current World Affairs, where he studied and wrote about the descendants of the Incas now living in Argentina. He was also an artist-in-residence at the Rockefeller Foundation Study and Conference Center in Bellagio, Italy. He received the Rolex Award for Enterprise to publish his multidisciplinary project, The Incas Road.

Alejandro Fogel's surviving works are currently disappearing in museums and private collections worldwide.

He lives in New York City with writer Shelley Berc.

1

My name is Alejandro Mario Fogel.

You would think that Alejandro is a Spanish name and Mario is Italian. But I was named after my two grandfathers: Avrum and Meir, a tailor and a butcher from Eastern Europe. They grew up in the Pale of Settlement, a large area that included present day Poland, Belarus, the Ukraine, Romania and Moldova.

The Pale was created by Catherine the Great at the end of the 18th century. This was the region where Jews were allowed to live. With over five million Jews, the Pale was the largest ghetto in history. Avrum and Meir both lived there, but they never met.

Two of their children found each other many years later on the other side of the world.

2

In 1905, Avrum, my grandfather

on my mother's side, left the Pale to escape the Russian draft. He and his wife Sofía arrived in Buenos Aires at the Hotel de los Inmigrantes with a samovar, a metal bed, a wall clock, and their language, Yiddish. They had five children and grew old in this city full of immigrants.

My grandfather on my father's side, Meir, decided instead to stay in the Pale. While Avrum's family was secular, Meir and his family were Hassidic. He didn't want to leave for fear that his children would stop practicing Judaism in a foreign land. On May 23, 1944, Meir and his wife Blime along with eight of their thirteen children were locked in a packed cattle car and sent to Auschwitz.

Alejandro Fogel, "Trains at Viseul de Sus", detail, series of 22 prints, Office Depot Laser Print Paper, non-acid-free, 24 lb, 8 1/8 by 6 1/8 in. Edition: 5 each

3

In July of 1953,

Moishe was in a train going to Argentina from La Paz, Bolivia.

In another train that week, Ernesto Guevara arrived in La Paz from Argentina.

The immigrant from Eastern Europe on his way to a new life in Argentina and the immigrant from Argentina on his way to a new life in Cuba.

The young man carrying his knowledge of Torah and Jewish mysticism, exhausted from persecution, war and poverty. The young man who had just became a physician, going to war to end persecution and poverty.

4

In June of 1952

protests against the tyrannical government of General Juan Perón erupted on the streets of Buenos Aires. Ernesto Guevara and Jorge Luis Borges were among the many rioting against Perón's Mussolini-inspired fascist policies. Ernesto Guevara, on his way to becoming a Marxist revolutionary, was back from the 5,000 miles long motorcycle trip that opened his eyes to the misery in Latin America. Jorge Luis Borges, a conservative anti-Marxist, had just published his major book of essays, Other Inquisitions. Ernesto and Jorge Luis never met. Their worlds were far apart and growing farther apart every moment. But for a brief time in history, they shared the same political view: they were against Peronism.

Decades later, just before Borges died, I followed him through the streets of Buenos Aires.

Half a century later, long after Che died, I coached him at the United Nations in New York City.

5

On the evening of October 10, 1967

when I got home from Hebrew school, I saw Che Guevara's picture on the front page of the newspaper. He had just been killed by the military in Bolivia.

I asked my parents about him. "A Communist," my mother told me. Six years later, as I was jumping out a window, escaping a bomb explosion at my university, Che Guevara entered my life.

ANUNCIAN EN BOLIVIA QUE MURIO EL "CHE" GUEVARA

SEGUNDA EDICION • 88 PAGINAS

Clarín 20 Pesos

Año XXIII   Diario de la Mañana   N° 7814

Buenos Aires, Martes 10 de Octubre de 1967

El General Zenteno Anaya Informó que el Dirigente Cubano Cayó en un Encuentro Librado con Tropas del Ejército ★ Se Espera Ahora un Anuncio Oficial del Gobierno

LA PAZ, 9 (Reuter, AFP y AP). — El famoso guerrillero argentino Ernesto "Che" Guevara, compañero de armas de Fidel Castro, cuya presencia en Bolivia, luego de su imprevista desaparición del escenario político de Cuba, fue repetidamente señalada por el gobierno boliviano, habría sido muerto en un encuentro librado entre fuerzas militares y un grupo guerrillero en la localidad de Las Higueras, cerca de Vallegrande. La noticia, dada a conocer por el general Zenteno Anaya, no ha sido todavía confirmada oficialmente, esperándose la identificación de los guerrilleros muertos. (Información en las páginas DOS y TRES).

ERNESTO "CHE" GUEVARA en una pose característica, cuando ocupaba el cargo de ministro de Industrias en Cuba. Ahora en Bolivia se informó oficialmente que fue muerto cuando integraba un grupo de guerrilleros

OTROS HECHOS IMPORTANTES DEL PANORAMA NACIONAL

Circulante El último balance señala un nuevo récord en la circulación monetaria. En la página 22.

Posición Costa Méndez reafirmó la posición argentina contra el castrismo. Información en la página 18.

ALALC Comenzó la reunión para considerar problemas atinentes al intercambio. Informac. en la página 26.

Becas Modificó la Universidad de Buenos Aires el régimen para estudios agropecuarios. Inform. en la página 31.

Donativo Recibió el H. de Niños un cardiosensor y un detector de pulso capilar. Inf. en la página 30.

Centros Establecieranse para la entrega de la libreta sanitaria a los alumnos de 7° grado. Inf. en la pág. 26

Bolsa Poca actividad y variaciones en títulos y valores. Hubo 56 bajas y 78 alzas. Información en la página 43.

Dólar Ligeras variantes en el área de futuros. Cotización oficial, 350 pesos. Ver información en la página 44.

Tornado Causó cuantiosos daños el que azotó una extensa zona de Río Cuarto. Inform. en la página 33.

Mendoza Récord absoluto de la industria vitivinícola: más de 18 millones de hectólitros. En la página 35.

Chaco Renunció el intendente de Resistencia, teniente coronel Raúl César Roldán. Informac. en la página 37.

Comisión Delibera la de cooperación económica argentina - española. Información en página 22.

Atletismo Se iniciará a las 15.30 la 2° jornada del Sudamericano. Informac. en la página 42.

EDITORIAL

La Secretaría de la OEA

La próxima renovación de la Secretaría General de la Organización de Estados Americanos abre la posibilidad de una gestión que lleve a un importante sitial a un candidato argentino, así todo si se tienen en cuenta las dificultades que plantea la elección de una figura aceptable para todos los países. (Página 12)

INTERVIENEN EL PODER JUDICIAL DE FORMOSA

ENTRE 37 REINAS de colectividades españolas de nuestro país, Lidia Esperanza Navarro fue consagrada anoche Miss Iberia. Pedirá ahora aspirar el título de Maja Internacional 1967 (Información en la página 27)

Así lo Anunció Borda ★ Ayer, el Gabinete Escuchó Informes de Costa Méndez y K. Vasena y Analizó la Racionalización

(INFORMACION EN LA MISMA PAGINA NUEVE Y DIEZ)

CAMINOS

Se Licitaron Obras Viales por Valor de 1.596.789.141 Pesos

(INFORMACION EN LA PAGINA VEINTISEIS)

PROMOCION

Se Alentará el Consumo de Carne Ovina en Capital y Gran Bs. Aires

(INFORMACION EN LA PAGINA CUARENTA Y TRES)

España
Eligen Hoy Diputados Por Sufragio Directo
(INFORMACION EN LA PAGINA OCHO)

Argel
Comienza la Reunión de Países en Desarrollo
(INFORMACION EN LA PAGINA CATORCE)

Uruguay
Grave Crisis ★ Impuso Gestido Medidas de Seguridad ★ Renunciaron Cuatro Ministros
(INFORMACION EN LA PAGINA SEIS)

Clarin newspaper cover, October 10, 1967

13

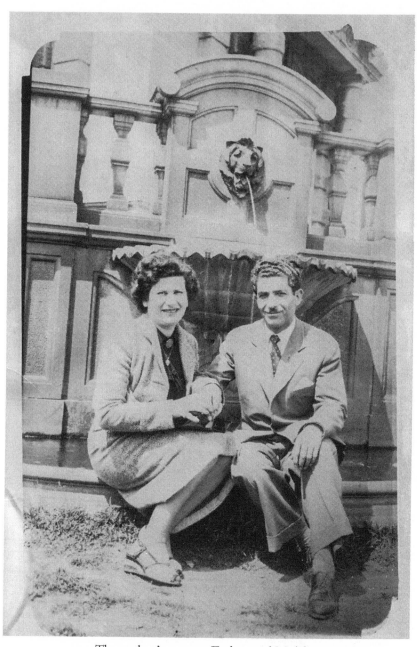

The author's parents Esther and Moishe

6

"Papá is dead"

my sister Ceci tells me on the telephone. My legs weaken. I have to sit down. She is crying, and I can barely speak. I'm holding the telephone and staring out the window. The Metropolitan Life building, illuminated in white and blue, is shining in the distance. "What happened?" was all I could think to say. As she tells me that his kidneys finally gave out, I feel my body growing cold and the entire living room, a tiny speck of real estate dust in Midtown Manhattan, gets dark and blurry. My dad's smile is fading. His olive skin is pale.

I finally say to my sister: "We'll be taking the first plane I can find." It is late in the evening here in New York City and the middle of the night in Israel. I can't stop thinking about Moishe lying in a hospital bed, his mouth slightly open, his eyes closed....

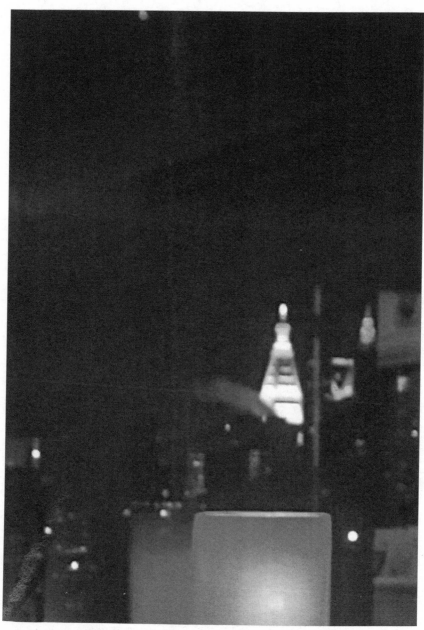

Alejandro Fogel, "The Night Moishe Died", detail, monoprint, Iris print on Somerset Velvet rag paper, 8 1/8 by 12 7/8 in.

The author and his sister Ceci

7

I'm going to write a few lines

about my father's funeral. I always thought I wouldn't include these lines in this book, but here they are:

We are in Kibbutz Beit Haemek in Western Galilee. Moishe's coffin is going down into his grave. We are all devastated. Ceci and Shelley, my wife, are crying. I can't cry. The hundred or so people gathered for the ceremony are watching Moishe slowly descend under a blistering sun. My Hassidic cousins, whom I never met before, are dressed in shiny black mourning suits, their black hats melting on their scalps, and their long, wild beards wet with sweat. They surround the grave, making sure everything has been done properly according to their religious protocols.

I hear a bird singing.... After a few seconds I realize that it isn't a bird, it's a cell phone ringtone. One of my Hassidic cousins quickly puts his right hand inside the pocket of his black silky vest and takes out his black phone. He looks at the Caller ID and picks up. "Alo?" he says, and goes on in a lengthy conversation that I can't understand. He withdraws a few feet from the grave as the coffin slowly goes down and finishes his chat.

I look at Shelley and Ceci, who are staring at the scene in disbelief, and say: "It must be God calling, otherwise he wouldn't answer."

I just arrived in Sacel

a small town in northern Transylvania, today part of Romania. I was so excited to come here, the mythical Sacel where my father was born. I've been talking about Sacel since I was a child. I would never refer to it by its name but as "the town where my Dad was born". It was always so far away, so remote. Unreachable. I've been longing for this moment for years.

I'd been to Romania a few years ago, to Bucharest, the capital. At that time, my friend Alexandru and I were going to drive out to Sacel, which lies at the foot of the Carpathian Mountains. But we had to cancel because the mountain roads were buried in snow. Romania then felt like a deep dark nightmare. The ghosts of the victims of Ceaucescu's dictatorship were walking around trying to get their stories heard. We lived in Bucharest at Strada Eminescu 252, apartment 17 for a week, and I listened to one of those ghosts.

But here I am today, walking the streets of Sacel with Shelley. We are a family and we are not Hassidic, an unimaginable thought for my grandfather Zvi Meir. He expected generations of Fogels to follow the teachings of the Baal Shem Tov, founder of Hassidism, as the family had done for over two centuries.

Rabbi Israel ben Eliezer, known as the Baal Shem Tov, was born in Poland in 1698. He gained a reputation as a miracle healer. He taught my family that one must worship God in everything, not just by traditional religious observances, but in daily life. His reputation as a miracle healer gained him a large circle of followers among ordinary people and scholars alike.

The Baal Shem Tov was a Kabbalist. I've been trying to understand the concept of Kabbalah for many years, always ending with a feeling similar to the one I had about Sacel: remote and unreachable.

It wasn't until I met Jorge Luis Borges that I understood the connection between me, my family and the Kabbalah.

Borges had answered my question without even knowing what it was. Just as he said, "chance has been ruled out." I was there, standing face to face with Jorge Luis Borges, years before the bomb exploded, years after Moishe knocked on the AMIA's door for the first time looking for work, so I can write this sentence, at this moment, and you, the reader, will finish reading it in this particular instant.

"Maestro, I'm so glad I've run into you. Can I ask you a question?"

"Sure," he responded. His eyes were focused somewhere high on the horizon. María Kodama was staring directly at me.

"My ancestors are Hassidic. I'm very curious about them and the Kabbalah. I'm thinking about determinism and I want to know...."

He interrupted me and said: "La Cábala es el libro que viene detras del Libro." "The Kabbalah is the book behind the Book. The Torah is "The Text," the literal word of God, which is the origin of all things. Kabbalah is the word of man attempting to comment upon and interpret Torah, while being faithful to it. Words have real volume in the Kabbalah. They are heavy and three-dimensional, numbered and measured, as if the words were actual beings and objects, themselves.

He thought for a moment, and then said: "Kabbalists believe that God dictates word by word what he wants to say. This means that "The Text" of the Torah is an absolute text in which change is measured as zero. What really attracts me is not the text itself, but the possibility of a text where chance has been ruled out."

We were standing in front of the building where my father used to work, the AMIA, the Jewish Aid Society. The building would be blown up by Iranian terrorists several years later. On that day Moishe was only two blocks from the AMIA, on his way to work there. His body lifted off the ground at the same time that some of his friends were blasted apart and buried in the rubble. I spoke to him on the phone a few hours after the explosion that killed 85 people and injured hundreds. He repeated what he had said to me many times over the years: "I am a lucky man. I escaped again."

The AMIA was the first place Moishe went looking for a job, when he first arrived in Buenos Aires at the Eva Perón train station.

Determinism: (n) All events are causally determined by a chain of prior events.

9

Jorge Luis Borges lived with his wife

María Kodama in an apartment in Buenos Aires at the corner of Calle French and Calle Bustamante, right across the street from my painting studio. The first time I saw them I was having breakfast at Café Literario, next door to their building. I was shocked to see The Master enter the room and take a table next to mine. They had coffee and *medialunas*. They were a stunning couple. He was in his eighties, blind and tall. She was in her early forties, half Argentinean and half Japanese. It seemed that everything grew quiet as they entered.

Over a period of several weeks I followed Borges on his wanderings through the streets of Buenos Aires without him knowing it. At first I had no idea what I was doing. Was it a travel-performance piece, like when I walked the Incas Road in the Andes mountains? At that time, me hiking the Road was the piece. Now, Borges was the main focus and the road, the streets of Buenos Aires, was the background landscape. The first time I followed Borges, he walked for about an hour holding María Kodama's arm and then went into a bookstore. After a few minutes they stopped at one of the display tables. María Kodama picked up a book and started reading to Borges in a low voice. The book was about the Kabbalah.

When they left the bookstore I followed for a few minutes and then stopped him.

9

Jorge Luis Borges lived with his wife

María Kodama in an apartment in Buenos Aires at the corner of Calle French and Calle Bustamante, right across the street from my painting studio. The first time I saw them I was having breakfast at Café Literario, next door to their building. I was shocked to see The Master enter the room and take a table next to mine. They had coffee and *medialunas*. They were a stunning couple. He was in his eighties, blind and tall. She was in her early forties, half Argentinean and half Japanese. It seemed that everything grew quiet as they entered.

Over a period of several weeks I followed Borges on his wanderings through the streets of Buenos Aires without him knowing it. At first I had no idea what I was doing. Was it a travel-performance piece, like when I walked the Incas Road in the Andes mountains? At that time, me hiking the Road was the piece. Now, Borges was the main focus and the road, the streets of Buenos Aires, was the background landscape. The first time I followed Borges, he walked for about an hour holding María Kodama's arm and then went into a bookstore. After a few minutes they stopped at one of the display tables. María Kodama picked up a book and started reading to Borges in a low voice. The book was about the Kabbalah.

When they left the bookstore I followed for a few minutes and then stopped him.

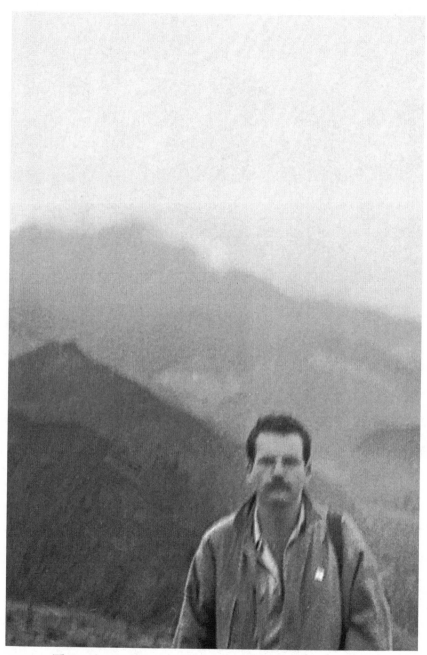

The author at Mount Aconcagua in the Andes Mountains

10

After I spoke with Borges

I kept wondering if this universe in which we live is not the only one. Maybe there are parallel universes, hidden from our eyes but not hidden to the flow of energy that causes our bodies to function.

Borges is the blind man who could see a parallel universe. A Kabbalist.

11

I'm in the Lake Como region

of northern Italy, standing in front of a plaque indicating the place where Benito Mussolini was executed in 1945. I'm staying in this area for the next five weeks at the Rockefeller Foundation's Bellagio Center as an artist-in-residence. A fellow resident took me on a reconnaissance trip. Unknowingly, we followed Mussolini's last steps from the city of Como to the town of Menaggio and stumbled upon this spot at Villa Belmonte where he was executed by Italian Partisans. Once we realized that we were trailing Mussolini's road to death, we decided to keep going and follow the body to its next stop: the Piazzale Loretto in Milan where the corpse was hung by his feet from a girder at an Esso gas station for public display.

My colleague is a historian and he's very excited about this unexpected macabre trip. I, on the other hand, am more interested in Leonardo's *The Last Supper* at the Santa Maria delle Grazie church, our agreed-upon next stop in Milan.

As we drive to Milan, one of Mussolini's most fervid students, the Argentinean general Juan Perón comes to mind. In 1945, just a few months after Mussolini's execution, Juan Perón became President of Argentina and picked up the torch of his beloved teacher.

I tried to see *The Last Supper*, fighting off tourists and trying to see through the bars of the restoration scaffold, but it was futile. I gave up and bought a poster of the painting instead.

Stopping to recover at a café down the street, we stand at the counter and order cappuccinos. As we wait, I'm looking at the many brands of liquors and wines on the shelves behind the bar. I can't believe my eyes when I see an extensive collection of wine bottles, all with the face of Mussolini on them. I ask the barista about the wine. He tells me that it's really good and that they also have this other one. He points to the shelf above it and, to my horror, I see several wine bottles with the picture of Hitler on them.

The official story after Mussolini's government fell is that the fascists were removed from power and Italy became a democracy. In reality, more than 40,000 fascists who committed horrific crimes during the war were given amnesty and went free. The amnesty didn't include the top leaders, but very few of those in the highest political and military ranks were indicted. In 1973, ninety-five percent of senior civil servants from Mussolini's government were still in their jobs.

Perón's own fascist dictatorship was overthrown by another fascist regime in 1955: the *Revolución Libertadora* or "Liberating Revolution" led by the Argentinean military. All of Perón's followers were purged from government. Even Perón's name was banned and replaced in official documents and the press with the euphemism "the deposed tyrant". People would refer to him for many years as *El Hombre* or *El Macho*. In 1973, Perón came out of exile in Spain and returned to Argentina. He was elected President for the third time. His government didn't last long. He died a few months after taking office. He had made his third wife, Isabelita (an ex-burlesque dancer), Vice President and after he died, she took over with the help of her astrologist. Her disastrous rule was also brief, because a Military Junta took over once again. They inaugurated the darkest period in Argentinean history: the Dirty War, in which 30,000 civilians disappeared. Among them was my friend Darío Bedne.

Alejandro Fogel, "Il Vino del Camerata", monoprint of an online image, Office
Depot Laser Print Paper non-acid-free, 24 lb, 8 1/2 by 6 1/8 in

12

I'm in Rome now

sitting on the steps of the Garibaldi Bridge. Moishe sat here once, too, one of the millions of people displaced by World War II. As I follow his steps, every time I see what he saw, stand where he stood, or sit where he sat, I learn a bit more about him. Since the time he left Sacel in 1941, he navigated his way in the world following one single clue: Jewish ethnicity. He believed that it was the only protection he had. The only way to survive was by finding others who spoke Yiddish. This end of the Garibaldi Bridge overlooks the Jewish part of town. Rome's Jews originally settled on the other side, in Trastevere, but by the 13th century they had started to move across the river. Via del Portico d'Ottavia, with its labyrinth of Roman, Medieval and Renaissance architecture, used to mark the Jewish ghetto's boundary. Today, it is the center of Jewish life, and it's a good place to sample Rome's Jewish cuisine. In fact, as I sit at the very end of the bridge, I'm eating some delicious deep fried artichokes, a Roman specialty, I got at a restaurant called Ba'Ghetto.

There are many people around me having their lunch on the bridge's promenade that runs parallel to the Tiber River. Most of them are Albanian refugees. I think about Moishe sitting here as a refugee, doing exactly the same thing most of these people are doing: waiting for help.

The word *ghetto* is Italian and was used for the first time in Venice, around the year 1516, to describe a neighborhood in which Jews were

confined to prevent them from mixing with the Christian population. They were forced to wear star-shaped yellow badges and yellow berets. The Albanians of the Garibaldi Bridge wear mostly jeans and t-shirts. Their chests advertise Hard Rock cafés, The GAP and Che Guevara.

The word "ghetto" came into popular use again in the mid-1930s when the Nazi came to power. This time it described a holding area for Jews who would be transported to the concentration camps. My grandparents and most of Moishe's siblings were taken to the Viseul de Sus ghetto in northern Romania before they were sent to Auschwitz.

I want to ask the Albanians some questions but none of them speak English. Anyhow, the answers are on their faces: exhaustion, loss of identity, fear. They are part of the 20 million refugees around the world. Twenty million people now like Moishe was then: homeless, displaced, on the move, following cosmic clues that will take them to their new realities. When I think about Moishe moving around Europe in the years after the war, I see him sitting on the roof of a train, closing his eyes to the wind, hoping that the next stop will be the end of the road. It took him seven years to find it.

13

We are having coffee

at Harvey Keitel's loft in Tribeca. We stayed on long after the party ended. Shelley and Harvey are discussing the *Book of Job* and thinking about collaborating on a one-man show about it. Shelley is specifically referring to Carl Jung's book *Answer to Job*. Jung saw the Holy Trinity as having a missing fourth part: Evil. For Jung, the Trinity is really a Quaternity, and Job is innocent.

I asked myself, assuming that God exists: can God be evil? One of those questions with no answer. We humans are so far from understanding the nature of the cosmos that very complex questions like this are absurd and pointless.

Harvey and I were disappointed that our families weren't from the same part of the Pale. His mom came from the South East of Romania and my Dad from the North West. No connection there.

But something remarkable happened at the party earlier that evening. I met a movie producer. Somehow we ended up talking about Che Guevara and my visit to La Higuera, where Che was killed in 1967. After a few minutes, she made me an offer I couldn't refuse.

14

I'm having an espresso

and talking about Mao Tse-tung with my friend Brian at Café Roma in Little Italy, a rapidly vanishing corner of Manhattan. Long gone are the days when Italian immigrants lived here on Mulberry Street. Hundreds of thousands of them went fleeing poverty and persecution in their homeland and settled in New York at the turn of the 20th century. The wave of refugees was so extraordinary in number that, in some cases, the population of a single Italian village ended up living on the same block of Little Italy or even in the same tenement building.

Little Italy has been gradually taken over by Chinatown and is now barely a couple of blocks lined with Italian restaurants. Chinatown is in full expansion. Its population has grown to about 150,000 residents. Some of them came in the 1960's, refugees from the Cultural Revolution. Mao Tse-tung believed that the old order and everyone in it must be destroyed to create a new one. Two days later I was whispering something similar into Che Guevara's ear.

15

It is going to be December 11, 1964
for the entire weekend. I'm inside the UN having lunch with the
delegates from Romania and Argentina. I approached them after
Che Guevara's third consecutive repetition of his "Colonialism is
Doomed" speech to the General Assembly. They graciously accepted
to have lunch with me and Alberto, Che's Cuban coach. We have one
hour before Che gives the speech once again.

In *Morel's Invention*, a 1940 novel by Argentinean writer Adolfo Bioy
Casares, the main character is a man evading justice. He escapes to a
strange island. As he observes the island's inhabitants, he realizes that
they can't see him, and they repeat the same movements, gestures and
dialogues over and over again.

The one exception to this endless repetition is a scientist named
Morel. It turns out he invented a very special machine. It runs on
tidal waves, so it is assumed to work forever.

This island has two moons and two suns, reality and recordings of
reality layered upon each other.

Morel used his invention on friends who visited the island. The
machine captured every single detail of their lives. The only problem
is that after the machine did its job of reproduction, the beings being
reproduced decayed and died, leaving only their holographic copies
replaying the same movements, gestures, dialogues for eternity.

For Nietzsche, the Eternal Return was a paralyzing thought: "What if some day or night a demon were to steal after you into your loneliest loneliness and say to you: "This life as you now live it and have lived it, you will have to live once more and innumerable times more; and there will be nothing new in it, but every pain and every joy and every thought and sigh and everything unutterably small or great in your life will have to return to you, all in the same succession and sequence-- even this spider and this moonlight between the trees, and even this moment and I myself."

Ernesto Che Guevara rises once again from his seat at the Cuban delegation and takes the podium. He gives his speech for the fourth time. His delivery is more resolute and secure than before. The slight Cuban and Argentinean cadences that he should have are still not quite right.

Che has on miniature headphones, and he alternatively listens to Alberto and me.

Che is back at the podium: "This session of the Assembly should not be remembered in the future solely by the number 19 that identifies it…"

Session 19 is not remembered by its number, but by the fact that it was the one in which Che Guevara spoke to the world. Films, videos, and web sites have been replaying it over and over for years —and every single bit and byte of it, ad nauseam. This virtual reality is being nourished by its repetitions to create reality. It is a measured, soulless, dead reality.

Before his next repetition of the speech, I leave the General Assembly room to get some fresh air. I am relieved to see there is only one sun shining in the sky.

In *The Shape of a Pocket*, John Berger writes :

"Everyday, all over the world, the media network replaces reality with

lies.

Substantial lies about what human and natural life is actually made of.

All the lies converge into one colossal falsehood: the supposition that life itself is a commodity and that those who can afford to buy it are, by definition, those who deserve it!

Imagine suddenly, the substantial material world (tomatoes, rain, birds, stones, melons, fish, eels, termites, mothers, dogs, mildew, salt water) in revolt against the endless stream of images which tell lies about them and in which they are imprisoned! Imagine them, as a reaction, claiming their freedom from all grammatical, digital, and pictorial representation, imagine an uprising of the represented."

I'm outside the General Assembly. One more break. First Avenue in Manhattan seems real. There is only one moon in the sky. I'm inclined to think that repetition in a non-virtual reality is virtually impossible. Although, against all common sense, this reality is telling me that what is being repeated so many times cannot be unreal.

I look back at the UN. Ernesto Che Guevara is about to speak again.

16

In History and Repetition

Kojin Karatani wrote:

"From ancient times, it has been said that history repeats itself. In truth, people study history precisely because it is not a one-time phenomenon but rather maintains the possibility of recurrence. For example, historians often say that those who are ignorant of history are doomed to repeat it. Does that mean, then, that those who have knowledge of history will be able to avoid its recurrence? Does the repetition of history actually exist? Such questions have never been properly considered. For even if they intuitively acknowledge the repetition of history, scholars, aspiring to be scientific, refrain from taking on the issue for fear of rendering their work unscientific. I believe in the existence of historical repetition, as well as in the possibility of engaging such repetition scientifically."

17

The first thing about Sacel

that doesn't fulfill my expectations is its size. When I was a child and my father spoke about his hometown, he made it sound as if it were small, like a couple of blocks. If that child went to Sacel today he would have felt it was enormous. Sacel is about two miles long and perhaps a mile or two wide on each side of its one main road. I remember asking my father for his address there and he would always answer: "I lived in the white house on the main road." Streets don't have names in Sacel. I'm currently standing on the main road under a scorching sun. I came to find Moishe's house. The only additional information I have is that it was next to the Catholic Church, on the left hand side.

I am looking around and notice that everyone on the street is staring at us. Not too many foreigners pass by Sacel since it is buried in the forested mountains and there are no main roads connecting it to the large cities in the area. I approach the closest local and ask him in English where the church is. He doesn't understand. I try in Spanish, another Latin language that is supposed to be close to Romanian, but he still doesn't have any idea what I am saying. I try with a few other people who come to help. No luck. Sign language then. When I draw a cross in the air, they finally get it. "Biserica!" the word for church in Romanian. They are all pointing one way.

As I walk in the direction they indicated, I really see Sacel for the first time. I'm on the main road; a tired, skinny horse and a mangy

51

sheep slowly pass by. A narrow river is just 100 yards away and I can see a few women doing their laundry there. The buildings are mostly one-story wooden houses. Some of them are surrounded by wooden fences with massive elaborate gates carved in the Transylvanian folk style. The gates have been built the same way since the Middle Ages. People became attached to their traditional gates, which aesthetically speaking have very little in common with the rough simplicity of their homes. I'm standing in front of one of these massive structures. The carving is primitive and intricate, rough and beautiful. There are a moon, a sun, and stars carved over the gate's arch. More carvings on the sides reveal a twisted vine growing upwards. There are traces of yellow paint on the weathered sun.

Alejandro Fogel, "Entering Sacel"

18

I'm in the ancient city of Tiahuanaco
in the Bolivian Andes, at 13,000 feet above sea level. I'm facing the
Gateway of the Sun, a 10 foot high arch carved from a single piece
of Andesite granite. It's dawn on the first day of spring and the sun
is coming up exactly through the center of the archway. As the sun
rises each day it moves along the horizon to a different spot. To
measure this movement the creators of the gateway envisioned it as a
giant clock. At the top of the structure there is a carving of the god
Viracocha, who the Incas believed was the creator of civilization and
their first king. He had one son, Inti, the sun. Holding a thunderbolt
in each hand, Viracocha is depicted as all-powerful.

Referring to this particular section of the Gateway, Joseph Campbell
wrote in *The Hero of a Thousand Faces:* "the grace that pours into the
universe through the sun door is the same as the energy of the bolt
that annihilates and is itself indestructible." A grandiose statement
I never understood until I was standing in front of the Gateway of
the Sun. I'm amazed by the quality of the carving and how the whole
structure reverberates with the landscape. The feeling is so different
from when I saw a life size cast of it at the Museum of Natural
History in La Plata, Argentina. The carving on the replica seemed
flat; the reproduction lifeless. It stands in a corner of one of the
museum's main halls, in the same building where Chief Fogel, the
19th century Patagonian tribal chief, was exhibited to the public.

Alejandro Fogel, "Lalliscka Pacha", oil on canvas, 6 ft. 56 in. by 4 ft. 92 in.

19

Every morning Moishe

and Yosef Shmil, his closest brother, ran to the Heder, the Jewish school that once stood on the street in Sacel where I'm standing now. Moishe's home was a simple wooden house with just three rooms. He lived there with his twelve brothers and sisters, his father Zvi Meir, who was the town's kosher butcher, and his mother Blime.

Blime means flower in Yiddish. There is no existing picture of her. Moishe told me that his parents were afraid of having their photograph taken because making pictures of people was forbidden by God. I always thought about her having a sweet wrinkled face and smelling like jasmine. She never made it to being an old grandmother. She was killed when she was in her late forties. Still, I always imagine her as old. As I walk through the streets of her hometown I carry my memory of her with me. I show her that there is still no running water in Sacel, there is electricity now, but it only works a few hours a day.

The old peasant women still dress like they've been dressing for hundreds of years with their *babushkas*, full skirts and handmade shoes that curl up at the toes. I stop to snap a picture of them. They graciously group together for the shot and I have the opportunity to observe around them without staring. They look like they are the age of the Blime I am showing around Sacel today. They were little girls when she was taken away to the train station at Viseu de Sus. After all the Jews were sent to Auschwitz, some of these then little girls and

their families stole their houses and still live in them.

Blime is coming along with me to find her home. After a few minutes I am at the Catholic Church. But her house isn't beside it. There is nothing there but an empty, fenced-in lot, full of weeds growing out of the dark Transylvanian soil. I'm taking pictures of the weeds and the ground. I'm collecting dirt from the lot in a plastic baggie to take home with me. I walk over to the river bank and pick some flowers. I leave them on the ground where I imagine my grandmother's house stood. The flowers are for Blime, the flower.

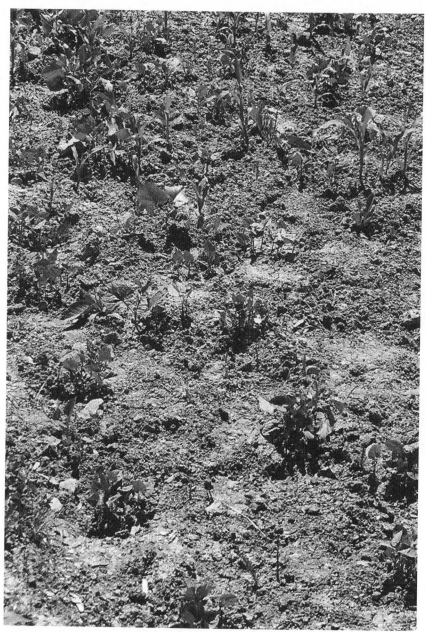

Alejandro Fogel, "The House that Wasn't There", series of 3 prints, Iris print on Somerset Velvet rag paper, 8 1/8 by 12 7/8 in. Edition: 25 each

Alejandro Fogel, "Ladies of Sacel"

20

Che Guevara goes in and out

of the United Nations sixteen times in the space of one hour. His cigar is the same size every time he reaches the podium. Everyone in the audience is frozen in the same place, one more time.

Mircea Eliade started writing *The Myth of the Eternal Return* in 1945, just after World War II, when Europe was in ruins and the Soviet Union was taking over Eastern Europe. The essay is about mankind's experience of time and history, especially the concepts of being and reality. It is about the terminal nature of human life and the infinite repetition of the cycles of nature. Borges would say that these cycles are really an infinite circle of which the center is everywhere and the circumference is so big that it looks like a straight line.

Many years after Eliade and Borges wrote their classic works, I stood with my Romanian double Alexandru in front of the mythologist's dilapidated house and withered garden. Winter in Bucharest was almost over and the dead garden was struggling to life again. For Alexandru and me it felt like we were trying to come full circle, too.

21

Todd Remis is suing

his photographers because the last fifteen minutes of his wedding party with Milena Grzibovska are missing. He says that those fifteen minutes are precious because they include their last dance and the moment his bride chose to toss the bouquet.

Mr. Remis wants to have those moments back.

He wants the photographers to pay for an exact recreation of the wedding, so those fifteen minutes that were not recorded, can be shot.

Justice Doris Ling-Cohan of the State Supreme Court in Manhattan determined that the suit should proceed.

The Justice quoted lyrics from the song "The Way We Were," in her opinion:

"This is a case in which it appears that the 'misty watercolor memories' and the 'scattered pictures of the smiles ... left behind' at the wedding were more important than the real thing."

22

When I was a child

I was fascinated by the spiky seed balls that grew on the plane tree outside my bedroom window. They started life as pretty delicate flowers, then hardened and transformed into hairy brown ping-pong balls. At the end of spring they fell to the ground. I was able to observe the entire process from my window. The best part was to collect the seed balls in a shoe box for experimentation. I would measure each one, weigh it and give it a number. Once a ball was numbered, I would hold it from its stem and swing it back and forth like a pendulum. I don't have my notes from that time, but I clearly remember that I wanted to get my pendulum balls to swing to the rhythm of our wall clock.

At the end of the experiment, for a reason I no longer remember, I would go to the edge of the roof and throw the balls at passing cars and people's heads.

On April 6, 2010, at the Musée des Arts et Métiers in Paris a cable holding a sixty pound brass ball snapped and the ball fell, shattering on the floor. This ball was part of the original Foucault's pendulum, designed in 1851 to prove the rotation of the earth. The authorities at the Museum announced that the damage was irreparable. The original Foucault's pendulum is gone. It has been replaced by a copy.

There are many copies of the pendulum around the world, one of which is in the lobby of the UN General Assembly.

Two Che Guevaras have stood below the UN's copy before they gave their speeches to the General Assembly.

A Foucault's pendulum is basically a heavy ball attached to a long wire. What makes it different from a regular clock pendulum is that it is allowed to rotate freely as it swings. Once in motion a Foucalt's pendulum appears to rotate slightly every minute. In reality the pendulum isn't rotating at all. What rotates is the Earth underneath it. The appearance of the rotation changes depending on where the pendulum is on earth. At the North Pole the pendulum will rotate clockwise full circle in 24 hours. Here at the UN in New York City at 40"47'25N the pendulum will rotate clockwise in 37 hours. At the Equator it remains in a fixed plane.

My interest in pendulums came back as an adult one day when I was watching the one encased in the wall clock my grandparents brought when they emigrated to Argentina. It is now on the wall of my sister Ceci's home in Israel. I was waiting for my father to take what turned out to be our last trip together before he died. We were going to the ancient city of Safed to try to find the synagogue my great grandfather built for the Rabbi of Vishnitz. I was impatient and as I looked at the time, I realized that the wall clock's pendulum and my watch were tick tocking together.

I'm in the Duomo in Pisa staring up at the altar lamps hanging from the ceiling. They are motionless now, but on a cold morning in 1583 one of the lamps was swinging rhythmically back and forth. It was the time of prayers. Galileo Galilei, a student at the University of Pisa, was observing the lamp and its regular motion. He realized that no matter how wide the oscillation, it took the lamp the same amount of time to cover different distances. In the absence of a clock, he timed the lamp swings against his pulse.

Christiaan Huygens invented the pendulum clock in 1665. He realized that the two pendulum clocks in his bedroom were swinging exactly at the same time. They were next to each other and swinging in

opposite directions. This phenomena has been explained scientifically as "coupled oscillations."

Steven Strogatz, a mathematician in chaos and complexity theory, describes how systems can synchronize themselves: from crickets in a field to electrons in a super conductor to inanimate objects like metronomes on a platform. A powerful tendency to spontaneous order.

In his book *Emergence*, Steven Johnson explains why the whole is smarter than the sum of its parts. Emergence refers to the connected lives of ants, brains, cities, and software. Ants have no leaders and not much individual brain power, but they organize themselves into complex colonies that become powerful organisms beautifully adapted to survive. As a whole they emerge as a very intelligent entity.

Jung's collective unconscious refers to all living creatures' unconsciouses, present, past and future, truly linked and sharing everything. A timeless, accumulating energy force spanning the universe. Jung says that we all have access to this energy. It seems there is a part of our conscious mind that naturally connects with the collective unconscious. We share this energy and everything that comes with it: images, thoughts, instincts, memories.

I was walking by the Duomo in Florence when I noticed a white marble circle on the pavement with an inscription that with time had become unreadable.

In January 27, 1601 lightning struck the cupola of the Duomo. The bronze ball at the top got hit and crashed to the ground. The white marble plaque commemorates that event.

After complaints from the neighbors that I was throwing balls at anything moving, my Dad banned me from climbing up to the roof. The ban was lifted years later when I saw an extraordinary picture in an encyclopedia.

Alejandro Fogel, "The Plaque by il Duomo", Walmart Faux Photo Canvas, 20 by 16 in. Edition: 10

23

Umberto Eco is one

of my favorite authors. In his novel *Foucalt's Pendulum*, the pendulum's fixed oscillation also proves that there is a single fixed point in the whole universe, and it is eternally unmoving. In Borges' short story, "The Aleph", that fixed point is in the basement of a house in Buenos Aires.

After re-reading this story, I went to see the original Foucault's pendulum at the Musée des Arts et Métiers. This was a few years before the ball crashed on the marble floor. My enthusiasm faded when I realized that several years before I had passed by this very pendulum without even noticing it. This time I hang around it for a while, watching the people walking by. Only a handful actually stop in front of it. They look at the pendulum for less than 15 seconds and continue hunting for more things they are supposed to see in the museum.

Later I went to the Louvre and the same thing happened. People stopped by each of the art pieces for just a second or two. If you've been in a museum lately you know what I mean. It's nothing new: the avalanche of images, the "must go to the Louvre when in Paris" pressure, and then, off to shop in its huge mall in the basement.

Something really interesting was happening the day I went to the Louvre to look at people rather than art. In one of the galleries I saw a student making a copy of a painting. People stopped for a long time,

ten, fifteen minutes, to watch her copy the painting. Practically no one stood by the real paintings that didn't have art students copying them for more than a few seconds. The adoration of the simulation? Or is it that people love action? After all, the painting is dead. The painter copying the painting is alive and moving.

On the other hand: Is the painting the real thing? If so, why are people more interested in the making of a copy?

I love going places where people I admire either lived or had a strong connection. "Being there" is a great source of inspiration for me. Today I'm writing these lines at Caffe del Commercianti on Strada Maggiore, Umberto Eco's favorite café in Bologna, where he taught for many years. I've come to test his theory that in Bologna they make the smallest most concentrated cup of espresso in the world. Eco wrote that "if you order a café ristreto in Bologna, all you get is a virtual coffee."

Alejandro Fogel, "Virtual ristretto in Bologna"

24

All of us at the UN

General Assembly are aware that the man speaking at the podium is not the real Che Guevara. We know that he is the actor Benicio del Toro playing Che. Behind him is a multimillion-dollar movie production that generates and amplifies the simulation. It is a simulation so real and powerful that it becomes reality; it becomes part of Che Guevara's history. For all of us in the room it is flesh and blood, it is the UN building, they are Che Guevara's words. For millions of people in the near future, sitting in front of movie screens and TV sets watching this film, it is going to be, at least during the projection, the best Che Guevara that ever was.

I entered the film dimension through a hole in time-space that was in Harvey Keitel's living room. I was asked to become Che Guevara's Argentinean dialect coach. In an ideal world I should have said no, of course, but I saw the job as a crucial part of this book. The Mother of all Simulations.

Baudrillard says that simulations have devoured reality and that replicas have taken precedence over real things. Simulations generate more simulations. The slow process of the simulation of life that started with ancient theater and literature has been accelerated exponentially in present times by mass media, becoming increasingly harder to separate or distinguish from reality in the public's perception. From films, to holograms, to video games, to high definition and virtual reality, people like spectacles better than reality, making simulation

more powerful than the real thing.

Dr. Nick Bostrom, director of the Future of Humanity Institute at Oxford, says it is mathematically certain that we live in someone else's computer simulation and we, all of us, are not really real.

As I write these lines, I google Ernesto Guevara New York City. I get one hit. There is an Ernesto Guevara alive today. He lives in Queens, across the river from where I live. He instantly becomes a character in this book. I go back to Baudrillard: "The simulation never conceals the truth. It is the truth that conceals that there is none. The simulation is true."

And then to Ezra Pound:

"We do not know the past in chronological sequence. It may be convenient to lay it out anesthetized on the table with dates posted on here and there, but what we know is by ripples and spirals eddying out from us and from our own time."

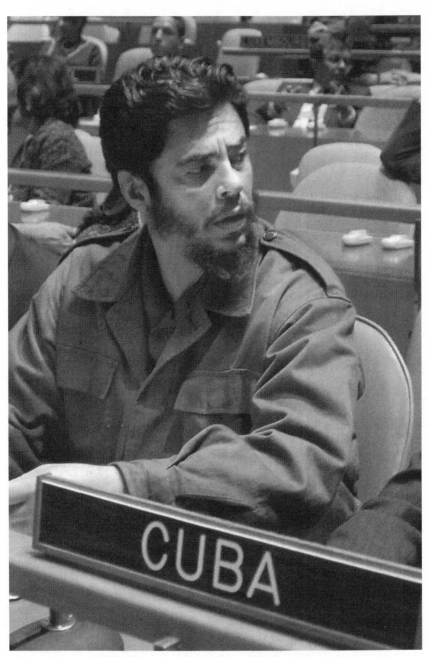

Alejandro Fogel, "One More Che Guevara"

25

My first memories of the Holocaust

came to me in the form of screams in the dark. They were my father's nightmares. I remember waking up in the middle of the night as his past was coming back to us, hearing my mother calming him down, and watching the shadows of the leaves of the enormous plane tree outside my window frantically moving through my room. I never asked my father about those dreams.

I was four when he first told me about running from the Nazis. It happened one day when I asked him about his petrified toenails. He was sitting on a chair in the living room of our Buenos Aires home with his feet in a pan of hot water. His toenails were different than mine. They were dark brown, bulbous as grapes and with the texture of petrified wood. I was very curious about them and began to ask questions. I was sitting on the floor looking at his feet soaking in a pan next to the kerosene heater. That was when he started to tell me his stories, and I began to understand his nightmares.

26

As I walk along the beach

on the island of Crete collecting sea shells, I keep thinking of spirals and labyrinths, and about Mar del Plata, a popular vacation beach town in Argentina. I remember listening to the sea inside the *caracoles*, nautilus shells that I picked up on the sand. I remember wondering how it could be possible for those shells to capture the sound of the sea and play it in my ear. I would listen to the waves inside the shell for a few moments, then listen to the sea directly and compare the two. There was the "live" sea and the "recorded" sea, side by side, overlapping in an eternal return of wave after wave after wave.

The nautilus shell I've just found is from Nea Hora, a beach on the northern coast of Crete. I'm walking on wet sand, the gentle waves lapping at my feet from time to time. The sun is about to set. I found two nautiluses today. When I saw the first one, I thought of the Minoan civilization and its famous labyrinth of the Minotaur. It's an easy connection, being in Crete where the Minoans, the oldest civilization in Europe, originated. Humans have been always fascinated by the labyrinth, especially its spiral shape. The spiral is an archetypal form imprinted deeply in our consciousness, perhaps because our DNA and the Milky Way, our galactic home, are spirals.

There is a web site from the Physics Department at the University of Wisconsin that shows two pictures side by side: a brain cell and a computer simulation of the universe. One is only a few micrometers wide, the other is billions of light-years across. Their patterns look so

similar.

From this human being's standpoint, the difference between the incommensurably minute shape of DNA and the incommensurably huge shape of our galaxy is just one more exercise of the imagination (barely a few electrical waves and brain cells interconnecting,) making sense inside the brain.

The second nautilus shell came into view several hours later as I kept thinking about summer and Mar del Plata. Each night I would ask my father to let me light the mosquito coil, a beautiful green spiral we would light to fight off the armies of mosquitoes. I loved the way the small orifice at the center of the spiral fit so beautifully in its metal base. The spiral seemed to float in the air, just a few inches above the little dish placed beneath it to collect the ashes. The next morning I'd always ask my mother not to wash the dish until I saw the spiral of ashes it left, the remnants of a galaxy that became extinct overnight. I can still feel the smell and the smoke of those burning spirals entering my nostrils, becoming one of my sharpest memories of childhood summers. I always asked for the mosquito spiral to be near my bed so when my parents shut off the light, I could see it burning, a small red dot from a galaxy glowing nearby or so far away. The brand name was Caracol. It means seashell in Spanish.

Finding the latest nautilus shell here, on a deserted beach in Crete, was like finding a Caracol spiral. A shell, a spiral, a labyrinth. The power of the shape and the color of things. I have a galaxy in the palm of my hand, spiraling out from its center outwards with beautiful regularity, the embodiment of nature's perfection and proportion: the golden ratio.

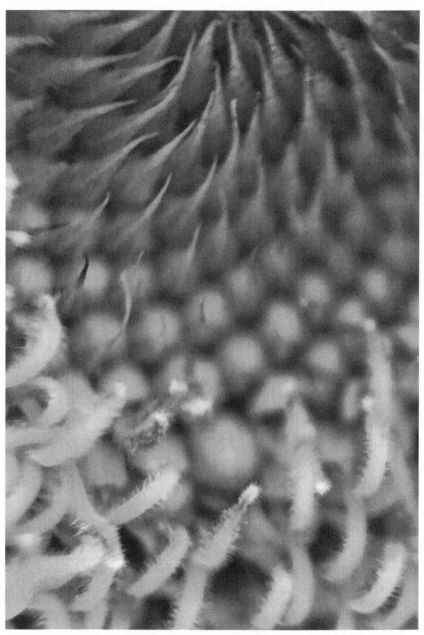

Alejandro Fogel, "Golden Ratio: Sunflower", series of 10 prints, Walmart Faux Photo Canvas, 11 by 14 in. Edition: 5 each

27

The first time I heard

about the golden ratio I was a teenager. My graphic design class was taught by a baldheaded chain smoker we called Jose Garra (Joe the Paw in English) because of his gigantic hands. I remember Jose Garra explaining the basis of the beauty of proportion in nature with his disproportionate hands. He would be juggling a burning cigarette in one hand and a piece of chalk in the other and becoming more and more excited about the knowledge he was about to pass on to us acne-ridden, gum-chewing teenagers.

He told us that the golden ratio is the ratio you obtain by dividing a line in such a way that the shorter section is to the longer section as the longer section is to the entire line. At this point everyone in the class was lost. He continued by saying that the longer section of the line is 1.618054 times longer than the shorter section. The shorter section is 0.618054 percent of the longer. I looked around the room and it seemed that we were all clueless.

Everything changed when he lit the next cigarette and offered an example. He said that a rectangle made with these proportions was the most pleasing shape known to man. He turned off the lights and started a slide show. He showed us pictures of paintings from Leonardo to Mondrian, different views of cathedrals from around the world, photos of historical monuments like the Parthenon, and how the golden ratio was used to create them all. But what really intrigued me was when he started showing pictures of nature--flowers, seeds,

shells--and demonstrated that the golden ratio proportions were there, too. They were a fundamental quality of the natural world, and part of the basic structure of the universe. He kept showing examples: fingerprints, tornadoes, DNA, the Milky Way.

I was stunned. At first, it looked like he was talking about some kind of esoteric, medieval theory, but when he drew on the blackboard a series of rectangles and squares within them, I saw it. A twirling spiral pattern that suggested it could go on forever. Then he connected a curve through the opposite corners of these concentric rectangles to form a golden spiral.

At this point Jose Garra had us all eating out of the palm of his extraordinary hand.

"The golden ratio is a very special relation between the whole and the part", he continued. "It has been in our consciousness forever," he announced.

He then asked his only question of the day: "Do you know why this phenomena occurs?" There was a long silence. His body projected a dark shadow, slightly softened by cigarette smoke, over a slide of the Coliseum. He waited a few moments and answered the question himself: "Nobody knows."

"*Nobody knows?*" I whispered as I looked around the class. "Is he implying that God exists? Or is he implying that God doesn't exist?" I wondered as Jose Garra and his magnificent paws left the classroom.

28

I fell asleep

watching *The Twilight Zone*. A huge explosion woke me. I opened my eyes to a room filled with the smokey blue light of the television screen. There was no programming in the middle of the night then, only blue static and a white steady noise. Many years later I learned that a portion of that static comes to us directly from the Big Bang. Nobel prize winners Arno Penzias and Robert Wilson discovered the phenomena by chance while installing an antenna in New Jersey. Here, in Buenos Aires, I had woken up to a live broadcast of the remnants of the beginning of the universe.

My parents and sister ran for cover as a second explosion rocked the building. This time I could also hear machine gun fire. It was a terrifying moment. But that was it. The rest of the night was very quiet. No ambulances nor police sirens. We never knew what happened, but it wasn't the Big Bang. The newspapers weren't reporting anything related to the war between the Argentinean military and the guerrillas. Bombs did not explode. People did not disappear. The war did not exist.

I went back to bed but I couldn't sleep. I opened my eyes and could only see the red light from my small green galaxy glowing in the dark.

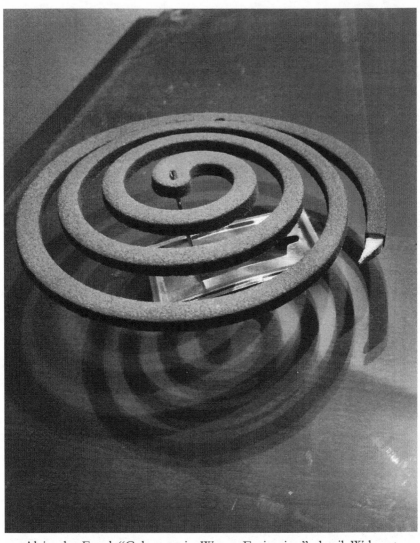

Alejandro Fogel, "Galaxy on its Way to Extinction", detail, Walmart
Faux Photo Canvas, 11 by 14 in. Edition: 10

29

Each time Shelley

and I took a trip abroad I'd call my parents and give them a contact number.

This time, we were going to Budapest. I called them. As we ended our brief conversation my Dad said:

"You know I lived there during the war when I was in hiding."

"You were in Hungary during the war?" I asked, surprised.

"I told you many times!" my Dad replied.

I wrote the address on a piece of paper, since every time he mentioned something about his life during the Holocaust, I quickly forgot it. All those stories about that time were stored somewhere in my brain, where they disappeared.

Shelley and I were having coffee with our friend Andras at Café Muvesz. In those days you could still smoke in public places in Budapest, and everyone was doing it with a vengeance. Muvesz had a great Bohemian atmosphere and the best pastries in town. As I took out my wallet to pay the bill, a scrap of paper fell out. It was my handwriting: "10 Rumbach Street," it said. And suddenly I remembered. I asked Andras if he knew where this street was. "Just a five-minute walk from here," he told me and pointed the way.

30

It took me 14 hours by car

to get from Sacel to Budapest. It took Moishe more than 2 weeks when he covered the same distance in 1941. He walked, rode horses, hopped trains. It was a scary trip for a 17-year old boy traveling alone, with no money, no ID, and who was constantly trying not to get captured. The police were rounding up Jews and sending them to labor camps. He finally reached Budapest and met someone who spoke Yiddish and helped him find a room in the heart of the Jewish ghetto.

Two years later, Moishe, hungry and exhausted, was arrested and put on a train to Auschwitz.

Standing here, in front of the building at 10 Rumbach Street where Moishe lived on and off between 1941 and 1943, I am my father and I have come back. We are so different, he and I, and at the same time we are the same person looking for our past. He could have been my son then, I think, as I watch the high school boys coming home from school.

Everything in Rumbach Street seems meaningful to me. The texture of the crumbling walls, the broken curb, the boarded up windows of the cellars, a piece of brick, the faint imprints of old shop signs that were taken away long ago. My father's building has a huge metal door and it is slightly open. I'm in the hallway looking up the dizzying spiral of stairs that leads to the apartments. The hallway has not been

painted for decades, the walls themselves are falling apart, a single bare light bulb swings from the ceiling and dimly lights the corridor.

I can see him in his room, a young man, my father before he was my father: shaving, sleeping, thinking. His voice is still here in 10 Rumbach Street.

I am speaking to the janitor in the courtyard of the building, hoping to find someone who knew my father then. She tells me that nobody from that time is left. "The last person who lived here in the 1940s died a few years ago," she says. She can't tell me much more. She confides that she knows some Jews lived in the building. When she pronounces the word "Jews" she lowers her voice.

The whispers of those trapped in the Budapest ghetto are still here. I can hear them on this run-down street and in the fragments of memory they left behind when they were taken away and never returned.

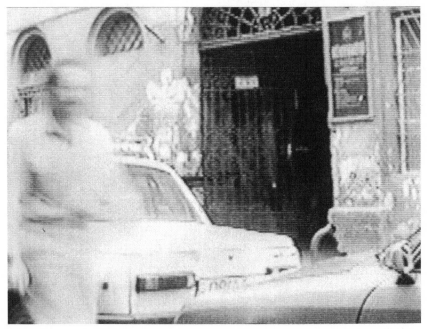

Alejandro Fogel, "Walking on Rumbach Street", video, 640 by 480, 1:15

Alejandro Fogel, "Root to Route", installation, partial view, at the
Ludwig Museum in Budapest (former Nazi Headquarters)

31

I was reading today

that researchers at Emory University's School of Medicine have determined that mice can pass on memories of traumatic experiences to subsequent generations. The rodents' brains show structural changes to their DNA caused by their reaction to a specific threat.

This genetic transformation is carried forth in the DNA of their descendants and is likely to affect their reactions to certain environmental or emotional stressors.

As I open *The Horse, the Wheel and Language* by David Anthony I read this:

"When you look in the mirror you see not just your face but a museum. Although your face, in one sense, is your own, it is composed of a collage of features you have inherited from your parents, grandparents, great-grandparents, and so on. The lips and eyes that either bother or please you are not yours alone but are also features of your ancestors, long dead perhaps as individuals but still very much alive as fragments in you.

Even complex qualities such as your sense of balance, musical abilities, shyness in crowds, or susceptibility to sickness have been lived before. We carry the past around with us all the time, and not just in our bodies. It lives also in our customs, including the way we speak. The past is a set of invisible lenses we wear constantly, and

through these we perceive the world and the world perceives us. We stand always on the shoulders of our ancestors, whether or not we look down to acknowledge them."

I place the four fingers of each of my hands on the table before me. I tap on it a few times. It is the same way my Dad used to tap and my uncle Yosef Shmil and my niece Naila. I wonder what else we are carrying with us, embedded in our ever-changing DNA?

32

It's my birthday and I'm celebrating

in Carlsbad, a mountain town in the Czech Republic famous for the healing properties of its thermal waters. I've come because my great grandfather, a Hassidic rabbi, spent his birthday here, too, only he was accompanied by other Hassidic rabbis. It was 1882 and they came to take the waters and discuss the Torah. The thermal baths haven't changed much since then. But Carlsbad has gone through a lot of political transformations: from belonging to the Austro-Hungarian Empire, to being occupied by Nazi Germany, to being part of Communist Czechoslovakia, which is now the democratic Czech Republic and a member of the European Union. My great grandfather and I are at opposite ends of this turbulent timeline. He saw the same grand buildings housing the baths as I do now. We both soaked in the same hot mineral waters. We both marveled at the beauty of the place.

My great grandfather had a clear purpose in coming to Carlsbad with his fellow rabbis. I can't help wondering about my own purpose in coming here, soaking in the thermal baths my great grandfather visited more than a century ago. I'm not trying to complete a family tree. I'm not on a linear quest from city to city in search of my roots nor do I care much about exact dates. I'm not trying to uncover a mystery.

As I'm thinking about why I'm following the footsteps of my family, I find a few clues in two books I brought with me: one by Martin

Buber and the other by Marshall McLuhan.

Buber tells the story of a Hassidic Jew who attended one of his lectures on moral philosophy: "It was obvious that the man did not understand a single word, but the way in which he received those words resembled the reactions of believers who do not need to know the content of a prayer since the arrangement of its sounds and rhythm give them more than any content could."

For McLuhan the medium is the content. He tells the story of a man in Africa who religiously tuned into the BBC every evening, even though he didn't understand a word of English. McLuhan wrote that "just to be in the presence of those sounds at 7 PM each day was enough for him."

33

Café Louvre is

in downtown Prague. The walls are pink, the window frames cream colored and the cigarette smoke is gray and thick. Being in this café is like being in a mountain cloud and reminds me of my journeys through the Andes. I used to climb mountain peaks just to be inside a cloud. I love the smell of clouds and the way colors change when you are inside them.

The view from Café Louvre is significantly different from the one I had up in the Andes. All I can see from the tall French windows is the reflection of a huge red Kmart sign on a glass building across the way.

I miss the Andes. They are so deeply imprinted in my mind that their presence comes back often and unexpectedly.

Franz Kafka sat here in Café Louvre in 1912 and inhaled a similar cloud of thick, gray smoke. I love Kafka's writings and I've been following his footsteps through Prague, his hometown, on and off for the last few years. I search for signs of him--a broken tile, a rusty pipe, a chunk of pavement that he might have seen and I am seeing now. There are tours that will take you to see the most significant places in Kafka's life for a fee. Two hundred Korunas will give you a glimpse of Kafka's Prague. For 350 Korunas they guarantee that you will see the cockroach. If you pay 3,500 you will become one for a day.

A few years ago I slept in Kafka's father's department store. It is a pension now and I just happened to be put up there by the university that invited me and Shelley to teach. On another visit, I went to the once grand building of the Worker's Accident Insurance Company, where Kafka worked for 22 years. The building was dilapidated, there were office chairs on the stairways and mountains of papers in every corner.

When I returned more recently, it had metamorphosized into a luxury hotel in the Mercure chain. Can you imagine? Just by a random cosmic act or due to a travel search engine algorithm, you could end up sleeping where Kafka's desk once stood.

This year I decide to visit his favorite café, the Louvre. I pick a good table by the window and order a Mattoni mineral water, bottled in Carlsbad. I sit back, wrapped in the tobacco fog, drinking the water from Carlsbad, enjoying the view of Kmart and the wonderful art deco building next to it and reading Kafka's correspondence to Max Brod.

Franz Kafka asked his life-long friend to burn all his writings after his death. Instead, Brod saved the manuscripts and later edited and published many of them including *The Trial*, *The Castle*, and *The Metamorphosis*. Max Brod took the last train out of Prague before the Nazis took over the city in 1939. With him he was carrying a suitcase full of Kafka's papers. He arrived in Tel Aviv a few weeks later. Until recently, all those papers were held by an old lady who had once been Brod's young secretary. She kept them in the cellar of her house on Spinoza Street, just a few miles from Bnei Brak where my father's youngest brother has his little shop selling Hassidic tschatkis and around the corner from the gallery that represented my paintings in Tel Aviv.

I'm sitting by Kafka's grave at the Straschnitz Cemetery in Prague. There is a modest tombstone with a cubist shape. The writing on the stone is in Hebrew and mentions his three sisters at the bottom:

Gabriele, Valerie and Ottilie.

Gabriele and Valerie are believed to have died in the Lodz ghetto. Ottilie perished in Auschwitz.

There were more than one hundred people crammed in a box car that could barely hold fifty. Moishe was standing over a dead body. An old man next to him was scratching the wall as he was slowly slipping to the floor. There was no air. In the middle of the night, Moishe was able to remove the bars covering the small window of the cattle car. He squeezed through and jumped out. The guards on top of this train bound for Auschwitz fired many times, but none of the bullets hit him. It was winter and he was running through snow fields somewhere between Czechoslovakia and Poland. This was where my father hid in the mountains and suffered frostbite on his feet, which turned his toenails bulbous and brown.

Alejandro Fogel, "Scratches in the Train VII", acrylic on cork, 20 by 17 in.

34

I'm at the Holocaust Museum

in Washington, DC. I'm inside of one the actual box cars used to transport people to Auschwitz. The ceiling height is about seven feet. The windows are 3 feet wide and 1 1/2 feet tall. There is a bar crossing the window leaving a space no more than a foot wide to squeeze through.

That's all I could do. Measure the space.

35

We never used my grandmother's

samovar, though it had a prominent spot in our house. I often sat close to it and observed my distorted reflection in the shiny silver surface. During the day the samovar reflected my plane tree outside the window. At night, sparkles of yellow from the overhead lamp made it look like it was gold. The blue glow from our black and white TV kept changing the reflection's shapes and shadows. The samovar was always present in one of my recurrent dreams as a child.

A spaceship lands late at night right across the street from my house. It is the shape and texture of a plane tree seed ball. The creatures that pilot it are coming for me and my girlfriend Graciela. They take us to the bar on the corner, tie us back-to-back in a chair and steal everything from the cash register.

In the dream, I could see everything happening to me in the bar while standing on a chair by the window in my bedroom. Down at the bar I was wearing my day clothes, short pants, and a beanie, while up in my room I was feeling the softness of my striped blue pajamas against my skin, a comforting sensation that made the scene in the bar look like just a bad dream.

The dream ends with the bar's fluorescent lights going into a flickering frenzy.

Ever since then, my memory of our family samovar is linked to that

spaceship-- a blue, black and white flickering object straight out of a 1960's TV series. Everyone in my family remembers the samovar and where it stood on a little table by the sofa.

I lived in the Abasto barrio of Buenos Aires, among the sons and daughters of Spanish and Italian immigrants. None of their families had samovars.

When my grandparents arrived in Buenos Aires about half of the population were foreigners. If you counted only the adults it went up to 70%. But the extraordinary number is that four out of five adult males were not born in Argentina.

Abasto was mysterious and scary sometimes. It got its name from the Mercado de Abasto, the main food distribution market of Buenos Aires, which was just a few blocks from my house. It was an elaborate 1930's Art Deco building occupying an entire block. Abandoned and decrepit for many years, it was bought recently by George Soros, the Hungarian immigrant turned billionaire power investor. He's turned it into one of the largest shopping malls in Argentina.

Alejandro Fogel, "Mercado de Abasto", monoprint of an online image of a photograph, Office Depot non-acid-free, 24 lb, 8 1/2 by 6 1/8 in.

36

I'm in Budapest at a party

given by symphony conductor Ivan Fischer, composer of the opera *The Red Heiffer*. The piece criticizes the anti-Semitic policies of the new ultra right-wing, nationalist government of Hungary.

It seems that a new era of persecution of Jews, homosexuals, and Gypsies has begun here in the second decade of the 21st century.

I'm sitting next to George Soros, famed billionaire businessman, philanthropist, and major benefactor of the Budapest Festival Orchestra. One word and Soros becomes a character in this book. I resist the temptation. He's being approached by countless people. My friend Kinga comes over to talk to him. I don't. It's so much better, at least for this book, that I am sitting next to George Soros and completely ignoring him.

In the early sixties, *el mercado* was a grey temple with interminable escalators like something out of an Escher drawing but with the aroma of fresh vegetables and fruit. I used to go there every week with my mother to buy groceries. We went really early in the morning to get the best produce. My mother was young and thin then and smelled like roses. She pushed *el changuito*, our little shopping cart on wheels, down the white marble stairs of our house on Calle Lavalle, and within a few minutes we could smell and hear the market. On our way there we went by piles of wooden crates full of produce, left on the curb at sunrise, by the truckers. They were usually sitting

on empty crates, their heads wrapped in colorful bandanas, drinking cheap wine and burping so outrageously loud that they elicited my deepest admiration. Their faces were unshaved, their clothes stained, and they always stared at my mother as we passed by.

I vividly remember the trucker's brightly painted trucks with their intricate arabesques of intertwined lines, images and words. The decorations, called *filetes*, became a tradition in Buenos Aires starting in the late 19th century. The artists were originally European immigrants who embellished their grey horse carts with garish paintings. By the mid 20th century many trucks and buses were painted similarly with flowers, animals, abstract designs and words usually referring to tango, love, pride, and misfortune. To me, these vehicles were a world of beauty and mystery that I discovered every Thursday when we went to the market.

Carlos Gardel's house was just across the street from the Abasto. He is the greatest tango singer of all times. People call him the "thrush of Abasto," "the mute," and "the smile that sings." A popular saying in Argentina is that "he sings better every day," even though he's been dead almost a century. Lots of truckers have Gardel's picture prominently displayed inside their cabins. For many people even now Gardel is more than a fantastic tango singer; he is a kind of saint they pray to and invoke. He died in a plane crash when he was only in his forties, which probably made him even more famous. Gardel grew up in poverty, with little education, working odd jobs until he was eighteen, when he discovered tango music and started singing. He is still a popular symbol of achievement. In Argentina when you do something really good for a friend or your community you *are* Gardel.

To me growing up, this "immortal" tango singer was a thing of the past. I knew some of his songs by heart since they were on the radio all the time, but that was about it. Gardel didn't even exist for my father. He grew up in a different world and, inexplicably, managed to stay there.

Moishe's world was one of rabbis and yeshivas with no electricity or running water. He witnessed a man landing on the Moon and owned a cell phone, but even in old age he was still the 17-year old Hassidic boy leaving medieval Transylvania. He was a man of contradictions. A man who believed in his religion, but at the same time defied it by putting on a disguise and eating pork chops incognito at a local restaurant after synagogue. A man who could encapsulate a crucial decade of life in a one-minute story or take a full hour to describe a brief encounter. He believed in destiny. A powerful force took him from Europe to Bolivia, where he managed to cross the border to Argentina, travel a thousand miles by train, and settle for a few months in a small town called Moises Ville, two hundred miles north of Buenos Aires, where he would finally settle.

It was in Moises Ville that he learned the invaluable secret he revealed to me when I was a child.

Alejandro Fogel, "Carlos Gardel", monoprint of an online image of a photograph, Office Depot Laser Print Paper non-acid-free, 24 lb, 8 1/2 by 6 1/8 in.

37

I arrived at La Higuera

the town where Che was executed, after a fourteen-hour road trip from La Paz, with a brief stop in Vallegrande, the town where his corpse was exhibited to the public. As with my father's hometown Sacel, I've been fantasizing about going to La Higuera for a long time. While Sacel was much larger than what I imagined, La Higuera was so much smaller that it almost isn't there. You can walk through its only street in just a few minutes. There are about twenty houses where 120 people live. The place is as deserted as when Che Guevara was imprisoned here half a century ago.

No one is on the street this afternoon. The heat is unbearable. When Che was captured by Bolivian soldiers in the jungle outside town, he was held at La Higuera's little school house. That's where the car I hired in Vallegrande left me. I knock but there is no answer. I try the door. It's open. The school house is a small room with some books and a few photos of Che and his comrades before they were caught. This is the moment when imagination becomes reality. I imagined this school house for years. I saw pictures of it taken at different times, but the fact that I'm actually under its roof makes me feel like I have closed a circle. Che Guevara was executed here. This is where his physical life ended and the myth of Che began.

A few houses away, there is a little market called *La Estrella*, The Star. There is a big poster of Che Guevara behind the counter where an old lady stands. I want to drink bottled water but she only has Coca-

Cola. As I drink my hot Coca-Cola, I ask her how long she's been working there. She says that if I'm wondering if she was here when they brought Che to the school, the answer is yes. Her name is Irma and she informs me that she cooked Che's last meal before he was executed: empanadas and eggs. She says that he is a saint. She prays to his poster every day and lights candles for him. She says that Che always helps her. She is now praying to him to bring electricity to town.

It feels unreal that I'm talking to someone in La Higuera who actually met him. "Che was very sad that day," Irma says. "He was very dirty and smelled bad. He thanked me for the food, and I left."

Irma tells me that wasn't the only time she saw Che Guevara. He came to visit with his comrades the day the town was celebrating a religious festival, a couple of weeks before he was killed. The guerrilla group danced, ate pork and drank liquor. Irma tells me more about La Higuera then, which doesn't sound much different than La Higuera now.

I'm about to leave, when she surprises me and asks for money. It turns out she charges for talking about Che. I pay her in Bolivianos. I say *"Wuaslegia, Sarjak"*. Both words mean good bye. The first one in Quechua and the second in Aymará, the two main indigenous languages of Bolivia. She responds with a *"Jajuechapeve"*. My Quechua and Aymará are non-existant so I ask what *"Jajuechapeve"* means.

"It means good bye in Guarani. I'm Guarani," she informs me. I tell her that I thought that the Guarani people only lived in neighboring Paraguay. She says that the borders created by the whites are fake. Her people always lived along a stretch of land covering Paraguay and South Eastern Bolivia. She is absolutely right. The artificial divisions created by the Spaniards over the centuries don't make much sense. When geographical conditions permit, the indigenous peoples of South America tend to ignore them.

I don't know much about the Guarani, except that they are credited with being the first to harvest and consume *yerba mate*, the herb used to make the favorite drink of Moishe, Ernesto, and me.

Alejandro Fogel, "Che drinking mate", monoprint of an online image of a photograph, Office Depot Laser Print Paper non-acid-free, 24 lb, 8 1/2 by 6 1/8 in.

38

When I was 10 years old

Moishe revealed to me the secret to making the perfect *mate* (pronounced MAH-teh).

Mate is a kind of herb tea that many Argentineans can't live without--much like the British feel about their black tea or Italians about coffee.

The traditional way to prepare mate is to put the dried *yerba* in a hollowed-out gourd, pour hot water over it and drink it through a filtering metal straw.

Mate tastes pleasantly bitter and smokey, like wood fire and pampas and spring. Another way to describe its taste is to imagine green tea mixed with coffee and a pinch of tobacco. Moishe loved it. He started drinking it as soon as he arrived in Moises Ville.

He was the one who prepared it for our family.

He filled the tea kettle with water and put it to boil on the stove. He filled the gourd half way with the green, straw-like yerba and gently he shook it, holding his hand cupped over the top so none of the mate would spill out. Then he put the *bombilla*, a metal drinking straw, in the gourd and stirred. He waited patiently for the water to heat to the perfect temperature for mate, that is, just before boiling, and poured it over the yerba. Moishe would always drink the first few rounds, which were the overly bitter ones, then he'd pour more

water over the mate and pass the gourd to my mother to drink. The last sips, weak but delicious, were reserved for me until I was ten and considered old enough to handle mate full strength.

Moishe's secret for making perfect mate was to add an extra bit of warm water to the yerba right before serving it. He said this "awakened" the natural flavor of the yerba.

He learned this precious secret that he passed down to me in Moises Ville, where he spent his first few weeks in Argentina as an illegal immigrant.

He claimed that his mate teachers were the famous Jewish Gauchos, who lived there.

Moises Ville was a large parcel of land bought by Baron Hirsch in 1889 for Eastern European Jews to escape the virulent anti-semitism of the Pale. Hirsch believed they would be better off becoming farmers in the New World than staying with their traditional city trades.

In the 1950's, when Moishe landed in Moises Ville, 4,500 Jews lived there and made up 90% of the population.

Two hundred miles from Buenos Aires, in the middle of nowhere, there was a thriving Jewish town with a synagogue, Hebrew school, and a kosher butcher and bakery.

It was in Moises Ville that my father was introduced to the man who would provide him with a fake Argentinean National ID card, the same ID card he'd use to marry my mother a few years later.

Moishe always said that the most exquisite combination is to drink mate with potato knishes.

Only 200 Jews live in Moises Ville now.

Moishe Fogel's fake Argentinean National ID card

39

In Argentina

I used to drink what we call *mate cocido*, or "cooked" mate, every day at school. It is a watered-down mate infusion sometimes mixed with milk and sugar and served in a glass. But honestly, for me and most real mate drinkers, the true experience comes when you drink it in a gourd, through a straw, and certainly without sugar and milk. The "ceremony" of drinking mate is a communal experience, something you do with family or friends. The gourd is passed around several times and everyone drinks from it.

Shelley can't stand it (even with milk and sugar). "I guess you have to grow up with it to like it," she laughs making a face, "it's so bitter".

I associate mate with rainy afternoons after school and with all-nighters studying for university exams and later on with long sessions painting my canvases.

On Sundays we had mate in the morning with fugacitas, white rolls, piping hot from the bakery across the street, topped with a little butter, and one or two anchovies. In the afternoon we had mate with *medialunas*, those small slightly heavy Argentinean versions of the croissant. On Saturday mornings my father usually made mate for himself before going to work as a cantor at the synagogue and again afterwards with my mother and me, when he returned home. For Passover we had mate with matzoh.

I wanted to know where mate came from, what its story was. Moishe didn't know. I asked my mother and my teacher; they didn't know either.

Years later, just after completing my military service, I decided on a whim to go to the Buenos Aires bus station and take the first bus out of the city and get off at the last stop.

This was my first trip to the Andes, and for me it was as remote and far away as the Himalayas. I knew absolutely nothing about the interior of Argentina. There were only vague references to it from my teachers, who dedicated as little time as possible discussing the original inhabitants of our hemisphere, mixing Mayas, Incas, and Aztecs in the same salad bowl. Their references were always about the aborigines of "the Latin American countries." They did not include Argentina in this category, because Argentina was obviously part of Europe.

That sleepy afternoon I arrived in Catamarca in the Northwest region of Argentina was a turning point in my life. There was somewhere else in Argentina besides Buenos Aires.

And finally I learned where mate came from.

Che Guevara's father owned a yerba mate plantation. Che, himself, traveled with his mate on all his missions. There is a great picture of him bare chested drinking from a mate gourd in the jungle.

If you google yerba mate, you'll find out that it is great for sleeping, staying awake, soothing indigestion, suppressing hunger, and curing cancer.

The history of yerba mate, like that of coffee, is tainted with exploitation and slavery.

Guarani Indians were forced to open long paths through the rainforest to facilitate the lucrative trade of yerba.

Long before the conquistadores adopted the habit, mate was drunk by the Guarani Indians as part of their sacred rituals. They considered it a gift from the gods. Poor people still drink it as an appetite suppressant to "trick the stomach" so they can survive their meager diet. Yerba mate was a kind of currency throughout the 20,000 miles of the Inca Empire's road system. Now it is only consumed in a relatively small part of South America that includes Paraguay, Argentina, Uruguay and Southern Brazil.

With its grassy, smokey taste and aroma, people say that drinking mate is like drinking the jungle itself.

I didn't know then that getting to Catamarca was just the beginning. That I was going to walk a very long road throughout the Incas Road for the next eight years.

Alejandro Fogel, "Incas Road Fragment", detail, mixed media: yerba mate, ceramics, dirt on canvas, 9 ft by 3 ft.

40

I'm standing at the corner

of Calle Fogel and Boulevard Almirante Brown in the city of Puerto Madryn in Patagonia. I have an open view of the Atlantic Ocean, just 100 yards away. It's sunny, windy and warm. I've come here for the opening of my work at a local gallery and decided to spend a few days exploring the area.

I'm staying with friends of friends. They picked me up at the airport and took me directly to their house on Calle Fogel.

Fogel! A long lost relative? My hosts don't know. They make a couple of phone calls to local history buffs and find out that their street is actually named after Chief Fogel, a 19th century local tribal leader. Fogel in this case is a Mapuche word.

I came here to show a series of my paintings very much influenced by the indigenous cultures of Argentina. I end up staying on a street named Fogel, in honor of a Mapuche tribal chief who shares my last name.

Coincidence: A remarkable concurrence of events or circumstances.

Synchronicity: a meaningful coincidence of events that seem related but are not explained by conventional mechanisms of causality.

I wish my students were here. After this week's events, the synchronicity between Chief Fogel, a Mapuche from Patagonia, and Alejandro

Fogel, the son of a Jew from Transylvania, empirically proves the existence of Carl Jung's theory of the collective unconscious.

According to Jung, the collective unconscious is an inherited knowledge that all humans are born with. The collective unconscious is entered when the human mind departs from its individuality and becomes part of and shares in the unconscious mind of mankind. As collective knowledge is shared, meaningful "coincidences" occur. Jung called these events "synchronous" and the theory of synchronicity was born.

Standing on this corner, in the immensity and emptiness of Patagonia I feel like the character in Borges' "The Aleph". He enters a dark basement in Buenos Aires and sees the Aleph, a singular point in the cosmos where everything material and immaterial converges.

I feel as though Chief Fogel and I are sharing a tiny space in the universe, where everything comes together at the same time from all angles, courtesy of synchronicity. I didn't know then that our paths had also crossed once before, in the center of Buenos Aires inside the Patricios 1st Infantry Regiment, a military compound.

Alejandro Fogel, "Chief Fogel", monoprint of an online image of a photograph, ·
Office Depot Laser Print Paper non-acid-free, 24 lb, 8 1/2 x by 6 1/8 in.

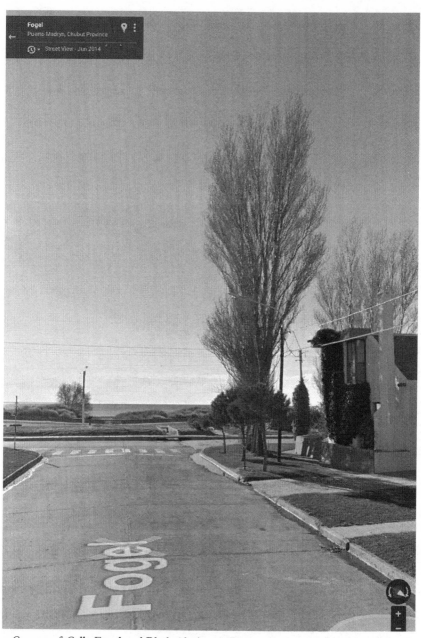

Corner of Calle Fogel and Blvd. Almirante Brown, Puerto Madryn, Argentina.
Google Street View: -42.778303, -65.021807

41

I'm following Borges. Again.

He is heading towards Recoleta, an elegant neighborhood known for its cemetery, with its elaborate marble mausoleums and famous corpses. The black granite tomb of Evita Perón, beloved wife of President Perón, is there among those of the wealthiest and most influential people in Argentina's history.

In the mid-1940s, when General Juan Domingo Perón became President of Argentina and Evita his right hand, Borges was fired from his post as Director of the National Library. He was demoted to "Inspector of Chickens and Rabbits" for a municipal market in the city of Buenos Aires. The Peróns wanted to humiliate Borges for his outspoken condemnation of their ideas.

Perón had waited to declare war on Japan and Germany until it was a sure thing that they were going to lose, which was just a few months before they surrendered to the Allies. In the aftermath of World War II, Perón secretly welcomed more than 9,000 Nazi war criminals to settle in Argentina.

In 1980 former Nazi Klaus Barbie helped the Argentinean military in a very special mission.

42

After being out-of-touch

for a long time I called my cousin Adriana who lives in Buenos Aires. She's a Gestalt psychotherapist, the daughter of my mother's brother, Shloime. Of course, she wanted to know what I was up to. I told her about this book and she asked if I could send her some pages to read. I did and I got an email back from her telling me that she was stunned. It turns out that just a week before I sent her my excerpt, she decided to start reading fiction again after years of reading nothing but books for her profession. She climbed up a ladder and picked up the first book that caught her eye. It was a book she'd read as a teenager, and it contained Jorge Luis Borges' "The Aleph."

Gestalt is about treating and alleviating the patients' symptoms but it also is about developing the individual's potential. It focuses on process rather than content. It is about awareness and experiencing the present moment.

Over the years Adriana has been integrating different Gestalt methods to create her own.

Adriana studied with the woman who introduced Gestalt therapy to Argentina in the 1970s, Florinda Glocer, who also happens to be my our cousin.

Argentina has the highest concentration of psychologists per capita in the world. There is even a neighborhood in Buenos Aires called

Villa Freud where most of the analysts live and work. Sigmund Freud himself would have been amazed by the proliferation of his theories in such a remote place. The first and only time he visited the Americas was at the beginning of the 20th century on a trip to the United States with Carl Jung.

During their stay at Hotel Manhattan in New York City on the corner of 42nd and Madison Avenue, on a particularly hot summer's night, Jung had a revelatory dream.

A century later I stood at that corner thinking about his dream.

43

I have to confess

that Borges wasn't the first person I ever followed. This activity has been a lifelong passion of mine. Borges was actually in my third wave of "following" people. The first period was when I was a child. I started following people in our neighborhood assisted by my friend Raúl. It was our main job on weekends. We followed them at random for hours at a time. Like detectives, we took elaborate notes of their itineraries and the clothes they wore; and we imagined their lives. At the end of the day we would have *café con leche* and review our findings.

The second wave of following people took place in my late teens just before the beginning of the Dirty War. This time my partner was Eduardo, my friend from high school. We published a Surrealist magazine called *The Lie*. Following people without them knowing it was part of our duties for the magazine as "conceptual reporters." We selected our victims at random and tailed them over time. We recorded their itineraries and "helped" them to discover an object we planted in their way. The object was usually a wallet with some money in it. Unbeknownst to them, each of our victims was released from surveillance the day they found and took the wallet, which was their reward for allowing us to see into one angle of the Aleph through a fragment of their lives.

In confronting Borges I did the unthinkable: I let the subject know I was following him.

44

Before he had a street

named after him, Chief Fogel had vast tribal territories south of the Nahuel Huapi Lake in Patagonia, where 30,000 indigenous people lived at the end of the 19th century. He was a great hunter and a master of the *boleadoras*, a lasso with wooden balls on the ends. The gauchos used it to catch cattle or wild game. Chief Fogel had better relations with the white men than any of the other local chiefs at the time. But he was finally betrayed by the whites and put in prison, so colonists would have less interference robbing the Indians of their land. They took the chief away from Patagonia and incarcerated him in an army garrison at the Patricios 1st Infantry Regiment in Buenos Aires. A century later, after refusing to be drafted and hiding out, I was caught by the military police, put in the same regiment, and forced to serve in the army.

Dario Bedne was also in the Patricios 1st Infantry Regiment. Dario and I were born just three months apart. We were friends from childhood. We lived in the same neighborhood, went to the same grade school, and enrolled in the same university in the same Faculty of Philosophy and Literature.

Very early on the morning of July 20, 1976 he went to Patricios. One of the soldiers standing guard at the main gate confirmed that he reported for duty. We never saw or heard from him again. He was "transferred" by the army.

From Marguerite Feitlowitz's *A Lexicon of Terror*:

Trasladar (v. To transfer, to move). To take prisoners away to be killed.

Traslado/a (n. Transfer). *Trasladado/a* (n. One who had been transferred, one who was a transfer, one who had "got his ticket").

Chief Fogel spent a year in prison at the 1st Regiment. He was then moved to the Museum of Natural History of La Plata to become an anthropological exhibition. His children were taken from him and "adopted" by Argentine families, who made them indentured servants (basically slaves), working as carpenters and locksmiths. His wife was forced to perform her traditional weaving in front of an audience every day. She, too, became part of the ethnological collection of the museum.

Darío Oscar Bedne
20-7-76

Dario Oscar Bedne, disappeared July 20, 1976

155

45

Something happened to Madonna

after starring in the film *Evita*. She came back to Manhattan and had some kind of religious epiphany. She named her new born daughter Lourdes, after the town in France where the Virgin Mary appeared to a young girl. And she joined a religious corporation, The Kabbalah Center International.

Brooklyn Life Insurance agent, Feivel Gruberberg went to Jerusalem to sell policies. There he met Rizka, the daughter of a famous Kabbalist, Rabbi Yehuda Branwein. They married and had eight children. Business was good. Feivel started an affair with his secretary, Karen, and the Kabbalist Rabbi died. Soon after, Feivel left his wife and children and ran off to Brooklyn with the secretary. He changed his name to Philip Berg and proclaimed himself "the world's foremost authority on Kabbalah." A Kabbalist by osmosis.

Berg proceeded to found the first Kabbalistic corporation in history. He owns one of the most coveted domains in the industry: kabbalah. com. If you google "Kabbalah" the first thing you see at the top of the search results is an ad for the Kabbalah Center directing you to their headquarters at 155 East 48th Street in New York City, a few blocks from the United Nations.

According to tradition, the practice of The Kabbalah started in the 10th century BCE. It quickly came to be practiced by more than one million people in the land of Canaan. But Jewish leaders soon closed

I'm going down

in an elevator. The digital display is counting years instead of floors. It stops on 12 BCE. The doors open to a large, dimly lit area, where I get off at the ancient city of Barcino. It is in ruins. There is no water running through the sewage system below my feet. The winery across the street is dry as bones. I wonder what and how long it took for this city to get buried so deep. People now live their lives 16 feet above us. They are in the 21st century, in the city of Barcelona. All the generations in between are of course gone and buried, making up the layers that separate the two cities. Dust, bones, and ashes separating these two realities.

Barcino was founded as a Roman colony in the first century BCE during the reign of Emperor Augustus. For the inhabitants of Barcino, Augustus was the potentate living in Rome. For the inhabitants of today's Barcelona sitting in front of their TV sets, Augustus is a group of electrons on an epic TV series called *Rome*.

The Romans built a temple in honor of Augustus on Mount Taber, right in the center of present day; modern Barcelona. Surprisingly the four columns of that temple are still standing in a medieval courtyard on Carrer del Paradiso. The columns are just a few hundred yards from Barcino but they seem much farther away. Barcino is underground but the ruins of the temple are still at the top of Mount Taber, where the temple was originally built. Mount Taber today is just an elevated street in a busy city that I must walk down to get to Las Ramblas, the

tree lined boulevard that runs through central Barcelona.

From street vendors selling the strangest birds to the best pick pockets in the Western Hemisphere and the most elaborate living statues, Las Ramblas is full of surprises. The name comes from the Arabic *raml*, which means "stream" in English, because the streets follow a stream that used to be there, before the 14th century. I wonder if there is anything left from Barcino below Las Ramblas?

My favorite café in Barcelona, Café L'Opera, is here. As I was walking there to have a coffee, I stopped cold when I saw Che Guevara standing at the corner.

He was in the middle of Las Ramblas haranguing a herd of tourists:

"En todos los lugares del mundo, el imperialismo trata de imponer su versión de lo que debe ser la coexistencia…" "Everywhere in the world imperialism tries to impose its version of how we should coexist… Only the oppresed masses, in alliance with the Socialist countries, are the ones that could teach us the real way to coexist. It is the obligation of the United Nations to support them…"

It seems that I have a magnet for fake Che Guevaras. Che is perched on a small platform. His guerrilla uniform is impeccable. He is one of Las Rambla's most popular living statues. After a few minutes he stops his speech and freezes his gaze on the horizon. Onlookers clap enthusiastically. I take out a one Euro coin and deposit it reverentially on the revolutionary beret by his feet to get him to resume his speech. Magically, a loudspeaker at his side goes on, and Che dubs Che.

His name is Rubén Pérez, he is Argentinean and one of the highest grossing statues in Spain. He reluctantly talked with me after I put five Euros in his beret. He says that he is on a mission to spread Che's message around the world. He goes to living statues conventions all over the world and promotes anything Che Guevara. I tell him about this book. He loves the idea. He offers to sell it on the streets of

Barcelona for a small fee.

We salute each other with a raised fist and I continue my trip over the ancient stream that was Las Ramblas. I walk towards the sea. After a few minutes I'm standing inside the infamous Admiral's gigantic body.

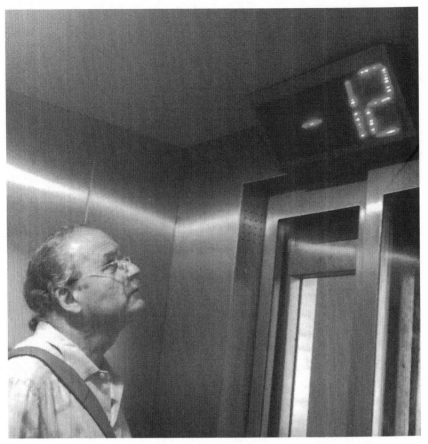

Alejandro Fogel, "Elevator to Barcino", video, 1080p, 0:24

48

I've been in Bolivia

for the last two weeks. As I leave Vallegrande, I meet Luis Lara, a Mojeño activist. We were both drinking water from a fountain across from Che's memorial monument. Luis tells me that he is on his way home after a long trip to Buenos Aires for an Indigenous Peoples Conference. Home is the Beni forest north of here. He kindly offers to give me a ride in his jeep to catch the bus to my next stop.

"We went from being "Indians" to "campesinos" to "indigenous people." What are they going to call us next?" he says.

Luis tells me that the Mojeños started a movement to completely separate from the White and Mestizo civilizations identified with the Conquista. They are in search of the "Holy Hill," the equivalent of Paradise in western civilization. Their aim is to recover the land that has been illegaly taken from them by the Bolivian state. "We want total separation and to be left alone. We don't want to be part of the political process. We leave that to our Quechua and Aymará brothers." We rode in silence for a while. As we reach the bus station Luis offers to help me buy a ticket since nobody speaks Spanish here, only Quechua or Aymará. I tell him that I took some lessons in Quechua before coming to Bolivia. He smiles and comes with me anyways.

The Quechua and Aymará are the largest indigenous groups in Bolivia. Quechua was the official language of the Incas and the

language of commerce along the entire Incas Road. Everybody in the Inca Empire spoke Quechua as well as their own mother tongue. At the bus station everyone is Aymará. The women have their hair in two long braids and wear bowler hats, fringed shawls, and many-layered red and blue pleated skirts. Some of them are sitting on the ground selling produce, garlic, lemons, and purple potatoes.

The Aymará were the first people to cultivate potatoes. They developed more than two hundred varieties and grew them at elevations over 10,000 feet.

After the Aymará were incorporated into the Inca Empire, potatoes became a major influence on the Inca culture. Inca units of time came to be correlated to how long it took for a potato to cook to various consistencies: soft, medium, or barely cooked. Potatoes were even used to predict the weather.

The men are in the bus station's bar. Most of them wear jeans and sneakers but some are wearing hand woven alpaca ponchos with green, yellow, and brown tassels. They are all drinking El Inca, a very sweet low-alcohol beer (not to be confused with Inca Cola, the most popular soda in Peru). I'm sitting at a table waiting for the bus and having something to eat. The waiter speaks a little Spanish and helps me decide on a meal. I'm having a *pique macho*--grilled chunks of llama with tomatoes and onions, served over potatoes. There is a heated discussion going on at the table next to me. I don't know what it is about, but the rhythm of speech accelerates, and the exchange of words and movement becomes a musical event.

The first time I learned there was an Aymará language was in an article in the *New York Times* about Iván Guzmán de Rojas. He is a Bolivian computer scientist, who converted Aymará into an algebraic code and pronounced it a "perfect language." As I researched the subject I found out that many scientists consider Aymará a "protolanguage" or one of the first languages from which all of humanity's 5,000 languages ultimately came. It looks like Aymará hasn't changed

since its creation, somewhere between 4,000 and 11,000 years ago, depending on who you ask. The word Aymará literally means "people from ancient times", and they call their language *Jaqui Aru* or "human language".

My llama arrived. My grilled llama that is. It smells exquisite.

As I chew on my llama, I think that the two people arguing next to me look so much like Tibetans. There are two main theories about the origin of the ancient peoples of the Americas: either they walked from Siberia to Alaska over a frozen Bering Strait, or they sailed in small boats across the seas from Polynesia. There is no mention of Tibet, although Bolivia is considered the "Tibet of South America" for its high and remote mountain geography and isolated native culture, the Aymará. The Aymará consider themselves the direct descendants of the builders of Tiahuanaco, my next stop. The waiter tells me not to worry about my two neighbors. They are just fighting about what costumes their children are going to wear for the centuries-old *Pasantes* festival.

I didn't know then that two weeks later and 1,700 miles south, I was going to personally participate in one of these festivals.

49

It all started when

my Dad gave me an encyclopedia. In it was a picture of one of Jackson Pollock's paintings from his drip period. I had never seen anything like it. To say it was a revelation is not an exaggeration. I wanted to paint. I wanted to paint my own Pollocks. So I did.

I was nine years old. I remember spending that hot summer afternoon on the roof of our house in Buenos Aires, painting with inks of various colors on large sheets of paper taped to the floor.

That day I completed several pieces and hung them on the clothesline. I sat on the floor and spent the end of the day admiring my work. At dark, the hanging paintings seemed to turn metallic against the starry sky. One of the stars, coming out from behind my pieces, was moving much faster than the rest. My eyes left the clothesline and kept following it. It was magical, a lone star moving across the sky. It took several minutes for it to finally disappear from sight.

That night, while my Mom was making dinner, I saw on TV that this wandering star was actually the American spacecraft *Gemini*, crossing the Southern skies on its orbit around the Earth.

50

General Juan Perón

is sitting down having a coffee. He wears a very elegant white jacket, a black bow tie and a charming smile. He is politely posing for a photograph with an excited Australian tourist. She is sitting on his lap with an arm around his shoulder, eying his famous onyx ring. The General is holding up his cup as if asking for another espresso. Two minutes later, a young man sits down next to Perón and talks to him while the staff photographer snaps another picture. Countless people come every day to sit at Perón's table and have a coffee with El General.

The place is called Un Café con Perón, a fancy coffee shop in the Recoleta neighborhood. It is located in the palace where Perón lived for much of his presidency and where Evita died in 1952. People say that sometimes you can still smell Evita's perfume in there. One employee confirms recent Evita sightings: she was seen sitting at the bottom of the main staircase, behind the curtain of a window on the second floor, reclining on a bench in the garden.

My friend Sergio is standing behind the photographer, acting as my reporter. He's giving me live coverage from the café via Skype on his cellphone. I'm in New York, but I get to see the parade of people taking their picture with Perón on my computer. The video is a bit blurry and pixelated, but it is exactly what I want.

Sergio is my childhood friend. We met the first day of grade

school and we remained friends ever since. We went to the Talmud Torah Horischono y Dr. Herzl School together. In the morning we learned the regular Argentinean curriculum in Spanish, and in the afternoon we studied Yiddish and Hebrew. We both hated it. We had to spent our entire day in school and there was no time to play.

Sergio is now interviewing the waiters for me. He tells me that Fernando Pugliese is the artist who created Perón's statue for the café. Sergio talks to the waiter while holding the cellphone facing Perón. "Fernando Pugliese is currently in Jerusalem and I'm going to interview him for you," Sergio says. "This is enough, Sergio," I tell him. "I don't need to talk to him." Sergio faces the camera and says: "You must talk to him. I'm going to Jerusalem right now." And with those words he hangs up the phone.

51

I am in the perfect position
to see what Christopher Columbus sees.

It took me a while to get here. From Café L'Opera I took Las Ramblas and walked almost all the way down to the sea where I found a circular platform surrounding a very tall metal column. I went inside the column, took an elevator, and 150 feet later, I find myself in this small room, the Mirador, from which I can see the Mediterranean. I'm just below Columbus's head. The Admiral is pointing to the sea. The tourist brochure says that he's pointing to the *nuevo mundo*. But if my geography is correct, he is pointing towards Italy. The statue was inaugurated in 1888 for the Universal Exhibition in Barcelona.

In the 19th century, Catalans considered Columbus to be one of their own. The statue was placed at the site where he arrived in 1493 from his famous trip to the New World and met with the Catholic Monarchs, Fernando and Isabel. Cristóbal Colón, as he was called when I was a child, changed his name a few times depending on which fundraising trip he was on. At the Dr. Herzl School, I was taught that he was born Cristoforo Colombo in the Republic of Genoa, Italy.

But Spain insists that Cristóbal Colón was born in the Spanish region of Pontevedra, 1,100 miles east of Genoa. We are not talking about the next town over. There is a serious distance between these two places. Not only that, Spain says that his father was Domingo Colón, a wool trader, while Italy claims that his father was Domenico Colombo, a watchtower sentinel. But then comes Portugal saying that Columbus was a pseudonym. They say that his real name was

Salvador Fernandez Zanco, son of Fernando, Duke of Beja and that he was born in the town of Cuba, in the Alentejo region of Portugal.

When I was a child I read an article in the Argentinean Yiddish paper *Di Idische Zeitung* claiming that Colón was a Jew. I dismissed it at the time, of course, since I was taught he was an Italian Catholic, but there are some major scholars saying that he could have been Italian, Spanish, Portuguese, whatever, but ultimately he was a *Marrano*, a converted Jew.

The term Marrano comes from "pig" in Spanish, a pejorative term used during the Inqusition to refer to Jews who practiced Judaism in secret while claiming they had converted to Catholicism. Thousands of Marranos were burned at the stake by the Grand Inquisitor Torquemada in the years before the Jews were expelled from Spain. The deadline set by the Inquisition for all the Jews and Muslims to leave Spain was July 31, 1492, just two days before Cristóbal Colón set sail for his trip to America.

The dialect the Spanish Jews used at the time of their expulsion is called Ladino. The language is a mix of old Castillian and an archaic dialect of Hebrew and Aramaic words. More than 500 years later, Ladino was the common language I spoke with my Turkish students in Istanbul.

Isabel (not the Catholic Monarch but my teaching assistant in Barcelona) is the one I should blame for getting me this ticket to visit the Columbus statue. The same day at the flea market she bought me an old edition of the *Apologetic History of the Indies* by Bartolome de las Casas, a 16th century priest and editor of Columbus' diaries.

I opened the book at random and read that when de las Casas arrived on Hispaniola, where Columbus established the first European colony in 1508, "there were 60,000 people living on this island, including the Indians; so that from 1494 to 1508, over 3 million people had perished from war, slavery, and the mines. Who in future generations

will believe this? I myself writing it as a knowledgeable eyewitness can hardly believe it...."

The 21st century brought another generation of Conquistadors to Latin America: the Spanish corporations. The new conquistadors were Repsol, Telefonica, Endesa and other multinationals. They purchased local oil, communications and energy companies from the state for much less than their real value in exchange for their promise to increase efficiency and worth. In the end they left the natives with smoke and mirrors. They pillaged the local companies by transferring their assets of value to Spain and then let them go bankrupt. Some of them had to be repurchased by the Latin American states that originally sold them, but now with less assets and with gigantic debts.

In one of those simple twists of fate I ended up moving to an apartment at One Columbus Place. Not in Genoa, Barcelona, or Pontevedra, but in the heart of New York City.

It is a fifty-story building with a golden sign. Every year on October 12, I briefly replace it. Just for a minute I cover the One Columbus Place sign with a sign saying One Incas Place.

I have confessed to several sins in this book. Here is one more: I have replaced Columbus street signs on October 12 in many places around the world, from San Francisco to Iowa City, from Buenos Aires to Barcelona, from Genoa to Madrid and New York City.

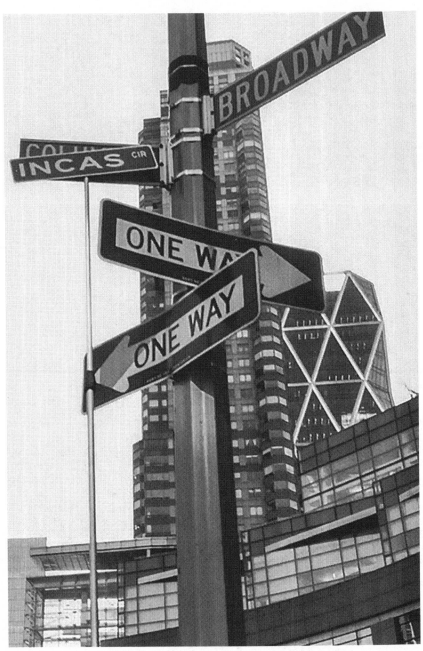

Alejandro Fogel, "Incas Circle", video, 720p, 2:35

52

I'm at the grocery store.

My phone rings. It's a Skype call from Sergio! As usual the Skype video is not very good. I can hear Sergio and see some buildings that don't belong in Buenos Aires. Sergio says: "I'm in Jerusalem!" "Yeah, and I'm in Beirut!" I laugh.

"No, I'm serious. Look. The Wailing Wall." When the video stops flickering, I can see a wall that, in fact, looks like The Wailing Wall. He slowly moves his cell phone towards a sign on the wall that says: *El Muro de los Lamentos*, The Wailing Wall.

"I'm in Jerusalem," Sergio says. "In Jerusalem, Buenos Aires. I'm in the Holy Land, the first religious theme park in Argentina. Fernando Pugliese, the sculptor who made the Perón statue, built this whole thing, too. This is big, man. I couldn't let you miss it."

As my phone and I head over to the fruits and vegetables, I see a close up of a living Jesus Christ carrying his cross.

Via Skype, my friend was bringing me some sort of poor man's parallel universe, where "fake" and "real" were both equally blurry, pixelated and unstable. Sergio was being ironic, playing with me and my obsessions. He was live streaming from an alternate Wailing Wall. With the rudimentary tools of Skype and a cell phone he was trying to capture the existence of a parallel universe.

The first time that a successfull experiment in real Quantum Physics

took place, it happened inside a refrigerator in Northern California.

The author and his friend Sergio

53

If parallel worlds

do exist, there is a good chance that I would be Hassidic. It's only logical given my family history. Please don't tell my wife I said this. She's terrified that one day I'll wake up and announce that I've started following the Rabbi of Vishnitz.

The small town of Kaser is thirty miles north of New York City. Its population of 3,000 is entirely Hassidic, all followers of the Rabbi of Vishnitz, my Dad's family's sect. The latest census says that 94% of Kaser's population claims Romanian ancestry, making Kaser the most Romanian place in the United States.

The racial makeup of Kaser is 98.61% Caucasian, while Hispanics are 0.54% of the population. This means that there are about 16 Hispanics in Kaser.

My name wouldn't be Alejandro Fogel if I lived there. It would be Avrum Fogel.

Alejandro Fogel, "Jerusalem, Buenos Aires", monoprint of an online image of a photograph, silver gelatin, Staples Laser Print Paper non-acid-free, 24 lb, 6 1/8 by 8 1/2 in.

My favorite Superman stories

were those in which he had a parallel life. Red Kryptonite or one of his other enemies would send him to another dimension where Jonas and Martha Kent were nasty villains and they raised Clark Kent to be a criminal.

Can Avrum and Alejandro Fogel live at the same time in a parallel universe?

Andrew Clelland at the University of California Santa Barbara, saw the most extraordinary thing in the refrigerator of his laboratory. A tiny piece of metal stood still *and* moved at the same time. At that moment Quantum Physics went from pure theory to a reality that can be observed with the naked eye. One object existed simultaneously in two separate areas of the fridge and in two different states: it was in motion and stillness at the same time.

Just like in my favorite Superman stories, we can now confirm that there are parallel universes.

The Alejandro Fogel writing these lines in Manhattan could be simultaneously studying the Talmud in the town of Kaser, New York.

My uncle Yosef Shmil goes to the Wailing Wall every day. He was there on July 3, 2002, when a mysterious damp patch appeared on The Wall, triggering hopes that the Messiah was coming. There is an ancient prophecy that says that when water starts trickling through

the stones of The Wailing Wall, it will be a sign that the Messiah's arrival is imminent. In this case, it was a false alarm. The Messiah didn't come that day.

For the Lubavitch Hassidim, the Messiah is already here. They believe their Rabbi Menahem Mendel Schneerson is the Messiah. He died in 1994, but they say he is still around.

Last night at midnight, Ricardo, an Argentinean psychotherapist, stood in front of Rabbi Schneerson's tomb. I met Ricardo years ago in Buenos Aires. He looked me up recently and found me in New York City. We are standing just across the street from The Dakota apartments, in the Strawberry Fields of Central Park, a shrine dedicated to John Lennon. There are a few cut flowers scattered over the word "Imagine", which is written in a black and white mosaic oval on the ground.

I feel sad every time I come here. John Lennon was such a big figure in my life growing up. Edgar Allan Poe is also present whenever I visit Strawberry Fields, for reasons the reader will find out later. I think from now on, Rabbi Schneerson will be here too. I find it very interesting that in his first visit to New York City, Ricardo went straight from the plane to pay homage to two of his most revered idols: Schneerson and Lennon. As I write these lines I also realize that there is someone else present: Simon Morley, the main character in one of my favorite novels, *Time and Again* by Jack Finney. In the book, Si travels back in time to the 19th century. He does so by using an apartment in The Dakota, where John Lennon lived and was later killed, as his port of entry. So here we are, John Lennon, Edgar Alan Poe, Rabbi Schneerson, Simon Morley, Ricardo, and me. All united by a thought across the collective unconscious.

55

My Dad, Shelley and

I are leaving Safed, after visiting the Rabbi of Vishnitz's synagogue. We hear that the Lubavitcher Chief Rabbi Levy Bistritzky was run over by a car in what was considered a hit and run attempted murder.

That same evening Meir Baranes called the press and confessed to the crime.

He told the press that Rabbi Bistritzky excommunicated Baranes for saying that Rabbi Schneerson was the Messiah. Many in the Lubavitch movement believe that Schneerson is back from the dead.

The next day, Baranes attempted to sue God in local court for not allowing the Messiah to come back to the Jews.

After this incident, the Messiah's face started following me everywhere.

Moishe in Safed

57

A group of mountaineers

decided to climb the tallest mountain in the Western Hemisphere, 23,000-foot Mount Aconcagua. The trip started at Puente del Inca, a natural formation used by the aboriginal people to travel across the mountains into Chile. The mountaineers did the climb slowly so as to get adapted to the altitude. Their particular route was very steep and difficult to climb. One of the climbers noticed in the distance a patch of green he thought was grass, which is very unusual at that height. When the group got close enough to investigate, they realized that it wasn't grass at all. It was a semicircular pile of stones and, within it, the most incredible thing they'd ever seen in the high mountains.

Inside the stone semicircle, long red and yellow feathers covered a carefully wrapped package.

58

I'm on the via

del Ghetto Vecchio, Old Ghetto Street, in Venice, Italy, facing the Messiah. He looks at me with his intense blue eyes and long white beard. His right arm is raised in a welcoming fashion. He could be the Santa Claus starring in "Miracle on 34th Street," if it wasn't for his black hat and coat.

I've seen him all over the world:

- On huge billboards in Jerusalem

- In a framed poster in Hebrew outside a modest house in Laos

- On the side of a white van with loudspeakers in New York City

- On the wall of a falafel store in Bangkok

- At a tango dancing salon in Buenos Aires

- On the cover of a book in a bookstore in Singapore

Rabbi Menachem Mendel Schneerson was proclaimed the Messiah by the Lubavitch, a proselytizing sect of the Hassidic movement. In this corner of the Jewish Ghetto there is a Lubavitch Judaica store with a large photo of the Rabbi on the window and he is staring intently at me. The presence of the Messiah here is relatively new. I should point out that "relative" in Messianic terms could be stretched to eternity.

Nevertheless, the Rabbi wasn't here when the first Jews settled in this area in the 15th century. There were no traces of Rabbi Schneerson when the walls of the Ghetto were built in 1516 and the Jews were forced to wear yellow badges. He still hadn't arrived in 1797, when Napoleon demolished the walls, or when the yellow badges came back during World War II.

In his place, a man who introduces himself as Leibele comes to greet me as I am taking photos of the store. He tells me that he used to live in Toronto and the Lubavitch sent him here to help spread the word.

He offered to wrap *teffilim* on my arm but I declined. "I'm not religious," I told him but went on to mention that my Dad's family comes from Romania and they followed the Rabbi of Vishnitz. He got really excited about my connection with Romania, He said he had visited the tomb of the Baal Shem Tov in the Ukraine and then went to visit his Satmar family in Satu Mare which is close to my father's home town of Sacel.

I asked him if he knew where the name Satu Mare comes from. He shrugged when I told him that it derives from Saint Mary, and that it seems odd that the Satmar Hassids would adopt such a Goyisch name. Leibele frowned and informed me that is not the correct origin of the word and went on to a lengthy and incomprehensible explanation.

I invited him to continue the discussion at a nearby café but he declined: "I'm the only one at the shop."

We shook hands, and I went to have my espresso.

Alejandro Fogel, "Venice Ghetto Window", detail, monoprint, Office Depot
Laser Print Paper non-acid-free, 24 lb, 6 1/8 by 8 1/2 in..

59

From the Associated Press

PALM BEACH, Florida (AP) - The Chabad House-Lubavitch of Palm Beach is offering a $1,000 reward -- no questions asked -- for the safe return of the $1 bill that was stolen Tuesday night during a burglary at the synagogue.

The thief, caught on surveillance camera, stole a special donation box at the Chabad center that included the bill, considered sacred because it was blessed by the movement's late grand rebbe, Menachem Mendel Schneerson.

During the late 1980s, Schneerson was known for handing out dollar bills to thousands of visitors who'd line up for hours to greet him on Sundays outside his Crown Heights, Brooklyn, headquarters.

60

Borges was walking again

holding onto María Kodama's arm as they took their slow customary outing among the tombs of Recoleta cemetery. I had been following them for quite a while when I stopped them.

"Buenos dias, Maestro. What a coincidence running into you once again." His wife looked at me skeptically. Borges seemed to recognize my voice and said impatiently:

"As I told you before, our destiny isn't horrible because it is unreal. It's horrible because it is irreversible."

"Can I ask you a question?"

"Of course, go ahead."

"My last name is Fogel. My family came from Eastern Europe. A few days ago I was standing at a street corner on Calle Fogel in Puerto Madryn, which is named after an Indian Chief, thinking about "The Aleph," my roots in Eastern Europe, and my roots in Argentina. Maestro, do you ever ponder the meaning of your roots?"

He paused for a moment and said:

"My ancestors were Spanish, Portuguese, and English. When I was a child, I thought of myself as being Argentinean. You know what I mean. You must be an Argentinean to understand it completely. Now at the end of my life, I seem to be going back to my English roots in

Northumberland. It is not a contradiction. I mean, I don't think of myself as having English, Spanish or Portuguese blood. I think what is really important is what one is now at the present moment."

Borges stopped for a moment, his blind eyes moving as if searching for a sign from the illuminated universe, and continued:

"I came up with the idea for 'The Aleph' when I thought that the whole universe, the entire external world, could be enclosed in a tiny space, for example, could be a small shining circle somewhere in a cellar in Buenos Aires and there the whole universe might be found. And there will be another Aleph inside that one, and so on, to infinity."

The next time I saw Borges was in 1987 at another cemetery, in Switzerland, his final resting place.

Two years after he died, I followed him again, this time in Cambridge, Massachusetts.

61

The town today

called Puerto Madryn was originally called Porth Madryn in Welsh. The area was inhabited by the Tehuelche Indians for 13,000 years. They were nomads from Patagonia traveling between the lowlands of today's Argentina and the high Andes in Chile. Magellan was the first European to land in their territory, which he did on March 31, 1520. He was searching for the passage between the Pacific and the Atlantic that now bears his name.

The Conquistadors were mainly interested in finding a connection between the two oceans. They didn't try to enslave the indigenous population at first. Tehuelche is a Mapuche word that means "Fierce People." The Spaniards called them *Patagones*. The etymology of the word is unclear but is widely believed that it comes from the word *pata*, or foot, in Italian. It was taken from the writings of Antonio Pigafetta, a resident of the Republic of Venice, who was on board one of Magellan's ships. The first accounts of the Conquistadors as they returned to Europe spoke of a race of giants with enormous feet living in the area. The land of the giant Patagons became Patagonia. I became interested in the Tehuelches when I traveled to the southern reaches of Patagonia and saw their extraordinary cave paintings.

I'm in a cave, sitting on the ground, staring at the stone wall painted with llamas, guanacos, snakes, abstractions, and hands. The hands are spray painted on. The painters apparently used tubes made of hollow reeds and slowly blew paint through them, like an ancient form of

spray painting. The hands are shades of red, black and yellow, colors obtained from the minerals and plants of the region. They were done by many generations of Tehuelches over 10,000 years ago. They used their own hands as stencils. At times they painted the outside edges of a hand, leaving the impression of a negative. Some of the hands are very small, while others are larger than normal. They are mostly left hands. There is one with six fingers. I'm fascinated by the beauty and texture of these prehistoric paintings. They were meticulously executed. There must be close to a thousand hands painted here.

I'm wondering what motivated the Tehuelche to do this. There is no way to know for sure, but it looks to me as if they got a great deal of satisfaction from it. I imagine that the artists were creating not just for their own eyes, but for others to appreciate, too. The paintings feel as if their makers had all the time in the world. I wonder what the passing of time was like for them?

Thousand of years later, the Tehuelches' extinction was expedited by the migration of another tribe into their land: the Mapuche. They invaded Tehuelche territory when they were being pushed out of Chile by the Spaniards. Mapuche culture overwhelmed the Tehuelches, and within a century their language disappeared and was replaced by Mapuche.

Mapuche belongs to the Arawak group of languages, the same Arawaks who greeted Christopher Columbus when he first landed in the Caribbean.

The Mapuches fought in vain against the newly formed and culturally Spanish governments of Argentina and Chile at the beginning of the 19th century. Yet, a Mapuche legend has it that a white visitor would appear to defend their native land from the invaders.

In 1860, a group of Mapuche chiefs elected the French lawyer Orelie-Antoine de Tounens to be King of Patagonia. De Tounens claimed that Patagonia didn't belong to Argentina or Chile; it belonged to the

Mapuches. He created a flag, a national anthem, and a constitution that proclaimed the land a Parliamentary Hereditary Monarchy made up of him and his heirs. The kingdom didn't last long. Chilean authorities detained de Tounens in 1862 and deported him back to France.

His monarchy, however displaced, is still alive. His great-great-grandchild, Baron Jean-Michel Parasiliti di Para, an Algerian War veteran, was recently crowned Prince Antoine IV, King of Araucania and Patagonia. He currently leads the Mapuche nation from his home in France.

Alejandro Fogel, "Cave of the Hands", Walmart Faux Photo Canvas, 20 by 16 in.
Edition: 10

62

On May 28th,1865

the ship Mimosa left the port of Liverpool for Patagonia with its first 150 Welsh immigrants.

I've always been interested in why people migrate. Poverty, hunger, and war are the usual answers. But the Welsh left Britain for remote Patagonia to keep their language and identity intact. Back home in Wales, the English language and culture were taking over.

There is a popular legend telling the story of prince Madoc. He supposedly arrived in America in 1170 and founded the first Welsh colony in the New World by the Mississippi River. This tale was invoked by the British Crown to support their claims on North America.

The final defeat of the Mapuche came in 1885 in the brutal Argentinean "Campaign of the Desert." The Mapuches' land was confiscated, they were reduced to extreme poverty, and banished to reservations.

One year later, Ceferino Namuncura was born. He was the son of a Mapuche Chief and a Cautiva, a white woman taken captive by Indians. He was the first South American aborigine to be made a saint by the Catholic Church.

When I was a teenager, I hitchhiked from Buenos Aires to Patagonia and back. A trucker left me in the town of Chimpay, Ceferino's

birthplace. I didn't know much about him. I remembered seeing his face on the popular *estampitas* or saint cards, and posters back in the city. There was a big one outside a Salesian Pio IX School near my old Abasto neighborhood. I used to pass it with my father every Sunday on the way to the playground. The poster portrayed Ceferino, a dark, sad, gentle child wearing an old fashioned jacket and tie. I found out many years later that Ceferino had been in the Salesian school chorus. He sang alongside a kid who was destined to become another popular icon of mythical proportions: tango maestro Carlos Gardel.

After his death, Ceferino was venerated by the working class, who saw him as one of their own. The Church made him a saint based on the account of a woman whose cancer disappeared when she asked Ceferino for help almost a century after he died.

There are now 6,000 Tehuelches living in Patagonia. Only four of them speak their native tongue.

There are 150,000 Mapuches living in Patagonia. 40,000 speak their native tongue.

There are 20,000 Welsh living in Patagonia. 5,000 speak their native tongue.

Alejandro Fogel, "Ceferino Namuncurá", monoprint of an online image of a photograph, Staples Laser Print Paper non-acid-free, 24 lb, 8 1/2 by 6 1/8 in.

63

I've come to

the American Museum of Natural History in New York to meet with one of its researchers, John Hyslop, a renowned scholar and author of *The Inca Road System*, one of the classics of Andean Archeology. I read the book many times and it was always in my backpack on my trips to the Andes.

On my way to Hyslop's office, I stop in front of one of my favorite objects in the museum: a huge piece of iron called Ahnighito. It is one of the largest meteorites on display in the world.

I've always been interested in space exploration. If you asked me when I was eight what would I like to be when I grew up I'd always say: an astronaut.

Ahnighito landed in Greenland thousands of years ago. For centuries, the Inuit people hammered at it to make their knives and harpoons. Robert Peary, the first American to reach the North Pole, brought Ahnighito to the United States.

He also brought six native Inuits and housed them in the basement of the Museum. One of them, Quisuk, died soon after arriving. His 6-year-old son Minik was told that his father's remains had been returned home. The truth is that the Museum staff removed Quizuk's flesh, cleaned his bones, and exhibited his skeleton to the public. A few years later, Minik was shocked to discover his father in one of the

Museum's display cases.

Not until 1993 were Quisuk's remains returned to his descendants in Greenland.

Chief Fogel's remains are buried in Patagonia.

64

I had the idea of

exploring the Incas Road when I first encountered traces of the actual old system in the Andes. I was in northwestern Argentina with a *baqueano*, an expert guide. We were drinking mate together and watching his son tending the llamas in the fields. His home happened to be right part of the old Incas Road which is still in use today. That sunny morning, I "found" the road. On and off for the next 8 years, I would travel through it.

It wasn't in any way a systematic exploration.

I just went here and there, stopping wherever something attracted me.

I'm looking at the building of Banco Santander on Calle Bandera 237 in Santiago, Chile. I didn't come for the purpose of getting money, but because remnants of the Incas Road were discovered on this spot.

Many of today's streets and avenues in Argentina, Chile, and Peru were built on existing Inca Roads. The Incas themselves used their ancestors' knowledge and established their roads on pre-existent paths, some dating back to 1,000 BCE. They go from beautifully paved sections nearly forty eight feet wide to just a tiny line of stones vanishing into the horizon.

I came to Santiago from Mendoza, Argentina, on the other side of the Andes, where I visited one of the last Inca *tambos*--the old

lodging stations for travelers of the Road--with Archeologist Roberto Bárcena.

"This is as far south as the Incas ventured in Argentina," he said.

A few days later, Roberto Barcena along with Hans Schobinger showed me their most precious possession, which was stored in a household freezer.

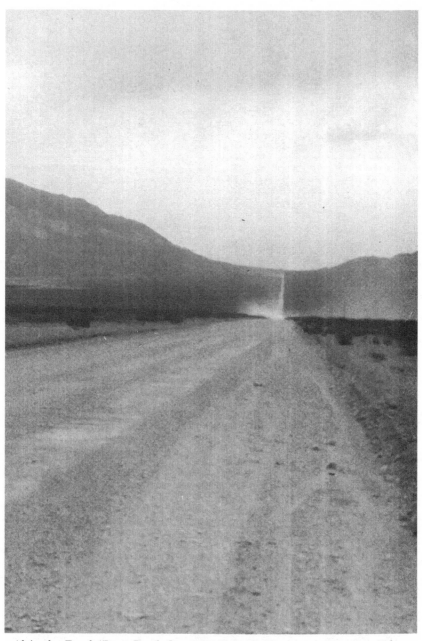

Alejandro Fogel, "Incas Road, Catamarca", detail, Iris print on Somerset Velvet
rag paper, 8 1/8 by 12 7/8 in. Edition: 25

Alejandro Fogel, "Incas Road, Iowa", environmental installation, 3,697 ft by 12.5 ft

65

Today is August 29.

I've come here, to the corner of Madison Avenue and 42nd Street, to visit the former site of Hotel Manhattan, where Carl Jung and Sigmund Freud stayed on this day in 1909. I read about their visit by chance this morning and decided to have a look.

The hotel is no longer here; it was demolished years ago.

In his book, *Memories, Dreams, Reflections*, Jung wrote that the concept of the collective unconscious originated in a dream he had while staying at this hotel.

He wrote that there is another layer of mind besides our conscious one: a second vast, universal knowing shared by all individual minds, which he called the collective unconscious. This layer is formed by universal archetypes, pre-existing elements inherited from all the individuals who ever lived.

The collective unconscious transforms itself at every moment. As we think, as we act, even as we die, new pieces are added to the universal puzzle. Past, present, and future seem to converge, creating new manifestations of past, present, and future.

It was at this same corner of Madison Avenue when years ago, on my way downtown, I heard a passer-by say that a plane had crashed into

the North Tower.

Alejandro Fogel, "Manhattan Hotel", Walmart Faux Photo Canvas, 8 by 10 in.
Edition: 10

66

In Borges' short story

"The Other," the main character Jorge Luis Borges, tells us that on a cold morning in February 1969, he was sitting on a bench facing the Charles River in Cambridge, Massachusetts. He was 69 years old. A stranger was sitting next to him. They started to talk, and Borges realized that this person was also Jorge Luis Borges. The only difference was that this other Borges was in Switzerland in 1918. He was nineteen years old and sitting on a bench by the Rhone in Geneva where he went to school. Borges and Borges were sitting together on a bench that existed in two times and two places.

The older Borges reflected that "if this morning is a dream, we should both think about ourselves as the dreamer. Maybe we will stop dreaming, maybe not. Meanwhile, our duty is to accept the dream, just like we accept the universe, the fact that we were created, that we can see with our eyes and breathe."

I sat on the bench facing the Charles River twenty years after the two Borges had found each other there. It was a cold morning in February 1989. Borges had died three years before. I couldn't resist following him again. This time I was following his ghost.

I'm adding the following lines in February 2009:

Today I take a train to Boston for the day to teach a workshop. On the way I keep thinking about that morning exactly twenty years

ago when I sat on the bench facing the Charles River where the two Borges met exactly twenty years before that. I think about going back to that bench now and writing about it for this book, forty and twenty years later. I google "bench on Charles River, Cambridge" and retrieve a photo, an instance, a single moment of a lonely bench by the river at sunset. As I arrive at South Station I'm debating whether to take the subway to the bench or a taxi to my hotel.

I'm thinking about the present becoming memories and the connection between the memories, when there is one. Everything indicates that I should go back to the bench and keep writing about Borges.

I decide to take a taxi to my hotel instead.

67

We just arrived in Bucharest.

My friend Alexandru picks us up at the airport in a borrowed Dacia. "Ceaucescu did a good job redesigning this car," he says. "His engineers copied a French Renault 12 and made it even more uncomfortable, inefficient, and uglier. One more form of Romanian torture," he laughs.

We've been driving for about thirty minutes. It is dark and cold. Being here with Alexandru is something I've wanted to do since we met in New York years ago. I was fascinated by our first encounter. His name is the Romanian version of my name. His father came from the same part of northern Transylvania as mine. After the war and the horrors of the Holocaust, his father moved to Bucharest, while my father made his way to Argentina. I was named after my maternal grandfather, Avrum. Alexandru, too, was named after his grandfather, Abraham.

We used to joke in New York about each other being "The Other", as in the Borges story.

Alexandru is so happy we are here. He stops the car on Strada Eminescu. Getting out of the blue Dacia, I notice all the cars parked on that block are also blue Dacias, except for one that is black. Alexandru sees the same thing. "A traitor," he laughs. He is trying to carry all the bags, but I am able to convince him that it wouldn't be good for his back. The apartment house is a gray concrete building,

probably from the late 1950's. We get in the elevator and go up to the fourth floor, to apartment number 17.

The first lock took eight turns to open. The second lock only three. What would become for me the characteristic smell of this place assaulted me for the first time. Still now, as I write this, I can smell that nauseating, unidentifiable smell. Then, standing in the hall in the dark, I regretted coming to Romania at all.

I mentioned to Shelley that I was writing about following Borges' ghost. She told me that in her new book she was creating a hero who lives among ghosts. This is what the character says:

"There are so many ghosts where I live and they are more present for me than the living. I have always heard them louder, seen them sharper and longer. The oddest part is that in the world of ghosts, I'm alive."

Shelley tells me that she started seeing what her character looks like after I wrote about its existence in my book. By being in this book, her character became "real" to her.

I thought about the two Borges and how much they changed in fifty years. The young Borges becoming the old Borges. The one who could see and the blind one. I sat with them both, watching the universe change through a slow winter sunset.

Alexandru apologizes. "This place is all I could find that has heat and electricity all day long. We are lucky because this is the embassy neighborhood and they have special gas pipelines." "You don't need to apologize," I say. "We'll be fine. We just need to clean the place and I am sure in daylight it will look much better." The light was dim. Shelley looks at me and tries to smile. What is wrong? Where are we?

"I rented the place from a woman who needed the money. She went to live with friends," Alexandru assures us. It is a common practice here. Pensions are as low as thirty dollars a month, sending thousands

of retirees begging in the streets. Alexandru left us to settle in. I open the window and take a deep breath of icy air. The night is very quiet. Someone is burning wood in a steel drum at the corner.

Shelley and I sat for a while on the sticky plastic-covered red sofa. There are dirty ashtrays everywhere. All the furniture is covered with faded red rugs. The dishes are almost all cracked. We found several small objects arranged like a shrine on a piece of dark wood in the kitchen: canning jars left open with some kind of thick, dark liquid inside, faded pictures of saints, a tube of lipstick, two empty perfume bottles, a dried out scrap of soap, and a plastic utensil I couldn't identify. They were all covered with a patina of grease. The only clean object in the whole apartment was high up on an archway facing our bed. It was a big framed photograph of a pretty little girl with a rosary hanging from it.

Marianna was born in Bucharest in 1961. She lived with her mother on Strada Eminescu 252, apartment 17. When she was sixteen years old she was kidnapped by the Securitate, the Romanian secret police. Her mother hadn't heard from her for twenty-five years, when she resurfaced in East Germany, where she had been sold to a prostitution ring by her captors years ago. In 1990, three months after the revolution that toppled the dictator Ceausescu, she came back to Romania to see her mother. They lived together in apartment 17 for four days until March 27. That morning, Marianna committed suicide by injecting herself with an overdose of heroin.

There is a small bronze plaque on a bare wall on Boulevardul Dacia, two blocks from apartment 17. Mircea Eliade once lived here. In *The Myth of the Eternal Return* he wrote that there's an ancient belief that each thing on Earth connects to its sacred, celestial other.

It is a small house with a small dead garden. Standing in front of it, I think about Alexandru and me. Our strange relationship through time, our Transylvanian blood, sometimes Romanian, sometimes Hungarian.

It is snowing. People are coming out with pots and jars full of stew from a small kiosk where a charity institution is running a soup kitchen. Gypsy girls are burning garbage on the corner to keep warm. What am I doing here? Where am I?

I should ask Alexandru.

There are no shutters on the windows of our apartment here, just a very thin curtain. I can't sleep. The moon comes out from behind one of the buildings across the street. The smell of the apartment, like a lethal antiseptic trying to cover up decay, is gradually becoming a familiar presence.

Shelley fell asleep and I did soon after.

The telephone is ringing. Alexandru wants to have breakfast with us.

We are in Casablanca, a small café downtown. Alexandru is upset. He couldn't sleep. It is his first time in Bucharest in many years, the first time since his parents killed themselves in the same room in which he is sleeping now.

His father had been very ill with Parkinson's disease. In Ceausescu's Romania it was impossible to get medicines if you weren't part of the official circle. Alexandru tried to mail him the medicines from New York, but they disappeared in Romanian customs. His parents' apartment didn't have heat and the electricity was restricted to just a few hours a day. They barely had any food to eat. They took a fatal overdose on the night of November 16th, 1987.

It is the first time Alexandru told us his parents' story. When he had spoken about Romania in the past, he talked about the suffocating repression and the Securitate's control over everything and everyone. He told us the story about Ceausescu and his wife Elena being decorated and getting honorary doctorates in the United States and Europe because of their supposed stand against the Soviet Union. Meanwhile at home, they were torturing and starving their whole

country. He talked about Ceaucescu's fifty-four palaces and his government building complex, larger than any other in the world, and about the systematic destruction of ancient villages all over Romania, the demolition of medieval churches, and the disappearance of thousands of people.

We sat in silence for a few minutes and then left the café. There is a synagogue across the street, a large building with a stone facade. It is empty and cold. The caretaker is lighting candles. We talk for a few minutes. He says that his family emigrated from the Pale to Bucharest. For a moment we all look at each other. Shimon the caretaker, Alexandru, Shelley, and I. We are all children of immigrants from the Pale.

Shimon's grandparents came to Bucharest from the Pale through the Gara du Nord train station in 1902.

Alexandru's grandparents came to Bucharest from the Pale through the Gara du Nord train station in 1905.

Shelley's grandparents came to the US from The Pale through Ellis Island in 1907.

My grandparents on my mother's side came to Buenos Aires from the Pale through the Hotel de los Immigrantes in 1905.

"Bucharest doesn't look like Buenos Aires," I tell Alexandru. He wants to go to Buenos Aires with me "to close our circle." He's feeling better. It is snowing again. We are moving on.

"To Mircea Eliade's dead garden?" I ask. 'Where else would we go?" he replies.

We lived in apartment 17 for one week.

68

On December 21, 1980

I dreamt there were only three Beatles instead of four. The next day John Lennon was assassinated.

I'm sitting at Café la Fortuna on West 71st Street, where Lennon used to come to drink espresso and write songs. He lived just a couple of blocks away at The Dakota, an apartment building opened in 1884 on the then sparsely populated Upper West Side of Manhattan. At the time, that building was so far from downtown that New Yorkers joked it was as far away as the Dakota Territory.

Forty years earlier, in 1844, and just a few yards west of here, Edgar Allan Poe walked every morning. He did not have enough money to take public transportation. So he walked six miles from Broadway and West 84th Street each way everyday to get to his job as a magazine editor on Wall Street. At a good pace it took him four hours round trip. Poe made such a long commute because he was determined that his consumptive wife should live in a place with fresh country air.

When he died John Lennon was so rich that his wife Yoko Ono inherited an estate valued in 450 million dollars.

When he died, Edgar Allan Poe was so poor that he left only debts.

I'm with Shelley at West 84th Street and Broadway sitting at one of the tables at Edgar's Café. Shelley has been doing research for her novel on Poe's wife, Virginia. The café is on the site occupied by

government decided to "conquer the desert." *La Conquista del Desierto* was a military campaign to exterminate and enslave the aboriginal peoples of Patagonia. In 1813 Argentina abolished slavery and freed the slaves. Nevertheless, during La Conquista del Desierto at the end of the nineteenth century, captured Indian children were regularly separated from their parents and sent to Buenos Aires as slaves.

The tribal chiefs were dumped on the Martín García Island across the river from Buenos Aires and left to die.

Isla Martín García

was used by the Argentinean Military governments of the twentieth century to jail deposed elected Presidents and their staff.

I've come here to visit the prison. It is now a tourist destination like every other retired notorious prison, concentration camp and torture chamber in the world. Don't get me wrong. I'm not opposed to people visiting horrific places, preserved as symbols of what we should never do again. What I find hard to digest is that they are sold as part of recreational tour packages. I haven't yet been able to bring myself to go to Auschwitz. Another place I have not visited is the ESMA, Escuela de Mecanica de la Armada, the largest concentration camp in Argentina during the Dirty War. The Blonde Angel of Death was based there.

Poe's funeral

was not publicly announced and less than ten people attended. Before his tombstone was placed, a train crashed into the stonecutter's yard and destroyed it. Since there was no money to buy another one, he was buried in an unmarked grave. His obituary, written by Rufus Griswold, his literary executor and, unbeknownst to Poe, his biggest enemy, made him out to be personally maniacal and artistically mediocre. This damaged Poe's reputation for years, even long after his dead.

A few years ago there was a re-enactment of Poe's funeral to try to repair his maligned reputation as a crazed alcoholic and 700 people attended.

Since his remains could not be found, a group of fans hired a special effects artist to create a new corpse. The new funeral was led by actor John Astin, who played Gomez on *The Addams Family*. Among the speakers was a fake Arthur Conan Doyle and a fake Sherlock Holmes.

72

Jean Baudrillard said

that everyone seeks to produce meaning but in reality meaning is killing us.

Did he mean too much meaning added to all the events in our lives is what's killing us, or is it that trying to interpret every single bit and byte that comes our way, including the meaning of his concept, is killing us?

73

We are in the outskirts

of the city of Mendoza in an enormous park that encompasses a botanical garden, a zoo, two museums, and a major university.

Archeologists Bárcena and Schobinger are waiting for us when we arrive at the University's Center for Science and Technological Research.

We go upstairs to a small office, chat for a few minutes, and drink Cachamai, an herbal tea of yerba mate, mint, and chamomile.

"Are you ready?" Barcena asks.

"We certainly are."

We walk through a dark hallway. At the end of it, there is a small white freezer with a big padlock. Schobinger unlocks it and slowly lifts the top.

The Inca mummy is inside. The 500-year-old boy is naked and beautifully preserved by the extreme cold of the Andes, where he was found curled up at 17,400 feet in an Inca shrine on Mount Aconcagua. I stop breathing for a few seconds. I look at Shelley. She is glowing with amazement. We get only a few minutes with the boy, who cannot be exposed to normal air temperature.

The white top is coming down. The boy's small reddish body gets darker and darker as it shuts.

"The Incas didn't consider the child a sacrificial victim but a voluntary messenger from the temporal world to the divine one," Barcena says.

The freezer is locked again, and the little Inca messenger goes back to his endless dream.

The author and his wife Shelley on the road

74

When I was growing up

in Argentina, the TV series *The Addams Family*, was called *Los Locos Addams* and John Astin's character, Gomez, was Homero Addams. *The Lone Ranger* was *El Llanero Solitario*, *The Man from U.N.C.L.E* was *El Hombre de C.I.P.O.L*; and *The Flinstones* were *Los Picapiedras*. I also read the same comic books as American kids, translated from English into Spanish. My favorite was *Batman*. My Bruce Wayne was Bruno Diaz, and Dick Grayson was Ricardo Tapia. These names were chosen by editors in Mexico. Mexican Spanish is so different from Argentinean Spanish that many of its words were foreign to me and I had to look them up in the dictionary.

I learned how to read in Yiddish and Spanish when I was two years old. Every evening my Dad and I would read parts of *Di Yiddishe Tsaytung*, one of Buenos Aires' daily Jewish newspapers. With my Mom, I learned Spanish by reading the *Adventures of Patoruzú*, a comic book in which the hero was the last Patagonian Tehuelche tribal chief turned millionaire. There were many Argentinean comic books. Besides Patoruzu, my favorite was *El Eternauta*. One of the captivating things about it was that the action was taking place right now in Buenos Aires. Everything was familiar, from the way people spoke to the names of the streets, and the places where the story occurred. The comic had local references, like the latest ads and current military coups.

The author was Hector Oesterheld, another son of immigrants: a

German Jewish father and a Spanish Basque mother. He was born and raised in Buenos Aires. Oesterheld plays himself in the comics, as a comic book writer who receives a visit from a time traveler. The story the traveler tells him becomes the main plot in "El Eternauta."

Oesterheld was kidnapped and made disappeared by the military in 1977, along with his four daughters Beatriz, Diana, Estela, and Marina and their husbands and the grandchildren. Only his wife survived the camp.

The rest of them were never found or heard from again. The last account of Oesterheld and his family came from Juan Carlos Scarpatti, another *desaparecido* who was allowed to survive. They were prisoners together in the concentration camp *El Campito* in Campo de Mayo, a major military base. Oesterheld was devastated. He told Scarpatti that in his latest torture session, the torturers showed him pictures of his daughters murdered.

Another survivor from the concentration camp was told by Oesterheld's wife that while she was in prison one of her kidnappers, Lieutenant Alfredo Astiz, gave her El Eternauta to read. He referred to it as the best Argentinean book ever.

They read Oesterheld books enthusiastically and they also killed him.

Hector Oesterheld was put on the government's black list as early as 1968, when his comic book biography of Che Guevara was published.

Alfredo Astiz, aka The Blond Angel of Death, is one of the most notorious Argetinean kidnappers and torturers in the Dirty War. He is in jail now. He was charged with the disappearance of Azucena Villaflor, one of the founders of Madres de Plaza de Mayo, a non-violent organization that doggedly continue to searche for the disappeared. She started the group after her son Néstor was kidnapped in 1976. Soon other mothers looking for their missing children and grandchildren joined her. Wearing their iconic white head scarves,

they began a silent weekly march every Thursday in front of the government house. It still goes on today.

Azucena Villaflor's remains were identified as one the bodies found floating in the Atlantic Ocean. She was a victim of of the so-called "Death Flights" organized by the Army. Prisoners were drugged, stripped naked and thrown out live from airplanes over the ocean. The Argentine Anthropologic Forensic Team (EAAF) has identified 120 bodies over the last few years. The EAAF is also well-known for its identification of Che Guevara's remains, which were found in Bolivia.

Hector Oesterheld, "El Eternauta"

75

I'm watching the

German movie *Labyrinth of Lies* about the ineffectual denazification of Germany after the war. It takes place in 1958. Thirteen years after World War II ended, when 90% of civil servants, many of them teachers, were classified as "ex" Nazis, German children had no idea of what Auschwitz was. This isn't a science fiction movie depicting an alternate reality. This a true story. I'm shocked. I had no idea how long Germany let so many of their Nazis go unpunished.

I realize that I always feared Germans. Just watching actors playing Germans makes me nervous. I fear even the "good" Germans in the movie. I have a phobia.

Psychiatrist Brian Dias has been working on how phobias, anxieties and post traumatic stress disorders develop. He believes that some phobias are based on the inherited experiences of the patient's ancestors, through chemical changes in those ancestors' DNA when exposed to trauma. Fear is literally in their DNA, and it influences the structure and function of the nervous systems of future generations.

As the movie ends I keep thinking about the possible biological transmission of the impact of memories. Memories are not exclusively our own; we can inherit them in our genes.

My fear of Germans however, is not as strong as my fear of police. I haven't been in jail or committed any crime, but when I see a policeman or a police car, I flinch. It's a very particular vibration that goes through my entire body. It lasts a second. Then I realize that I

haven't done anything, I'm not in Buenos Aires during the Dirty War now, and these police are not those police.

I don't have children. These fears end with me.

76

The Espresso at Edgar's café

is pretty bad. John Lennon was having much better luck at Café la Fortuna.

I clearly remember the first time I listened to a song by The Beatles. It played on the radio in the bus that was taking me home from grade school. The date was June 6, 1966. That date had some significance for me because my teacher told us that 6/6/66 happens only once in a century.

Later that year Ernesto Che Guevara partially shaved his head and traveled to Bolivia disguised as a Uruguayan businessman. He was about to start his guerrilla war in the Bolivian jungle. The CIA turned to Klaus Barbie for help; they didn't want another Cuba in Latin America. Barbie had been a high-ranking Nazi officer during War World II. He was responsible for the death of more than 14,000 people. Barbie was one of the heads of the counter-guerrilla insurgency against the French Resistance. He executed its leader Jean Moulin in 1943, the same year Moishe joined the partisans in the mountains of Poland after his train escape.

Barbie became a U.S. counter-intelligence agent in 1947. In 1980 he participated with the 601st battalion of the Argentinean Army in a violent and ruthless coup d'etat that brought military drug traffickers to power. It was known as the "Cocaine" coup.

The 601st battalion was very active during the Dirty War. One of its

261

bases was Campo de Mayo where the infamous concentration camp El Campito was established.

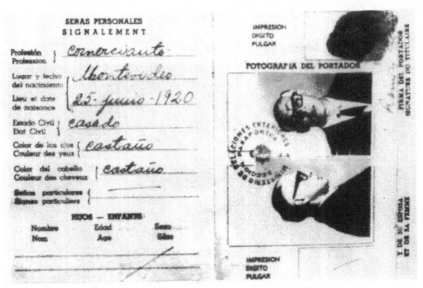

Ernesto Che Guevara as Alberto Mena Gonzalez. Fake Uruguayan passport

Moishe Fogel, soldier in the Russian Army, World War II

77

I join Sara Rus

one sunny afternoon and walk around the pyramid in Plaza de Mayo with her.

Sara met Bernardo when they were teenagers in the Lodz Ghetto in Poland. They fell in love and were separated when Sara was deported to Auschwitz. When the camps were liberated in 1945, she was eighteen years old, weighed fifty-seven pounds, and could barely walk. She and Bernardo were reunited, got married, and two years later made it to Buenos Aires. They had two children, Daniel and Natalia.

Daniel Rus became a nuclear physicist and worked for the National Commission for Nuclear Energy. On July 15, 1977, he and twenty of his colleagues were detained by a military patrol. No one knows why.

That was the last time anybody saw him.

Sara Rus joined the Mothers of Plaza de Mayo.

Since public gatherings of three or more people were forbidden, they grabbed each other in pairs and started walking in circles around the plaza, where she and I are walking now.

Almost four decades after Daniel's disappearance, Sara Rus still goes to the Plaza de Mayo every Thursday and circles the square with other mothers whose children disappeared during Argentina's Dirty War.

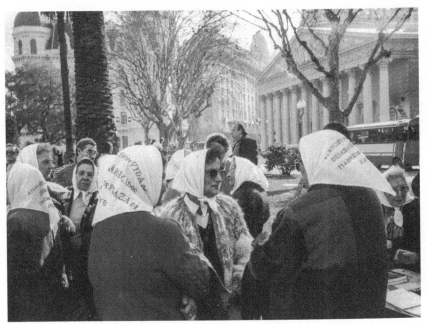

Alejandro Fogel, "Mothers of Plaza de Mayo"

78

I'm lying on a beach

in the Caribbean. The sand is almost white and the sea deep blue.
There are some palm trees and small straw huts where you can seek
refuge from the sun. Northeast of here, Christopher Columbus
landed in the New World for the first time in 1492 and met with the
Arawak Indians. A few years later, every single Arawak in the area was
taken away to work in the mines on the island of Hispaniola.

Arawak religion was a mixture of nature and ancestor worship.

So strong was their belief in their forebears that the Conquistadors
were able to lure them away from their homes to slavery on another
island by the promise they would meet their ancestors there.

which is German mixed with Hebrew and Aramaic, and Ladino, a blend of Old Spanish, Hebrew and Aramaic.

It is late in the evening on the Caribbean island of Aruba. Two young men are cleaning the beach. They exchange a few words that sound familiar to me but I cannot understand them. I learn that they are speaking Papiamento, a Pidgin language. It is a mixture of Spanish, Arawak, Portuguese, English, Dutch. Papiamento started evolving as a quick and efficient means of communication between speakers of different tongues. It became the lingua franca of the natives western traders, many of them Jews who had emigrated from Europe, in Curacao, Bonaire, and Aruba, the former Netherlands Antilles. I'm listening to them and enjoying the beautiful melody of the language. I love the rhythm and the cadences. It reminds me of Ladino, which some of my Turkish Jewish students used to communicate with me.

My students and I would sit in a café by the Galata Tower on the European side of the Bosphorus. The neighborhood was densely packed with electronics stores and classic Ottoman houses. We sipped sweet apple tea from little tulip shaped glasses and talked for hours. I'd speak Spanish and they would answer in Ladino. We loved this practice and enjoyed pointing out at the similarities and the differences between the two languages. We marveled at how easy it was for us to talk with each other, even though we were speaking different tongues. My Turkish students were direct descendants of the Jews who escaped from Spain to Istanbul in 1492, when the Jews were expelled by the Inquisition.

Their languages and the language spoken by the Dutch of this island ultimately merged and became Papiamento, from Portuguese papear to speak.

The Jews who came to Aruba from Brazil in 1654 were also descendants of Jews who fled Spain in 1492. They traded with the few Arawak Indians left alive after their forced labor in the mines. This was just before they became extinct. The Arawak of this island had their own

version of the seventy-three languages called Arawakan, which is still spoken by tribes from the Caribbean to the Andes, from the Amazon to Chile and Bolivia.

80

I'm sitting at a café

in an outdoor shopping mall. It is actually nicer than your average American mall. They don't have Banana Republic, Starbucks, or any major brand stores. They call it a "Shopping Village." It's one of those malls built to resemble a small town in pre-mall America. All the shopkeepers are locals. There are a few antique stores, clothing and travel equipment boutiques, a bookstore, and this café.

Why am I telling you about this mall? The answer is relatively simple: I dreamt about writing about it last night, and in the dream I did, right before I woke up.

I come here every morning to work on this book. The buildings in this mall are meant to look old, although they are obviously new. The place has a good feeling about it, and they don't play music, which I hate to hear when I'm trying to write.

Now that I've mentioned my dream and written about it, I feel free to start writing what I had planned to write this morning. I frequently use the "Hemingway Principle": Hemingway would stop writing in the middle of a sentence at the end of each day so he'd know exactly where to start the next morning.

Yesterday I stopped writing in the middle of this sentence:

"The Hassidim did not wear woolen cloth, only silk because..."

Since it is the beginning of my writing day I'm going to finish that sentence just as Hemingway suggested.

Dear Reader: there is a problem. I finished the sentence but I edited the story to which it belongs, and now it will be in Volume 2 of this book. Sorry but you'll have to wait until then.

As you enter Princes Square

shopping mall in Glasgow, you can't miss the copy of Foucault's pendulum hanging from the ceiling, not too far from a Starbucks. At Starbucks they sell *madeleines*, those delicious little buttery cakes known for triggering Marcel Proust's memories and instigating his six-volume masterpiece *In Search of Lost Time*.

I've seen these madeleines in several Starbucks around the world: New York, Paris, Singapore, Barcelona. Before the birth of Starbucks you could only find them in France. Inevitably, as I see the madeleines packaged in plastic at the counter, it triggers the memory of triggering memories. I wonder who came up with the idea of selling madeleines at Starbucks or naming the company after a character in Moby Dick.

Scott Bedbury, the former Chief Marketing Officer of Starbucks, personally led the creation of the company's brand. In his book, *A New Brand World*, he explains the Starbucks core identity as "being less about engineering a great cup of coffee than about providing a great coffee *experience*.... The Starbucks brand is about the coffee Gestalt, the atmospherics.

As a boy, Marcel Proust spent his summers in the small town of Illiers. In his monumental book, a bite of a madeleine triggers a flood of memories of his time growing up in the fictional village of Combray. On July 10, 1971, exactly 100 years after Proust was born, his ancestral town of Illiers renamed itself Illiers-Combray to honor

him and his work and to attract tourists.

The town that scorned Proust for being a homosexual, an atheist, and a Jew in the end recreated itself based on his memory of itself.

I'm standing outside Madame Benoist's patisserie chewing on a "real" madeleine, rather than a Starbucks' knock off. Before the town changed its name, the patisserie sold a handful of madeleines per month. Now they sell them in the thousands, mostly to "Proustourists." They land here for a few hours to get the "feeling" of Proust's fictionalized memory of his childhood. Just like me right now. I, however, have the excuse that I came here for research purposes.

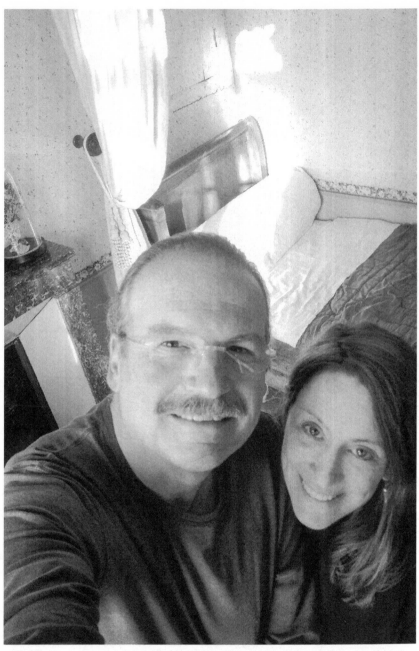

Shelley Berc and Alejandro Fogel. Selfie in Marcel Proust's childhood bedroom

82

I'm in Aix-en-Provence

a college town close to Marseilles, eating another madeleine and drinking *café au lait* at Les Deux Garçons. This is the café where Paul Cézanne and Émile Zola used to meet as teenagers before they moved to Paris and had their legendary fight.

The intense heat of summer in Provence makes the waiters even more impatient than usual. I'm trying to get a Badoit mineral water, "the water that refreshes your ideas" according to their advertising, but I might have to wait for some time.

The golden light that Cézanne revered is now illuminating the sky, dappling the leaves of the plane trees carefully aligned on the Cours Mirabeau, and landing at last on the blue, purple, and gray cobblestones. All these elements were here when teenagers Paul and Émile sat at one of these outdoor tables and had a cup of coffee.

The waiter buzzed by and left without hearing my Badoit request. He's trying to take care of twenty tables at the same time. It appears he is the only waiter for the whole café.

I find this dehydrating wait very positive. It allows me to concentrate on the boulevard before me in almost an hallucinatory way, trying to isolate what Cézanne and Zola saw from all the elements added in the 20th and 21st centuries to which I am now subjected.

I'm eating my madeleine, making associations from present to past,

83

I'm in Carmel, California

facing the Pacific Ocean, walking on a seemingly endless sandy beach as the sun slowly goes down. Today is the first day of fall in the Northern Hemisphere. It is the Equinox, a day perfectly divided between twelve hours of light and twelve hours of darkness. Right now we are close to the moment at which light and dark meet.

When I was in grade school, I learned about the earth rotating like a gyroscope and how the 23.5 degree tilt of its axis causes what we call "the seasons." The Fall Equinox has been celebrated for thousands of years by people all over the world. It is known by many other names: Alban Elfed, Cornucopia, Feast of Avilon, Festival of Dionysus, Harvest Tide, Mabon, Night of the Hunter, Witch's Thanksgiving, and The First Day of Autumn, which is closest to how I feel about it.

Monotheistic religions, like Christianity, Judaism, and Islam tend to view time as linear and going forward in only one direction: the future. Aboriginal religions, on the other hand, see time as circular and repetitive, past to future, future to past, in an endless round.

Just south of here, the Native American Chumash tribe celebrates the Fall Equinox with a sun ceremony after they've gathered and stored their harvest. The festival tells the story of the death and rebirth of life.

Just like the Chumash of Southern California, Jews all over the

world celebrate harvest time. The festival is called *Sukkot*. During the seven days it lasts, Jews are supposed to build little make-shift huts. There are neither doors nor windows, the walls are rough wooden planks and the roofs, covered with tree branches, are open to the sky. These days you can still make your own *sukkah* or you can buy a ready-made one online at sukkahdepot.com. If you aren't much of a do-it-yourselfer you can rent one at sukkahrentals.com: "We deliver, assemble, take apart, and remove."

I loved the sukkahs we had every year in the small barren patio/playground of Dr. Herzl School. Every fall, it suddenly grew a roof of leafy branches. The unobstructed sunlight was now covered over with tree boughs that glowed a luminous purple-brown and transformed our playing into a new, mysterious place of light and shadows. Each year, when the sukkah first went up, I wanted to spend the whole day in there. But the novelty quickly wore off, and the hut in the playground just looked dark and gloomy.

84

In 1936

Walter Benjamin wrote about how reproduction was changing the art world.

He said that the "soul" of a piece of art disappears when it is reproduced.

Not only art, but all human products, objects, and ideas, lose their uniqueness when reproduced, their authenticity and the critical magic of their aliveness in the here and now, are extinguished.

I wonder what recent technologies are doing to us. If we see a high definition photograph of Machu Picchu taken with the right light and filters before we go to the real place, we are being conditioned by it. Even if the photograph is seen after visiting the place, our memory of it gets glossy like the photograph, which grows more real than what we have seen "in the flesh" as time goes on.

A group of tourists race by our door. We are in the village of Oia on the island of Santorini. Our little cave faces the Caldera, the magnificent canyon of water left when the resident volcano unexpectedly exploded and destroyed much of this island. Now, many centuries later, it is beautiful and tranquil.

Shelley and I know where they are headed. We've been going to the same place everyday day since we got here, along with hundreds of other tourists squeezed onto some stairs overlooking the Caldera.

We follow them and there it is: the most extraordinary sunset ever. Every day.

You probably noticed

by now that I'm a little obsessed with the issue of fake things becoming
real and real things becoming fake.

In 1946, the Buenos Aires paper *Di Yiddishe Tsaytung* published a
text found in the ruins of the Warsaw Ghetto. It was written by Yosl
Rakover, one of the Ghetto's doomed defenders. He wrote an angry
lamentation to God. You can't help but think about Job and his rant
to Our Maker. "Yosl Rakover talks to God" was widely translated
and became famous. When Thomas Mann heard the German version
on *Radio Freies Berlin*, he declared it a holy text. French philosopher
Emmanuel Levinas called Rakover a genius of literature and theology.

For twenty years, the story of Yosl Rakover was believed to be an
eyewitness account of the ghetto's final days. It turns out that the
supposed author, Yosl Rakover didn't exist. The story was really
written by Zvi Kolitz, a Lithuanian Jew who escaped the Holocaust
by going to Palestine. He became a Zionist activist and wrote the tale
while promoting the Israeli cause. He didn't intend to create a fake
document—he simply wrote a story from the point of view of a
fictional freedom fighter. Unbeknownst to Zvi Kolitz, his name had
been mistakenly omitted in one of the early publications of the text,
which was then translated all over the world. His story became an
"authentic document" of a victim of the Holocaust. The true identity
of "Yosl Rakowetz" was established in 1992 by journalist Paul Badde,
who had discovered a copy of the original work. He came to the

United States and found Zvi Kolitz in his Columbus Circle apartment in Manhattan.

Badde had come across the only copy left of the *Di Yiddishe Tsaytung* edition of September 25, 1946, in which the real author of "Yosl Rakover talks to God" was credited. That copy disappeared under the rubble of AMIA, the Jewish Aid Society, when it was bombed in 1994.

Philosophy: (n. from Greek). Love of wisdom.

In a concentration camp during War World II, Emmanuel Levinas challenged the traditional meaning of philosophy. What he wrote about it in the camp became part of his series of lectures, "The Times and The Other." He countered that philosophy is not as we suppose "the love of wisdom," but rather "the wisdom of love." The basis for existence is love and the ethics and responsibilities that go with it. Those qualities take precedence over any objective search for the truth. Levinas wrote: "with the appearance of the human-- and this is my entire philosophy-- there is something more important than my life, and that is the life of the other."

86

As we are driving

to the airport on Route 204, I see a meaningful road sign. I ask the driver if we can take the next exit.

My friend Pavel, a scientist, had told me about some research being done here in Prague. At first I laughed, but the issue in question had been on my mind for the last few days. Since I was interested, Pavel gave me some of his research to read.

The phenomenon described in the study fascinates me because it seems to prove that the earth's magnetic field has a strong physical effect on the behavior of living creatures.

I asked the taxi driver to stop because the road sign pointed the way to the Czech University of Life Sciences where Pavel's study was conducted.

Please don't laugh (like I did) when I tell you the subject of the research.

Dog shit.

Pavel and his fellow scientists have been studying how the dogs relieve themselves, geographically speaking.

The study took two years to complete and it involved twelve scientists,

and thirty-seven dog breeds. The data from 1,893 canine defecations reveal that dogs defecate standing in a north-south direction 100% of the time. The study, published in the academic journal "Frontiers of Zoology," posits that the dogs' shitting positions are caused by small variations in the earth's magnetic field.

Being in Barcelona

always takes me back to growing up in Buenos Aires. I'm sitting at an outdoor café on Carrer Enric Granados. My espresso cup, the buildings surrounding me, the old ladies' 1950s flowered dresses, the light, the smells, even the way plants hang over the balconies, everything feels like Buenos Aires. A peaceful Buenos Aires with no military dictatorships or random street violence.

My Argentinian friend Alberto lives just a few yards from here in a modernist building, with a beautiful tiled mural on the wall of the foyer. Mirta and Alberto came to Barcelona in the 1970's, like many Argentineans during the time of the Dirty War. We are a few blocks from La Pedrera, one of Antonin Gaudi's most dramatic buildings. Or I should say, one of his funniest buildings. I'm sorry, but Gaudi makes me laugh. He was such a wonderful artist, a serious genius who changed the face of Barcelona in just a few decades. Still, I always find his buildings, with their fairy references, which he transformed into stone, delightfully comical.

Hundreds of thousands of Argentinians live in Spain because of military or economic terrorism, that made them flee their country. Many of them legally live here as citizens, thanks to the "law of return," which allows any direct descendants of Spanish citizens of the last two generations to receive automatic citizenship. They could return home for good, because Argentina is a democracy now. But they only go briefly at a time to visit family or for some brief work-

related activity. Economic terrorism still thrives in Argentina. It has submerged millions of poor people into the most abject poverty since the military governments of the 1970's took power. And it has finally caught up with and gutted Argentina's traditionally strong middle class, courtesy of the policies of Peronist governments of the 1990's and 2,000s.

I call Peronism the ideology of "everything." If you want to be a Peronist, it's easy. You just have to say: "I am a Peronist," and Peronism will magically adapt to your platform. In reality, Peronism is essentially a Fascist movement created by a military man, General Juan Perón.

Throughout his life (1895 – 1974), Perón had a fascinating gift; he conned people from opposing ideologies into following him. He was the head of the Peronist "movement," which included Trotskyites, Nazis, Jews, Centrists, even Buddhists in its enthusiastic ranks.

I'm at a copy store in the Eixample neighborhood of Barcelona, waiting in line to get some copies done. As I finally approach the counter, I glance to my right and feel a blast of Arctic air hit me. It's *him*. "Firmenich," I find myself saying aloud as if I'm seeing a ghost. In the 1970's, Mario Firmenich was the leader of the Montoneros, the largest and most deadly Peronist Marxist guerrilla organization in Argentina. They called themselves the "soldiers of Perón" and claimed to be for a "Socialist Homeland," even though their leaders, Firmenich included, started their careers in a Neo-Nazi youth group. Firmenich, himself, is believed to have secretly collaborated with the Military Junta and sent most of his Montoneros comrades to certain death.

Having Firmenich right before my eyes sends me back years ago to a supermarket in Buenos Aires, when I grabbed a can of sardines at the same time that another customer did. We were fighting for possession of the can, and as I looked at my competitor's face, I had that same feeling of ice run through my veins. It was General Reynaldo Bignone.

For a few seconds I held onto the same tin of sardines as one of the top members of the Junta that governed Argentina through seven years of the most death and destruction the country ever suffered. General Bignone gave up possession and left when he realized that I recognized him.

Mario Firmenich is currently a Professor of Economics at the University of Barcelona. He is married to an Argentinian aristocrat, a "Peronist" of course.

General Bignone was a free man until the amnesty of military men involved in the Dirty War was revoked in 2007. He is now serving a life sentence in prison.

I met another prominent Peronist, Governor Carlos Menem, in his home province of La Rioja in the days when I was traveling through the Incas Road in Argentina. He was dressed all in white and had big, bushy sideburns. It was obvious that he was trying to look like his hero, the 19th century strongman Facundo Quiroga, whom Menem starred on all the currency his province was printing. By the way, this money was worthless outside La Rioja. Picture the governor of Iowa taking it upon himself to print money, and instead of calling the bills dollars, he called them "Iowans," and instead of putting Washington or Franklin on those bills he substituted some other, less savory historical figure who, coincidentally, looked very much like himself. I had a long conversation with the Governor in La Rioja's government house when I was invited there to attend a local celebration. He explained to me his Peronist philosophy, a mix of Karl Marx, Machiavelli, and Ronald Reagan.

I had a picture taken of Menem and me shaking hands. I printed an edition of 100 copies, and called it "Alejandro Fogel's pesos." This art piece turned into a nightmare come true when Carlos Menem became President of Argentina a few years later. He won the elections as a "people's Peronist," while adopting the economic policies of The Chicago Boys, carefully sealing the barriers between rich and

poor through deregulation and wild capitalism, leaving hundred of thousands of people on the streets, unprotected and homeless.

Alejandro Fogel, "Alejandro Fogel's pesos", photo print 4 1/2 by 6 1/2 in.
Edition: 100

88

I'm standing in front of

a mural by Joan Miró at the National Museum of Catalunya. I'm here because I want to take a picture of one of his iconic stars. These stars were often the first thing Miró painted on his canvases. He said that once they were there, the canvas wasn't empty anymore and that helped relieve his fear of the blank surface.

Miró hated bourgeois art; he considered it a new form of pleasing the wealthy and affirming their beliefs. He also loathed art critics as egomaniacs, who were always trying to justify their own philosophies through someone else's work.

In 1927, he declared that he wanted to "assassinate painting."

"The only thing that's clear to me is that I intend to destroy, destroy everything that exists in painting. I have an utter contempt for painting. The only thing that interests me is the spirit itself, and I only use the customary artist's tools - brushes, canvas, paints - in order to get the best effects... I'm not interested in any school or in any artist. Not one. I'm only interested in anonymous art, the kind that springs from the collective unconscious. I paint the way I walk along the street.... When I stand in front of a canvas, I never know what I'm going to do, and nobody is more surprised than I at what comes out."

Miró's work was one of my first inspirations as an artist. He is still one of my favorite artists. I take a photograph of the star in his mural

while Shelley takes a picture of me taking the picture.

Miró's mural, made up of 406 ceramic tiles, hangs alone in a large empty space in the museum. If you stand some distance away, you can really appreciate its magnitude. The Museum sits on a hill overlooking the city. As we are walking down the hill, we see a large flock of robins drawing lines in the sky. They are flying south.

The orange-breasted European robin migrates every fall. It travels from Scandinavia to North Africa, where it stays for the winter.

In 1972, Wolfgang and Roswitha Wiltschko proved that robins navigate their journeys through an internal compass that is moved by the earth's magnetic field. This built-in avian GPS is called magnetoreception. The earth's magnetic field sensed by these birds is actually 100 times weaker than a refrigerator magnet. How is that a force so insignificant can have an effect powerful enough to guide them on their one-thousand mile journey?

Carl Jung said that in all chaos there is a cosmos, in all disorder a secret order.

Below the surface of our everyday chaotic reality there is a hidden realm of unity and absolute knowledge: the *Unus Mundus*.

It is connected to us all and we are all influenced by it, whether we are conscious of it or not.

Quantum entanglement is when two particles are far apart, and yet remain in contact and affect each other over vast distances.

In the robin's retina there is a light-sensitive protein known as cryptochrome.

If you go deep into the structure of the cryptochrome, you will find two electrons that are far apart from each other, yet quantumly entangled.

The robins connect with the earth magnetic field through that infinitesimally small quantum entanglement, and it guides them where they need to go.

Watching the robins grow smaller and smaller as they fly away, I think about the central principle of quantum mechanics: the act of watching a quantum object actually changes it. However slightly, my

gaze is changing the journey of those birds.

89

Every time I'm by the sea

I think of my father. Moishe loved the sea. The first time he ever saw it was in the port of Marseilles, where he arrived on the roof of a train, just like thousands of other displaced people after the war.

I like to imagine that moment he first encountered it; his green eyes turned aquamarine and his smile grew wider. He was in his mid-twenties, navigating a destroyed Europe, homeless, alone, only knowing a few words of every language of every country he passed through. What word came to mind when he first saw the sea? "Iam," the Yiddish word for it or the Romanian "mare?" Or did he think the newly learned French, "la mer?"

Moishe showed me the sea for the first time when I was seven years old. We went for summer vacation to Mar del Plata, a popular beach resort south of Buenos Aires.

"Mirá que grande que es el mar," he exclaimed. "Look, see how big the sea is." We would go in together and he'd become a child, too. He didn't know how to swim. He would just get wet and jump with the waves.

As I walk by the Mediterranean in Marseilles I remember my father. We are communicating through the same salty air, through the same sand dunes, through the sounds of seagulls gathering on a roof from his time then to my time now.

Our routes were so far apart that they finally touched. Full circle.

I'm at a crossroads alone with him now, alone with his petrified toenails and our dreams.

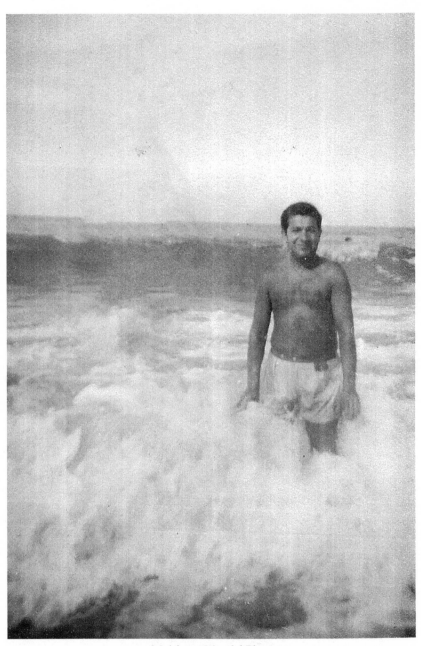

Moishe at Mar del Plata

90

A bomb exploded

at the university, in the School of Philosophy while I was in semantics class.

Before this happened, I remember having recurrent nightmares about something like this happening. As the bomb went off in my nightmares, all the windows shattered and a thick cloud of brown smoke entered the room. I always woke up from these dreams in a cold sweat, and unable to breath, but relieved it was just a dream. This time it was real. The windows shattered, but there was no smoke.

There was a brief moment of deep silence after the explosion and then people started to scream all over the building. Blood all over the floor and walls. Everyone was cut by flying glass, though luckily no one was badly injured. The only way to escape was through the blown-out windows. There was no time to think. We ran and we jumped.

As I was falling, the first thing I saw was Che Guevara's face painted on a gigantic banner across the street and the words: *Patria o Muerte*, Homeland or Death. That moment of terrible fear and falling is forever imprinted in my mind and merged with Che Guevara's face.

Now when I think about Che, the first image that comes to me is that window and the sound of the shattering glass.

My nightmares never went away, nor did they for Argentina.

Leftist and rightist paramilitary organizations were battling for

control of the country. Believe it or not, both sides were Peronists. In the end, 30,000 people disappeared. The vast majority of them were guilty of helping the poor, studying philosophy, teaching journalism or just being in somebody's phonebook. They were labeled traitors to the fatherland, materialists and atheists, enemies of Western Christian values.

The Military Dictatorship bulldozed the School of Philosophy and Literature in 1980. Even now, it remains a concrete park.

The day of the bomb changed my life. I never went back to the university. At that time all males between the ages of 18 and 30 were being drafted into the army and had to serve for one year. I went home after the bomb, took my induction letter and threw it in the garbage can. I packed a bag with books and a few clothes. I told my parents "I'm not going to the Army" and left.

Four years later, in military court, I would look Colonel Boglia in the eye and tell him why.

I'm in a hallway sitting on a bench next to other young men. Soldiers dressed in combat clothes run back and forth to various offices. I'm the only one in civilian clothes and I am shaking with cold and fear. The "recruitment" office is at the end of the hall. I am told to wait here until I'm called. They take away my National ID card and in its place I get a piece of paper with the letterhead of the Patricios 1st Infantry Regiment. They staple my photo to the paper and stamp it. I look awful.

I've been sitting on this bench for 2 hours. From the recruitment office they are calling people by alphabetical order. When his name is called, each person stands up, enters the office and closes the door. We can't hear anything that goes on in there. One by one, they come out with somber faces. Looks like we are being sent to a punitive platoon for draft evaders, one thousand miles from Buenos Aires. We are getting close to the letter "F" and it's going to be my turn.

They just called Luis Fernandez. I must be next. A few minutes later they call Gustavo Fumagalli. Why didn't they called me?

Alberto García... Jorge Grimblat... What's going on?

Daniel Zadunaisky... Jorge Zervera....

That was it. They skipped Fogel. I'm sitting on the same bench, but now I'm the only one there. Everyone else is on their way to a platoon in Patagonia, in the middle of nowhere.
For a long time I sit frozen, debating what to do. Should I run? Should I ask someone in the recruitment office what's going on?
I finally get up and knock. A thunderous voice tells me to come in.
I opened the door and stood by it.
A sergeant sitting behind a desk looks at me and asks:
"Who are you?"

91

The Cuban company

Labiofam created an extraordinary product: Ernesto. They spent more than a year working with a French perfume company to get the right scent.

The irony is that Guevara, besides being called "Che," was known as "the pig" because he hated washing. Getting close to Che Guevara wasn't fun, even by the standards of jungle guerrilas.

As I read the news of the Ernesto perfume launch on my daily Che Guevara feed, I am reminded how powerful odor is.

Smell is time travel for me. Nothing brings back the past as quickly and with such immediacy as smell. It seems that it has something to do with the regions of the brain where we keep long term memories, and our sense of smell live in close proximity. The olfactory nerves perceive a familiar scent and send you back years in the past.

I often play with my olfactory sense, my built-in time machine. Food is one of my favorite trips. I like looking at and smelling a freshly grilled steak with mashed potatoes. I get transported immediately and quite vividly to the kitchen table of my childhood. I can describe the room detail by detail. I see my Mom's hands putting the sizzling platter on the table. I see the neatly placed silverware, and my special drinking glass with my favorite soccer team's insignia on it.

As I am instantly transported from present-day New York City to

the Buenos Aires of my childhood, I realize that I can also isolate the smells of the steak and the potatoes from each other. By itself, the steak takes me to Sunday lunch at the Costanera, a riverside promenade with the best meat in Buenos Aires. Curiously, the mashed potatoes alone send me back to the nine year-old Alejandro watching puffy cumulous clouds from our rooftop and being struck by the idea that mashed potatoes and clouds look very much alike.

Proust refers to the madeleine as a special conduit to his past; but it isn't just the taste, it is the combination of taste and smell that takes him on his time travel trip. He writes:

"When from a long distant past nothing subsists, after the people are dead, after the things are broken and scattered, taste and smell alone, more fragile but enduring, more unsubstantial, more persistent, more faithful, remain poised a long time, like souls, remembering, waiting, hoping, amid the ruins of all the rest; and bear unflinchingly, in the tiny and almost impalpable drop of their essence, the vast structure of recollection."

The thing is that our memory rewrites the past. Every time I remember the steak, my hippocampus edits the tape. It's not a static documentary, it's a constantly changing video reflecting not only the past experience, but what I smell, taste, hear, and see now.

I buy a bottle of Ernesto perfume and open the stopper. Let's see where this time machine goes next.

END OF VOLUME 1

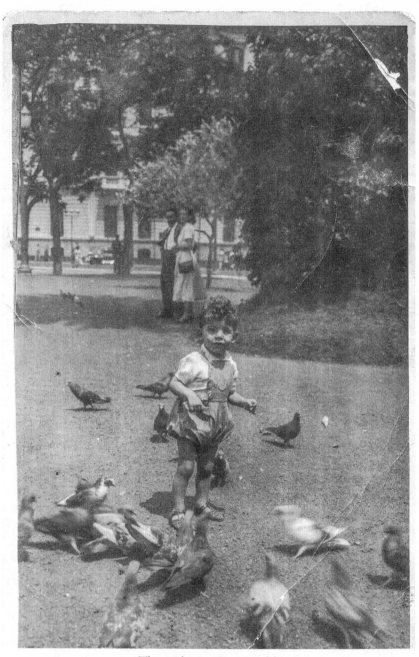

The author at 2 years old

Made in the USA
Lexington, KY
12 December 2016

List of Plates

For Shelley, as always

This is not a work of fiction.
Some names and dates have been changed to protect the privacy of those involved.
For more on Alejandro Fogel's work visit: coachingche.com

Paperback (Illustrated - Color) ISBN-978-0-9975388-0-9
Paperback (Illustrated - Black and White) ISBN-978-0-9975388-1-6
eBook (Illustrated - Color) ISBN-978-0-9975388-2-3
Cover design: David Wilder

RANDOM BOOKS,
NEW YORK

Coaching Che Guevara

Alejandro Fogel

RANDOM
BOOKS

NEW YORK

Thou wast not born for death, Immortal
  Bird!
No hungry generations tread thee down;
The voice I hear this passing night was
  heard
In ancient days by emperor and clown:
Perhaps the self-same song that found a
  path
Through the sad heart of Ruth, when, sick
  for home,
She stood in tears amid the alien corn;
The same that ofttimes hath
Charm'd magic casements, opening on the
  foam
Of perilous seas, in faery lands forlorn.
　　　　　— From "Ode to a Nightingale"
　　　　　by John Keats (1795–1821)

■ ■ ■ ■

PART I

■ ■ ■ ■

CHAPTER 1

I am walking up Prospect Avenue with my twelve-year-old son, striding side by side along the mottled sidewalk, when it strikes me he has not grown for a while. I look across at him. Damon's head — that flamed-red, leonine head — still falls below my shoulders, roughly where it had reached the previous year. He is so vital and engaging one easily forgets his size. But now his clipped stature feels like a withholding of fruition, as if his legs were young shoots held back by a clinging, invisible vine. I want to reach down and cut him loose so he can sprout. I don't want a big change but I feel he needs a little nudge, one more click to get him over the next hump of development.

"So how was school?" I ask. Damon wears baggy jeans, a gray hooded sweatshirt, and Adidas sneakers, with a Walkman round his neck and a cell phone on his belt loop.

11

"Good. I got picked to read my essay for Kick Butts day." He speeds up as we talk, swinging his arms to keep up with me, and explains that Hillary Clinton, now running for a Senate seat, is part of the visiting delegation for this stop-smoking educational campaign.

"Congrats." I salute him. "Need any help with the essay?"

"I'll do a draft and show you," Damon says. We stop at Venus Video and select a musical for his audition. "Can Jon sleep over Saturday?" he asks.

"If you get your work done, I don't see why not." I pay for the rental.

"Yes! Thanks, Dad!" Damon smiles as we exit, his cerulean eyes dancing with open vistas. But as we continue strolling up the avenue, I again ponder his unsprung height.

He is due for a growth spurt — he is overdue — and I don't need a tape measure or a doctor to verify my judgment. I can always gauge the slightest change in his body, to a hair's breadth, and I have a built-in monitor of his progress embedded deep inside me, like a microchip — or is it a mirror? If we are not exactly joined at the hip, we have more than the usual father-son bond connecting us.

Damon is the oldest of our three children.

12

Born on 8/8/88 — a date so fortuitous that in China they performed premature Cesarians to snag this birthday — he was an only child for nearly five years before his brother, Sam, arrived. For most of this time, he also was a sick child who required, and received, extraordinary love and attention from his mother, Shealagh, and from me. Even after his sister, Miranda, appeared in 1995, a healthier Damon remained the focus of our family, the pacesetter.

He was born with a malformed heart, for no known reason.

Most notably, Damon lacks a second ventricle like you and I have. His good ventricle, the left, pumps red, oxygen-rich blood throughout his body. But when the blood returns from his body to the lower right chamber of his heart — blue blood now because it has given up its oxygen — there is no second ventricle to pump it back into the lungs, where it can pick up fresh oxygen and expel carbon dioxide. So Damon was a "blue baby" whose organs and tissues did not get enough oxygen. He was smaller and weaker than other infants and his gross motor skills developed more slowly. But his brain, his manual and verbal dexterity, and his imagination never lagged.

By age four, Damon had undergone two

open-heart surgeries, and the second operation, known as a modified Fontan, alleviated his problem. A "passive flow" system, it bypasses his right side altogether and shunts the returning blue blood directly to his lungs, where it can take on vital oxygen and discharge carbon dioxide.

After the modified Fontan, Damon's body received sufficient oxygen-rich blood, and he flourished.

He grew and scrambled back onto the growth charts for height and weight, even catching up to some of his friends. His color improved, his energy increased, and he became physically more active. He is a tortoise, not a hare, but he is intrepid and takes delight in activity of all kinds, from karate and kayaking to soccer and skiing.

Damon is in seventh grade now, attending the Salk School of Science in Manhattan, where he excels academically. He also is an actor who performs in every school play and then in more advanced theater workshops outside school. And he's become increasingly popular in middle school, more of a star than he's ever been. When he spiffs up his unruly red hair and dons a dress shirt for the school dance, cruising the room like a confident young blade, he makes an impression. He outshines the taller boys because he actually dances and *talks* to the girls.

Damon is never going to be the biggest kid in the class or run a four-minute mile, but otherwise he's in great shape. He's been healthy for the eight years since his last operation and free of all medications. He sees his cardiologist every six months and she marvels at his progress.

I am keenly aware of all this as we walk together this afternoon. We have lived through a protracted nightmare and survived to talk about it as a page from history, a backstory. I know all about patience and keeping your eye on the fundamentals. Shealagh and I have our own set of milestones for Damon, outside the standard configuration, and we feel inordinately proud of his advancement and the kind of person he's become.

So on this early fall day of the first year of the new millennium, with the soft yellow leaves raining down from the sky and starting to blur the margins of the pavement, I dismiss my concerns as exaggerated, a common defensive ploy to contemplate the worst, just so you can say it ain't so.

We turn into the wide embrace of Terrace Place, with the great park at one end, and walk up the front porch into our two-story brick house with its long driveway and small backyard that boasts a bona fide peach tree and a fig tree, our own patch of Eden.

CHAPTER 2

A perfect spring evening at Yankee Stadium.
The air is warm, with the slightest breeze
ruffling the flag. The baselines and foul lines
are stamped in fresh white chalk.

I have taken Damon and two of his closest friends, Kyle and Keith, to a night game
against the Boston Red Sox. The stadium is
packed, the fight songs blaring and the beer
flowing, as befits these longtime archrivals.
But the three teens don't really care. They
enjoy the aesthetics and ambience of the
game as much as the competition.

"Check out the body-paint dudes!" Keith
points at the bleachers, where seven rowdy
males spell "Go Yanks!" in bold lettering
across bare torsos.

"I think they're drunk." Kyle wrinkles her
nose at the beefy, soft-bellied roisterers.

"Man with crazy chef's hat, six o'clock!"
Damon gestures three rows ahead, where a
fan sits in a billowing, brimless white hat.

"The Mad Hatter is blocking the view —"

"It's called a toque." Kyle corrects Damon with her sweet Natalie Portman smile.

"Duh, I think it's a mascot for Sheffield — he's 'the Chef,'" Keith interjects, correcting Kyle.

"Really? Whatever . . ." Kyle giggles as she takes in the information.

"Hey, Dad, can we get Cracker Jacks? Kyle needs brain food."

Kyle is Damon's oldest and closest friend, a girl he rescued in kindergarten when the school bus dropped her off at the wrong stop. They are the same age but Damon is a grade ahead, which makes him the sage elder. Now almost thirteen, Kyle changes her hair color every week — today it's purple with blond streaks — and she wears bangles and bracelets and layers of colorful clothing. She is bright, vital, and quite beautiful, but her identity shifts like a kaleidoscope, with a propensity toward the darker hues.

The Cracker Jacks arrive in a giant box and Kyle and Keith dive in looking for the prize. "If it's a ring, it's mine!" Keith smiles.

Keith is a tall, wiry African American, wry, sensitive, and hyperarticulate. He and Damon attend Salk together. Handsome and fine-featured, like a model, Keith lives

18

alone with his young single mother in Harlem and spends weekends with his grandmother in Queens.

"Okay, guys, we need to root for the Yankees," Damon announces late in the game. "I think they're losing" — he checks the scoreboard — "and we don't want my dad to go home unhappy."

And indeed, after eight lackluster innings, the Yanks rally and pull out the game with two home runs in the bottom of the ninth. The stadium erupts. Damon and I exchange excited high fives, connecting in the moment's primitive ecstasy. Although not a committed fan, Damon appreciates raw emotion and the thrill of the come-from-behind. And he is impressed by my militant cheerleading for someone other than him. As he embraces Kyle in the pandemonium, I note he looks a little hamstrung, as if nursing an injury.

I wonder if it's the aftereffects of his "fight." Five weeks earlier, Damon came home from school with deep cuts and a grapefruit-sized swelling across his forehead. He'd gotten into an altercation with the school bully, a humongous lout twice his size.

"This kid kept shoving me and trying to get in my face," Damon explained. "He bumped me with his chest: 'Come on, little guy, fight me!' I told him I wasn't afraid of him but I didn't want to fight, so I started to walk away when he rushed me from behind and smashed my head against the cafeteria table. I never saw him coming."

Damon sustained contusions, a hematoma, and a concussion. Head injuries even in healthy people are notoriously complex, as both Shealagh and I know: Shealagh did research on war veterans with head wounds at the Radcliffe Infirmary Neuropsychology Unit at Oxford, where we met, and I boxed for Oxford University and learned about concussions firsthand. We kept Damon at home while I initiated disciplinary action against his attacker, a notorious troublemaker, and made sure this could never happen again.

Damon appeared physically traumatized yet stubbornly proud, incised with fresh, deep wounds he's worn since like a badge of honor. He recovered, and his standing up to the class bully only enhanced his status in school as a leader. But the incident forced me to confront his vulnerability, and my own possible complicity in it. I had always taught Damon to stand up for himself and to hold his ground. But now I felt torn between a father's pride at his son's courage and concern that Damon not follow my example too closely, because he lacks the physical resources to defend himself. I quickly realized, however, that any cautionary advice at this stage was futile because Damon's character had long been formed. All I could do was hug my brave-hearted bantamweight while privately resolving to watch him like a hawk.

We return from Yankee Stadium in high spirits, dropping Keith off in Harlem and Kyle in Ditmas Park. Shealagh, waiting up, gets a full report from her beaming son as we sit in the downstairs kitchen. Damon even eats his mother's rhubarb pie as he fills her in on the triumphant game.

It's been a good day. But now it's late and there's school tomorrow, so Damon moseys up to the middle floor, where he and Sam have adjacent bedrooms. Shealagh goes to talk to him and get a little private time — mother and son have their own very special bond — before she kisses him good night and leaves.

As I pass through on my way to the top floor, Damon cracks the bathroom door and calls to me from the doorway. "Hey, Dad, can you come here a minute?"

I can sense something amiss as I head to the bathroom. Normally Damon asks his mother about routine matters and saves me for the big stuff.

As I walk inside, Damon closes the bathroom door with mysterious urgency. I feel the burden of a pending revelation and brace myself.

"I wanted to show you this, Dad . . ."

Damon pulls down his pants and lowers his boxers under the overhead bulb.

"Oh man!" I shake my head. "What happened?" His testicles hang down, hugely swollen. They look four times their normal size. He's a young kid and I am all for his sexual development, but this is alarming. "When did . . . ?"

"I noticed it Friday but thought I should wait a day. But it hasn't gotten better."

"Poor guy . . . Does it hurt, D-man?"

He hesitates. "It's uncomfortable." Damon has experienced real pain and never exaggerates about such matters. "And it's kinda awkward, you know —"

"Sure. Okay, this isn't right and we're going to take care of it. Pronto!"

I talk to Shealagh, then call a few doctor friends. Two scenarios emerge. A hernia, the most likely, or a twisted testicle, rarer and more urgent. And given Damon's history, there's always an extra element of uncertainty and fear.

We decide not to risk waiting until morning and call my parents to come over and babysit Sam and Miranda before we speed off to Columbia Presbyterian Hospital, which has treated Damon since shortly after his birth. It's a long drive, but Columbia knows his complex case and we trust them. It's past midnight when we reach the sprawling medical complex in Washington Heights.

Eons ago, we did hard time in this hospital and feared we'd never escape. Once, when he weighed only eleven pounds, Damon spent thirty days in the ICU, trying to come off the respirator. Now as we arrive, the dread memories rise up.

We walk past ambulances, EMT personnel, and two burly cops and enter into the perpetual twilight zone of the emergency room, a cacophony of coughing, moaning, shouting, and crying. We pick our way through the tumult and despair and request immediate care for our son. Damon's cardiologist, Dr. Hayes, has called ahead and told them to expect us.

The admissions clerk nods, unimpressed, and gives us forms to fill out.

A well-organized unit, we establish ourselves on three plastic chairs. Shealagh distributes juice and snacks and fills out forms, I call home to check on the kids and gather intel from the staff, and Damon, after sweeping the room, disappears into his copy of *The Subtle Knife* by Philip Pullman.

Eventually an intake nurse admits us and we enter a more orderly if still-hectic space. Someone takes Damon's vitals and he gets a bed with a flimsy half curtain. We wait until a young resident pops by. He checks Damon's groin and instantly declares he has a hernia. A bona fide inguinal hernia, the gross rupture will need to be surgically repaired, but he finds no twisted testicle or undue cause for alarm.

I feel a measure of relief but continue talking to the doctor as he examines Damon. Because he is unfamiliar with my son's anatomy — Damon's heart is on the right side and several other organs are reversed — I fill him in while he asks questions and offers observations. I've long grasped that medicine is an imperfect art, fifty to a hundred years from being an exact science, so I gather information from every possible source. I've also learned that good doctors are not necessarily the senior people with fancy reputations — often quite the opposite — and a young resident, if he observes thoroughly and with an open mind, can tell me as much as anyone.

This resident — he has the gift; you can

tell in the first thirty seconds — palpates Damon's abdomen and casually mentions his liver is enlarged, which I've never heard before. When I inquire further, he lets me feel how the liver presses against the abdomen, its margins extending beyond the normal range. Damon watches us with quiet, alert eyes, always the model patient, and I wonder if this enlarged liver could explain why his belly protrudes, giving him a slouching appearance. Even in karate class, with his *gi* neatly belted and his back erect, his stomach seems to slump forward, and zipped into a black wet suit for swimming, he looks paunchy despite his leanness.

Shealagh and I have questioned his cardiologist about this anomaly and we once dragged Damon to a chiropractor to try to sort it out. We exhort our son to stand up straight and pull his shoulders back. Now it strikes us a protruding liver could explain his posture more than any deficiency of spine or will. We feel a stab of guilt that we held Damon even partially responsible. Later, when we pursue the oversized liver with the chief of surgery, he says it is completely normal for children with Damon's heart condition and he sees it frequently. We wonder why no one ever told us this before.

We schedule the surgery promptly but try to minimize the disruption to Damon's life. He hates to miss school and has started rehearsal for *Charlie and the Chocolate Factory.*

CHAPTER 3

When the morning of his hernia operation dawns, we tell ourselves it is a routine procedure, but with Damon's medical history, nothing is routine. We envy all our friends who freak out over their kids' colds.

On the ride in, Damon and I discuss a new play I'm supporting with Alan Alda playing the Nobel Prize–winning physicist Richard Feynman. I work for a well-established philanthropic foundation and one of my roles is to help develop plays, films, and television shows with science and technology themes.

We arrive at the hospital, sign in, and go to the fourth-floor pediatrics ward.

The secretary makes several copies of our insurance and asks us to fill out the same form about Damon's medical history, several pages long, for the umpteenth time.

A nurse takes Damon's blood pressure and temperature, weighs and measures him, and exchanges his familiar jeans and T-shirt for a hospital gown that ties loosely at the back. A hearty, decent sort, she means well but her idea of small talk is to ask him three times if he's nervous. "A little," Damon says to mollify her.

Another nurse comes in to start an IV. Damon has pale, spidery veins and sticking him requires precision. After an initial adjustment, she gets the line in.

Then a young doctor, bright-eyed with self-importance, saunters in and beams at Damon. "Hi, I'm the resident. Have you ever had any serious medical conditions?"

At first, we think he's kidding, but he's not. Damon turns away, too polite to sneer, and Shealagh groans in disbelief. I fire off a rapid, testy medical summary. "Next time do your homework and read the chart!" I say. He slinks out of the room, red-faced.

We wait with other tense parents and their sick children until they send us to the pre-operative holding area. A fountain of gurgling water, pink-lit, is meant to soothe our nerves. A tall doctor with a Hungarian accent walks in and mumbles that they want to put Damon under general anesthesia because a local injection could lower his blood pressure, and his pressure is already low. The anesthesiologist tries to rush our consent but we won't give it until he answers each of our questions and reviews all the options. General anesthesia carries a known risk of mortality, compounded, like everything else, in Damon's case, and we have learned not to take anything for granted.

The surgeon arrives in his scrubs and quickly runs through the procedure. An affable, highly competent man, he does not anticipate problems and wants to get started. We each ask questions, including Damon — "When can I go back to my karate class?" — before signaling that we are ready. The nurse releases the brakes on the gurney and the anesthesiologist, turning to follow the rolling bed, suggests we say our good-byes now.

"No," I tell him. "We always go into the operating room with our son. It's part of our routine." Damon watches us from the gurney, upset — we touch his arm to calm him — before the surgeon tells the anesthesiologist it's okay for us to accompany our son.

We quickly throw yellow moon suits over our clothes and don protective face masks before plodding down the corridor beside Damon's gurney like a team of sterilized astronauts. We turn and push through sealed doors into the operating theater.

It's a large, cool, brilliantly lit room with state-of-the-art medical equipment surrounded by a tinted observation booth. A lone bed rises in the center, with a giant stainless steel arm arcing above it. A modern setting for sacrifice and, hopefully, healing — a place for testing one's faith.

I tell myself it's not as dire this time — this is standard procedure for a hernia — but still, I can't believe we're going through this ordeal *again*.

I keep up a running banter with Damon as they wheel him into position and Shealagh chimes in with reassuring comments. Damon remains stoic and game throughout but he likes having us nearby. I want Mom and Dad to be the last thing he sees when he closes his eyes and the first when he opens them again.

Damon climbs onto the narrow steel bed and they immediately place a mask over his head and tell him to inhale. A team of nurses, doctors, and assistants attaches lines and sensors to Damon. They prick his finger with a needle and he says "ouch" through the mask, but then the nitrous oxide reaches his central nervous system and he begins to laugh. We watch his lips pull back over his large front teeth all the way to the gums as he giggles uncontrollably. His big face with

30

the bright red hair and pale skin fills with induced mirth. Then he is out cold. An array of monitors reads live data input from his unconscious body. We kiss him one last time and leave the operating theater.

We sit in a common room with gray lockers and a coffeepot. We make our calls, try to read the paper, stare into space.

The wait that lasts an eternity.

At some point, the surgeon emerges and walks toward us. We scour his face and body language for clues to our son's fate. He reaches us and immediately says, "Everything's okay." So time begins again, and now we can listen to what he says.

It was a surprisingly big hernia that demanded more surgery than anticipated — "The hernia of the week," the surgeon confides with a trace of professional pride — but all is well now. We should see improvement within seventy-two hours. Damon will be sore for a few days but the rupture is repaired and the problem solved.

We thank the surgeon profusely, then go to the recovery room to see Damon.

"Hi, sweetie." Shealagh hugs Damon, who's groggy from the anesthesia.

"You did great, D-man." I kiss his brow and congratulate him. He smiles weakly.

We sit by the bedside, each of us holding

one of his pale, slender hands. We feed him ice chips until he's permitted to drink.

The next morning we leave the hospital and take Damon home.

Everything seems to have gone well. Damon had a hernia, which any healthy person can get, and now it's fixed. There is no apparent connection to his underlying heart disease, nor any long-term ramification. He'll be back at school within a week and right as rain. We had a spot of bad luck but it's behind us now.

We try to reassure ourselves with this official prognosis but sense in our depths that something has changed, some seismic but as yet undetectable shift.

Something *has* changed, but we do not understand it yet.

CHAPTER 4

"Help, help me!"

I am jolted awake. It is early on a Saturday morning and somewhere in the house, Shealagh is screaming.

I leap out of bed and follow the trail of cries down the long staircase.

My wife hovers on the middle steps, bent over in agony.

Her back has seized up and she cannot move.

Shealagh has experienced back trouble for the past few years. A tall, robust young woman and a competitive athlete when we met — swimming, rowing, riding — she no longer competes but maintains a physically active life, so the worsening condition takes its toll.

She works three twelve-hour days a week as a therapist for the New York City Health and Hospitals Corporation, shuttling to a clinic in East New York, where she ministers to an underprivileged minority clientele. Meanwhile, she chauffeurs her three kids everywhere; kneels down with them over class projects; helps design and build sets and costumes, especially for Damon's theatricals; and cleans, cooks, shops, and gardens.

Now she's beginning to slow down, and it's not just from passing forty. She gets out of breath and uses an inhaler. Her afflicted back makes sitting at a desk for long periods untenable. Often, she must lie down in the middle of the day. She is less mobile and energetic and needs assistance with routine chores.

I pick up some slack and also get outside help. But I fret about this atypical lassitude in such a strong, vigorous person, and I worry about my wife.

One friend suggests it is partly psychological, a delayed result of Damon's illness and the stress surrounding those early years. Now that Damon is better and we have three wonderful kids, none of which came easily, now that our lives and careers are flourishing, the suppressed trauma of that period is returning for a full accounting.

I fear the worst when I find Shealagh frozen on the stairs this Saturday morning. She hangs on to the banister like a lifeline, paralyzed and sobbing in pain.

"I can't move!" she cries.

Slowly, with excruciating care, I maneuver Shealagh down the steps and into our car. We drive straight to the emergency room — the nearest one, in Brooklyn, this time.

Several long days, intrusive MRIs, and expert consults later, the consensus is that Shealagh requires back surgery. She has extrusion and disc herniation, with severe compression of the nerve root. She has lost some sensation and mobility in her left leg — she has minor "neurological deficit" — and the doctors don't want to risk more damage.

It is late July and we have planned our big August vacation on the Isle of Skye, our traditional retreat in the Scottish Hebrides. Shealagh will need four to six weeks of rest and rehab following the surgery, so Skye is out of the question for her. I'm beginning to feel like a professional caretaker and I'm ready to cancel all our plans so I can focus on Shealagh. My tenderhearted wife, the devoted mother of my three children and my dearest friend and confidante, she also is my secret sharer in the special project that is Damon. Our union has deep roots. On a more mundane level, Shealagh is Super Mom, whereas Dad, useful for schoolwork, sports, and outdoor adventure, mostly writes in the summer, so it's unclear how the kids would eat, dress, or sleep on clean sheets with *him* in charge.

But Shealagh does not want her children deprived of their big summer holiday and wonders if we can go on vacation without her. Maybe, too, she needs a break from us so she can concentrate on her rehabilitation and get some personal time. Her biggest concern is whether we four can survive with Dad as the sole parent, especially since I planned to do my summer writing in Skye. I assure her I'm up to the task and will defer the writing if I must. She should stop worrying about anything but her recovery.

Shealagh's spine surgery is considered elective but proves more harrowing than we expected, especially after our recent experience with Damon.

My wife lies sprawled on her side as they lift the back muscles off her spine and expose the nerve root, forcing aside the protective membrane so they can remove any obstructive disc matter. I sit alone in the hospital's designated waiting area and call my best friend, David, who lives in Seattle, to get my mind off the unthinkable.

Damon is very concerned about his mother's well-being but helps to divert Sam and

Miranda, who stay with him at my parents' house. I phone him to provide updates. He talks to me from the room I slept in when I was his age and I feel like I'm talking to my younger self, only an improved version.

"So when will the surgery be over?" Damon asks pointedly. Responsibility comes naturally to him.

"Another hour or so. It's always longer than they say. This is routine, D-man."

"I know. Sam wanted to talk to Mom but I said she was sleeping."

"That's true, well done," I praise him. "So the little ones are okay?"

"Yeah. They're watching *Jungle Book* on the VCR and eating ice cream with Grandma and Granddad. Miranda's already asleep but Sam is being stubborn."

"He'll drop off soon . . . I'll call you when Mom's out of the OR. Okay?"

"Don't worry about me, Dad. Just watch over Mom's doctors like you watch over mine."

Shealagh's flashy, expensive surgeon shows up in the waiting room after the surgery wearing a tux. He says the patient is fine, he did his job, and now we must wait to see if they got all the disc material out — because of course you can never tell.

After the surgery, Shealagh invites her best

friend, Sonja, who is single and mobile and also happens to be a doctor, to stay in our house through August. My wife wants us to go on holiday with a clear conscience. Sonja is a very kind, loyal, and super-efficient friend, so we couldn't leave Shealagh in better hands. Still, the kids and I all feel a pang, and not a few gnawing doubts, when, loaded with suitcases, backpacks, and wet suits, we set off for our summer vacation in Scotland without Mom.

CHAPTER 5

Damon assists me from the start of our motherless Hebridean sojourn, even before we've landed. He supervises Sam and Miranda on the airplane, escorting them to the toilet, refereeing card games, and showing them how to work the in-flight remote.

At Glasgow airport, he insists on pushing the second luggage cart, even when it proves unwieldy and spins around on him. On the winding drive through northwest Scotland, he entertains his younger siblings with stories. When they get cranky and fight, he adroitly applies the carrot and stick — "You want to hear what happened next? Then stop bickering!" — until they beg him to continue, promising peace treaties until the end of time.

My own exhortations to look out the window at the lochs, mountains, and medieval castles dotting the Scottish Highlands fall on deaf, jet-lagged ears. Nevertheless, the Isle of Skye casts its misty magic the instant we make landfall, and we are transported as we drive through the magnificent twisting Black Cuillin. Snowcaps gleam while lush vegetation flourishes — purple heather, yellow gorse, and red rowans dazzle our bleary eyes — and torpid sheep blithely cross the highway.

We drive toward Portree harbor, then veer off the highway, singing "Donald, Where's Your Troosers?" as we skirt the moors along a serpentine valley road. Across from us rises a broad, heather-clad mountain, Ben Tianavaig, which overlooks the cold blue bay that reputedly welcomed Bonnie Prince Charlie ashore in the eighteenth century.

We descend sharply into the tiny loch-lapped village of Camastianavaig and head for the White Cottage, a compact stone croft house with a slate roof. The somnolent village consists of about twenty houses with small plots and open grazing land dotted about a paved circle that loops the picturesque bay at the base of Ben Tianavaig. Government subsidies keep this rural crofting community afloat and support the few die-hards who still tend the ubiquitous, black-faced sheep, who outnumber the cars and the people and overrun the place at will.

"Sheep attack!" Damon grins at the familiar swarm of waddling, woolly frames, bleating faces, and clipping hooves that greets us.

Although we are outsiders, Shealagh is a maternal descendant of the island's ruling clan, the Macleods, and entitled by tradition to wear the tartan. Her ancestors cannot lay claim to Dunvegan Castle, the imposing twelfth-century Macleod seat that still draws tourists, but her great-grandfather Jack Macleod bottled Macleod whiskey and made his fortune bootlegging to the States during Prohibition. He built schools and hotels on the island and his offspring prospered, several becoming members of Parliament and one marrying the daughter of a billionaire media tycoon. My own link is far more tenuous but I spent a year living alone in the isolated family croft two decades earlier, without heating save for coal-banked fires and without a phone. We weren't married yet — I'd graduated Oxford and Shealagh still had a year to go — so I paid rent and wrote every day in near-perfect solitude, developing the daily discipline that's sustained me since and forming a deep attachment to this wind-swept Celtic aerie. I may also harbor a sweet spot for Scotland because my father grew up in Glasgow and still speaks with a faint brogue.

Now our kids have discovered the splendors of this rugged island. Our sheltered bay gives them the freedom to play outdoors and run wild with other parent-free children, and they fit right in with their bright hair and fair, freckled complexions.

Damon and Miranda — she's a vivid blonde, unlike her two redheaded brothers, but her general coloration matches — both have friends in the village from previous visits, while Sam, the middle child, tags along, buffeted between competing camps. Because the village has a limited pool of children, the kids are more adaptable and less finicky about age differences — seventeen-year-olds willingly play with seven-year-olds — but sibling rivalry and group exclusion appear immutable.

Damon is leader of the pack and chief organizer, ruling his siblings and negotiating between two main friends, Lachlann and Jamie. Lachlann, compact, agile, and mischievous, has a six-year-old sister, Kerry, who plays with Miranda, and an older brother, Alasdair, who sometimes joins the boys. Jamie, tall, handsome, and soft-spoken, lives down the hill with his parents and offers a quieter alternative.

We quickly develop a routine. I rise around five A.M., stroll down to the bay — examining tidal seaweed and occasionally spotting a seal or a heron — then pick up fresh eggs from Lachlann's house (his mother raises chickens) after depositing a brass one-pound coin in the squeaky metal honor box. I return to the croft and write for several hours before anyone wakes up.

Sam rises first and I give him writing assignments. His work is meticulous but spare, and I must coax him to explicitness.

"What you wrote is very good, but you need more than one paragraph!"

Sam at eight has curly red hair, lighter than Damon's; pale blue eyes; and a dusting of freckles across winsome features. He is lean and rubbery with a sweet disposition. Mostly quiet and self-contained, he also possesses a stubborn streak that can erupt into tantrums. We call him El Shrieko for his piercing cry. He is our wild card.

"Can you help me write a postcard to Marwan?" Sam asks today.

"Sure," I say, nodding. Marwan is a Palestinian boy from Lebanon who Sam met in first grade and with whom he formed a tight, biblical-style friendship. Marwan's family, lacking a green card, had to leave Brooklyn for the United Arab Emirates, but despite the distance and the passing years, the two boys call each other almost every week and stay in close touch.

After Sam, Miranda comes tumbling down the narrow stairs. I give her juice and a sheet of math problems, which she knocks off in a trice.

"All done!" Miranda beams. She is quick and clever, a loquacious six-year-old charmer dubbed "the blond bombshell" by her brothers. Sensitive but pragmatic, Miranda is always thinking two steps ahead.

I enjoy these private morning sessions with Sam and Miranda but when Damon gets up — I hear him prop open the skylight upstairs and can visualize him inhaling the pristine air and the dazzling bay in one luxurious gulp — I usually let him slide on the schoolwork. I want him to relax and recharge, and after years of working with him, I know he's absorbed my lessons and internalized my approach.

"Morning, D-man. How'd you sleep?" I smile at him in the low doorway.

"Good. I always have the deepest sleeps here." He yawns. "What time is it?"

While Damon washes up in the one tiny bathroom, I prepare a big communal breakfast. This first meal of the day becomes increasingly well attended, just like our lunches and dinners. The kids' friends drift in at mealtimes because they've discovered I'm a naïve profligate — I over-shop — and a soft touch, at least where food is concerned. I smile as they tear into Nutella sandwiches and stacks of funny-face ham and frosted wheat cereal that comes in sheets.

After breakfast, I stand on the metal grate by the door and make my restive offspring put on sun hats, sunscreen — it doubles as a midge repellent, so they don't complain so much — and Wellington boots. The high rubber boots prove practical not only for the marshy bogs and moors but as protection against the sheep shit that litters our front yard. The sheep have discovered a gap in our sagging wire fence.

Damon, the ringleader, claps on his blue canvas legionnaire's hat, which has side flaps and covers the back of his neck. He wears bottle-green wellies, scraggly shorts, and a *Save the Panda* T-shirt. I make sure he takes his EpiPen — an emergency shot of epinephrine against bee stings, to which he's allergic.

Once the kids have passed inspection, I unhook the big swinging front gate and let them all out with their friends. "See you for lunch," I say, waving, as they scamper off.

Damon, who dominates indoors with his force of personality, immediately falls behind as all the kids run up the hill to Lachlann's. He follows his own meandering path to obscure this fact, veering off to beat the roadside thistles with a stick and bending down to discover natural wonders en route.

When he can, Damon also deploys his younger siblings as cover. Sam, though gangly, benign, and worshipful of his older brother, is already too fast, but little Miranda happily lingers for Damon's attentions. Damon takes her by the hand and carries her off to the side of the road when a car comes by. He lifts her over a puddle or ditch, as if she were more helpless than she is.

"Don't worry, I got you, Mirandy," Damon says protectively.

Miranda plays along with her adored big brother until she gets bored and races off with the fleet Kerry — "Gonna beat you, Kerry!" — leaving Damon exposed again.

The others wait at the top as Damon slogs up the steep hill to join them. I watch him swing his hips and push his upper body forward while his striving legs lift and his feet drag and scrape the ground in their clunky rubber boots.

Damon struggles, but he always smiles and maintains his self-possession, and he always gets there. He's not even that far behind.

"Okay, guys, what are we doing?" He catches his breath at the crest and quickly reestablishes leadership. "I know. Let's go on a treasure hunt!"

CHAPTER 6

Due to his medical history, Damon has never learned to ride a bicycle. At home, I practice with him in the anonymity of Prospect Park, but it's a struggle because it's taken so long and now he's afraid to let go. I wait for the summer, when we'll have more time together. A few more falling-down sessions and I know we'll get there.

But it's trickier than I anticipated once we're in Skye. Damon is almost thirteen now; there's no privacy in this tiny village, and I don't want to embarrass him in front of his friends and his siblings. I watch Lachlann do amazing wheelies and other high-wire tricks on his bicycle and I decide to ask him to teach Damon. For a fee, of course. Lachlann loves commerce and jumps on the idea — I offer him a hundred dollars, which makes his eyes pop.

"Och aye, I'll teach him to bike up Ben Tianavaig for a hundred dollars!" Lachlann says, beaming.

Damon likes the idea too. It's a challenge and an adventure for two twelve-year-old boys. They spend the next few days practicing nonstop. I can hear fragments and catch glimpses of their budding collaboration from my study window. They come down the hill at a good clip, Lachlann running alongside Damon's bicycle with one hand on the handlebars.

"Good job, Damon . . . Och, but keep the damn thing straight, man!"

"I'm trying," Damon squeals, "but it has a mind of its own — oh no . . . !"

Damon takes several spills, gasping and giggling as he scrapes his leg or tumbles over Lachlann. I give the boys a stern safety lecture and make them practice on the flat parts, but I do not stop them. They're having a great time together. And I know, underneath the playfulness, how much this matters. I can see Damon's confidence and comfort level grow by the day.

One afternoon Damon calls to me from the road. "Hey, Dad, come out here for a minute, I have something to show you!" I step out of the croft. The sun pours gold over the entire valley, the granite peaks of the Red Cuillin glow, and the glassy blue bay shimmers.

"Come on, Dad!" Damon grins, beckoning me closer.

He perches over a black mountain bike at the top of the hill.

"You watching?" he asks excitedly. I nod. I have seen him perform onstage many times but this is a riskier kind of role for him. He straddles the metal frame and counts off, rehearsing in his head. "Ready?" he says, priming himself as much as me.

"Just do it, Damon!" Lachlann cries. "Before the bloody midges eat us alive."

Damon places one tentative foot on the upraised pedal. He takes a deep breath, then pushes off more authoritatively with his back leg.

The impelled bike immediately starts to zigzag in wide arcs.

"Whoa!" Damon tries to get a grip on the shaky handlebars but the bicycle careens toward a roadside gully, making straight for the gutter.

"No!" Damon yells, bracing for disaster. But with the bike rim on the verge of the ditch, he recovers and steers it back to the center of the road.

Still a tad off-kilter, Damon hunkers forward and to the left as the bike leans to the right. I've never seen anything like this, except maybe at the circus.

Damon and his bicycle tilt in *opposite* directions.

"Hang on, Damon!" Lachlann shouts, fearing the worst.

I hold my breath. Damon appears to be falling out of the saddle as he overcompensates on the left to offset the rightward drift of the bicycle. The bike sways and jitters as if it's about to spin away from him. But somehow Damon manages to keep it balanced and finds a strange new equilibrium.

A tightly focused Damon now pedals past me with set jaw. In the corners of his mouth, I spot the wisp of a proud smile forming. He grips the handlebars with tremulous intensity and turns right on a steep slope, speeding downhill. The bike wobbles but Damon confidently hangs on and stays astride all the way to the bay.

"Attaboy, D-man!" I holler and whoop, startling the sheep. Lachlann stands by a gorse bush, beaming at his student and avidly contemplating payday.

My son pushes his bike up the hill, breathless with excitement. "See that, Dad?"

I flash a thumbs-up as Damon remounts and pushes off again. He's got the hang of it now, and he's having fun. A panicked sheep runs out in front of him and Damon swerves expertly around it. "Naughty ewe!"

he chides, grinning.

The look on his face as he makes the bicycle do his bidding is extraordinary to behold. I watch him grasp all the lost ground he's recovered and the new powers he's unleashed as he rejoins his cohort and celebrates a major rite of passage.

I call Shealagh in New York. "Guess what your son did today?" Delighted, she wants to congratulate Damon, so he trudges into the croft and indulges his mother with nonchalant teen pride — "Yeah, Mom, I know" — before running out again.

Shealagh is mending and Sonja is taking excellent care of her. She misses us all but is happy her kids are having a great summer in such a beautiful place. We discuss the progress of each child, then linger over Damon's latest accomplishment.

"This is huge," Shealagh says. "A few years late, but he did it. Our Damon!"

The Skye idyll continues, with a few minor setbacks. One day, a breathless Sam slips into the croft with a garbled tale that he and Damon had gone into the woods searching for a tree house, and now Damon is apparently injured and needs help!

Frantic, I race out the door and down the valley to the bay, then charge up the facing hill, searching through bushes and a thick copse of birch that Sam points me to.

"I don't see him, Sam! You sure this is the place? Think carefully!"

Sam is flustered and confused so I ask him to calm down and retrace their route.

We scour the area in a wide swath. I cup my hands and yell. Nothing.

Just when I'm wondering if this is a bad dream — the dense wooded hillside, though visible from the croft, would take me hours to comb through, and it's already growing dark — we stumble upon Damon lolling on a bed of bracken. He reclines on one elbow, enacting a battle scene on the peaty ground with twigs deployed as toy soldiers.

"Hey, Dad." He greets me as if I've just dropped by his room. It transpires my venturesome firstborn was swinging on a rotten tree branch when it collapsed under his weight. He tried to walk back but it became too painful so he sent Sam for help.

I hoist Damon onto my back and carry him down the hill and back up to the croft. Inside, I lay him on the couch and examine him carefully for injuries. Sam insists he was only a foot off the ground when he fell, and in truth, he does not appear seriously hurt. A couple of minor scrapes and bruises, a sore ankle. But he's had a scare, and so have I.

I'm struck by Damon's frailty as I carry him through the sinking twilight back to the croft, how small and fragile he feels in my arms and how tightly he clings to me. It takes so little to knock him off course. And I'm struck by my own powerlessness, how hard it is for me to safeguard my son if I also want him to have a normal life.

Back home, Damon explains how his little brother propped him up and carried him down the hill until it got too hard and Sam ran for help. We both agree eight-year-old Sam showed impressive maturity and presence of mind.

I cook Damon his favorite dishes and read to him on the couch while he mends. Sam and Miranda get bedtime stories but Damon needs more mature fare — all three kids bunk in the same room — so I select literary works for him, which we two discuss.

On request, I also give my recuperating son therapeutic massages. He has a stiff upper body with a thick neck and a relatively narrow back, solid and compact, except for two bony shoulder blades. You can see where his powerful underlying frame, the rugged core that is Damon's original blueprint, has been attenuated by cardiac insufficiency. I knead the tight, sensitive muscles around his scapula and gently work out the knots, praying that the young body at my fingertips reaches its full potential.

One day, when I return from a run with a bad cramp in my own back, Damon offers to give *me* a massage. I'm glad he's feeling better but I tell him it's not necessary. Besides, my back has defeated trained people twice his size. But Damon insists.

I sit on the edge of the couch bowed in grateful wonder, a hunched father in sopping T-shirt, as my diligent son bends over the knotted, sweaty terrain of my back and, asking for feedback, zeroes in on my cramp. "Wow, Dad, it's like a rock!"

I feel the fierce, loving, and focused determination as Damon pinpoints the area of tightness and exerts precise force with his elbows and thumbs. It's a sweet treat, and I enjoy the pleasant sense of bonding with my own flesh and blood.

As the summer wears on, I undertake more outings with the kids. We go to the Skye Highland Games in Portree and the sheepdog trials in Talisker Bay. When the sun's out, we slide down boulders and splash in the bone-cold Varragill River. Damon's lips turn purple but his smiling enthusiasm for our watering hole is undimmed.

We take riding lessons at the Portree stables. All the kids enjoy horseback riding and Damon proves surprisingly adept. During one exercise, I glance over my shoulder and catch him clearly outclassing me as he trots.

"Nice, D-man!" I yell, realizing with a start that this is how it's supposed to be.

I throw Damon a big thirteenth-birthday party with a big cake, inviting half the village to celebrate. "Make a Skye wish!" Miranda says as Damon blows out his candles. His vivid face glows before the moors, the lochs, and the mountains.

Per tradition, we drive down to visit Shealagh's uncle and aunt in their remote summer retreat, running into huge, gorgeous cattle lolling on the single-track road, until we reach the loch-edged house with its daunting view of the Black Cuillin.

Philip and Catriona are warm, genuine people, not what you'd necessarily assume from their upper-class English accents and manor house in Berkshire, England. They've long been like surrogate parents to Shealagh and very hospitable to me, and they embrace our kids and welcome them amid their visiting children and grandchildren.

We putter on a small motorboat and

picnic on Coral Island before heading back to the house, where it's tea, juice, and gingerbread with lots of kids, including my children's lovely teenage cousins, flitting about. Damon seizes the moment, enthralling the coltish girls with his patter and mimicry. He stands on a stool and impersonates a cartoonish cigar-chomping American mogul. The girls applaud and ask for more, which Damon happily provides, but I can't help noticing how he shivered out on the water and looks puffier in the face now.

CHAPTER 7

We have been waiting for a clear day to climb Ben Tianavaig. The mountain behind our croft is only about fourteen hundred feet high, but the weather changes very fast on the Misty Isle, and we cannot risk getting fogged out. Every year, climbers on the Cuillin disappear due to inclement weather. Ben Tianavaig is tamer, a pleasant hour-and-a-half hike under the right conditions, but none of my kids has ever reached the top.

On a crystalline blue day, we set off on a path behind our house. I carry a backpack with food, water, and sweaters — it gets chilly at the top — and Lachlann, for whom the ascent is a dawdle, carries a second pack. He also annoys us all by blasting "Lucy in the Sky with Diamonds" on his tape player and screeching along nonstop.

We pass behind a neighboring croft, following a well-trod path through bracken and fern up the first steep slope. Damon and Lachlann lead while I bring up the rear, taking Miranda by the hand. Sam, the middle child, walks in the middle.

It's narrow during the initial climb, and we hike single file through dense overgrowth. Damon, in a broad khaki hat, marches proudly ahead while Lachlann flits on the margins beside him, ducking to avoid scratches. Damon beats the bushes with a stick, kicks obstacles from the path, and relishes being in front. I know it won't last but I enjoy watching Damon feel his oats. He's a natural-born leader who rarely gets to exercise physical command, but now he's unchallengeably in the lead.

"Wow, that's sharp!" Damon whacks a stinging nettle.

Sam, in a Buzz Lightyear T-shirt and a flap hat, eagerly follows behind the two older boys, nipping at Damon's heels. Sam has a high, darting gait, like a show horse, and he's bursting with raw energy. "Easy — no tailgating!" I warn Sam, recognizing his impulse to prove himself and pass his big brother. Part of me roots for Sam — I know about being the second child — while another part seeks to restrain Sam for Damon's sake. I want both my boys to succeed, but just now, it's Damon who needs my help.

As we advance up the mountain, the valley quickly drops away and recedes into a tiny, sun-drenched hollow of lines and colors — grass-green, peat-brown, and gorse-gold, with streaks of heath-purple — revealing other mountains and moors and cliffs, a vast geology of which it is only one small part.

I notice Damon straining and Miranda slowing. "Let's take a break," I announce.

We stretch out on a carpet of bell heather and pass around the water bottle. Lachlann discovers McVitie's chocolate cookies and devours them with yelps of pleasure. Damon pushes up his hat and scans the horizon like a veteran climber.

"It's nice up here. Everything looks so *small.*" Damon eyes the neat cliffs and tidy bay at the mouth of our little valley, savoring the infinitesimal scale.

"Isn't that Lachlann's house?" Miranda points to a far-off tiny green roof.

"No way!" Sam dismisses both the idea and its proponent.

"Aye, that's our wee shed glinting through the trees," Lachlann replies.

"Good eye, Mirandy!" Damon pats his sister, and Miranda sticks her tongue out at Sam. The pesky midges swarm and I spray the kids with more insect repellent.

"Midges don't bother you above one thousand feet," I tell them.

We resume climbing and make slow but steady progress. Only there's a catch.

Ben Tianavaig rises out of the ocean like a rough volcanic pyramid, with its southern flank — the side that shelters our croft and village, the side we climb — sliced diagonally with a series of sweeping setbacks that can deceive the first-time climber, who experiences two "false" summits before reaching the third and final, or "true," apex.

So despite my admonitions, the kids believe they've reached the top long before we get there. Miranda rides on my back while the others struggle but won't admit it.

Damon propels himself through sheer will. He's like a car on empty, determined to squeeze every drop from the reserve tank and then push from behind if necessary. Sam too is exhausted but still intent on beating Damon. He stumbles about, complaining — "Are we there yet? How much farther?" — but then he shoots up the hillside in a sudden spurt to join Lachlann and smiles down at us. Damon glances up at his younger brother and his friend, frustrated and quietly seething.

I call several breaks but Damon insists it's

not necessary.

"No, let's keep going," he says between clenched teeth. "I'm fine, Dad."

Finally I stop by a boulder. "I need a rest from carrying Miranda." I set my daughter down and make Damon sit too. I give them each juice, then pull him aside.

"Listen, D-man, you're doing great. With your oxygen level, you're carrying *three* Mirandas . . . So let's not overdo it. If we don't make it this time, we'll try another day."

Damon nods at what I'm saying but his mind, or rather his iron will, is set.

"I'm okay, Dad. I just needed to catch my breath." He glances up the mountain. "It's farther than it looks — and steeper!" He grins, then snaps his fingers. "Let's do it!"

He stands with his windblown lion's mane flapping and his hat flying behind him on a tie-string. He's got everything it takes, all the heart in the world, just not the heart function. I cheer silently and send him invisible boosts and rungs of support.

We march on. The scrub trees have long yielded to stubbly mountain grass. No more heather at this height. Not even thistles. It's hot, arduous, and unforgiving.

My kids look dazed and punch-drunk. But no one wants to give up.

I trail Damon with Miranda on my back, lending a hand when he starts to falter and taking a longer but more graduated path to help him pace the ascent.

"We're almost there now!" I say, wondering if he can hang on.

We pass the second false summit and see the true peak up ahead. Damon's eyes light up, his arms swing into action, and his stride quickens. He end-runs Sam, who's flagging again, and makes for the finish line. A violent wind suddenly rushes in from all sides and swirls about him, creating a turbulent barrier.

"Arrrgh!" Damon charges, locking on the column that marks the mountaintop.

Sam spots the column too, but he's been outflanked by his older brother, so he just makes a run for it. But Damon hits the target first. Lachlann swoops in beside Damon, landing like an eagle. Miranda scrambles off my back and agrees to walk the final stretch. She grabs my hand as we all reach the apex and converge at the column.

Ben Tianavaig lifts its high craggy shoulders, with a sheer drop over the ridge. We teeter on the naked, windswept summit, with cliffs and rocky precipices below.

"Awesome!" Damon's eyes glint at the

harsh confluence of land, sea, and sky.

A lowering storm suddenly looms above our heads as fast-moving clouds scud across the peak. The clouds turn into chunks of mist and pelt us like hailstones, engulfing the summit and shrouding us in blinding swirls of fog. We get pummeled.

Just as quickly as they came, the storm clouds move past, and sunshine pours down again from a luminous blue vault, revealing a sparkling, vertiginous panorama.

No one speaks. Damon leans a proprietary arm against the summit column, catching his breath. His brow is damp, his cheeks flushed, but his chest swells proudly.

The Black Cuillin hover beyond our sunlit valley like a pale, jagged mirage.

"We're on top of the world!" Damon grins like a conquistador and hoists an unsuspecting Miranda onto the summit shaft, planting her there like a flag.

Miranda, frightened at first, relaxes and leans back, her legs extending from her torso like a ballerina's as her golden tresses fly in the wind. Damon guards his baby sister, slinging her legs across his shoulder, while Sam presses close, holding down his flap hat. Lachlann beams in the pure ether, a humble knight to my trio.

We're close to heaven, and everyone feels it.

A chill, bitter wind eventually forces us down to a lower spot. Lachlann inflates orange balloons and shows the others how to tie them into swords so they can fight and duel on the mountain. Swashbuckling Damon, who's reading *The Count of Monte Cristo,* corners the slippery Lachlann while Sam jabs him and Miranda jumps on his back. Their yodeling carries down the valley and in no time Lachlann's sister and mother, out on their own trek, clamber up to join our cavorting.

For the finale, inspired and cued by Damon, we set all the balloons free, watching as they catch the fierce wind and float over the valley like migrating orange swallows.

CHAPTER 8

A week before leaving Skye, after I've asked
Damon to review for his high school entrance exams, he steps out of the croft to
talk to me. I'm sitting in a white patio chair
facing what's left of the sun, reading foundation proposals FedExed to me from New
York, when he stands in the doorway and
looks at me with a curious expression.

"I got this funny feeling in my side, Dad."

I put down my papers and walk over.
"What kind of feeling?"

"I don't know. But it hurts in a weird way,
like a shooting pain."

"That's not good." I put my hand on his
shoulder. "When did this start?"

"Not sure. I had it Tuesday but then it
went away. But just now I felt it again."

I lean over him, peering. "Where exactly
is the pain?"

He points to a large area, running his
hand from his rib cage to his hip.

"Could you have fallen down and gotten bruised without knowing it?" I ask.

"No, it's not like that . . ."

"Then what's it like, D-man?" I press because he's starting to worry me.

"I don't know . . ." He frowns. "It just went through me and it felt really weird."

Just then something weird goes through *me* — right through *my* side — and I do not like the feeling. If there's an innocent or logical explanation, why can't I think of one?

"It's not that bad, Dad," Damon finally says, reading my unquiet thoughts. "I just thought you should know."

I watch him closely over the next days but he insists the pain is gone. He believes it was a false alarm, maybe even growing pains, but I remain uneasy. I start seeing warning signs everywhere but maybe I'm looking for them.

The day before departing, I take the kids to the Portree stables. We plan to skip the lesson for a big farewell trek. Damon's regular horse, Bootise, is indisposed, so they give him a bigger horse, Jasper. We're about to roll out when I notice Damon is close to tears. He can't tell me what's wrong but it seems the immense horse, close to eighteen hands tall, has him rattled. Damon says he's

67

too far off the ground and he wants to get down.

We dismount and he calms somewhat. But he's still too overwrought to try a different horse and I won't force him, even if it means canceling our last ride.

I've rarely seen Damon so distraught and I'm baffled by it. Until today, he's shown complete confidence and proficiency on a horse. Did I push him too fast? It's always a balancing act but he seemed to enjoy the riding as much as his siblings and he's even started to surpass us. Maybe the sudden chill has affected him? It's been raining and the temperature has dropped sharply, as it does at the end of August.

Or maybe he's upset we're leaving Skye and wants more time with his friends? Or he got into a fight and didn't tell us, as happened once before?

I can't figure it out but it's completely out of character. I tell a disappointed Sam and Miranda that the trek is off and take them for fish and chips by the harbor.

We sit by a railing overlooking the brackish quay and watch as swift hands fry each fresh fillet of cod, anoint glazed chips with salt and vinegar, and wrap it all up in thick white paper. Damon perks up with the hearty food and laughs when a big, cheeky seagull swoops onto our cramped table and steals a fry right out of my hand.

He seems to have recovered by evening and is up to his old tricks with his pals. They goof around and play hide and seek. They jump on the trampoline. When Harry's white van makes its weekly visit, Damon braves the midges to buy treats from the mobile grocery while Harry, the white-haired Wizard of Skye, tells me about Damon's island ancestors, who looked just like him.

That night I invite our village friends for farewell drinks and food. The kids play video games and have pillow fights choreographed by Damon with boisterous hilarity.

When we leave the Isle of Skye the following morning, everyone agrees it was a great summer. But as we drive over the bridge at Kyleakin, I cannot shake an inchoate sense of dread about Damon. I check for him in the rearview mirror and watch him surreptitiously in the backseat, where he retreats with a Walkman and a book into his gray hooded sweatshirt, stares glumly out the window, and dozes off for long stretches.

CHAPTER 9

On the eve of September 11, 2001, ten days after returning from Skye, I sense, along with many people in the United States, that something nasty is brewing.

I read the papers and track news coverage from around the world. I'm aware of public threats made by al-Qaeda and other Islamic fundamentalist groups, and of U.S. government alerts responding to those threats. Although I have no security clearances, my job puts me in touch with a range of government officials — at State, Defense, the CIA — and I know many leading scientists and policymakers.

I also have less-mainstream connections and more offbeat sources. As a former taxi driver who regularly takes cabs, I talk to cabbies and listen to their chatter. I'm also writing a thriller set in the Middle East — I was born in Israel and spent the first seven years of my life in the Levant — and I've read widely about Jihadism and terrorism.

So I develop a palpable sense of impending attack, and I even think I know the occasion: a September 23 Salute to Israel parade, when Governor George Pataki will welcome Israeli prime minister Ariel Sharon to New York. My mistake is, I'm working off an outdated model — the 1980s assassination of President Bashir Gemayel in Beirut, Lebanon — and I do not just overshoot the date by twelve days, but I miscalculate the number of deaths and the level of destruction by several orders of magnitude.

There is something sickeningly familiar, as well as shocking and monstrous, about what happens on 9/11. I've seen it, in paler versions, before — as a child in Israel, whenever I revisit the Middle East, and even in Europe. But never *here,* not in America and in the quintessentially progressive, tolerant city where I live with my family. It belongs back there, in the feudalistic, tribal world I left behind.

Like most people, on the day itself my immediate concern is my family. Sam and Miranda attend PS 29, very near to the Brooklyn Heights clinic where Shealagh now works. I reach my wife on the phone — she can see the burning tower from her window on Montague Street — and we agree she should pick up the two younger children because she has the car, while I decide what to do about Damon, who's in Manhattan.

Shealagh leaves for the school on Henry Street. The wind blows east, from downtown Manhattan to Brooklyn. Out on the street, thick smoke fills the air and white ash floats down like dirty snowflakes on Shealagh's head. She hurries, worried about the white ash, which is asbestos from the towers, though officials will deny it for months.

Inside the school, hundreds of frightened children gather in the auditorium, where teachers in face masks organize the evacuation. Panicked parents rush in, clutch their kids, and sign them out. Some kids will wait all day because several PS 29 parents work in the World Trade Center and never will make it out alive.

While Shealagh collects Sam and Miranda, I ponder what to do about Damon. His school is near Gramercy Park, but the bridges and subways are closed. When my wife returns with the car, I'm ready to drive in anyway, but Shealagh's seen police stopping drivers on the bridge and doesn't want me to go. I suggest riding my bike past the roadblock but she worries I'll be arrested; even if I get across, my wife doesn't want

72

me cycling back with Damon on the handle-bars. She feels he's safe at school — we track the news nonstop — and doesn't want us to risk further family separation.

I call my sister, Anat, on a landline — cell phones still don't work. She lives near Damon's school and reports all is calm in the area. I ask her to check up on Damon for me. She walks to East Twentieth Street, upwind of the explosions, where everything appears normal. Classes remain in session and Damon wants to stay. My sister agrees to meet him after school and take him back to her apartment, where he can spend the night.

I speak to my parents in Queens and they're okay too.

The next day I take the subway to Four-teenth Street and pick up Damon from my sister's apartment. It's a relief to have him back with me. We walk south but stay clear of Canal Street, where a security cordon has been set up with soldiers and army vehicles. The air is dense, fetid.

Damon looks the same but seems oddly marginalized, as if the crisis has diminished his footprint. Even in the subway, a state of emergency prevails. The cops wear white masks with carbon filters while travelers eye each other warily.

"How were things at school?" I ask as we board the train. "Did people panic?"

"Not really," Damon says. "We heard a boom and then they came and told us about it. Everybody stayed pretty calm, except kids whose parents work in the towers."

"Doesn't Jon and Kirsten's father work in one of the towers?"

"Yeah, but he's an architect, so when he saw the first tower get hit, he bolted, even though they told people to stay put. He escaped just before the second plane hit and walked over the Brooklyn Bridge all the way home in a daze."

"Good for him!" I say, then add, "We're all in a kind of daze, D-man."

My son looks at me. "Didn't you show me an article on this, like, a month ago?"

"Yes, people knew they were planning *something* but not on this scale . . ." I nudge him. "Maybe now you'll start reading the papers?"

Back home, Shealagh and I note how subdued Damon seems. He tiptoes by us like a pale bird, making tentative inquiries in a muted voice.

"He's not the main focus. Something bigger has our attention," Shealagh remarks.

Damon helps his siblings adjust, especially Sam, who saw the smoking towers from his class window. He invites Sam to his room, a rare treat. They have long chats, play Doom, and listen to Coldplay. Damon even allows six-year-old Miranda to join as they huddle over cards and board games, forming a stable, self-contained sibling crew.

I feel relieved because everyone in my family is safe. Of course, no one can predict the psychological fallout on the children. An entire generation will grow up remembering this date. Not just the devastation but the fact that we, their parents, were rendered so helpless and vulnerable. Why couldn't we stop this? What else can't we protect them from? Is there a limit to our power, and thus to our authority?

I feel this acutely with Damon, who stops by for increasingly serious talks. He turns his gentle, searching blue eyes on me and analyzes my face, as well as my words.

"Could they attack New York again?" he asks on the first Sunday after 9/11, when I return from Ground Zero on my bike. We sit in my study as I towel down.

"Sure," I reply. "But the Pentagon attack worries me even more. Because you can never protect every civilian building but we have only one national military headquarters — and it seems to have been penetrated with remarkable ease."

"No one's talking about that," Damon says. He's reading the papers daily now.

"No, it's too upsetting. Just like why we didn't foresee the global nature of this conflict. Remember my military tour in July?" I point to an F-16 photo on my wall.

Damon nods. I got him souvenirs from all four armed services.

"During one briefing, I asked a four-star general if the military was worried about the rising tide of anti-Americanism I saw whenever I went abroad. This general dismissed my question as irrelevant, too far below the radar to merit a serious answer."

"Why would he do that?" Damon screws up his features.

"Beats me . . . But I thought of that general today, when I rode my bike over the Manhattan Bridge and went to see firsthand what they'd done to our beautiful city."

"And you wouldn't take me with you!" Damon chides. "I can ride now, Dad."

"I know, D-man, but it's still too dicey. Place is like a toxic, bombed-out war zone, with army troops in battle gear, sewage-filled streets, and rescue workers sifting for human remains. And it stinks! I had to take shallow breaths on my bike not to puke. Site's still smoldering five days after impact!"

"Wow," Damon says, rapt. "You find your friend and his family?"

"I tried but their building was roped off and they weren't in the queue to go back in . . . It was surreal. People held signs with names of relatives and handed out photos of the missing. Like a displaced persons camp after World War Two!" I scowl.

"You sound angry, like it's personal," Damon observes.

"That's how it feels, like a violation. This is my city, and I know all these streets and lanes intimately. When I drove the night shift as a cabbie, I used to tuck the sleeping city into bed every night . . ."

"That sounds cool, Dad, I'd like to try that!" Damon says.

"Maybe one day you will." I smile at him. "Though today, D-man, all I could do was jump on my bike and get the hell out of that cesspool! My one consolation was cycling back over the Brooklyn Bridge, which was completely deserted — not one vehicle or pedestrian along the entire span! I stood up in the saddle at the crest, alone under that great filigree of cables, with a clear sight line to the statue and the harbor mouth."

"I want to come with you next time!" Damon cries. "Can I? Please, Dad!"

I hesitate but Damon's ardor is irresistible.

"Okay, I'll take you. But only after things improve, including the air quality."

"Cool. Thanks, Dad." Damon beams and deftly pockets my IOU.

I continue conversing with Damon and trying to make sense of what happened when I receive an e-mail from a friend saying that his father, a top official in the fire department, rushed into one of the towers just before it collapsed. Although I know that several hundred firefighters and rescue workers have died, not to mention thousands of civilians, this is the first victim I am acquainted with, and suddenly all the talk of bodies and funerals is personal and real. This man was not just my friend's dad but also the grandfather of two of Damon's childhood friends, Kelsey and Siobhan.

"I have some bad news," I tell my son in his room. "Billy's father ran into the southern tower to rescue his men, and he never made it out . . ."

Damon's face drops and his eyes mist over, while I begin to get a glimmer of understanding for a tragedy whose true dimensions I can never grasp nor adequately explain to my own children.

CHAPTER 10

Two weeks after 9/11, I am sitting with my wife and three children in Temple Beth Emeth for the Yom Kippur service, the holiest date in the Jewish calendar and the one day we attend synagogue. Because I hope to have Damon Bar Mitzvahed in June, I have joined this congregation, paid dues, and tried to act more observant than I am.

I make the kids dress up, which means no T-shirts or sneakers. Damon wears stiff black shoes that squeak heavily as he walks and an open-necked blue shirt that shows the tip of his midline scar and buttons tightly across his belly. His unruly shock of red hair is combed and wetted down, and he glistens with pale, reproachful handsomeness. Sam and Miranda, two beautiful if bored children, shine in their clean outfits, and all three kids look like flowers ablaze with color in this dour ecclesiastical setting.

We are listening to a thunderous sermon

about the unprecedented terrorist attack on U.S. soil when word comes that Shealagh's father has died.

Philip Rosenthal was eighty-four and living in Germany, so we did not see him much. But he was a complex, outsize figure and the only father Shealagh has known, and his death is a shock to us all — and another blow to Shealagh, still recovering from back surgery.

We are not especially close to Shealagh's family. Her parents are separated; they live in Europe and have led largely self-involved lives. Shealagh's mother, in particular, has not treated her daughter well. But Shealagh's father, a celebrated industrialist and politician who publicly disinherited his children and joined the Socialist Party under Willy Brandt, rising to secretary of state, has reached out to her in his latter years, and Shealagh has made her peace with him. His overtures to our family, especially to Damon, have been genuine, and he and I have a mutually respectful if wary understanding.

On getting the news, we quickly return to our house and check on flights to Germany. While Shealagh calls her family to discuss arrangements, Damon stops by my study, a notebook and tape player under his arm.

"Can I go to Germany with you?" Damon asks, his face full of urgent tenderness.

His request takes me by surprise, even though he's gone with us before.

"Let's wait and ask Mom. We want to be sensitive to her and her family."

Damon nods and I ask him about the tape. He explains it's an interview he did with his grandpa for a school history project. "I also wrote a class essay, 'My Grandfather,' and worked out a family tree." He opens his notebook and shows me the material.

Philip Rosenthal's life intrigued Damon. A Catholic who joined the Hitler Youth at fourteen, ignorant of his father's conversion from Judaism, Philip had to flee Nazi Germany for England when the Gestapo appropriated his father's china company. After boarding school in Broadstairs and rowing at Oxford — the same college, Exeter, where I would later meet his daughter — young Rosenthal tried joining the British Army to fight Hitler but was rejected as a German national. So he enlisted in the French Foreign Legion, where the most action he saw was with the woman who convinced him, belly with child, to make the first of his five unsuccessful forays down the aisle. After many attempts, he finally escaped the legion and its lifetime indenture. He drifted in England and then returned to Germany, where, aided by his family name and significant reparations, he reclaimed his father's china firm and led it to new heights during the German postwar economic boom. He was also elected to parliament as a proponent of worker participation, joined the cabinet, and became a leading statesman and celebrity.

"It's good you got him on tape," I tell Damon. "He told many stories and even if some were self-mythology, he was a fascinating guy and a real embodiment of history."

"With his own castle and pool!" Damon's eyes twinkle.

The family lived in a 1740s *Schloss* modernized into a sleek mansion with contemporary art. Damon favored the Party Room, converted from a former stable into a *La Dolce Vita*-style cavern featuring an indoor pool, alcoves, recessed lighting, and a vaulted ceiling. Every year Philip organized a big fireworks display in the front courtyard of the *Schloss*. The dazzling spectacle attracted many denizens of the small china-manufacturing town where he ruled like the revered local prince, with a flamingo-fronted factory designed by Walter Gropius, state-of-the-art amenities for workers, and streets named after him and his father, also called Philip.

"It was cool going on walks with Grandpa because everywhere we went people pointed to him and he pretended not to notice," Damon says. "But I think he liked it."

A big, handsome figure with a touch of the white-haired John Huston, circa *Chinatown*, about him, Philip walked around the *Schloss* in a flowing djellaba and sandals and slept on a sand floor under tented fabric with artificial stars. He climbed the Himalayas, flew his own plane, and walked, swam, or rowed across ten European nations in a two-decade odyssey he proudly charted on a huge map in the *Schloss*.

"Grandpa did a lot, but I don't think he had many friends," Damon says quietly.

"No, but he was very fond of you. And he loved that your name was 'nomad' spelled backward," I remind Damon. "It made him feel closer to you, since he saw himself as a wanderer. That and the fact that he had a heart murmur as a boy."

"And he introduced me to pig's trotters!" Damon grins.

Shealagh wanders into my study, red eyed, and says her siblings have decided that no one is bringing children, so we can't take Damon. She's still in shock.

"You gonna be okay, Mom?" Damon instantly forgets his own disappointment.

We leave the kids with my parents and fly that night to Germany, meeting up in the *Schloss* the following afternoon.

Only the immediate family is invited, as stipulated by Philip, who's planned every detail of his postmortem in the Teutonic way. There will be no funeral or public ceremony. No trace of religion of any kind. He wants to be cremated and the ashes, housed in a black porcelain Rosenthal urn, lowered into the ground under the beech tree in the front garden of the *Schloss*. He's written his own epitaph — at once pompous and true — and had it carved on a headstone with only the date of his death left blank: OF PORCELAIN THIS SO-CALLED KING KNEW LITTLE. HE LEARNED MORE FROM HIS SOCIALIST BROTHERS AND FELLOW MAN AND FROM ROWING.

His death is on the front pages and on television. The chancellor issues a statement, as does Rosenthal China. But we keep the family end very small and private.

Shealagh, her three siblings and their spouses, and her older half sister attend. Philip's devoted executive assistant, PR handler, nurse, companion, onetime lover, and caretaker oversees things, aided by and occasionally clashing with his eldest son.

Shealagh's mother, not on the invite list, crashes the gathering. She's technically still married to Philip even if she decamped for London decades earlier. The *Schloss,* once celebrated in designer magazines as the home of an innovative, world-class company, is crumbling now. Philip had donated it to the firm in a typically grand gesture, keeping a small flat for himself. But the renowned china company, formerly the product of true vision and a unique, rigorous aesthetic, has since been sold and debased, and Philip ousted. Marginalized, even mocked, by crass salesmen and bean counters, the former CEO and founder's son was consigned to a tiny, decaying remnant of his onetime kingdom.

I've been to very few funerals and Philip is one of the first people I am close to whose corpse I behold. When I see him laid out in the casket in his custom-made brown suede jacket with his sparse white hair and his willful, prominent, and subtly curved nose — a medieval portrait worthy of Rembrandt — I also see his carefully obscured Semitic roots and I understand him in his full historical dimensions. It's a dramatic revelation, as if death has swept away any last illusions, and it makes me appreciate the

85

monumental project of self-invention and determined adventure that was his life.

I draw lessons for myself but also for Damon, who has a part — a physically recognizable part as well as specific character traits — of his grandpa in him. Because I like to imagine myself the founder of a new line — I harbor big dreams for my family — I see Damon as *my* Philip, the scion whose father started things but who took them to new heights. So as I gaze at my son's grandfather, I look into the future as well as the past.

But mostly, as I stand by the casket, I am filled with sorrow and speechlessness at the mystery of silence, of no-moreness, that is death. It's hard to believe that Philip, such a dominant force, whom I loved sparring with, is gone. After comforting my wife as best I can, when no one is looking, I wipe away my own tear.

CHAPTER 11

Shortly after returning from Germany, oppressed by sadness and the lingering national doldrums, we decide to stride forward and, in the spirit of Philip, initiate our own family walkabout.

Growing up, Shealagh hiked through most of Germany, Italy, and Turkey, joining her father for large sections of his European peregrination. Many of her school vacations were commandeered by his odyssey — especially when he wanted a press photo — but she also has fond memories of these times spent together as a family.

We've considered a U.S. variation of this Continental theme before, but now the time seems ripe. And we know that Damon, a poor runner but a tireless anaerobic hiker, can walk his siblings into the ground.

We decide we won't march straight across America, at least not on this first go-round, but instead we will limit ourselves to the mid-Atlantic region. We'll start from Brooklyn, pass through Manhattan and the Bronx, and continue upstate along the Hudson. All distances will be covered on foot or on bicycle. Each section of the journey will begin where the previous part ended. After a few segments, we'll need to drive to our starting-off point and leave the car. We'll do it on weekends, holidays, summers, whenever the opportunity presents.

Shealagh's back remains an issue but she is game — it's her family tradition and her dad we're honoring — as long as I promise not to race ahead.

The kids, fresh from their outdoor triumphs in Skye and cognizant of the homage to their grandfather, readily agree to our plan. On the last day in September, a blustery Sunday, the five of us don comfortable shoes and light jackets, stuff a backpack with sweaters and water bottles, and walk to the end of our street, entering Prospect Park by the Vanderbilt playground. We skirt the still blue lake, pass two lumbering horses on the bridle path, and climb past Lookout Hill, where scouts scanned for German U-boats during World War II. A stream of cyclists, runners, and Rollerbladers zips by as we round the corner by Bartel-Pritchard Circle, where a new multiplex and cafés attest to the area's gentrification. Everyone in the family seems primed for this historic inaugural march.

Damon takes the lead by my side, with Sam hot on our trail, as we traverse the meadow's perimeter, crunching leaves and twigs. Miranda ambles with her mother, two handsome Victorian ladies on a nature tour. The terrain is flat, and we make good progress.

I keep my eye on Damon as he whacks tree trunks with his latest sword-branch. He wears a gray hooded sweatshirt emblazoned with the fiery words NO FEAR and at first he appears energized. But soon he begins to dawdle. He veers off to thump trees and loiters, appearing distracted.

By the time we reach the northern end of the park, Damon clearly lags and is struggling to keep up. Shealagh flashes me a worried look as we wait for the traffic light by the intersection. The light turns green and we cross to Grand Army Plaza. Now Damon appears in distress. I point the kids to the big triumphal arch and walk over to Damon.

"What's up, D-man? You feeling okay?"

"Yeah, I just need a minute to catch my breath . . ." He waves me off and walks away with hands on hips, looking pale and listless.

Shealagh wanders over to me, half-accusing. "What's going on?"

"I don't know," I reply. Sam and Miranda pretend to study the victorious bronze charioteer crowning the monumental arch. "He seems tired, out of breath."

Shealagh shakes her head. "That's not like him. We haven't walked that far and it's only the flat bits so far. He can usually go for hours."

I sigh. "He hasn't been himself for a while."

Shealagh stands with arms akimbo, catching her own breath. "Maybe he's dehydrated. He didn't drink that much today." She unzips a water bottle from my backpack and approaches Damon. He takes a perfunctory sip and hands the bottle back to her.

"I'm okay, Mom," Damon says with a halfhearted teenage smirk.

He doesn't look okay, but we grab more downtime in the island plaza, with cars streaming in about us. I spot a small bronze bust of John F. Kennedy.

"Now, there was grace under pressure . . ." I show Damon the inscription and we discuss our thirty-fifth president, whose assassination when I was in third grade marked a black day like 9/11 for my genera-

90

tion. Damon gets swept up in the historical drama and his eyes gleam. Even his color starts to return.

"Come on, let's go," he says after a spell, as if we've been holding him back.

We cross the wide roadway and head down Flatbush Avenue. It's busier here and a little grungier but it's mostly downhill, with frequent rest stops for Damon at the traffic lights. He uses them artfully, catching his breath on each street corner. We make for the Brooklyn Academy of Music, maintaining a semblance of purposefulness.

But both Shealagh and I are nervous now, our excitement at this inaugural family outing marred by our anxiety about Damon. We can sense his unease, the uncharacteristic hesitation in his step.

We go slower and stop at a candy store, hoping to revive him.

Sam and Miranda can feel something's off. They too begin to flag. They grumble they're tired and bored. A few blocks later, Shealagh starts to falter. I can't tell if it's her back, her asthma, or her concern about Damon, but everyone's losing heart.

I try to keep them all moving, like the group leader prodding his straggling, dispirited charges. This is not the communal, milestone-setting march I had in mind. It's not going well. But I'm desperate to keep my family on course, any course, before they give up and call it a day.

Everyone perks up as we approach the great spidery span of the Brooklyn Bridge. We ascend slowly along the elegant steel structure, letting Damon linger at various spots on the promenade, until we reach the crest, a windy crow's nest.

A small, excited crowd mills at the top. Three weeks after 9/11, the city remains under lockdown, but irrepressible signs of life appear from this sweeping height. We stand on the deck of a great ship, lashed by a sharp ocean breeze, and savor the spectacular vista of Lower Manhattan and Upper New York Bay. Damon grins between the soaring cables and lofts outstretched arms. His hair flaps wildly in the wind and his eyes sparkle as he's buffeted from all sides. Sam and Miranda come alive, galvanized by the gusty heights and by their giddy brother. Shealagh and I beam.

Only the absence of the Twin Towers jolts, like an erasure from the skyline.

When we reach the Manhattan side by city hall and the wind subsides, we can smell the foulness from Ground Zero. An acrid pall still hangs over the wounded city.

We turn south along the East River. The

waterfront area appears spectral, semi-deserted. Damon starts to drag again, and we all feel the gloom.

We find a restaurant by South Street Seaport and try to replenish ourselves with a big lunch. But even the food does not quite fill the void. Looking around the table at my family, I realize we've gone as far as we can. Sam and Miranda are ornery, the air quality is suspect, and Damon looks pale and out of sorts. His mother is not faring much better.

I go to hail a cab while they wait inside. There are no taxis and I walk for miles by the icy water, my fingers bitten, before I finally find a cab. I try not to lose heart as we ride back across the river. We didn't go as far as I'd hoped but at least we clocked the first few miles. And we need to sort out Damon's problem before resuming.

Back in the house, Shealagh offers Damon her asthma inhaler and shows him how to use it. Damon inhales, awkwardly at first, but then he gets a few good puffs in and the bronchodilator appears to take effect. His breathing eases and he starts to unwind. By evening, he seems okay again. He does his homework, watches TV, and hangs out with me.

I'm relieved Damon's problem seems

concrete and remediable. He's had allergies before and this may be a natural progression. More and more children have asthma, especially in urban areas. His mother has it, so there's a family history. And we know from Shealagh's experience how to treat and manage the problem.

But both Shealagh and I concur that since it's Damon we're talking about, he should see a doctor right away, just to be sure.

CHAPTER 12

We take Damon to Columbia Presbyterian Hospital to see his cardiologist, Dr. Constance Hayes, who has overseen Damon's case since he was three days old. A diminutive woman with short gray hair and austere features, Dr. Hayes is an accomplished professional who is caring but cautious and spare in manner, giving the term "tight-lipped" new meaning. But she is conscientious and kind, her recommendations are usually first-rate, and she has rarely steered us wrong. Now she listens to Damon's latest problem and suggests we see a pulmonologist she knows.

We meet with the lung specialist, who gives Damon a thorough exam and tests. He confirms that Damon's breathing problem appears to be asthmatic but reminds us " 'asthma' is an umbrella term covering many symptoms." When we tell him about Damon's enlarged liver and his heart condition, he explains that pressure on the diaphragm — from the liver, the heart, or other stressed organs — "can cause or mimic the airway constriction that is a hallmark of asthma." This wouldn't change Damon's treatment for now but could suggest other, confounding factors at work. He prescribes a bronchodilator and an antihistamine and tells us to keep an eye on things.

Shealagh gives her son a few more lessons and helps him administer the new regimen daily. She makes sure he always carries his inhaler. The therapy seems to work, and Damon's breathing difficulties subside. The problem appears under control.

Damon is in eighth grade now, engrossed in the challenges and excitement of a new semester. Sam is in third grade and Miranda has started first grade. The next week, Sam is due to see a doctor about a minor procedure. Shealagh asks if we can defer Damon's checkup because he's just seen Dr. Hayes and our calendar is tight. But, reversing our roles, I insist Damon keep his appointment because I retain a bad feeling from the summer I'd like banished.

Shealagh gets Damon the same date as Sam. I have several meetings that day, so she'll take Damon for his usual tests in the morning and I'll come up from the office after. We have Damon's checkup down to a routine, but we've never met Sam's doctor, so he's the main event.

On the day in question, my last meeting runs over and I arrive at the hospital a few minutes late, just missing Dr. Hayes. She was called to the OR, but not before revealing to Shealagh disturbing new test results for Damon.

"What exactly did they find?" I press. My wife looks very upset and is doubly constrained because Damon and Sam are in the waiting room nearby.

"They think it's something called PLE," Shealagh says in a low, fraught voice. "He's not keeping protein in his body."

"Never heard of it . . . What's the treatment?" I ask, assuming a new medication.

"Dr. Hayes says they'll see if they can fix the problem in the cath lab or redo his original operation, but otherwise he will need a heart transplant."

"What?" I shake my head in disbelief. "Hold on! How do we go from 'He's doing so well' in one checkup to 'It's all falling apart' in the next? Where did this *come* from?"

"That's what Dr. Hayes told me," Shealagh says. "I was too upset to ask questions and then she had to go. Maybe you can get more out of her." She stifles a sob.

"Okay, I'll talk to her." I don't want to let it go except we can see Damon and Sam in the adjoining room, playing with Sam's action figures. The boys can see us too.

Sam's doctor calls us in and I sit through the meeting in a daze. All looks good for Sam and his routine procedure, but it makes the contrast with Damon even more incredible.

I've had my concerns about Damon since the summer, but not on this scale! He goes to school every day, participates in sports and extracurricular activities, parties and horses around with his friends — he leads a full and active life. How can everything just *unravel?* Without any warning from Dr. Hayes, whom I grill on every occasion?

At our last checkup, Dr. Hayes told us how proud she was of Damon's progress. She stood by the upright scales with arms crossed over her white lab coat, beaming at his development. As he sat on the paper-lined exam table with his shirt pulled up, Dr. Hayes listened to his chest and lungs, as well as his latest exploits, with a big smile. She is fond of our son and delights in his success in the world, like a benevolent if slightly stern godmother, which is how we've come to regard her.

Troubleshooting as usual, the biggest worry I could come up with on that last checkup was whether, as Damon reaches puberty, his anomalous blood flow could affect his sex life. Dr. Hayes, a thin, reserved woman, blinked at me and checked Shealagh before acknowledging it's a valid question. She told us she'd look into it and get back to us.

From such mundane concerns to this life-threatening crisis seems too great a leap. I refuse to panic until I know more. I page Dr. Hayes, but she's still in the OR. I redial several times, without success. Reluctantly, I go home with Shealagh and the boys. I can't let Damon see how rattled I am. He looks to me for guidance and can read my moods as well as I can read his — maybe better, since his survival depends on it.

In his room, we listen to the Top Ten on Z100 and discuss his upcoming exams.

"I'm thinking of going out for Model UN," Damon proudly confides. He suspects nothing, as far as I can tell.

Up in my study, I consult a medical text on PLE and browse the Internet. I don't like what I read, but I have no definitive data or diagnosis yet. Although Shealagh has more formal scientific training, she lets me take the lead on Damon. I've written a

99

couple of medical books, I work with top scientists and researchers, and I'm relentless in my digging. I also successfully shepherded both my parents through health crises.

I have one basic rule: if we can't understand an issue or a medical approach makes no sense to us, it's the doctor's problem, not ours. No mumbo-jumbo. We must always know exactly what's going on so we can help ensure the best decisions are made. The most capable physicians supply the clearest explanations — equally clear about what they don't know as what they do — and only the mediocre take refuge in obfuscation or omniscience. I tell myself that once we have more facts, we'll sort this out.

I finally set up a phone appointment with Dr. Hayes while on a business trip in Los Angeles. I clear my morning schedule, hang a DO NOT DISTURB sign outside my door, and sit on the bed with pen and pad, perching anxiously by the phone. I can feel my heart hammering in my chest as I wait for the appointed hour to call.

I need to hear straight from Dr. Hayes and to know things are not as bad as I imagine. I cannot grasp how the same voice that has seen us through two open-heart surgeries and countless medical difficulties to the verge of young adulthood, the same voice that has bantered with us about skiing and schoolwork and Damon's plays, the voice that's been so full of optimism and encouragement about my son and never, not *once,* breathed a word about the possibility of a new disease — which, if he has it, has been developing for some time — how this same voice could so suddenly change its tune.

But Dr. Hayes, after pleasantries notably more strained than usual, does not have much good news for me. She explains that PLE, or protein-losing enteropathy, is a very serious illness that develops in about 10 percent of children who've had Damon's Fontan heart operation. The albumin count — albumin is the critical protein molecule that keeps vital components flowing inside the vessels — plummets, and all the vital proteins necessary for the functions of life leak out of the body. If the leakage cannot be stopped, the patient will eventually "starve" to death. No one really knows what causes PLE — though many suspect a link to higher pressures in the heart — nor has anyone found a cure.

But before assuming the worst, Dr. Hayes says, there are many things we can do.

First, they will take Damon to the cath lab and see if there is any obstruction that could account for his PLE-like symptoms. Sometimes it's a simple problem doctors can correct on the spot — in effect, a false alarm. If that doesn't work, they'll check if the original Fontan surgery is starting to unravel. (Damon has a Gore-Tex patch in his heart, made of the same material as my winter coat.) If there is a flaw in the repair, a Fontan "redo" could fix things. Then we can try various therapies — diet, drugs, injections, minor surgery — culminating in a heart transplant if nothing else works.

There seem to be multiple variables and approaches, so I press Dr. Hayes on data and outcomes, much of which she cannot supply. The disease is rare, the patient population small, and the published literature scarce. Yet even surfing the Net, I tell Dr. Hayes, I noted many papers from the U.S. and abroad, so it can't be *that* uncommon.

"Yes," Dr. Hayes says, "PLE is known and recognized, if poorly understood. It's complex." She offers to send me a recent paper on it. "I rarely recommend scientific articles to patients' families, but because of your background, I feel you can handle it."

I thank Dr. Hayes but ask why she never hinted to me before that anything like this could happen. "Haven't I always asked for more information about my son?" I say.

Dr. Hayes tries dancing around my question but I force her to go back to Damon's last checkup — and to all his previous checkups over the last nine years.

"Surely a condition like this does not occur overnight but develops gradually over many *years?*" I say. "The albumin is a liver count. Could PLE be connected to Damon's enlarged liver and the protruding belly we've asked about for several years? What about the recent slowdown in his growth? Could PLE also explain his asthma-like symptoms? Even his hernia? Why didn't you ever give us *a hint* about this possibility?"

There is a long silence on the other end. "Damon was doing so well and I was so encouraged by his tremendous success that I didn't want to believe it *myself,*" Dr. Hayes admits. "Until his last albumin count went so low, and it became undeniable . . ."

I'm dismayed by what I hear even though I know Dr. Hayes is a caring doctor — it's her excess of concern, rather than unconcern, that led to her behavior. And she still has hopeful options to offer us, which we desperately need.

Dr. Hayes and I dwell on the best-case scenario and toss around the possibility of a quick fix in the cath lab. Dr. Hayes has seen this work before but we won't know until we go in and explore Damon's anatomy. We agree to schedule the catheterization without delay. Maybe we can head this thing off now. And even if we can't resolve it all in the cath lab, we can always repeat the Fontan. Damon responded so well to the first operation — he's had nine great years! — this must bode well for a second repair.

Dr. Hayes agrees we still have many options. As we pull back from the brink and prepare to end our conversation on a brighter note, I suggest that maybe this whole thing is manageable and will soon blow over. Dr. Hayes hears what I'm trying to do — hasn't she tried to do something similar? — but this time she will not go that far. She repeats she remains very hopeful but she believes this is a "significant" development.

The word sticks in my craw and makes me queasy. I want to ignore it and roll back the clock to where we were before I ever heard this dread news, to return to the triumphant narrative of Damon — his name means "he who conquers" in Greek — that we have all recited like a heroic epic since his birth.

But Dr. Hayes, perhaps cognizant of my

recent criticism and not wishing to compound it, will not give me this satisfaction. Despite all my transparent efforts to downsize the crisis and reduce the alert level, Dr. Hayes repeats in a dry, all-too-practiced voice words that sound more chilling for their bland, clinical understatement:

"I believe this will be a significant event in his life."

I hang up the phone, still reeling, and stagger to the louvered windows. The room spins and shakes around me. I grope for the blinds and open them.

Outside, the California sun still shines and the palm trees sway.

The world carries on as before.

But underneath my feet, deep cracks and fissures appear. I shiver and hear someone who sounds suspiciously like myself begin to sob and scream.

"No!" I yell, slamming the wall and listening to my own wailing as if it came from another. "You can't take him from me . . . No, I won't let this happen! No, no, no!"

I barely recognize the deranged person howling inside my body but he seems to know more than me, as if a deep-buried and long-suppressed nightmare has returned.

My firstborn son, Damon, age thirteen, has been diagnosed with a severe, life-threatening illness. His congenital heart impairment, once believed successfully palliated, has erupted into a full-blown, potentially fatal disease!

There are many steps and hopes and therapies and trials along the way — and I'm going to explore and exhaust every one of them, and invent some of my own — but at that moment, the bottom falls out, and I stare down into the abyss.

I have a beautiful family, a loving wife and three wonderful kids, a nice home, good friends, a satisfying job, my own creative work and ever-rising prospects . . . I have a great life, but in that instant, it all turns to shit.

The original diagnosis occurs on October 11, 2001 — exactly one month after the tragic terrorist attacks of 9/11. But now, for me and my family — and for the person whom I love with all my heart and soul, for Damon — the terror really begins.

PART II

CHAPTER 13

The week following my conversation with Dr. Hayes is like a powerful but invisible aftershock that pursues me from California back to New York.

No one else in the family understands yet how grave things are. And I fear saying anything until I know more and can prepare them better.

I pore over the scientific paper Dr. Hayes has sent, a multicenter study that aggregates much of the available data on PLE. I track down the original sources and references and read everything I can get my hands on.

All the peer-reviewed literature in all the best medical journals, though couched in staid jargon, seems to reflect a similar bafflement bordering on helplessness:

- "Protein-losing enteropathy (PLE) is an enigmatic disease with significant morbidity and mortality seen after the

Fontan operation. It is unclear why its onset occurs months or even years after Fontan surgery."

- "PLE, defined as severe loss of serum protein into the intestine, occurs in about 4–13% of patients after the Fontan procedure and carries a dismal prognosis with a five-year survival rate between 46% and 59%."
- "PLE after the Fontan operation is a life-threatening complication that may be refractory to medical treatment. Preventive strategies and new therapeutic approaches are necessary."

I refuse to get discouraged and focus on treatments that have worked. I analyze all the therapeutic possibilities and outcomes in the literature, including any anecdotal data, and follow every footnote. I do my own calculations and make a list of options, arranging them in order of least intrusive (diet supplements, oral medication) to most intrusive (assist device, heart transplant).

I know that I will see things more clearly at the beginning, before anyone has raised false hopes or muddied the facts — and before the need for shielding myself and my family overtakes reality. I am single-minded in using hard statistics to understand the odds. I can always search for unheralded treatments and unconventional approaches, encourage or devise new solutions myself, or hope for miracles or at least a break, but I need to know what we're up against.

What we are up against is a devastating, little-understood disease with no known cure. It kills 50 percent of its victims within five years and 80 percent within ten years. And because no one has checked Damon's albumin for several years, and because Shealagh and I have observed what turns out to be PLE symptoms for an indefinite period, I don't know how long ago the illness started or how much of Damon's time it has already consumed.

I talk to half a dozen pediatric cardiology experts across the country who've dealt with PLE. I consult many other smart doctors and scientists I know. The generalists voice more optimism than the specialists, who, when pressed, admit they do not really understand this dread illness or how to cure it. But they all have their preferred treatments, each of which has worked for *some* people in *some* cases. Because the disease is rare and data scarce, I make a note of each case and add any new therapy I don't already have, be it standard or experimental, controversial or not, to my growing list.

I will deploy this master list, built up and refined over time, like a series of fortifications thrown up against an advancing enemy. The list gives me a rough battle plan to follow and a semblance, or illusion, of control.

My scientist friends with medical backgrounds, like Jeffrey Friedman, a leading molecular biologist at the Rockefeller University, and Robert Ben Ezra, an accomplished cell biologist at Memorial Sloan-Kettering Cancer Center, initially try to reassure me. I mustn't overreact. This is the twenty-first century, with molecular medicine and biotechnology, and medical care advancing by leaps and bounds. They'll look into PLE for me, talk to their expert friends, and return with an answer. Invariably, they call back and speak in more careful, subdued tones. This is a very tough illness with an uncertain prognosis.

Perhaps the hardest thing in those first days, after I've begun to grasp the grim parameters of this disease for myself, is how to convey the news to Shealagh and to Damon. I've accepted that I am breaking down inside — I feel emotionally paralyzed all day and twisted up all night, and I cry at odd moments — but I know how to continue functioning in the world. I do not know how Shealagh and Damon will react or how to broach this subject with them. And then there are Sam and Miranda to explain this to . . .

I want to tell Shealagh everything immediately and to share the terrible burden with her. We have always been full partners regarding Damon's care. But Shealagh has suffered a succession of unspeakable blows within a very short time — back surgery, her father's death, and now Damon's diagnosis, absent the dire statistics I've just learned — and I feel unsure about her frame of mind. Her best friend, Sonja, a physician who assisted her over the summer and now helps me research PLE, warns against upsetting Shealagh with too much depressing information. But we both agree she must know the big picture right away.

On a Friday morning after the kids have left for school, I invite Shealagh for coffee in the downstairs kitchen. It's a bit chilly for my taste because the door to the backyard is flung open, but Shealagh prefers fresh air at any temperature and I want to make her as comfortable as possible. I rub my arms and blow into my cupped hands by the dishwasher.

"Wear a sweater if you're cold, silly," Shealagh says in her pragmatic, English way.

"I'm fine." I fill the coffeemaker with filtered water from our sink and grind up the coffee beans in an automatic grinder that whirs and roars. Shealagh waters the heather and the flowering cacti on our windowsill with a copper watering can. Then she wipes down the counter with a sponge and deposits an empty milk carton in the recycling bin.

We cleave to our rituals, avoiding the subject at hand. Shealagh knows I must give her an update on Damon but she has not pressed me and seems content to stay in the dark. As she settles into a high-backed chair around our rustic kitchen table, I consider letting things slide. My wife looks fragile and tense in her soft lamb's-wool cardigan as she pencils in Miranda's Irish dance class on the monthly calendar. All she wants is the routine of parenthood, the daily satisfaction of bringing up her children. I'd do anything to spare her and maintain our hard-won equilibrium, but I know — we both know — that things have already deteriorated, and a reckoning is overdue.

I finish brewing the coffee and heat the milk in a giant china mug, as Shealagh likes it. I join her at the trestle table, our legs touching under the broad surface.

I look into Shealagh's wary face with its

remarkable pale blue eyes — palely luminous, like the sky — as I start explaining what I've learned: how serious PLE is and how little understood; how there are various things to try but no consensus on a cure; how we confront a very formidable disease and will have to marshal all our resources to beat it.

I summarize the papers I've read and relate my conversations with numerous doctors and scientists. I describe the situation as delicately but accurately as possible, because we must be clear-eyed if we hope to persevere. It's tough, awkward going. I can find the silver lining in the darkest cloud, but first I have to tell Shealagh how overcast it really is.

"So basically, no one really understands why the Fontan circulation breaks down and why the body starts leaking protein from the gut," I say. "But it can't go on indefinitely because he needs the protein to grow and thrive."

"But he was doing so well!" Shealagh cries. She understands the medical information but it still doesn't make sense. "Why is this happening?"

"I don't know." I cover her hand with mine, trying to cushion the blow.

My wife trusts me to protect her and take

care of things and now I must let her down, even hurt her. I feel culpable, as if I'm not keeping up my end of the bargain. And I feel shocked all over again, as if I am just learning the truth anew.

"My best guess is that it's related to the original congenital heart disease — remember how severe Damon's was? And that the Fontan is only a temporary fix, despite what they told us," I hazard.

Shealagh looks as if she's seen a ghost, and suddenly it feels as if time has collapsed and the past thirteen years have been erased.

We are back to the dark days of Damon's birth . . .

Shealagh's labor and delivery goes smoothly and out pops a handsome, fair, eight-pound, two-and-a-half-ounce baby boy with big hands and big feet and a gorgeous full-lipped smile. He looks well formed and capable.

The first two days are blissful, with mother and child bonding at the breast. The proud father dispenses cigars and rushes back to the hospital from work. Everyone in the family rejoices.

On the third day, we discover our newborn has a serious heart problem. The slower heart rate detected in utero is the result of a malformed heart that does not deliver sufficient oxygen to the body.

The doctors snatch Damon from his mother and rush him to the neonatal intensive care unit. He is placed inside an incubator. The room is filled with many premature, tiny-sized infants encased in similar apparatuses, struggling for survival. Damon, full-sized and pale skinned, stands out.

We watch our newly quarantined baby get extra oxygen from a high-tech helmet that squats on his head and sends a steady spray of mist wreathing about his nose and mouth. His oxygen saturation, which should be 98 percent, hovers around 72 percent before the Olympic Oxyhelmet boosts him to 90 percent. A pulsing red sensor attached to his tiny foot sends a stream of data to an overhead monitor, which flashes continuously.

Three-day-old Damon lays inside a clear bubble, separated from us by modern technology, a pint-sized astronaut marooned in his own world. We slip our hands through little portholes to touch him, but this only brings home how distant and sealed-off he is.

Shealagh suffers withdrawal, shock, grief. Her newborn is suddenly a captive of the medical profession. When they come to lance Damon's heel for a blood sample, his mother wants to hold him but they won't allow it. He must remain inside the incubator and we must step back and let the technicians proceed. As the long needle pierces his skin, an outraged Damon starts to cry behind his solitary barrier. We stand at a distance and watch the big syringe fill with bright red blood as the plunger pulls back. The forlorn cries of our exsanguinating infant in his caged apparatus pierce us. Shealagh, blocked from going to comfort her distressed baby, breaks down. I lead her out of the ICU, propping her up.

Shealagh, so ready for motherhood, is crushed. She can't establish a bond with her newborn and may only nurse him at strict intervals set by the ICU. To keep her milk flowing, she must sit on a stool and pump.

Meanwhile, we hear about Damon's pulmonary stenosis, a narrowing of the artery leading to the lungs that prevents the blood from receiving enough oxygen.

We are told of his atrioventricular (AV) canal, a hole in the heart that sends blood back to the right chamber, so it must be pumped again, raising pressures.

We learn that, best case, Damon will need a major operation in four to five years, and another procedure much sooner if he devel-

118

ops any sign of blueness.

The doctors, explaining that many of Damon's organs are reversed, inform us he has no spleen and will need daily lifetime medication. We are crestfallen until they return an hour later to report they've "discovered" a spleen on his right side. So we are spared this extra cross to bear and feel, perversely, lucky.

Finally Damon is discharged but Shealagh cannot take her baby home. She must relinquish him to another hospital for more tests. My heart cringes as I watch my young, nursing wife on the steps of Brooklyn Hospital, her arms empty, while they place her baby in an ambulance bound for Columbia Presbyterian Hospital. She sobs inconsolably in the sunlight as the ambulance pulls away.

I feel my wife's suffering more acutely than my own, because my powerful feelings for Damon have not yet developed — fatherhood remains largely an abstraction to me — and I don't understand that this little pale infant with his reddish tuft of hair will become the center of my life. It is Shealagh's privation, her harsh and unnatural introduction to motherhood, that affects me most deeply.

But sometime during those first weeks, a

change comes over me too. I watch my newborn son as the doctors tell me he will always have a heart defect and never be like other children. I am overwhelmed by his complex congenital heart syndrome and devastated by our misfortune. Shealagh and I both enjoy robust good health, and there is no trace of any illness resembling Damon's on either side of the family. How could this happen to us?

I take in all the bad news, I listen to the gloomy prognosis. But to my eyes, this child still looks beautiful and full of life. Damon lays there, a sweet, thoughtful-looking infant, placid but supremely alert. He's primed for engagement with the world. And he's ours; we made him. Already, Shealagh points out how he sleeps like me, right arm draped by shoulder, left hand poised by jaw.

I conclude that nothing we've heard from the doctors, daunting as it may sound, precludes ultimate victory. We have a fighting chance and together we can beat this.

And for thirteen years, we do.

Damon undergoes two successful open-heart operations, thrives and succeeds beyond anyone's imagination.

Now Shealagh casts her eye to the refrigerator, settling on a recent photo of a beaming, sunburned Damon fishing off a boat on Cape Cod. Nearby is his certificate of excellence from karate with a raised gold seal.

"He's going to be okay?" Shealagh says. "There are effective treatments against this disease, right?"

"Yes," I reply. "We have lots of things to try. And many people make it. But the numbers are not great." I look down at the floor, then across at my wife. "We need to face that — and then we can figure out how to beat PLE."

"But Damon is not a number," Shealagh says with unimpeachable authority.

"No, exactly," I reply. "He's extraordinary, he's our amazing Damon."

Shealagh takes it very hard but nothing can rival Damon's reaction when he learns that he will have to go in for an unexpected procedure the following week. Shealagh tells him about it when she picks him up one evening from theater rehearsal. Damon asks why he needs a catheterization and Shealagh mumbles about problems that showed up on a previous test. She promises his father will explain it to him back home.

By the time Damon walks into the house, he knows something is wrong. The look on his face as he marches into the kitchen to confront me is excruciating to behold:

anger, fear, bewilderment, accusation, and pleading vie across his boyish features. He dumps his heavy backpack by the door but his shoulders stay hunched, as if flexing against a great, unjust weight. He strides forward with his wide gait and slams his cell phone, MetroCard, and play script onto the counter. The top page flutters to the ground. A gentle, supremely rational boy, he can barely contain his fury at this incomprehensible turn of events.

Damon can't yet grasp what's happening, but he knows it's bad and that it doesn't fit any template we've previously discussed. He says not one cross word to me but his reproachful look effectively screams in my face: *This wasn't part of our game plan, Dad! What's going on?*

My son's look pierces me. I've been his coach and his mentor from the start, and together we've developed a true collaboration and a careful winning strategy. But now we've run into a fierce hurdle I could not prepare him for because I knew nothing about it. By choosing not to warn me about even the *possibility* of such a setback — believing we were better off *not* knowing — Damon's doctors have undermined my role and made me shirk my obligations to my son.

As we go up to Damon's room, I try to explain what's going on. Damon has matured and possesses a first-rate mind. He also has a diagram of the human heart pinned to his wall and a model skeleton standing atop his dresser, so I assume he'll want all the details.

"We believe it's related to your original heart problem," I say. "Your body is losing protein because the heart isn't pumping enough oxygen to your cells."

"Will I need another operation if the Fontan isn't working?" Damon asks. He doesn't look happy but at least he's thinking clearly.

"If it's PLE — we're not even sure yet — then we'll have to try various things. An operation is the last resort. But you've been through worse, and you'll get through this." I try to reassure him by drawing on his past record of success.

"Will I have to miss school?" Damon focuses on practical matters.

"No, not now. But it's complicated, so we'll have to keep our eye on it."

I'm ready to tell him more — all I know, in fact — but it turns out I'm wrong about my teenage son's inclinations. Damon extracts the gist of his problem from me but he decides early on not to immerse himself in his own medical case. He's more inter-

123

ested in attending school and participating in theater workshops and being with his friends. He doesn't want to learn all the details of his illness or the history of PLE or the latest research, but trusts me to manage these things for him and to report back any major developments.

It's a decision that surprises and even disappoints me at first — I respect Damon's ability and believe he could help himself, and even assist me with his insights — but it's a decision whose wisdom I learn to appreciate over time.

Damon just wants to lead a normal life.

CHAPTER 14

The morning of Damon's catheterization Channel One reports snarled traffic, so after seeing Sam and Miranda off on the school bus — we tell them Damon has a routine procedure — we leave our car in the driveway and take the subway in.

Shealagh packs two oversized bags, one with Damon's things and one with hers. A devoted mother ready to serve her son in any capacity, she is the designated hospital overnighter. We both bring work, knowing the drill.

We take the F train, each immersed in a different section of the paper as we sit with our luggage. At Jay Street–Borough Hall, we switch to the A train.

Damon wears frayed black shorts and a pale green T-shirt with palm trees on it. He looks a tad drawn — I note a small raccoon blotch under each eye — but otherwise he appears in decent shape. The Zyrtec he's been taking for allergies has reduced the puffiness in his face, and his belly seems less protuberant. His red hair gives him a bright luster even in drab surroundings.

Damon soon grows bored with the paper — he reads it dutifully but the daily habit has not quite taken — and pulls out an *Animorphs* series book. The cover shows five kids who morph into animals and fight evil with enhanced powers.

"You know, there's a theory that the structure of the modern human brain still retains traces of our ancestral evolution," I tell him. "It says we have remnants of a snake brain and an early mammal brain, like a cat, which means we are not so distant from our animal past . . . So there may be a scientific basis for such tales."

"Yeah, I know, Dad." Damon gives a dreamy, cunning smile. He's familiar with this idea, even if just now he's more interested in escapism than realism.

We disembark at 168th Street and pass the newsstand and the peanut vendor before entering the giant hospital complex and going up to the third floor.

"I feel a little nervous." Damon smiles awkwardly, as if it's just hit him.

"You've been through this twice before,

126

when you were much younger." I touch his back.

"And both times you sailed through with flying colors," Shealagh says.

We sign in; Damon gets the standard checks and is told to prepare. There are no changing rooms available and Damon is too self-conscious to change in front of his mother, so we find a private bathroom down the hall. I help him slip into his hospital gown, noting how his abdomen seems marginally less swollen. I attribute this to two new medications prescribed recently. From my reading, I estimate 25 percent of patients with PLE can resolve their symptoms with medication alone, and I pray that Damon will fall into this category.

I carry his clothes as he pads out in thin gray slipper socks and a green gown.

Dr. Donnelly, the head of the cath team, comes to talk to us before the procedure. She has polished manners and is eager to begin. But first I want her views on fenestration: creating a small opening between the chambers of the heart to relieve pressure, which has reputedly resolved many PLE cases.

"We've heard it's effective and can even be done in the cath lab," I say.

Dr. Donnelly smiles. "We'll be proactive if

we find anything small to do but the primary purpose of this procedure is to gather information."

Dr. Donnelly says they will likely go in through Damon's neck rather than the groin because the veins around Damon's groin are blocked from his previous catheterizations. Damon moans at this and becomes visibly agitated. I press Dr. Donnelly for alternative access points but apparently there are none. She promises they will numb the neck area before entering and give Damon additional sedation so that he remains "comfortable."

"How long do you expect this procedure to last?" Shealagh asks tensely.

"Two hours if we only take pictures, but longer if we need to do anything."

We accompany Damon to the cath lab, a dark, chilled, cavernous room. The nurses tip him from the gurney onto a flat board encircled by huge swinging steel arms housing imaging equipment that feeds into a bank of large, overhead monitors.

Damon lies twitching on the narrow bed, restless and uneasy. He is wary of being stuck, so they give him numbing cream. But the resident who tries inserting the needle misses Damon's vein several times, sending him into a paroxysm of squirming. Shealagh squeezes his hand and I stroke his arm, glaring at the fumbling resident, while Damon continues to wriggle and yelp like a recalcitrant puppy on the vet's table.

A Jamaican technician seizes Damon's lower body to steady him. A big, gentle man, the Jamaican needs to tape his genital area but Damon is too riled to lie still. He's also too embarrassed. Shealagh squats by his head, whispering that she can't see anything and his privacy is protected. I try guy talk — "It's a homemade jockstrap, D-man!" — as I help the Jamaican to stabilize my writhing son, heartsick at his frail thrashing but quietly thankful the technician is male.

Damon continues to wiggle and twist against this ignominious violation. I've rarely seen him so wild. He kicks and bucks. I wince as I hold his legs down, hating myself for the role I'm forced to play. Better me, I rationalize, than an impersonal pair of hands. But it's humiliating, for both of us. The Jamaican applies three strips of tape, diapering my teenage son, and I quickly let go of his legs.

"No, I don't want it!" Damon cries as a nurse finally gets the needle in.

Shealagh and I are told to exit the OR but Damon pleads for us to stay. He's unusually skittish and clingy and we don't want to leave him in such a state.

I stroke his hair. "Hey, D-man, forget where you are and think of something nice. What would you most like? I'll get you anything you want . . ."

He's so upset I'm not sure if he's following me, but then Damon suddenly pipes up. "Can you have Lachlann fly in for my Bar Mitzvah?"

I smile. "You got it."

It's a brief respite before multiple, criss-crossing hands attach wires and sensors to his body, sticking him like a pincushion. Damon whimpers and again begs us not to go. We ask to stay until his eyes close but the OR staff won't hear of it. They must put him to sleep in stages, and we must exit so they can begin.

Shealagh and I harden ourselves and kiss him good-bye. Damon cries as we leave the room. Shealagh waits until the door closes before daubing her tears while I try to suppress the grisly image of Abraham sacrificing Isaac as I leave my son alone on his altar bed. I tell myself the biblical story turned out well — it was only a test, after all — but it feels like scant consolation.

Shealagh and I spread out in the waiting room and buckle down with our diversions:

chitchat, reading, phone calls, coffee. After an hour, we grab a quick bite and hurry back to our stations. There's no telling when Damon might get out.

I work until Shealagh, under great stress, falls asleep on the couch beside me. I move to the plastic chair, giving her room, and continue reading proposals.

After three hours, I begin to grow restless. Usually, if it's taking this long, a nurse comes out with a progress report. But we still haven't heard a peep from the cath lab.

I page Dr. Hayes, Damon's cardiologist and still our go-to person at Columbia. Her assistant says Dr. Hayes is in the OR but will get back to me ASAP.

At some point, Dr. Hayes materializes, hands tucked demurely inside the pockets of her white coat. I rise and give her a searching glance.

"Everything so far is okay," she says in her small voice.

I let out a sigh. We chat and I explain that Shealagh, sleeping on the couch below us, has had a terrible few months. We agree she should not be disturbed.

Dr. Hayes reports that Dr. Donnelly, a cath lab veteran, feels Damon looks "surprisingly good" and is "impressed" by his overall condition.

"They haven't found anything yet." Dr. Hayes smiles softly. "We're hopeful they've caught any problem he might develop early enough so it's manageable."

Dr. Hayes also discussed the case with Dr. Hohrdoff, head of the whole cath lab, and he agreed that Damon's hemodynamics looked "wonderful."

Dr. Hayes sounds almost chipper, as if she's trying to cheer us both up.

I'm pleased to hear good news but ask Dr. Hayes if we hadn't perversely hoped to find something *wrong* that would explain the PLE, so that we could fix it.

"Bad news leading to good, rather than vice versa, which is what I fear you're telling me?" I explain.

Dr. Hayes turns grim. "Yes, it's true," she sighs, as if on a separate subject. "No one knows why these children with perfect pressures go on to develop PLE."

I wince. "So we're back to square one?"

Dr. Hayes doesn't answer, but such is the temptation to extract hope and seek solace that I find myself focusing on the positive aspects she's emphasized — Damon looks good and his numbers are good — even though I know it's not so simple or straightforward.

It's not simple because Damon lacks a

working ventricle to pump blood returning from the body to the lungs, so his body must maintain artificially high pressures *continuously* just to let this blood reach the lungs. And even with higher pressures, the fluid sometimes backs up and leaks into other organs, requiring even higher pressures in a vicious cycle. So even "perfect pressures" for a child with a Fontan would be abnormally high for you and me, and may not address the underlying problem.

But I don't dwell on such counterintuitive facts as Dr. Hayes departs — I cleave to the positive and share the good news with Shealagh when she wakes. My wife nods but starts to worry as more hours pass without a word. At five P.M., the receptionist leaves and the hallways empty out. Someone turns off the lights.

"What's going on? Why hasn't anyone come to update us?" Shealagh asks fretfully.

I page Dr. Hayes and try her assistant, but I only get voice mail. I scamper across the dark, deserted floors and yell along the empty halls but all I hear is my own echo. I too start to fret. It's twilight, and we're in a very weird zone.

Finally, well after seven P.M., Dr. Donnelly emerges in scrubs and tells us all is well. I note she's refreshed her makeup. She quickly sketches a diagram of Damon's anatomy and shares two findings: Damon had developed some collateral veins, which they coiled off, and this should improve his saturation; and they noted a very small fenestration from his first surgery, suggesting some mixing was already occurring, so a new fenestration might not provide much additional benefit.

"Otherwise," Dr. Donnelly reports, "all was fine and Damon tolerated the procedure well. Absent his cardiac anomaly, we found nothing wrong with him."

"So there's no identifiable problem you can fix?" I point out.

"Yes, from the cath lab point of view, Damon is in good shape," Dr. Donnelly says, sidestepping my question. "You can go see him in the recovery room now."

I thank Dr. Donnelly and follow Shealagh into recovery.

Damon lies behind a half-drawn curtain, encircled by monitors. He looks wan but dogged, his plume of hair a pale, diluted crest across the pillow.

"How are you, sweetie?" Shealagh says as we rush to his side.

"Okay, but it was pretty rough," Damon says. His eyes are groggy and bloodshot and his mouth turned down.

Our son reports he was awake for the entire procedure and experienced acute discomfort and distress. When they inserted the catheter, he was aware of being pierced and could sense the wriggly tube snaking through his veins. He felt a stinging sensation when they injected contrast dye in his arteries and a burning nausea as the hot dye spread to his heart. His body cramped from lying still so long. And he felt physically abused and morally ignored as they manipulated his body.

"Once when they hurt me, I cried in pain and they told me to be quiet . . . I thought I imagined it but when I did it again, they yelled, 'Stop talking!' " Damon says with ashen incredulity.

I have to stifle my own anger. Damon is stoic and rarely complains, so it must really have been bad.

By eight thirty P.M., we're out of recovery and up on the floor. The nurses enter constantly to monitor Damon. He must lie flat and use the chamber pot.

Shealagh unpacks and, like a good mother, tries to make our room more homey. We check in with Sam and Miranda, then find a movie on the overhead TV. Shealagh wanders up the hall — she knows all the hiding places — and returns with crackers

135

and cheese and soft drinks, plus extra pillows and blankets. We sit around Damon's bed, eating, watching the movie, and making a small party of it.

After the film, I pull the chair-bed out for Shealagh. While she goes to change, Damon and I chat. He is still weak and sore but I detect the glimmers of a comeback on his face. I describe the initial catheterization results and relay to him the positive news Dr. Hayes emphasized to me. Damon asks when he can return to school and I say as soon as he feels up to it, which seems to satisfy him.

Shealagh returns in a long T-shirt nightgown with her skin scrubbed and her thick hair pushed back by a velvet hair band. Her myopic blue eyes look lost before she adjusts to the makeshift hospital accommodations. I dislike leaving her alone in such surroundings but they only allow one parent overnight and Sam and Miranda wait for me at home. And I know that Shealagh is steadfast and will do whatever is required for her children.

I linger for a spell, wondering why an exploratory test Damon has undergone twice before felt so harrowing this time, before I kiss my son and my wife good night and ride the subway back to Brooklyn.

CHAPTER 15

It takes Damon longer than expected to bounce back from his catheterization, as if the sharp and protracted medical probing he underwent has disrupted his basic equilibrium, the secret bargain he's struck with his body.

At least that's what I tell myself, because the doctors have no explanation.

He comes home the following day and goes straight to his room to rest. Shealagh, too, is exhausted from her labors and retreats upstairs to our bedroom.

When I return from the office, Shealagh is napping and Damon lies on his loft bed, staring up at the ceiling fan and listening to soft music on his clock radio. I catch up with my wife and son, check in with Sam and Miranda, order dinner.

When the food comes, I place Shealagh's meal on a tray, add a glass of red wine, and carry it to the top floor. Shealagh's back is acting up and she's wiped out. But Damon, despite fatigue and lingering soreness, insists on eating with us in the downstairs kitchen. He descends gingerly from his loft bed and waddles from the middle to the bottom floor, grasping the stair rail and protecting his groin.

I sit with the kids and watch Damon hold court at the table. He slumps forward on weary elbows and is a little short-fused with his siblings — what can they know of his aches and pains, his travails? — but he's also affectionate and playful with them.

"Damon, what did you eat at the hospital?" Miranda asks.

"Hospital food," Damon says, tucking into his seafood salad.

"What's that?" Miranda misses the irony.

"Chicken, mashed potatoes, carrots — but it all tastes like applesauce."

"Yuck," Miranda cries, grinning. She and Sam delight in their big brother's return and hang on his every word and gesture.

"Mirandy, how do you like Ms. Garvey? Me and Sam both had her," Damon says.

"I know. She keeps asking me why I don't have red hair," Miranda replies, pouting.

"Because you're a girl," Sam teases. "And you're silly."

"Sam, don't be annoying!" Damon says.

"Girls have red hair just like boys."

"Yeah," Miranda says. "Look at Pippi Longstocking!"

After dinner, Miranda volunteers to dash upstairs, change into pj's, brush teeth, and even forgo a good-night story if she can watch *Lizzy McGuire.* Sam and Damon groan but I consent because I connect with my daughter by watching this show with her. After Miranda goes to bed, we tune in to *The Fresh Prince of Bel-Air.* Damon likes Will Smith, and Sam likes watching with Damon.

The phone rings. It's an employee from the hospital pharmacy informing me, in broken English, of a mix-up in Damon's prescription. It sounds like a bad joke from one of our sitcoms, except it's not. The guy can't answer any of my questions, so I hang up and call Dr. Hayes, leaving an urgent message. Eventually, I get a call back from the attending doctor, who's covering for Dr. Hayes. She beats around the bush until I get her to reveal that Damon was supposed to get 1.25 milligrams of enalapril, a drug that opens the blood vessels, but instead the hospital mistakenly filled a prescription for *12.5* milligrams.

"You mean you gave my son *ten times* the approved dosage of his heart medication!" I raise my voice, though it's nothing compared to my anxiety level.

"I didn't do anything, I'm only relaying information for your benefit." The attending sounds blithely detached, almost condescending, as if she's doing me a favor. She asks how Damon is and explains the peak effect from the overdose would have been six hours ago, so we're past the danger point — assuming I haven't given him another dose. She suggests picking up a new prescription tomorrow. The doctor also warns me that enalapril lowers blood pressure so we need to watch out for dizziness or fainting. "No warm baths or sitting up suddenly. Otherwise he should be fine, though of course you must stay vigilant."

I thank the attending and hang up in dismay. I check with two physician friends who confirm the peak danger should have passed but that a tenfold increase in dosage is significant and could cause kidney problems. They tell me to keep an eye on Damon and add that such an error constitutes malpractice.

The next day, I take the morning off to be with Damon. He's still weak and dizzy but not significantly worse to my eyes. We rent *My Cousin Vinny* and laugh together. I watch him closely for signs of an overdose effect before going to work.

When I return that evening, my parents bustle in our kitchen. They have driven over from Queens and prepared a wonderful Friday-night meal, replete with Helga's homemade chicken soup, a favorite of Damon's. Shealagh is grateful for a night off.

The seven of us stand around the brimming table and light the Sabbath candles — the single ritual my parents observed when I was a boy, and one I honor only sporadically now — and then I bless my children. This is a new tradition I haphazardly inaugurated a few years ago. I read about it or saw someone do it and it spoke to me, so I adopted it.

I walk around the table and place my hands over Damon's and Sam's heads. The bright, flickering light from the Sabbath candles shines on their two thatches like the sun gilding a russet field. They bow their heads before me — Damon's is a deeper, richer red; Sam's has lighter tones — and both bask in my embrace. With my palms covering their resplendent crowns, and Miranda excitedly waiting across the table for her turn, I look at my wife and my parents and feel like the richest man in the world.

I smile upon my two beaming sons, stroke their hair, and recite the blessing:

May God make you like Ephraim and Menashe.
May God bless you and watch over you.
May God shine his face toward you and show you favor.
May God be favorably disposed toward you and grant you peace.

Ephraim and Menashe were Jacob's grandsons, whom he praised as role models, a "blessing," for the people of Israel. I've explained this to my children several times but all they know is that Dad is touching them and saying nice things about them. They understand it's part of his tradition — their mother has converted to Judaism, though no one is very observant or consistent in this house — and they grasp they are valued and loved. And that's good enough for them. For me too.

The minute I finish the boys' blessing, Miranda beckons me to her side, yanking at my arms. She looks like she might burst with pride as she helps install my hand over her crown. She bows her shimmering blond head, radiant in her solo glory, while I repeat the benediction, changing only the role model names, to the righteous matri-archs this time: "May God make you like Sarah, Rebecca, Rachel, and Leah . . ."

The candles burn and we bless the wine and the bread and sit down to eat. Damon still sags a little in his chair but he eats respectably and engages actively with my parents, two of his biggest fans. My mother, who used to help with his day care as a tod-dler, now accompanies Damon to the the-ater, and my father, who plays soccer and catch and any game going with his grand-son, and who shares a penchant for telling stories and jokes and performing, is teach-ing him Hebrew in preparation for his Bar Mitzvah.

"How are your lessons coming?" my mother asks, smiling at her grandson.

"Okay. I'm still having a little trouble with the vowels," Damon admits.

"You've almost got it, laddie — a wee bit more practice is all you need," my father says.

On Saturday, Damon sleeps late and then the two of us hop the subway into the city. On the way in, Damon complains of tight-ness on his left side, from the ribs back to the kidney, and I give him a massage. I'm not sure if it helps but he thanks me sweetly.

We pick up one schoolmate, Kiri — a

compact girl with a witty, tomboyish air —
on Fourteenth Street, and wait for another,
Keith, at Rockefeller Center. Keith's mother
— she's so young, at first I mistake her for
another student — drops him off by the
Atlas statue before we proceed into the
International Building and ride the elevator
to my office on the twenty-fifth floor. I
serve, in a voluntary capacity, as secretary
of the New York State Selection Committee
for the Rhodes Scholarship, and Damon
and his friends have come to help me
process the applications, which must shortly
be sent to my fellow committee members.
It's a labor-intensive task and I pay the kids
for their efforts, but it's also a social outing
and a good way for Damon, who's missed
school the past three days, to catch up with
his friends.

We lay out nine copies of each application
on a big conference table. I stress that each
file is confidential and represents a lifetime
of hard work and dreams, so they must treat
it with respect. But invariably, teen irrever-
ence creeps in.

"Check out Miss America!" Keith bran-
dishes a glossy headshot. "Is that a *halter
top?* Oh, she wants to work in *global health,*
so this shows she's ready to fly to the
developing world twenty-four/seven and *get*

down with the heat and the jungle."

Kiri smiles. She holds little truck with glamour shots but, perhaps out of gender solidarity, she shows a slick male photo that would do a politician proud.

"Would you buy a used car from *this* man?" she deadpans.

"No, but tell me what toothpaste he's using!" Keith shrieks.

Damon walks around the long table — I notice he drags a little — and inspects the photo. He grins. "That's scary." Then, beaming wickedly, he holds up a sheet.

"Another essay beginning with a hardship case that inspired someone to enter public service . . ." He flutters the paper with comical, hard-nosed skepticism. "Is that, like, the secret formula, Dad?"

I chuckle, then glance at the meager number of completed files on the table.

"Hey, I'm sure when you guys apply, you'll knock it out of the park, but how about a little more work? If we finish on time, I'll take you to the movies."

Damon returns to school on Monday though he's still not back to full strength. I drop him off in a taxi in the morning and Shealagh picks him up at three P.M. That night we go celebrate my mother's birthday at a restaurant on Smith Street, even though we worry Damon is not really up to it.

The trendy little restaurant has a "minor plumbing problem" and all night a kitchen hand feverishly swabs the floor. Meanwhile our food is late and everyone grows peckish. "Even the *Titanic* kept serving!" my father grumbles. Damon sags in his chair, exhausted. A car alarm goes off and shrieks uncontrollably. When the food finally arrives, Damon forces down a few bites and then jumps to his feet, looking queasy. Everyone stares at him.

"You feeling all right, sweetie?" Shealagh asks nervously.

Damon's mouth is sealed but he lifts one finger as if to say, "Just a minute." Then he bolts out the door. I follow him to the street and catch up just as he bends over a trash can and vomits neatly into the receptacle.

I put my arm around his shoulder. "Better?"

He leans against me, pale and weary, and his eyes roll back in their sockets.

I stroke his drooping head. "It's gonna be okay, D-man."

We return to the restaurant, clean him up, and resume our meal. Damon is game but he's just not himself. He sits there, weak and dispirited, trying to cope. I wish we'd brought along a friend for him. His big puppy eyes, so sweet and knowing, flash disconcertingly at us and then beyond us, as if registering in their objective sweep that things are awry.

We try to cheer him up but he has only one thing on his mind.

"When do we get my cath results so I can stop taking so many meds?"

We don't answer directly because this is a white lie to help him adjust to his new regimen. He must swallow half a dozen medications, some several times a day, plus vitamin pills and protein supplements and fatty oils that nauseate him and kill his appetite. Damon bitterly resents this daily ordeal and blames it for his current malaise. And I don't yet have the heart to tell him I only pray he can *keep* taking these medications so we won't need to do anything more drastic.

"We just have to monitor things and see how it goes," I tell him.

The waiter brings a cake with candles and we dutifully toast my mother's seventy-fourth birthday, but everyone feels the uncelebratory weight of the evening.

Damon continues to have a rough few weeks. When he gets home from school, he often wants to lie down and rest, highly irregular behavior for him.

One day he storms into the house and cries, "I can't breathe!" He's having an asthma attack. Once he uses his inhaler, the attack subsides, but it's a bad sign.

His disorientation persists, and for the first time in his life he experiences motion sickness. Previously, he could read for hours in a speeding car without any discomfort. Now he gets dizzy just sitting in the backseat. Even the rolling subway affects him. I worry he has lost a fundamental layer of his immunity, like a turtle or a snail deprived of its shell. His filtering defenses have been compromised and life suddenly assails him. I can't tell if it's the effects of his catheterization or if his diagnosis has accelerated things, the way naming a problem can hasten its onset.

Damon's doctors can't tell either, so we remain baffled and concerned.

In the fall, I take Damon to the entrance exams for New York's specialized high schools. Like most aspirants, Damon has practiced for this test and attended a prep course, but in the last two months he's trailed off, as with so much else.

"You can wait until you feel better to take

the test," I tell Damon. "I'm sure we can get you a medical deferment and even if we can't, your health comes first."

"But I want to take the test with everyone else. I'll be fine," Damon insists.

I drive him to the test site, an immense public high school, on a Saturday morning. When we get there, hundreds of students are already lined up outside the building. The first thing I notice is how big and physically developed these kids look, and how small and pale Damon appears by comparison. As we walk along the sprawling queue, I feel like I'm bringing a child to an adult competition and console myself this is not an athletic contest. Nevertheless, Damon appears dwarfed by these strapping adolescents bursting with hormones and rude health.

He gets in line and I hand him juice and energy bars. "Don't forget to eat and drink," I tell him. I watch other parents giving similar last-minute advice and supplies, including enough number 2 pencils to repopulate a forest. I smile ruefully because while I'm normally competitive for my kids, my main concern now is that my ailing son not fall asleep during the three-hour exam and embarrass himself.

I suddenly realize I no longer care about

this test — I know how smart Damon is — because I'm too preoccupied with his physical well-being and his medical, rather than his academic, prognosis. I look out at the sea of aspiring young faces, many from families with big stakes in this race, and I decide I'd gladly trade ten points off Damon's IQ with any one of them for a single point on his albumin level. Let them have their Ivy Leagues and all the scholastic laurels; I just want a healthy kid!

"You can go, Dad," Damon says. "I'll be fine."

I give him a final pat on the back — no kisses in front of this group! — and head back to the car.

As I walk off, I glance back at my son standing in the middle of this great, hulking crowd. He appears small and isolated with his protruding abdomen, and I worry I'm leaving him all alone; yet I also note how Damon maintains his own center of gravity, casual but self-possessed. Within seconds, he engages a new student and proffers advice to his grateful family. He speaks with easy authority while others, less sure, drift to him. Checking out the wider action, he nods at an attractive girl with chopped, purple hair and she nods back at him.

I smile. You'd think Damon shouldn't be

here, yet here he is, on his own terms, with everyone else. He even possesses a certain coolness, in his compact, mop-headed, jeans-low-on-hips slouch. I want to tell him how proud he makes me, that in my eyes he's already passed the test, but I don't dare cheat him of this important rite of passage with his peers.

Bullhorns bark and the students file in.

I depart but return early, uncertain what to expect. At the appointed hour, Damon walks out of the building with the other kids, looking nonchalant, and casually strolls toward me.

"So how was it?" I scan him for any hint of distress or a blowout.

"Fine. Maybe a little harder than I expected." Damon looks calm and unfazed. "I had to rush at the end but I think I did okay."

"You didn't get tired?" I'm amazed at his serenity. "No special problems?"

"No, except I had to get up and go to the bathroom all the time. From all the diuretics I'm taking . . . And the proctor kept giving me dirty looks, like I was cheating. So for the last hour, I just held it in. Which was a little distracting."

"Well, congrats on getting through it, D-man. That's an achievement itself."

151

Now he admits he feels a little tired, and even before we get home from the test, he dozes off beside me in the car.

Although we won't learn the results for several months, Damon winds up winning entrance to Bronx High School of Science and Brooklyn Technical High School, two of the city's top three schools. It's an impressive performance, better than anyone else from his middle school.

CHAPTER 16

Damon gradually recovers from his catheterization and crawls back to sea level. The motion sickness fades. The asthma attacks cease. He seems more like himself and resumes a normal, or near normal, pace. Or have our expectations just changed?

One Saturday I'm working in my second-floor study, revising my five-hundred-page first novel after an initial round of rejections, when I hear footsteps pounding up the stairs and Shealagh and the three kids burst into the room. They surround me with great, nervous excitement and heavy breathing. Hushed, conspiratorial giggling fills the room.

They have a secret, a *surprise* for me.

The kids, led by Damon, push their mother forward. Shealagh carries a black Sherpa bag with nylon mesh at either end. A rustling movement issues from inside the bag.

153

Miranda and Sam look like they're going to explode from the suspense.

Shealagh unzips the bag and removes from it the long, reddish-brown neck of what appears to be a large, lively rodent. Everyone looks expectantly at me.

"A ferret?" I frown, trying to be a good sport. I recall once discussing with the kids getting a rabbit or a guinea pig but never a ferret. "Aren't they a little wild for house pets?"

An awkward silence, followed by laughter.

"No, Dad. It's a dog!" Miranda reproaches me on everyone's behalf.

"A *dog?*" I study the tiny creature. It's under four pounds with a smooth-coated body, muscular neck, pointy ears, and docked tail. "Doesn't look like a dog."

"He's a *miniature pinscher,*" Damon informs me with a bright-eyed look and stilted pronunciation suggesting he's just learned this fact for himself.

"He's a cross between an Italian greyhound and a dachshund, a mini-pin," Shealagh says, a mite sheepishly. She knows she's on shaky ground but she's counting on mitigating circumstances. We used to have a real dog, a Gordon setter named Ophelia who died when Damon was five and whom we all adored. But Shealagh and

154

I had agreed, or I thought we had, that the family wasn't ready for a new dog. And when we were, we'd choose together.

"Please, Dad, can we keep him? Please!" Sam is near tears. He's never had a dog — Ophelia died shortly after his birth — and he's clamored relentlessly for one this past year.

"Mom and I will walk him," Damon says, as if they've rehearsed this. "Every day."

"And clean up after him." Shealagh delivers her lines, smiling.

"Oh sure —" I start to express my skepticism, but I don't get to finish.

"You won't have to do anything, Dad, except maybe let him out in the morning because you get up first," Miranda chimes in.

"And he's so little we can take him on the plane to Skye," Damon says.

I pause. Given recent events, it seems churlish to deny anyone, especially Damon and Shealagh, any opportunity for joy.

"His name is Freddie!" Sam announces, sensing vacillation on my part.

"Freddie is a purebred Kentucky gentleman," Shealagh adds with her plummiest English accent. "He comes from a very distinguished Southern family."

"His father was called Little Red Flame,"

Damon says, his eyes twinkling at me.

"We have a certified pedigree from the American Kennel Club," Shealagh boasts wryly. "He has a most impressive lineage stretching back many generations."

"Yeah, that's why he was so expensive!" Miranda blurts.

"He's not *that* expensive . . . ," Shealagh says defensively.

"Yes, he is. That's why you had to sneak back into the house and get more money," Miranda reports with oblivious precision.

Damon gives a toothy, embarrassed grin while his mother tries a broader perspective. "We could breed him. Mini-pins are very popular. And his pedigree is compiled from official stud book records so his offspring would fetch a handsome price."

"I don't want to *breed* Freddie." Damon looks horrified. He picks up the puppy. "Unless *he* wants to. Huh, Freddie?" The dog snuggles against him.

"Not now, he's far too young," Shealagh reassures Damon, eyeing Freddie's microscopic breeding equipment. "Anyway, it's just a suggestion."

"Who came up with his name?" I ask, impressed by the pace of events.

"Damon did," Sam replies.

"But I saw him same time as Damon,"

Miranda asserts.

"We went to Little Angels for haircuts and the pet store is just across the street," Shealagh explains. "But we had *no intention* of buying a dog when we left the house."

My wife always cites original motive as a moral indicator, even a defense, whereas I tend to focus more on outcome. But now it seems the outcome is clear. I've rarely seen my family so excited and united. And we've certainly had enough bad news.

As Damon leans his head against Freddie's coat, I note how they form a match, as if cut from similar cloth. "They have almost identical coloring — that same brownish-red shade," I remark.

"Yes!" Shealagh senses victory. "Freddie's official pedigree color is *rust*."

Damon cradles Freddie, posing for a dual shot. Not for nothing he's an actor.

"This woman walked into the pet store and saw Damon sitting on the floor and holding Freddie and she said we *had* to buy that dog because the two of them looked so alike, as if they belonged together." Shealagh smiles. "Almost like they were related."

"Well, don't exaggerate," I say, admonishing her.

Miranda tries to help, tactlessly. "They're both kind of small."

Damon winces. "That's not what Dad meant."

"Damon's a lot bigger than you!" Sam assails Miranda and defends Damon, a twofer.

"He's bigger than you too," Miranda retorts, more from rhyme than reason.

"Okay, guys. Relax." I blow the whistle. "Let's enjoy what we have."

A pause. Sam leans in shrewdly to me. "That mean we can keep Freddie, Dad?"

"Please, please pretty please, Dad!" Miranda begs.

"Come on, you know you really like dogs," Shealagh coaxes.

"Yes." I sigh. "But he's a *ferret.*" I pick up the tiny creature in one hand, holding him aloft as he swipes at me with his mini-paws. "Freddie the ferret," I dub him.

"No, Dad, don't say that," Miranda pleads. "He's a dog." She rescues Freddie from my hands but then almost drops him until Damon intervenes with a surer grip.

"A cute ferret?" I offer.

"No, he's a dog!" They drown me out in unison, feigning offense even if they realize the tide is turning in their favor.

"So how about it, Dad?" Damon speaks up in a manly tone but beseeches me with big eyes.

I flash back to Damon at four, dawdling

158

with Ophelia on our little postage stamp of a beach on Indian Lake in the Adirondacks. It was before his second surgery, so he was less active, but he would sit all day on the sand with his dog, building things and playing by the big, tranquil lake. Ophelia, with her lustrous black-and-tan coat and floppy ears, was both beautiful and vain, but she also made a loving and loyal guard dog. She'd watch over Damon and bark at anyone or anything that moved across the lake or approached from the road. Damon would stroke Ophelia's pretty head and pet her silky wattles — we called her Pouch for the soft undulation beneath her chin — and throw sticks into the water that she fetched in her stately manner, lovely head held high above the surface as she paddled primly along. She was a good-sized Gordon setter, much bigger than Damon, but she had a way of wriggling on her belly and making herself small to accommodate him and insinuate herself into his embraces.

Now minuscule Freddie cocks a cropped ear and watches me with shiny, alert eyes.

Damon presses me. "Can we keep him, Dad?" His mother stands silently behind him, plaintiff, judge, and head of the ambush party that surrounds me in a tight circle of love.

"Do I have a choice?" I smile and throw up my hands, stroking Freddie's head before I move up the evolutionary ladder and muss my elder son's hair.

"Yes!" Damon pumps his fist into the air.

They break out into cheers and applause and I receive a cascade of free kisses, including a sloppy, wet one from Freddie.

CHAPTER 17

Damon continues to function reasonably well under his new regimen and Dr. Hayes professes satisfaction with his progress. She finds the decrease of his ascites — fluid retention, most notably in the belly — "very encouraging."

But I've learned not to drop my guard and I no longer trust any single voice on Damon's illness. Everything we are seeing could be real improvement, as we devoutly hope, but it could also be the relentless pattern of PLE, with minor progress at the margins unavailing against the core onslaught.

One of the first people I turn to for guidance is the Columbia surgeon who performed Damon's original Fontan operation nine years earlier. Dr. Jan Quaegebeur, or "Dr. Q" as he is known, is an internationally renowned cardiothoracic surgeon who trained with Dr. Fontan himself. Dr. Q, a

Belgian, is among the top people in the world in his field, he operates a hundred times a year with an amazing success rate, and he enjoys a quasi-cult following. We can vouch for his extraordinary skill and the masterful surgery that gave Damon an excellent quality of life, at least until he developed his most recent problems.

However, not unlike other high-powered surgical stars, Dr. Q manifests a self-assurance some might construe as arrogance. He is very hard to reach, especially now that we're not scheduling an operation. I'm advised not to bother the great man, that it's out of his hands now.

But I'm on a sacred quest and I can't afford such advice. I keep calling and leaving messages, making it clear to Dr. Q's underlings there's no way he can avoid me. As Shealagh points out, Dr. Q owes us — and her personally, she feels — an explanation. After Damon's successful Fontan procedure, the supremely confident surgeon breezily told my wife to go home and have a good life, her son was fine and our troubles forever behind us.

"He laughed at my worries and promised me everything would be okay from here on, and I believed him!" Shealagh cries.

But now everything is *not* okay and we

need to understand from the person who knows Damon's anatomy best what exactly went wrong and how we can fix it.

Eventually, when it's clear I won't stop, Dr. Q returns my call.

"I'm sorry Damon is not doing well but I doubt it's PLE, which is extremely rare," he says preemptively.

"Excuse me, but if ten percent of Fontans now develop PLE, it may be uncommon but it's not rare," I reply, upset at his dismissiveness. "You can't pretend you never see it."

"No, this ten percent is exaggerated. And among *my* patients, it is rare!" Dr. Q declares. "Damon's pressures are very good, so he shouldn't have developed this problem at all. And Dr. Hayes is still unsure what is causing it. I think you're overreacting and things may not be as bad as you're making them," he chides. "Why not follow Dr. Hayes's protocol and give it a chance? I'm sorry, but there's nothing more I can offer you."

I'm surprised by Dr. Q's defensiveness and hasten to assure him I'm not questioning his performance, which everyone acknowledges was first-rate. Rather, I'm asking him to help me understand, and try to solve, my son's cardiac problem. A problem that bears all the symptoms of a progressive, and potentially calamitous, case of PLE.

The Fontan, I propose over Dr. Q's objections, gave Damon nine great years, but now it's failing him. Is it possible this operation provides a wonderful but temporary respite from the underlying cardiac anomaly? That in future it will be seen as a bridge therapy, and a more permanent cure is required? And if so, what would he recommend as the next best treatment for a patient like Damon, whose Fontan has clearly expired?

But Dr. Q cannot, or will not, follow me here. He won't accept that Damon has PLE, as if admitting this might somehow taint the reputation of his brilliant procedure. "We do not know what Damon's problem is," he asserts with an adamance bordering on hostility.

Nevertheless, because I still crave any glimmer of insight from this world expert, I ask Dr. Q about fenestration, which shows a promising outcome in the literature. He says flatly, "It doesn't work." I tell him about the Mayo Clinic and Children's Hospital of Philadelphia, which reported several PLE cures from fenestration, and he says: "If you believe that, maybe you should take your son *there*." I mention other treatments, and he's equally dismissive.

"Damon should continue with the diet and meds," he insists.

"Yes," I say, "but what if they *don't work?*"

Dr. Q repeats, with the same stern disapproval, that I should not leap to conclusions. "We do not know what is going on, so why assume the worst?"

"Because it's my son and I'm worried about his *survival.*"

"Don't exaggerate!" Dr. Q admonishes me. "Things are not at this stage. Dr. Hayes does not believe Damon's life or anything like that is at stake."

"But what if his life *is* at stake?" I say. "Do you know any way to *stop* PLE?"

Dr. Q gives a long sigh. "If Damon continues to deteriorate, and if none of the drugs helps, then the only way to stop PLE is a heart transplant. But that is way down the line . . ."

I feel my blood freeze but force myself to confront this now. I ask Dr. Q about the outcomes for a heart transplant, for which surgery he's also celebrated.

"It's far too early to consider such an option!" Dr. Q chides. "Damon, if he ever comes to it, is at least two to three years away from a transplant, so why discuss it now?"

Two or three years is like *tomorrow* for me. We are talking about my son's *life,* and the specter of such radical surgery and the alarming deterioration it prefigures horrifies me now. But for Dr. Q, with his daily lineup of patients, it must seem like eons away. He appears to think sequentially, in terms of his day-to-day tasks, and to avoid such out-of-sequence speculations. In fact, he seems offended that I'm posing the question at all. Now I'm just a hysterical parent wasting his time, and he wants to get me off the phone.

"I'm busy, I must go," he announces.

"PLE kills fifty percent of its patients within five years and I'm not going to let my son just drift away!" I tell him.

"I don't believe this fifty percent figure — statistics can be used to support anything. But you can do what you want, I have to go now!"

There is a tense silence as Dr. Q retreats into his remote treetop and I consider cutting him down to size. It's not his self-importance that bothers me but his inability to live up to his reputation. He seems to take little responsibility for his former patient, now that he's not a success story, and even denies his problem. Here's a man who's internationally feted and richly rewarded for his surgical specialty — he earns millions of dollars a year, with all the perks — yet he can't seem to face up to the technique's limitations.

I'm so irate I'm ready to track down the legendary Dr. Fontan himself — I've learned he's retired in full laurel to his vineyards in France — and threaten to expose him, with his protégé, unless he can explain this imperfection in his legacy!

But, wisely, I count to ten and suppress my indignation. My sole objective is to help Damon, and each action must be analyzed in those terms. While I hope at all costs to avoid a heart transplant for my son, if ever I must go that route, Columbia is a pioneer in heart transplantation and Dr. Q is a leading transplant surgeon. So I still may need Dr. Q in the future and antagonizing him now is counterproductive. I swallow my anger and thank him for his time and his help.

At the other end of the spectrum, around this time I get an introduction to Dr. Alvin Chin of Children's Hospital of Philadelphia (CHOP). Chin is a pediatric cardiologist who grew so frustrated with the lack of knowledge about a single-ventricle, Fontan-type circulation such as Damon's — and the debilitating problems, like PLE, he kept seeing at the bedside of these children — that he switched to bench science to grapple with this disease.

A professor of pediatrics and biology at the University of Pennsylvania School of Medicine and an attending cardiologist at CHOP, Dr. Chin has lobbied for more federally financed research into this poorly understood disease. He believes more scientific knowledge at the molecular and cellular level holds the key to progress.

From the outset, Dr. Chin readily admits what I've observed but what every other medical expert seems intent on denying: that no one knows how to treat PLE because they don't yet grasp its basic mechanisms or causes.

"We don't even have an animal model for this disease, which is the gold standard in scientific medicine!" Dr. Chin says.

Dr. Chin believes the incidence of PLE is higher than reported and that many top institutions such as Columbia pretend they never see it because they regard it as a blot on their reputations and an impediment to luring patients. He also thinks PLE will increase as the young adult Fontan population in the United States more than doubles in the next ten years.

Dr. Chin and I begin a regular e-mail correspondence that will last several years and constitutes a veritable tutorial on PLE, cardiology, and the modern practice of medicine. Our common goal is to help Damon and crack the PLE code, and Dr. Chin educates me as needed:

> In the late 1980s, the prevailing attitude was, If we get a bit better with the technical aspects of the single ventricle surgical procedures, and if we offer the surgery in infancy rather than later childhood, the long-term sequelae like PLE will vanish. This attitude had worked for all other congenital heart defects . . . Needless to say, essentially ignoring the problem did not work in the case of single ventricle. It will take an extraordinary individual to mobilize an Apollo Project–like effort in this country.

In preparation for our first meeting after months of cyber-contact, I send Dr. Chin Damon's complete medical records. But he keeps asking for *more:* echo reports, Holters (heart monitoring data), growth curves, and all protein and albumin readings since his Fontan. We discover no one has measured Damon's liver function for years, so we can't tell if his levels have been low for a long time or if the drop is more recent. The startling gaps in Columbia's records — no other hospital tracks this either — convince Dr. Chin to begin measuring liver function more frequently at CHOP.

In January, Shealagh and I drive with Damon to Philadelphia to meet Dr. Chin. It's a bleak, wintry day, made starker by our hurtling across slippery bridges and icy highways. Shealagh's back still acts up and she gripes I drive too fast. We are both tense and bicker along the snow-blown turnpike while Damon, the object of all our anxiety, sits unperturbed in the back, blithely listening to CDs on his headset. He loves music and is an old hand at tuning out his squabbling parents.

Dr. Chin is gentler looking and more soft-spoken than I pictured from his sharp, iconoclastic e-mails. He gives Damon a careful physical exam and speaks to him in a warm, respectful manner. As Damon removes his Salk T-shirt, he reveals thin upper arms and a pale, distended abdomen crisscrossed by blue veins. Dr. Chin nods sympathetically.

"That's his liver wrapping around his middle like a belt." He touches Damon's belly tenderly. There's something reassuring about Chin, even when he explains troubling things, and we all respond to his calm handling of Damon.

"The liver is full of fluid that's backed up from his high pressures because his heart has to pump so hard to get blood to the lungs," Chin says as he probes Damon's abdomen with sensitivity.

"But his belly is less swollen. The Aldactone seems to be working," I say.

"Yes, but it may not be addressing the protein loss — it's a diuretic that's drying him out. He's peeing out fluids, but this does not mean his PLE is better."

"Oh, I see." I try not to show my disappointment.

Dr. Chin says one also needs protein for growth, which may explain why Damon's development has stalled. Damon, listening closely, suddenly pipes up.

"I used to be one of the shorter kids in the class but now I'm the shortest."

Dr. Chin gives a poignant nod. "Well, Damon, we've seen growth hormone help with some PLE patients," he says, and I watch my son perk up.

We agree to look into this and keep an open mind.

After listening to Damon's heartbeat and taking his pulse, Dr. Chin informs us Da-

171

mon has a "slow heart rate." He warns this could be a problem — but one that CHOP has effectively managed in several similar cases with "a pacemaker."

I wince and sense a kindred shudder from Shealagh but Dr. Chin assures us a pacemaker can be implanted via a simple procedure using long leads so Damon can grow, while the battery "lasts eight to ten years." This bionic tidbit does little to allay our unease, even when Dr. Chin says it can improve cardiac output.

"In that case, you can put in the electrodes now but hold off on the external generator box, so we don't initiate pacing until you're ready," Dr. Chin says.

I glance across at Damon and realize how hard this must be for him. Although he chose to stay in the room with us, this doesn't mitigate the blow. I recall how upset I was when they told me I had to wear eyeglasses as a kid — I quickly opted for contact lenses — and now my son has to confront *this*. It doesn't seem fair. Shealagh also looks riled. Her father had a pacemaker implanted, but not before his late sixties; Damon is thirteen.

We agree to explore this further but we remain deeply skeptical. In fact, Dr. Chin will never persuade us to go this route, despite his best efforts. He is a wonderful mentor and a trusted adviser, but we always do our own research and solicit input from many sources before making a decision.

The area where we find almost complete accord with Dr. Chin is fenestration.

"Fenestration is not always a solution," Dr. Chin admits. "The benefits last five years on average — though some people are still good after ten years — but it's the most consistently effective therapy against PLE. And it's not as invasive, irreversible, or dangerous as a heart transplant. We've had many successes with it."

"Won't it make me more blue?" Damon asks, recalling Dr. Hayes's concern.

Dr. Chin nods. "The trade-off for punching a hole between the chambers of the heart is some blood mixing. So you will see greater blueness and lower oxygen saturation. But this does *not* necessarily mean you'll have less energy, because the oxygen deficit may be offset by a more efficient liver producing higher levels of protein that yield *more* energy. Plus, you won't have PLE!"

"It's the safest, most effective weapon we know," I tell Damon. "It comes up in all my literature searches. And Dr. Chin has seen it work for many patients."

The key, we all concur, is not *whether* but

when to try fenestration. How long do we give less intrusive approaches to work? We won't risk cutting Damon's oxygen unless we must, but we can't wait too long. We agree to revisit by summer.

As the meeting ends, Dr. Chin talks to Damon about graduation and his interest in theater. When Shealagh leaves to show Damon to the bathroom, I find myself alone with Dr. Chin for the first time. He tells me what a nice family I have and how bright Damon and Shealagh are, and I commend his bedside manner and his clear medical explanations. Then I lean forward and look him in the eye.

"So what do you think now that you've seen Damon in the flesh?" I smile. Despite our long exchanges, until today Dr. Chin has only viewed medical records of my son and heard about him secondhand.

Dr. Chin pauses, weighing his words. We've been sharing thoughts and ideas very freely, but now I see him trying to reconcile this openness with my being the boy's father.

"I think he looks about the same as other PLE patients I've seen," Dr. Chin says.

I feel a sharp letdown and suddenly realize I'd wanted Dr. Chin to tell me what I heard at Columbia: that Damon looks too

174

good for PLE and it's all a big mistake.

Dr. Chin is my second opinion — in the next months, I'll solicit a dozen more expert medical views — but he is confirming, in the most diplomatic manner, what I've dreaded.

CHAPTER 18

Weekdays I rise at four forty-five A.M. to write, stealing a few quiet hours in my study before we get the kids up for school and ourselves off to work. The energy consumed as I sit in a chair and cogitate over a keyboard in my sealed chamber generates so much heat and sweat that I must strip down to my underwear, even in winter, while the windows fog up like steamy portholes. When Shealagh barges in to tell me my time's up — ideally carrying a fresh cup of coffee — she is assaulted by the humid, tropical heat and the sight of a semi-naked, wildly oblivious man. She throws open the windows, laughing at the human "steam furnace," and reminds me to put on some clothes.

Only now, it's no longer Shealagh but Damon who first enters my hothouse at dawn. Damon has such an exacting diet with so many pills to swallow that he needs extra time in the morning, and we take turns trying to give him a hand.

He knocks with a light touch and slips unobtrusively into my study around six A.M., perching on the wicker chair by the door like a polite bird. "Hey."

"Hey, D-man." I swivel from my desk and check the state of his puffiness, which is most pronounced in the morning. He checks me out too, ignoring the familiar nakedness but scanning my book-lined shelves and project-strewn desk.

"How's the novel?" Damon asks. He knows I've cut it and resubmitted.

"Good. I've got some real interest, more than I had before. We'll see."

"Cool." My son is pleased for me. He believes in my unheralded creative work, making him special indeed. "So what you working on now?" He cranes toward my laptop.

Among the papers, I spot a copy of Dr. Chin's lab results, stating, *Damon's PLE and liver dysfunction are quite severe.* I quickly turn the report facedown.

"I'm outlining an idea for a new novel — a heist with a moral rationale — and story-boarding that film about Grandma and Granddad." I point to my camcorder.

"You gonna show the film at their party?"

Damon asks.

"If I finish on time." I'm making a short film about my parents for a fifty-second wedding anniversary party planned for the night before Damon's Bar Mitzvah.

"Getting close, huh?" Damon chuckles. He still has lots of prep work.

We've decided to carry on with both events, even though we planned them before Damon's diagnosis, which has altered everything.

Shealagh and I debated whether we were putting Damon under too much pressure but he insists he's up to it. He regularly attends Hebrew classes and Bar Mitzvah lessons while keeping up with his schoolwork, extracurricular activities, and social calendar. He may be a half step slower but he's as focused and determined as ever. He's even resumed karate class, after an eight-month hiatus.

"It's still fun," he says.

Taking a cue from Damon, we've decided not to make any concessions to his illness unless we have to. Even my parents, thrilled with the idea of their party, offer to let me put it off, fearing we may be taking on too much. But they've had their own ups and downs and I've wanted to do this for them for a long time. I also know that if we start to give up on a normal life, we're done for.

"Hey." I tap my wristwatch. "It's time!" We shuffle down to the kitchen. I prepare breakfast while Damon feeds Freddie, then jogs with him in our backyard, exercising them both. That sly ferret-dog, who craps under my desk and chews the heads off Miranda's Barbie dolls, is a godsend for Damon.

"How you feeling?" I ask Damon when he comes back in, flushed and panting.

"I get a little more tired than before, but otherwise I feel okay," Damon replies.

I count out his morning meds on the counter, laying out the pills in a white egg-cup: enalapril, Aldactone, Zantac, Adeks, calcium, baby aspirin. The Lasix and Zyrtec are for the evening but now he also must swallow a big spoonful of greasy MCT oil, which contains medium-chain triglycerides for easy absorption. To help it go down, I give him a glass of orange juice. Then I peel a kiwi and slice an apple for him.

"Thanks, Dad," Damon says, using the sweet, palatable fruit to chase down the pills.

While Damon sits on a high stool at the counter and gets through his meds, I cook him a soft-boiled egg, which he spoons avidly from the shell. The news plays quietly on the TV above the counter.

Damon often requests a second egg, which I happily supply. Once, when I'm by the stove, he gets up for the salt, stepping on the low, mobile platform that lives on the kitchen floor, a ridged booster step for little Miranda. He notices I'm watching — I dislike the step, which trips me up and reminds me of his dependency — and he turns to face me.

"Ever since the doctors started talking about how I haven't grown, I suddenly feel small," Damon says huskily. His eyes moisten and I wonder if he's going to cry. Shealagh says he puts on a brave front for me but she gets more tears. But now Damon's mouth turns wry. "I'll be one of the smallest Bar Mitzvah boys ever. Tom Thumb at the Torah."

"You'll be fine, Damon," I assure him. "And you'll be a man, more than I can say for many people twice your size."

As the Bar Mitzvah nears, Damon and I plan to meet at Brooks Brothers to buy him a new suit. The store is on Fifth Avenue, by my office, but Damon is late — he's coming up from school — so I stand out on the sidewalk and look for him. The ceaseless press of humanity, which I pass unthinkingly every day, suddenly looks daunting. This is a special day — I recall when my

father bought me my Bar Mitzvah suit —
and I want it to go well.

After scanning the throng and trying his
cell, I finally spot Damon on the street. He's
unmistakable, even in this dense crowd: a
pale, compact, ginger-haired boy motoring
forward at a surprisingly vigorous clip, like
a speed-walker with a battery pack strapped
to his back. He swings his arms like pistons.
The minute he recognizes me, he breaks
into a smile and slows down, shutting off
his engine. We walk into the store arm in
arm.

In short order, we pick out a classic dark
suit, a couple of dress shirts and silk ties,
then throw in a pair of new shoes. We go to
the fitting room, where a natty man with a
tape measure bends over Damon. The jacket
only needs minor alterations but the pants
must be recut at the waist. The tailor, hum-
ming an aria and exuding cologne, wields
his measuring tape with silken dexterity,
makes a few brisk chalk marks, and previews
the final product in the full-length mirror:

"What a handsome boy. He look like a
prince, a young lion!"

The night before the Bar Mitzvah, we host
my parents' anniversary at the Century
Club. Many relatives and close friends join
us, flying in from many countries. But the

most exciting arrival for Damon is Lachlann, who materializes from the Isle of Skye with his wiry hardiness and gorse-bush accent.

"Och aye, let's get smashed!"

Now the two young rascals cruise the stately reception hall, set with a dozen handsome tables, a screen, and a podium. Damon looks sharp and jaunty in his dark new suit. He greets guests with confident aplomb, then sidles up to me at the projector.

"Hey, Dad, you nervous? Grandma said they love that you're doing this for them, she just hopes it won't be too embarrassing." He dims the lights for the film, which begins with a 1949 map of Europe and the theme music from *Casablanca*. My father as a scrappy, leather-jacketed youth with cigarette dangling from mouth in old sepia photos has always conjured up Bogie for me, while my mother, a tall, striking European blonde, bore a real likeness to Ingrid Bergman.

But it's my parents in their unglamorous seventies, sitting together at their Rego Park kitchen table in a tight two-shot, who are the heart of the film: Robert, grayer and stouter, more like Edward G. Robinson than Bogie now, in a burly cable-knit sweater. A nimble athlete, a pleaser of ladies, and a witty, well-defended, warm-hearted Glaswegian, born in Budapest, with a decade of pioneer work in Israel and then a business career, at first highly successful and then less so, in America; and Helga, still beautiful and dignified, and still tragic and self-dramatizing, with high cheekbones and her long, stately nose in the air, a little sadder about the eyes, and a little rounder, a survivor of cancer and of Leipzig, Germany, where the Nazis wiped out her entire family. She escaped with her brother on the Kindertransport to England, where she met Robert, in Liverpool, from whence they journeyed, via France and Italy, to a kibbutz in Israel, marriage, and children, and then, by chance, to America. Now wearing a vivid red turtleneck and mauve lipstick, she fluffs her thick, frosted hair with die-hard female vanity, an elegant and eloquent woman, upright, vicarious, and true.

They sat side by side for hours — I taped them over several months, from across the kitchen table where I ate my meals as a boy — and they spar, bicker, and one-up each other, rolling their eyes at the camera and expressing the frustrations and self-justifications of a long marriage: "A lifetime or a life sentence? A little of both," Helga quips. But somehow, as they talk about their upbringing and their own parents, the impact of momentous historical events on their lives, and their meeting, courtship, and subsequent marriage, culminating in two children and three grandchildren, one of whom is Damon, whose sharp gaze I can feel beside me, the years peel away, and part of the mystery of love is revealed.

The film is followed by laudatory speeches. My parents are royalty for this one night, which pleases me greatly, and appropriate homage is paid.

Damon, Sam, and Miranda are last to speak and marched up to the front by a take-charge Damon. Their mere appearance at the podium brings smiles and murmurs of delight.

As Sam and Miranda hide behind him, squirming and giggling, a decidedly mature Damon lowers the microphone and speaks about the three kids' close relationship with their grandparents and how they were always there, "Especially," he says, "when we wanted to get away from our own parents." As the crowd laughs, Damon displays a keen appreciation of time. "I feel this has been a pretty long week for me, but for my grandparents' marriage, it's been two thousand, seven hundred and four weeks, one hundred and eighty thousand days, twenty-seven million minutes, or one point eight billion seconds."

Flashing a big smile, Damon wishes his grandparents a happy anniversary, then beckons his siblings to follow suit as they've all rehearsed. "Okay, guys, now!"

Shy, giggly, dashing Sam sidles up with rubbery limbs, juggling his assigned words like a hot potato, which he quickly tosses to the audience before darting back. But gap-toothed, golden-haired Miranda is stymied because she's too short to reach the podium. Without a pause, Damon bends down and heaves his sister in her blue sash dress right up to the podium mike.

"Happy anniversary, Grandma and Granddad!" all three kids blurt in unison.

CHAPTER 19

The day of Damon's Bar Mitzvah begins badly.

It's pouring rain, a washout, which will not only impede our preparations but augurs poorly for the turnout. We still have several hours of setup in the synagogue's banquet hall — they needed it for another function the previous night — and it must be ready by ten A.M.

Even more upsetting, Damon had a rough night. He says he feels okay now, a big relief, but his face has swollen up, making him appear more frog than handsome prince, and his body drags, dampening his ebullience.

"It's rotten luck because all eyes will be on him today," Shealagh says.

But the day improves. And under Shealagh's direction, we transform the banquet hall with bright hangings, fine chair coverings, fresh flowers, and balloons — hundreds of colorful balloons in thick clumps and bunches, rising from the tables and descending from the ceiling. We finish by draping bold rainbow streamers and kites, throw in a popcorn machine, karaoke, raffle balls, candy, and wrapped gifts, and the room looks ready for a party and Shealagh's idea of "jollification."

Upstairs, the majestic if somewhat faded turn-of-the-century sanctuary of Temple Beth Emeth v'Ohr ("House of Truth and Light") fills up with nearly two hundred and fifty of our guests plus regular congregants. Key members of my family fly in, as do all Shealagh's siblings. And most of our close friends make it in from points far and wide, along with many neighbors and local friends. Even the sun, miraculously, makes a belated appearance.

We enter the sanctuary from the rabbi's office behind the podium. Damon looks sharp in his dark new Brooks Brothers suit, a little less frog and more prince. A bright blue silk yarmulke rides high on his crown and a striped prayer shawl adorns his shoulders. He shuffles through a folder with his key papers — speeches, blessings, prayers. He looks nervous but totally focused and ready.

I sit on the stage in a high, carved armchair with a scalloped crest, facing the congregation, and listen to Damon, his back to me, recite the first of innumerable blessings in praise of God:

"The Lord is the earth and fullness thereof, the world and they that dwell therein . . ."

I normally don't have much patience for this stuff but since Damon's diagnosis, I keep a more open mind and search for clues everywhere, much as I scan the medical literature. So now when Damon reads "Who shall stand in God's holy place?" and answers, in his high, clear, and firm voice, "One that hath clean hands and a pure heart," I *know* that my son qualifies. I look up at the ark and tell whoever is minding the store that there is no one better or purer to receive "the blessing of the Lord and justice from the God of salvation."

I emphasize the word "justice," shaking an imaginary finger up at the tabernacle.

Rabbi William Kloner, regal in long black robe and gold braided prayer shawl, commands the congregation to rise. Damon climbs three steps and opens the hammered bronze doors of the ark, revealing a large and a small Torah book under a gleaming light. Rabbi Kloner hands Damon the small Torah and carries the big Torah, the crown jewel, to center stage. The rabbi prods

Damon, who is cradling his junior Torah just under his chin, and Damon recites from the prayer book.

As the congregation's singing rises to an ecstatic pitch, Rabbi Kloner and Damon descend from the stage. They march up the aisle carrying their respective Torahs like two beaming Moseses, young and old. Members crowd in to touch the mantle, using bare fingers or their prayer shawls, then kiss the holy spot. The two figures return to the stage, unsheathe the Torah, and roll open the parchment. As Damon chants from the Torah, his mastery of the material is unmistakable. Once, toward the end, he stumbles but recovers so seamlessly few realize he's tripped up. He never loses command.

The performance is impressive to us not just because of Damon's diagnosis but because he was rejected as a Bar Mitzvah candidate by the first two Park Slope synagogues we approached. The rabbis felt one year was not sufficient time to prepare. At least *three years* were required, during which one had to be a paying member of their congregation. When I explained that Damon was a trained actor who could learn major parts in weeks, and that my father and I could help him with the Hebrew, it did not matter. Nor did they budge when I said, without specifying Damon's medical past, that timeliness was a factor.

It surprised me that at a time when a majority of American Jews have assimilated and synagogue membership is flagging, they would refuse us, but they did. Rabbi William Kloner, our final try, was also wary about any appearance of a shortcut. However, being a navy chaplain and lifelong student of history, as well as a Reform rabbi with an aging congregation, he was more sensitive to the "survival of the flock" argument. He did not say yes right away but agreed to let us try it out on a "let's see if he's as good as you say" basis.

As Damon finishes singing, Rabbi Eric, the younger, second-in-command rabbi, praises his "phenomenal" job and takes Damon to the side, offering him a personal blessing that no one can hear.

I am handed the Torah while Damon recites more blessings, until Rabbi Kloner removes the weighty scroll from my arms, where I confess it's growing heavy, and places it back in the ark. Following this consummation, I am sent from my privileged perch back down to the congregation, where I take my place beside Shealagh, Sam, and Miranda.

Damon now delivers the talk on his Torah portion, focusing on the Ten Commandments. He reminds us that even this document is based on a "photocopy," the original lying somewhere at the bottom of Mount Sinai, smashed into a thousand pieces.

"So no one," Damon says with a twinkle in his eye, not even Moses or the Israelites, "likes rules." Yet rules, or a "single set of uniform laws that uphold absolute values and principles," are essential if people want "to live together and avoid chaos." Accepting rules means "you accept responsibility for your actions" and the fact that "you don't live alone."

As Damon speaks, alternately playful and serious, I note how his eyes lift off the page and scan the room. He has undeniable presence and a natural eloquence, but I'm also struck, now that I see him head-on, by his pallor and the lingering puffiness in his face. I tell myself to relax and enjoy his triumph. Even at three-quarters strength, Damon shines.

I tune back in as Damon concludes: "I still plan to enjoy myself and to make my life into something original, but I accept the Ten Commandments as a moral code to guide me as I go forward in the world to find my own place."

■ ■ ■ ■

Downstairs, after the kiddush, the party is in full swing. Jolly music plays while wide-eyed children wander through the billowing, festooned banquet hall as in a wonderland, tugging at the coiling ribbons that stream down from canopies of bright balloons. Our seating chart quickly gets jettisoned as people plunk themselves down wherever. Miranda and her cousins Lucas and Harry spray over seat name tags with cans of Silly String. Only my parents' elderly friends, who have trouble standing, quickly find their assigned seats and tuck into the food.

Damon, happily dazed, accepts handshakes and greetings as he makes straight for his friends, a multicultural assortment of young teens sprawled across three tables. Kyle is there, barefoot in a strapless black dress with her hair swept off her neck. Daniel, an old friend from music school, hovers awkwardly because he doesn't know the other kids. Brenda, a big, precocious blonde, finds Jason, a math whiz, two pals from elementary school. Keith leads the middle school contingent, a sharp figure in dress slacks and tie, while Kiri has cleaned up nicely, even if she still wears pants. Most of the other girls are dolled up in party dresses and gowns. It's a month before graduation, and they are excitedly trying things out, showing off new outfits and makeup and hair. Maddy, a leggy six-foot classmate, bends down to kiss Damon, towering over him even more than the other girls. But Damon takes it all in stride, accepting embraces from a bevy of admirers.

Damon hands his skullcap to Kirsten, who wants to try it on, then removes his prayer shawl too, unwinding as he realizes this part of his day is over now. He snaps his fingers, glances at his sea of friends, and breaks into a wide smile. "Party time!"

The master of ceremonies, I make the rounds and check that all is in order. There's food and drinks galore and representatives from all stages of our lives. Everywhere I turn, I see people I like, people who matter to me. It's an amazing turnout. Yet even with all these special people here to celebrate Damon's coming-of-age, and even with all the decorations and the champagne and the music, I cannot quite shake my lingering sense of fretfulness.

Shealagh sidles up in her willfully giddy party mode and instantly recognizes my thoughts as we share a silent high five at bringing this whole thing off. My wife shoots me a pleading look and shoves a glass of wine in my hand. Since our CHOP visit, I've taken Damon to three more hospitals across the country.

"Have a drink, you look too sober!" Shealagh says, as much for her sake as mine.

And I do have a drink, several in fact. I notice my second son has already exchanged his tie and jacket for a blue T-shirt he wears inside out, while Miranda, pretty in a pink dress with a big bow, snaps photos with a disposable camera and interviews adults about life.

I take the mike by the karaoke machine and call up family and friends to toast Damon. When it's my turn, I talk about Damon's incredible courage, his beautiful mind, and his unbelievable messiness, three areas with little in common except, perhaps, that he's already surpassed me in each. In citing his courage, I glancingly address the elephant in the room — most of the guests know nothing of his diagnosis — remarking that Damon was born with congenital heart disease, so his whole life has been a battle, and he's far braver than he realizes.

Then Damon graciously thanks everyone. "And it's great to see so many of my friends show up, it's so cool, you guys, even if I know you mostly came for the food and the gift bags."

Damon speaks with ease and panache and this crowd adores him, but I can't help noticing again that something's off. There's an odd catch, a furry thickness, in his voice, and a faint, rabbity twitch about his nose.

After Damon, Shealagh, the grand event designer, raises her champagne glass and toasts her son's wonderful courage and amazing character. Then in time-honored tradition, his school friends, aided by assorted adults, place Damon in a chair and lift him off the ground. They form a snaking line and raise him above their shoulders, clapping, chanting, and swaying.

The stomping and pounding grows wilder, and the surging crowd more frenzied. The boy on his throne is small and light and the mob intoxicated with its massed, heaving power. The pack hurls Damon into the air with intensifying force. He must hold on to the flying chair to keep from falling off. His disheveled mane bobs up and down, his jaunty shoulders flop, and he bounces hard on the seat, soaring above the heads of the celebrants.

It looks like he's losing his balance, but he isn't. He's having the time of his life.

CHAPTER 20

"In middle school it was all about fitting in, but in high school you have to find your own way . . ."

In June, Damon graduates from the Salk School of Science in a ceremony held at the First Avenue campus of New York University School of Medicine, a Salk affiliate. By virtue of his size, Damon leads the processional of sixty students down the aisle as Elgar's "Pomp and Circumstance" issues from a solo trumpet. The teens look alternately mischievous and somber as they fan out to their seats. Damon wears a purple silk graduation gown while the long horse's-tail tassel on his mortarboard swishes merrily. He plops down one row in front of Keith and turns around in his seat, smiling puckishly.

"Hey, Keith." Damon points his disposable camera at his friend, who is a foot taller with a brash buzz cut, and Keith swivels his head. "Gotcha!" Damon grins and shoots.

We listen to inspirational speeches and student poems. When the awards are handed out, we're surprised to see Damon repeatedly called to the stage, winning prizes for academic excellence, for leadership, for writing, and for science. He marches to the podium in compact triumph, lit by a luminous smile and his own warm spotlight as his classmates cheer.

After the mortarboards go sailing into the air, Damon hugs friends and bids farewell to teachers.

It's a proud day for us all, but the normal, bittersweet joys of graduation are marred by our abnormal anxiety about what the future holds for our son. Damon's protein levels have not budged, despite daily medications and a strict diet.

"He hasn't improved, so what do we try now?" Shealagh asks that night.

"It's between heparin and fenestration," I reply, and list the differing views of four hospitals we consult with closely: Columbia, CHOP, Boston Children's, and the Mayo Clinic. "Heparin is less invasive, so we'll probably try that first."

Shealagh sighs. "Oh well, I guess we're not going to Skye this summer!"

"We can't. And no sleepaway camp for

Damon either," I say ruefully.

I still remember waiting for the returning camp bus on Damon's maiden outing the previous summer, wondering how he'd survived in such a close, unrelentingly physical environment for a whole month. I was worried, so I kept my eyes peeled on the door as the kids poured out of the bus. There was no sign of Damon for a long time, and my anxiety mounted. But the instant he appeared at the top of the bus steps and stood there with his shaggy, unkempt new swagger, I felt elated. I took in his blazingly defiant, sunburned face; his sinewy, mosquito-bitten arms; and the proud, faintly rebellious smile on his cocky lips — that heady flowering of freedom and new powers that summer camp can confer on a boy — and I knew he'd held his own with his peers and tasted true independence for the first time.

"Hey, D-man. How you doing?" I gave him a brief hug as he stepped down.

"Good," he said in a more mature, aloof voice. "Very good!" He grinned.

But now we cannot let him return to the six-thousand-acre mountain playground in Frost Valley, New York, much as we'd like to. Fortunately, instead of camp, Damon sets his sights on auditioning for New York

University's Looking for Shakespeare summer theater workshop. It's part of the Educational Theatre division, where graduate-student teachers direct an ensemble of thirteen-to-eighteen-year-olds to create and perform an original adaptation of a Shakespeare play. The production takes place at the historic Provincetown Playhouse.

For his audition, Damon prepares two soliloquies, modern and classical. He also gets an improvised scene to perform. "I don't think I did that well," Damon says as we exit the theater on MacDougal Street. The program is a notch up from any stage work Damon has done before but I also wonder if his condition has started hindering him. But two weeks later, a letter arrives saying he's been selected for *Cymbeline,* making him among the youngest actors in the program.

Damon attends the workshop five days a week, and on weekends as the production date nears. Each session includes warm-up exercises, stretching, vocals, and ensemble-building activities run by the gifted stage manager, Krista, who turns out to live on our Brooklyn block and becomes Damon's friend. The directors cast Shakespeare's *Cymbeline* and then create a contemporary frame story where each actor writes a new role based on his or her character.

Damon quickly establishes himself. He learns all his lines and then helps others with their lines. When no one else will do it, Damon dons a pair of antlers and hangs upside down off a broom, playing a dead deer. "I don't mind except my arms get a little tired," he tells me. He befriends several actors and hangs out with the cast after rehearsals. Afternoons, they go down the street to the Olive Tree Café and eat Middle Eastern fare while doing loud, wicked imitations. "They almost threw us out today when we got a little rowdy," Damon says with a smile.

On the first Friday in August we drive to the Provincetown Playhouse, where Eugene O'Neill and Edna St. Vincent Millay debuted their work. A bold, graffiti-strewn urban backdrop sprawls across the stage.

In the frame story, Damon plays Raven, a pizzeria owner mediating between rival tribes. Amid the strutting gang members who tower over him in do-rags and leather, Raven, in checked apron and brown fedora, exudes quiet authority and calm reason. "Oh, sorry," he jibes, "is fighting the only thing you're good at?"

In *Cymbeline* proper, Damon enters

grand, eliciting laughter and applause as he rises through a trapdoor and emerges in full regalia as Zeus the Thunderer on the back of an eagle. He sparks great mirth with flamboyant, deadpan godliness.

After the show, one woman so admires Damon's performance that she gives us her card and invites us to consider letting him join her small acting company.

"He's very castable. You should let him develop his talent," she advises.

As we watch Damon clasp hands and bow onstage with his fellow actors, grinning in bright costume and makeup, I'm struck by how natural he looks in this setting, like a bird that can only display its full plumage in a native habitat.

"Did you enjoy it?" Damon asks in the car after, invigorated and hungry for feedback. "What'd you like most? Was the frame story okay? What didn't work?"

After we've supplied detailed critiques of his performance and analyses of all the other cast members, Damon also solicits our views on the directing, writing, staging, and costumes.

Two days later, we're back at Columbia for more tests and visits.

In the morning, Damon goes to the X-ray department, where a radiologist conducts an upper gastrointestinal series. The aim is to see if there's any problem in his digestive tract that could account for his protein leak. "It's unlikely but you want to rule out any possibility, especially a treatable one," the GI expert advises. The test is unpleasant but Damon hangs in. We'll get the results in two or three days.

After the test, we go meet with a pediatric endocrinologist. Discussing delayed growth with an adolescent boy is a delicate matter under any circumstances, and we've already had one bad experience at Columbia, so we're uneasy about this meeting. But the reserved-seeming Dr. Mary Horlick quickly impresses Shealagh and me with her up-to-date knowledge and unobtrusive empathy. Which doesn't mean seeing her is a pleasant experience for Damon, only that Dr. Horlick makes the best of a very tough situation.

"Let's get your exact weight and height, okay, Damon?" Dr. Horlick has Damon remove his sweatshirt and sneakers before stepping on the digital scale, then measures his height with a state-of-the-art stadiometer. Although I know there's been no progress, I hold my breath as Dr. Horlick adjusts the sliding headpiece over Damon's crown. She takes three different measurements in her thorough and meticulous way, but each time we get the same read: fifty-six inches. It's as if Damon is stuck and can't get past that ceiling.

"Dr. Chin suggested a bone-density test if we're considering heparin and growth hormone," I mention, wondering how she'll react to outside advice.

"Yes, and a bone-age scan too." Dr. Horlick nods. "I have a lab at St. Luke's where we can test him. We'll also want a full blood workup for Damon's hormone levels."

"That's just a blood test, right?" Shealagh asks as Damon watches keenly.

"Yes." Dr. Horlick pauses. "But to get a full picture of Damon's status, I also need to give him a physical exam, including a manual check of his testes." She winces for us. "I promise it won't hurt, and I'll make it as quick as possible, but there's no other way!"

I've forewarned my son and he looks resigned if very leery.

Dr. Horlick chats with a nervous Damon about school and other activities, then asks with an apologetic smile if he can change into a gown.

"Okay." Damon swallows. "But, Mom, can you, like, wait outside or something?"

Shealagh is thrown but only for a second.

"Of course." As she leaves the tense room, she does not look totally unhappy, and I watch her exit with a mix of emotions.

Damon changes into a loose green gown and lies back on the exam table, looking pale, apprehensive, and excruciatingly self-conscious. I make small talk as Dr. Horlick dons thin surgical gloves and approaches Damon's side. She lifts his gown and gently probes Damon's testes with one hand while holding a string of numbered wooden beads in the other. The beads, arranged in ascending order on a rosary, correspond to testicle size, and testicle size "correlates directly with puberty and developmental age," Dr. Horlick explains.

"Oww!" Damon jumps and squirms as Dr. Horlick, who's being very careful and correct, palpates his privates. She's totally professional but there's no escaping what's happening and I cringe for my fourteen-year-old son, whose entire body now seems fair game for probing. Previously, when a more insensitive doctor gave him a digital rectal exam, Damon cried, "It's not fair!" and I feel a terrible, guilty helplessness at his continuing ordeal.

Dr. Horlick finishes and seems almost as relieved as Damon as she covers him back up. "You can get dressed now," she says thoughtfully. I open the door for Shealagh but she's gone. I go down the hall and find her sitting by a sunny window with a coffee and a pastry, trying to create a small oasis for herself. It's all very hard on my wife, and I hesitate before breaking in on her.

"Well, Damon," Dr. Horlick says once we've all reassembled in her office, "you've officially entered puberty!" She smiles at him in his jeans and sweatshirt. "You're at the earliest stage but it's definitely started."

Damon raises an eyebrow at this unexpected sign of progress and Shealagh and I pause to savor it too. But we also know what's *not* happening.

Dr. Horlick explains that Damon's development remains "nascent" — she points between the second and third beads on the chain — and the "major cascade" of hormones and other pubescent markers has not yet begun. "But this is a good thing," she says, "because it means you still have time to develop and catch up once full puberty kicks in."

She seems pleased but warns there is only a finite interval or "critical period" when normal growth is possible. "After that, the growth plates close and are replaced by solid bone." To boost Damon's chances of benefitting from this narrow window, Dr.

Horlick suggests we consider growth hormone. "Results vary, and you'd have to vet the idea with Damon's cardiologists before proceeding, but the downside is minimal, and I've seen kids shoot up half a foot in ten weeks," she says. "I think it makes sense to try it for Damon."

Damon's eyes light up. It's the best news we've heard in a long time.

Food is much on our minds these days. With Damon's albumin levels still too low, he must eat three high-protein meals daily, plus two protein supplements. I'm stricter and less forgiving than Shealagh about it. When he sleeps past noon on weekends, I worry he's already missed a meal and we must play catch-up. I morph into the food police, demanding a daily inventory of his dietary intake and verbally frisking him when he comes home.

One day he calls me at four thirty P.M., after theater, and asks if he can go to Jon's house.

"Sure," I say. "What'd you eat for lunch?" He usually has a bite at the Olive Tree.

Damon hems. "We went to a fast food place today, so I didn't eat anything."

"What!" I cry. He's losing protein nonstop, so he must refill himself constantly.

"By now you should be on your *second* supplement and you haven't even had lunch!"

"I didn't want to eat bad food," Damon says, both defensive and defiant.

"Damon, I give you extra money so you can always buy good food, whatever it costs . . . You've got to stop screwing around and take this diet more seriously!"

I still let Damon go to his friend's house — it's summer and I want him to enjoy himself, after all — but I demand he return for dinner so I can make sure he eats properly.

He comes home late and sits down with us at the table but says he doesn't have an appetite. He looks tired, pale, and sulky. I feel for him but insist he at least eat his chicken, a good protein source. By now, he's *two* meals behind, and I won't take no for an answer.

I keep the pressure on while we sit at the table — "Come on, Damon, three more bites!" — until he jumps up, makes a retching sound, and bolts from the kitchen as if to vomit. I follow him to the bathroom, filled with remorse, and place my hand on his back as he leans over the sink and opens his mouth, gagging. I hold a bucket under his chin.

Now I've really gone too far, and I feel ashamed of myself.

But Damon's attack passes and he keeps his food down. It's possible he exaggerated to teach me a lesson. Regardless, he's won the argument, and I leave him alone about eating for the rest of that day, wondering what to try next. I can see the protein leaking out of him daily, and I want desperately to plug the leak.

Damon still has his spirit, which manifests in surprising ways.

One day we're in Prospect Park, playing a makeshift game of soccer, with an oak and jacket for goalposts. It's Miranda and me against Damon and my father, who used to play semiprofessionally. My father still likes to kick and head the ball and he still has fancy moves. But at seventy-five, with high blood pressure, a previous mild heart attack, and extra pounds, he runs out of breath and is less fleet.

I was never as adept as my father at this game but my relative youth gives me an advantage, and Miranda and I take the lead and dominate. But Damon surprises us with his skill and tenacity. I often have to run to Miranda's aid to stop Damon, who powers past her and heads for our goal. Once, I allow Damon to score as a reward for his impressive efforts, and Miranda screams at me.

"No, Dad! You let him do that!" She must win and won't tolerate any laxity.

But Damon doesn't need much slack. Even when I stop him and recover the ball, leaving our goal unattended as I run up-field, he comes right back after me, chasing me the entire way. He just *won't give up.*

Once, as I near the goal and feint left to fool my father, Damon sneaks up from behind and steals the ball. It's a brilliant move, and I'm impressed. But Miranda doesn't share my admiration. "No, Dad, get it from him!" she cries, egging me on until I run Damon down and steal back the ball. Damon puts up a furious fight, refusing to relinquish his prize, until I overpower him. He kicks at my legs, livid, and screams as I advance with the ball, elude my father, and score.

Shealagh comes by and Damon complains he and my father are getting creamed. So Shealagh joins Damon's side, altering the dynamic. Now I must cover the goal closely and poor Miranda is overwhelmed by three bigger players. I can't stop them either, and they go ahead. Everyone is satisfied now, save for Miranda, who yells, "Three against two isn't fair!" I tell her she's playing great, but she's still upset. So I rush out and score on a booming kick, making her smile. But mostly I'm stuck guarding the goal and we have no offense, so our fate is sealed.

We've been playing for a long time and it's getting dark, making injuries likelier. I'm also worried about my father, who's panting, so I suggest we stop and go for dinner. Shealagh agrees and my father says he will accede to the majority.

I'm picking up the jacket that delineates the goalpost when Damon storms over.

"Why are we stopping?" he demands, irate.

"Because it's dark and it's late and we've all had enough," I reply evenly.

"No, let's keep playing!" He kicks the ground, fired up. "I wanna play!"

"Listen, D-man. My father's tired, I'm tired, your mother has other things to do . . . We had a good game. You played a terrific match."

"No. I want to play more!" he snarls. "We were just starting to do well."

"Hey, you *won*," I say, surprised by his anger. "You defeated us."

"No, you stopped trying, Dad. Play more!" Damon is seething, his adrenaline is pumping, and he refuses to be mollified. He's taken the game far more seriously than

I realized, and he still wants satisfaction. Miranda, too, gets into the act and bawls, insisting we play on. Shealagh tries to reason with them, as does my father, to no avail. The two children kick at the grass and wail.

I'm amazed at how overwrought Damon looks, how choked with fury. It's so unlike him. Yet as I watch my son continue to fume and curse, sputtering uncontrollably, I can't help but be impressed. There's such an incredible fighting spirit beneath his tantrum. He's already mobilized for war.

I decide to refrain from any further reprimand, because I wish to preserve that spirit. Even if it's misplaced here, this fieriness will serve him well in future contests.

CHAPTER 21

We haven't been to our country house in over a year, so when we get there the first priority is cutting the weed-choked, waist-high grass that overruns our Catskill Park property. The deer and field mice carry ticks, and we don't need Lyme disease added to Damon's ills, nor our own.

"Can I help, Dad?" Damon watches me rev up the old mower and don goggles.

"No, I want you inside with the others until I clear the area." I make him go back in.

The house, a two-story modified cape, sits on a terraced lot with a stone wall, a garage, and a writer's shack, all nestled between a brook and a hilly forest. Damon stands in the family room and tracks me from the big picture window while I mow down the meadow. As soon as there's a path, he runs out in boots and long pants and trails me, raking the cuttings into black trash bags.

He feels excluded if he cannot lend a hand.

"I got it, Dad!" He helps me lug the bags to the compost heap behind the garage.

Meanwhile, Shealagh has us get the house operational. We switch on the water pump and water heater, clean out mouse turds and spiderwebs, activate the fridge and fill it with groceries, and buy coupon books for the town dump.

We're almost done when we find a dozen wasp's nests on our property.

"They're everywhere!" Shealagh cries. Damon once had a severe allergic reaction to a hornet sting, so we call pest control to come clear the hives.

With our house functional, we head down to the Olympic-sized town pool by the fairground. Damon leaves Sam and Miranda at the gate. All three of our kids are water rats and can frolic for hours in the pool, but today Damon wants to pass the diving test before his friends come up for a visit.

Damon trundles over to the water with an impish smile. His body above his red trunks is pale and tubular, with skinny arms, a sloping belly, and a zipper scar down his chest. Unabashed, he takes a running start and hurls himself full-tilt across the pool, letting out a booming cry. His eyes glitter as he tumbles downward, yodeling fiercely in the giddy, free-falling moment before impact. Then he crashes with a thunderous splash. His large head drops like a stone and drags his body down with it.

When he resurfaces after a breathless interval, Damon's wet hair shimmers like a crown and his features glisten.

"Whenever you're ready," the lifeguard tells Damon. He must swim halfway across the pool, tread water for one minute, then swim back.

Damon nods, steeples his hands before his chest, and begins. He doesn't swim so much as paw and grope his way forward with both arms while jerking his torso and legs. After each spasmodic lunge, his weighted body begins to sink to the bottom. You can see his patient, smiling face as he drifts underwater and calmly waits to stop sinking, exuding mirthful bubbles. It's hard to grasp how he can ever resume buoyancy but each time Damon manages to return to the surface. He swims like a seal on land, rolling up and down via ill-suited flippers but making undeniable progress.

Damon reaches the halfway mark and begins to dog-paddle. He appears to be struggling as he tilts his head back and gasps. But he stays afloat, grinning as the water laps his purple lips.

"Okay, you're good." The lifeguard signals his minute is up.

Exhausted but sensing victory, Damon swims back in the same awkward hodge-podge, except the transition between rolls and lunges is smoother. He knows he's going to make it now, and he's more confident in his undulations.

He reaches the end of the pool and taps the ledge, glancing over his shoulder for the official result. The guard gives a thumbs-up.

"Heya! I can dive off the big board now," Damon says exultantly.

That evening we celebrate Damon's four-teenth birthday at a local eatery, Mr. Willy's. It's a quiet affair, especially after his Bar Mitzvah and graduation, but it suits our mood. Back at the house, Damon sets up his "movie theater" and sells tickets and refreshments before introducing a film for our screening pleasure.

One day we pack the kids and their friends in the Eurovan and go tubing in the Delaware River. We get a brief "mini-lesson," then everyone grabs a life jacket and an inflated rubber tube and heads down to the rocky banks of the river.

There's a long, flat stretch before you hit the rapids and the water suddenly drops.

Shealagh ties Miranda's tube to hers, so she's secure, and paddles calmly downstream with her daughter in tow, while Sam flails away.

Damon has the most trouble getting started. He rocks fruitlessly from side to side while his friends, after spinning in circles, gradually work it out and slip off downstream in their tubes.

As Damon's efforts grow more frantic, his tube tips over and his life jacket, which he deliberately left untied, slips off. It's broad daylight but I'm watching a nightmare. I paddle over at top speed and yank him out of the water.

"You okay, D-man?" I wrap the life jacket around him and pull it tight, snapping the buckles. He's shaken up and so am I. "Listen, I understand about independence, but this is going *too* far. You've got to keep this tied on at all times!" I help him back into the tube.

Damon is ashen and silent. I'm struck by the panic on his face. He got a real fright, rare for him, and he's also embarrassed and very angry with himself. He's not doing well — his disadvantage is showing — while his friends have all streaked ahead. Plus, he's got his father, whom he needs to defy and impress, on his case.

"Use your limbs as paddles," I advise. "You can make this work, I promise."

"No, I can't, because I'm too short to reach the water," Damon says, sulking.

"Don't use your size as an excuse, I know you can do this!" I show him how to position himself in the tube for better leverage.

Damon begins to move, then stalls out again. It's just not happening.

"Okay, I'll help you get to where your friends are. It's easier out there."

I place my feet in Damon's tube, he grabs on to my legs, and I backstroke with my arms. It takes a moment to coordinate, but soon we're cruising downstream and everything around us is in motion. The trees on the riverbank whiz by.

"Yeah!" Damon smiles as we gather speed, breaking his long inertia. He perks up as we overtake other tubers, relishing our swift passage over the water.

We're racing when we pass Sam, still floundering. He spots us and throws a fit. "Why are you helping Damon and not me? It's not fair! I'm younger. Help me!"

Sam protests bitterly until I drag him along too. Not only is everyone staring at us — Sam's sharp voice skitters over the water — but Sam has a point.

Now I place one leg in each son's tube,

217

and they both grab on to my ankles as I haul off. It's hard going, much harder than before. I struggle to hold the two tubes together with my legs as I backstroke furiously with my arms. It feels like we're hardly moving but the boys relish my flailing on their behalf. Slowly, I muscle us forward and manage to drag them with me. By the time we hit the rapids, I'm so focused on keeping both boys afloat in their tubes that I forget about my own, and it suddenly flips from under me. I tumble out, smacking my knee against the rocks, but am able to hold on to Damon's tube while pushing Sam's into a safe channel. The water foams and hisses about me, angrier than expected. I'm soaked and bruised but my precious cargo is dry and unscathed.

I retrieve my tube and climb back in, only to discover the electronic car key is gone from the dry pocket of my shorts! Shealagh berates me and all agree I was a fool to keep the key on me even if there are no lockers. I go inside and call a taxi so I can return to our country house for the spare key.

The taxi is late, and the kids grow hungry. But our picnic lunch is locked in the car, along with my wallet. Everyone gives me dirty looks, especially Damon, who's still chafing over his tube troubles. I convince the on-site shop to let us start a tab but tussle with Damon when he opts for a big bag of tortilla chips.

"There's nothing healthy here, so I have to eat junk food!" Damon argues.

Two hours later, when I return with the car key, Damon's mood has lifted. He's been practicing all afternoon, and he's finally got the hang of tubing.

He's devised his own system, which consists of lying flat on his stomach in the lower end of the tube with his legs dangling over the edge while his hands seize the side grips. Now he can use his small legs like propellers, kicking and churning with surprising efficiency as he motors along and drives the tube at will. Soon he's outracing all his pals and scooting down the rapids with abandon.

It's a wondrous sight, a grinning boy in a purple life jacket bouncing giddily in a bright orange tube that tosses like a cork on the dark green Delaware River. Damon is borne by the swift-running current, racing fearlessly for new thrills.

After his friends leave, Damon and I prepare to go camping in our forest.

"Can I come?" Sam asks at the last minute. I'm pleased at his interest but promise him a separate outing. This is my traditional one-on-one birthday excursion with Damon.

We pack a tent and sleeping bags and throw in food and water before heading into the family woods. I haul the tent and supplies while Damon carries a light knapsack on his back, a canteen on his belt, and a bow and arrow in hand. We spot spent red cartridges gleaming amid the ground vegetation. The previous owner leased the land to hunters, and deer-tracking platforms still dot the area.

"You won't let them hunt on our land, right, Dad?" Damon scowls.

"That's why we have No Trespassing signs." I point to the yellow posters on our trees, though I worry more about my children getting shot than the deer.

We've hiked a distance and Damon is not quite his energetic self, so we find a nice carpet of fern and some flat rocks and put up our gray, four-man tent. Inside, it's low but roomy. We unroll two pads and two sleeping bags, unzip the rainfly, then step back out.

"Don't leave any food," I remind Damon as I hammer a tent peg with a rock. "Put anything edible up in that tree, away from the tent. In case of coyotes . . ."

"Or bears, right, Dad?" Damon lets out a

grim chuckle. He's heard all about the recent freak attack in our area. A black bear wandered into a bungalow colony and stole a five-month-old baby from her stroller on the porch. The mother, hearing cries of "Bear!" pushed her two other children into the house and rushed to her baby, but the bear had already made off with the infant in its mouth. The father chased the bear with rocks but by the time the bear dropped the baby and ran back into the woods, the infant's neck and head injuries were too severe and it died. Authorities later shot the animal, claiming bears didn't attack humans and they couldn't remember a similar case in thirty years.

"That was a total anomaly," I tell Damon. "Bears usually avoid humans. But this bear was probably habituated to people because they were leaving food out."

"Gee, Dad, that's reassuring . . . Okay, no food in the tent!" He hands me a bag, which I knot and hang off a tree.

We muck around in the woods, hurl stones, climb boulders, spot rabbit and deer, and pick strange flowers and fungi. Then we take the bow and arrow and practice shooting. I mark the target on a tree and demonstrate with the first shot. Then I let Damon try.

He holds the powerful recurve bow by its molded grip and inserts an arrow into the built-in arrow shelf. I assist Damon as he pulls back on the taut drawstring and releases. Although the first arrow falls short, he immediately senses the tremendous force in his hands. "Cool!" He smiles at me.

Damon grips the bow and shoots a dozen times, until he's hitting the tree with ease. He has a sharp eye and a steady hand and his brain calculates quickly. And because there is no cardiovascular component, Damon lacks any impediment.

Dusk falls fast as we head back to camp. Unsure of our whereabouts, we stumble through the alien woods until our tent crops up like a sudden outpost. We prepare our fire on an incline, away from the tent. As I hold a matchbox, Damon asks if they really used to start fires with rocks. "Sure." I smile at him and grab two stones, rubbing them repeatedly together. I manage to elicit a few puny sparks but fail to ignite a leaf before Damon takes pity on me and says, "It's okay, Dad, I get it!"

Reprieved, I strike a match and toss it in. The fire catches nicely and is so warm and consoling, I decide to keep feeding it. We're in a clear area, and it feels like an assertion of our humanity in this forbidding forest.

Damon watches intently as the flames leap into the sky. I keep a sharp eye on the surrounding forest as I continue stoking the fire until I feel the flesh of my cheeks burn and my dungaree-clad thighs bake. I turn to warn my son but Damon stands right behind me, riveted by the conflagration. The wild flames lick his bright hair and scorch his rapt features.

"Careful!" I say, even as I recognize my own reckless fascination in his eyes.

I let the fire die down, then open two cans of baked beans and pork with my Swiss Army knife. I burn the food but it still tastes good. Damon watches me guzzle a beer.

"Want a pull?" I offer. He sips the beer but returns to his ginger ale. We break into a bag of sweet white marshmallows but after burning or dropping one too many, we eat them raw. Then we go piss under the woodsy stars.

We slither into our sleeping bags, zip up, and huddle with our heads on either side of the center pole. The dark forest beyond comes alive with mysterious night creatures and night noises. I turn on the flashlight and place it facedown, trapping a bright ring of light, and tell Damon the eerie buzzing and yowling is the animals' nightly chatter — we're on their turf, after all. Damon finishes his pills, and we chat until we hear the furtive stirring of branches and a loud *snap.*

"What's that, a bear?" Damon cries, and for a moment I wonder too.

"Not likely, D-man." I again explain how unusual the recent attack was. "Besides," I growl, thumping the rolled-up jeans under my head, "I have a big, sharp hunting knife with me, so no one's gonna mess with us."

Damon chuckles and relaxes and we talk by the glow for a long time, covering many topics, from family and visiting friends to bears and books.

Damon is growing up and our relationship is changing. He's more independent-minded and oriented more toward his peers, and also dealing with the isolation of illness. I'm a smaller part of his day-to-day world. But our bond is deep and unshakable.

I kiss his forehead and turn off the flashlight. "Night, D-man."

"Night, Dad."

I wake up once in the still of night and grow alarmed when I can't see Damon in the pitch-black tent. I sit up and cock my ear but I still can't detect any evidence of him. Could he have gone outside to pee?

I unzip the flap and peer into the forest but it's equally dark out there and I can't see or hear a thing. I withdraw back into the tent. Where is he?

I reach over and grope in the empty darkness, my heart pounding, until my hand brushes the edge of a sleeping bag that has rolled into a dip. I palpate the mummy shell, which feels vacant, until I work up to something solid, squeeze and identify a human leg. It's small but I'm on the right track.

I reach over and locate a shaggy head, then tenderly touch Damon's slumbering face to confirm his presence.

Otherwise, he remains hushed, still, and completely undetectable in the dark.

It's amazing how silently and self-effacingly my son sleeps.

CHAPTER 22

In the fall, Damon enters Brooklyn Technical High School, New York City's largest public high school and one of the nation's leading magnet schools. He leaves the safe hothouse of Salk, with a student body of two hundred, for a sprawling twelve-story institution that occupies a square city block and houses five thousand students.

"My God, it's like a college!" Shealagh says. "Tech," as it's dubbed, boasts a wall of famous alumni, including two Nobelists, and a university-style system of majors. It might bewilder any kid with a freshman case of jitters, let alone a life-threatening case of PLE.

"Bronx High School of Science has half the students," I remind Damon.

Shealagh objects. "It's three hours a day on the subway! Too far from home."

"What about private school?" I ask Damon, not for the first time.

"Nah, I don't want to be one of those private school kids." Damon frowns. "And Tech's cool. I want to go there!"

Shealagh gets dizzy just going on the tour, while I'm more familiar with the setup because I also attended a vast New York City public high school. But I was healthy and full-size, whereas Damon is one of the smallest kids to ever walk through the heavy steel doors on South Elliott Place. His light complexion and hair and eye color make him even more conspicuous: 75 percent of Tech is non-Caucasian.

"I don't need a special elevator key," Damon scoffs. He's intent on a normal school experience and refuses any preferential treatment, arriving ten minutes early so he can walk up to his classes on the huge, teeming staircases. He's just as adamant about participating in all aspects of physical education.

"That kid never even had surgery!" Damon says of a boy who sits out each gym class due to a minor heart problem. Damon disdains medical excuses and performs every drill and completes every exercise, even when he's lapped on the track and comes in dead last on the mile run.

"Damon Weber?" The gruff coach doesn't even check his roster. Besieged by parents during our first mass conference in the chaotic gymnasium, he explains it's too soon to know the names of his hundreds of new students. Yet our son, not exactly varsity material, has already caught his eye.

"Damon's got a great attitude. Tell him to keep it up!"

It's another story with math, where Damon has failed two tests and is struggling. Partly it's the poor preparation at Salk, plus stiffer competition at a specialized math and science school. And it's never been Damon's best subject. But partly it's also the teacher.

"He never explains a thing," Damon says. "He just expects us to know it."

I come prepared to lock horns with the teacher but the sly old fox spots trouble a mile away and totally disarms me with his shrewd patter and practiced geniality. We agree to get Damon tutoring and let him catch up in the next term.

At first, Damon doesn't have a single friend at his new school and he struggles to find his niche. It's daunting. But he's naturally sociable and outgoing. In the school cafeteria, he sits at the senior table, where he strikes up conversation with the older students. But he's still a solo act.

"What about the theater program?" I ask. "You always make friends there."

"Yeah, if I could only find where it is!" Damon sighs. Theater is so irregular and so low-profile, it takes Damon weeks to track it down. Finally, he locates the tiny drama club in the vast, labyrinthine institution.

He auditions and immediately lands a part in the big fall play.

"I'm Dr. Chasuble in *The Importance of Being Earnest!*" Damon proudly informs us. It's a feat for a freshman and provides his first real opening in the Tech social scene.

Damon's daily homework load increases steeply at Tech, and he stays up late to get it all done. Shealagh, a semi-insomniac, worries about Damon's lack of sleep. She stays up with him, helps where she can, and makes him soups and late-night snacks. She cajoles and pesters him to knock off early until Damon, in exasperation, quips, "Mom, you're the only parent in the world who tells their kid to *stop* studying and *not* do their homework!"

Damon still has a full regimen of pills and supplements to swallow. But now he also starts daily heparin injections. It takes about one hour of prep time each night, and there's a lot of waiting-around time, which I try to help alleviate.

"Want to watch with me? I'm screening a doc we commissioned," I tell him.

"Yeah, just give me a minute." Damon retrieves from the closet a big box with all his "fixings." First, he disinfects the injection site with alcohol swabs. Then he applies a yellowish smear of anesthetic cream to his abdomen and covers the cream with a thin patch of cellophane, which he fastens with a makeshift belt. Normally he'd kill the next hour while waiting for the cream to numb his skin but tonight he joins me downstairs.

"Hey, Dad, this your show?" He settles near me on the sofa. "What's it on?"

"The impact of the genetics revolution — fifty years since the double helix."

"Cool," Damon says. We watch together until the cream has done its work. Then Damon unwraps a fresh syringe and needle and inserts the needle into a small ampoule of heparin. He retracts the plunger and fills the syringe with the clear, straw-colored liquid to just the right level, flicking it to ensure there are no bubbles or floating particles.

Then, with a determined sigh, Damon jabs himself.

The needle is tiny but it pierces the skin and leaves dark bruises on the surface. Damon becomes proficient and the technique routine, but there's always the flicker of insult at having to stick himself, and an angry band of discolored marks along his abdomen.

After seeing Dr. Hayes and others at Columbia — they advise that he should take the heparin for three months before expecting results — Damon heads to our local pediatrician for his regular checkup.

Dr. Satish Tandon, who also treats Sam and Miranda, has a solo family practice around the corner from us. People bring their kids with colds and coughs and rashes, and to get their shots and fill out school health forms.

Dr. Tandon always wears a tie and is polite and unassuming, with a big poster of Barney and lollipops for the kids. He's also a first-rate doctor and diagnostician whose thorough competence we've learned to appreciate.

Today, Dr. Tandon puts Damon on the height scale and informs us he's now fifty-six and a half inches, meaning he's grown half an inch since before the summer. This normally falls within the margin of error, but Dr. Tandon is precise, and it cheers us to think Damon has finally broken through that ceiling. Maybe he's about to break out in other ways.

"You saw it too? I prayed it was a pimple!"

Shealagh chuckles over the tiny red blemish we both spotted on Damon's face. We scan avidly for any sign of puberty's onset. I'm hopeful but wary, recalling how Damon once complained of growing pains in his shin and we all felt excited until I read, with a pang, that shin pain was a symptom of PLE.

"His liver feels larger and harder than before the summer," Dr. Tandon observes. Using a tape measure, he confirms that the liver now protrudes eight to nine centimeters below the rib margin. In May, it was three to four centimeters, so this is a significant increase.

"This July," I now recall in dismay, "a GI guy in Boston estimated the liver at six centimeters. Which would confirm your read, and the idea of a progressive enlargement . . ."

"But Dr. Hayes said nothing about it at last week's visit," Shealagh notes.

"Still better to follow up," Dr. Tandon says. "There's a good liver man at Columbia." He gives us the name of a Dr. Stephen Lubritto, whom we go see.

Dr. Lubritto, short, round, and fast-talking, says the enlarged liver could be due to fluid overload, which diuretics can reduce. But it could also be a sign of "pump failure," which only a heart transplant can fix. "Let's hope for the former," he says.

By November, when Damon and his pals come to my office to help process the annual Rhodes Scholarship applications, I observe it's his reliable old gang and no new friends from Tech are there. All the kids have shot up except for Damon, who appears slight and pallid by comparison. I notice his hands and wrists look thin, almost diaphanous. But nothing seems to deter his ebullience. We make a party of it, going out after with all his friends to the Hard Rock Cafe.

Kyle also stays very much in the picture as Damon enters high school. One night I invite her and Damon to a play at a theater I'm affiliated with. It's a chilly evening and I tell Damon to take his coat. Kyle wears a jacket and dresses in multiple warm layers while Damon is clad only in a sweatshirt; he has the sniffles — he's been battling a cold for weeks — and looks pale and worn. But my son stubbornly resists and refuses to bundle up.

"Damon, I'm not taking you without a coat!" I finally say. I'm sympathetic but I can't allow teen fashion or rebelliousness to override serious and pressing health concerns. Teed off, Damon resentfully takes the coat and tosses it in the car.

We drive into the city, get snagged in traffic, and park blocks from the theater. It's curtain time, so we make a run for it. A biting wind cuts down the avenue and knifes through us. I clutch my coat collar and glance at Damon to see how he's coping, when it hits me he's wearing only a sweatshirt!

"Damon, where's your coat?" I realize with a sickening jolt he must've left it in the car. And it's too late to go back, or we'll miss the play. "Don't tell me . . . !"

"I took it with me, like you said." Damon stands looking innocent.

"You gotta be kidding!" I feel like a fool for taking my eye off him but I always try to give my son extra space with Kyle, and in our rush, I blew it. The frigid air stings us. "I can't believe you deliberately left your coat behind!" I yell.

"But I wasn't cold," Damon replies defiantly as the icy wind lashes us.

"Goddamn it, Damon, it's fucking freezing!" I blow my stack. What I don't say, in deference to Kyle, is that he's a very sick boy with a compromised immune system, and we can't afford such games. Even as I chastise him, I want to wrap his frail, stubborn body in my arms and shield him from

234

the cold. He's so vulnerable. But all that comes out is my shrieking anger. *"I won't stand for this bullshit, Damon!"*

As I detonate, I become painfully aware of my own shrillness and loss of control. The ceaseless anxiety over my son's health has taken a toll on my nerves, and I can hear the raw, unnatural strain in my voice. The words explode from my mouth, angrier and fiercer than I intended. Damon reacts in a frozen tableau, glaring silently and bitterly at my dread authority. I've long been prepared to find every age-appropriate emotion, hatred included, in his eyes, and in my calmer moments, I even consider it my paternal duty to give him obdurate steel against which to toughen himself. But this outburst is unplanned, unpleasant, and mutually mortifying. Kyle looks like she wants to crawl into the ground.

We make it to the theater and dash to our seats as the xylophone chimes its last reminder. Kyle sits between Damon and me, a sweet buffer, but we're all so overwrought that at first it's hard to concentrate. Several times, I hear Damon try to muffle a fitful, hacking cough, a disturbing form of vindication I don't need.

But the play is surprisingly engaging, and by intermission we're all swept up in the tale and have almost forgotten our tiff. After, I take Damon and Kyle backstage and introduce them to the actors. The male lead talks shop with Damon.

We leave on a high note and walk down the street to a good restaurant. Kyle is impressed by the high-ceilinged room with its live menu of sprawling, iridescent fish; by the exorbitant prices; and by the beautiful people. But to me, Damon and Kyle are the two most alluring people in the place.

I recall taking them to another play years earlier, when Damon was in third grade and Kyle in second. After the Madison Square Garden show, we went to Lindy's for dessert and I watched the two of them banter and flirt in the most innocent, entrancing way. They were young children without a clue about romance or sexuality yet there was something electric between them that was extraordinary to behold.

"I don't know why you make me laugh so much!" pretty, wide-lipped, eight-year-old Kyle giggled at Damon from across the table.

"Kyle, your sleeve is in your ice cream!" Suave eight-year-old Damon leaned forward and grasped Kyle's arm, lofting a handsome ginger eyebrow.

I sat mesmerized and completely invisible

to them. They brought their heads closer, two kindred spirits groping toward beauty and self-knowledge.

Now, many years later, we're sitting at another restaurant, after another play. Damon and Kyle, both fourteen, remain best friends and soul mates but Kyle, who loves Damon as much as ever, does not want to change their relationship in any fundamental way. I've walked into Damon's room and found them sweetly entwined on his loft bed, and nothing can ever truly separate them. But Damon wants a girl-friend and Kyle wants things to stay as they are, more or less.

It's not been easy for Damon but he's begun to swallow his disappointment and, impelled by his natural vigor and resiliency, to look elsewhere. I've caught the rumors of a girl at Tech, and there's much I don't catch. Whereas with Kyle, Damon now affects the role of indulgent older brother and bemused confidante, which helps them both negotiate their complex feelings for one another.

This evening, perhaps animated by their surroundings, they seem freer and more direct with each other. And they retain their abiding and matchless affinity.

"Here's to the two of you." I hoist a glass

to Damon and Kyle.

"Thanks for inviting me." Kyle smiles with her long ice cream spoon in the air. "I really liked the play. And this is *so* nice." She points to the elegant restaurant. "But tell me one thing." She frowns in intellectual puzzlement. "How can they charge seventeen dollars for a fruit platter — a *fruit* platter?"

"That's for the small fruit platter. The big one is thirty-one dollars!" Damon grins.

"It's not always about price," I say to the two bright-eyed friends, forever young. "Remember that certain occasions, like tonight, are priceless."

CHAPTER 23

In early December, Damon's blood test shows a dramatic spike in his serum protein levels, presumably a result of the heparin injections. His albumin nearly doubles, jumping from alarmingly low (2.2) to normal (3.7). The total protein, a measure of all the proteins in the fluid portion of the blood, also soars, suggesting the PLE has abated.

"Wow, this is unbelievable!" I cry, staring deliriously at the new figures. Although we started the heparin treatment with precisely this goal in mind, and although we've learned that such positive effects, when you're lucky enough to see them, tend to diminish over time, the news brings immediate joy and relief.

"That's fantastic!" Shealagh exults as we stare incredulously at one another. "It's the first time since he was diagnosed that Damon has normal protein levels."

"And it proves we can stop and even reverse this relentless disease," I say.

Shealagh pauses. "Though he still looks small, and he's still not growing . . ."

"And it still could be only a temporary blip," I admit. "But if these numbers hold up, we could climb out of this hole and get our lives back!"

Shealagh and I share a double high five. We both feel cautiously, giddily optimistic.

Pondering this sudden change of fortune, I'm struck by how everything reduces to these two key measures, albumin and total protein. Two simple, naked numbers. Which, after stubbornly refusing to budge for over a year, have suddenly rocketed into positive territory.

So I decide to jot down these two numbers on a yellow Post-it, in two columns, and to carry them with me wherever I go. I enter the numerals from a year before on the same Post-it, so I can see how far we've come:

(Date)	(Albumin)	(Total Protein)
10/2001:	2.2	3.9
12/2002:	3.7	5.8

I will keep this little yellow Post-it in my wallet, and throughout Damon's illness, I will register any significant change in the two readings on this postage-stamp-sized ledger. At the oddest times, say in the middle of a meeting or in a movie theater, I will peek inside my wallet and ponder their pattern and meaning. While Damon's medical case only gains in complexity, and the available data and inputs multiply exponentially — and while many doctors tell me to ignore such crude measures — these two numbers are my secret bottom line. For a long time, their slightest tick, up or down, will predict my mood, functioning like stock prices for investors, final scores for sports fans, or casualty figures for war generals.

Once we get the good news about Damon's protein levels, we begin to look for, and find, hopeful signs under every rock.

"Hey, D-man, why you up so late?" I ask one night when I catch him on the stairs.

"I was really *hungry,*" Damon confesses, blushing. He gets food cravings and goes on eating binges. His body appears more solid, more substantial. His color improves.

Our reenergized son invites us to the Brooklyn Tech production of *The Importance of Being Earnest.* The show is held in the massive school auditorium, a 4,200-seat, two-balcony theater space, but fortunately the actors are miked.

Damon does not have one of the leads so we have to wait until Act 2 for his first appearance. But the moment he steps onto the stage with his slicked-up pompadour, twinkling eyes, and pompous thumbs hooked into Victorian lapels, Damon commands our attention as the Reverend Canon Chasuble. His colorful presence, comic timing, clear voice, and superb diction make him stand out.

It's becoming clear to us that Damon is at home on the stage, liberated by his gift for impersonation, his social intelligence, and his limitless imagination. We're equally pleased to see, once the curtain descends, that he's mingling with a new set of friends. It's first semester of his freshman year and he's found his niche.

A few days later, I take Damon to the Annual Daughters and Sons Meeting at the Council on Foreign Relations. It's a chance for members to bring their high school and college age children to this renowned foreign policy enclave, a cross between a wonky think tank and an exclusive club where you can rub shoulders with world leaders and dignitaries.

I leave my office after work and wait for Damon by the neoclassical town house on Park Avenue. Shealagh has put our son in a cab and I'm apprehensive, not just about whether he'll arrive safely and on time but about whether he's up to this event.

"You sure this might not be too stressful for you right now?" I ask Damon that morning. His face looks puffy and his voice sounds reedy to me.

"Yeah, Dad, I'm really interested in this stuff!" Damon says. "I'm doing Model UN and I might want to major in international relations."

Now he steps from the cab in the requisite suit and tie but everything's a little askew: the top button of his dress shirt pops open, revealing the secret pallor of his chest; an ill-knotted rep tie bunches at his collar; and his low-hanging pants droop below a distended belly. He's a study in disarray but I have to chuckle because despite his unique case, Damon shares with me a rumpled quality I recognize.

But this is a formal place, and we don't want to draw undue attention.

"Let me help you with that," I say as we walk through the detector and pick up our two name tags. I peel off the backing and lean forward to affix Damon's tag, surreptitiously trying to straighten his tie, a role we're both so unaccustomed to that Damon involuntarily flinches.

243

"Dad! What're you doing?" He's not sure whether to be upset or amused.

"Sorry, D-man." I attempt to close his collar, but he grimaces with such suffocating forbearance, like a mirror of my younger self, that I give up.

We are directed past Venetian doors to a formal drawing room with a bar and a table of appetizers. Damon's big black dress shoes squeak on the parquet floor. As other members arrive with their rangy offspring, I note Damon is by far the smallest and youngest-looking person in the room, and I'm ready to present his high school ID if challenged. The chairman walks over and chats with Damon, breaking the ice. Then I introduce my son to an air force colonel I know.

The bell sounds and we all file to the meeting hall for the featured speaker, a former deputy secretary of state waiting for the next administration so he can be secretary of state. He provides a good overview of post-9/11 security challenges.

Like most members, I'm pleased to be sitting here with my son as we're briefed by an insider. Beyond the analysis and insight, I want Damon to realize the country is run by people not much different from him, so he can grasp that its challenges are his, and his generation's.

Later, after a couple of confident college kids have asked questions from the audience, Damon's hand creeps up. It stays up, even when he's not called on right away. I smile, recalling the first time Damon raised his hand in public. He was four and sat on the floor amid a crowd of nattering, fidgeting tykes in his Saturday drawing class at the Brooklyn Museum. The instructor asked about a famous painting in front of them but none of the children made a sound until one hand shot up. I was impressed then, as I am impressed now, even though Damon never gets to ask his question because the session ends promptly, per council tradition.

"What were you going to ask?" I query Damon as we exit.

"If they *really* can't find bin Laden. My Pakistani cabbie said everyone in Pakistan knows where he is, but if they tell us, they'll lose their leverage."

Damon continues on a roll through the holiday season. After celebrating Hanukkah at my parents', we go for a week of skiing in Holiday Mountain, a family resort near our country house. Bavarian-born Shealagh, the ablest skier among us, has long given up on her husband, but she wants her kids to ski properly. This year her bad back keeps her

245

off the slopes but she still instructs Miranda how to snowplow, and Sam, when he listens, how to turn.

Damon practices with me for several days before his friend Jon comes up. His lessons have paid off, and he shows great progress. One cold, bright day, Damon and I are riding the chair lift when it stops halfway to the top, and we find ourselves stalled in midair, suspended over a steep ravine. We hear the windy creak as the aerial chair twists and dangles off its solitary cable.

"How do we get down if the lift is broken?" Damon asks, laughing nervously.

"Easy. They could use a harness, a bucket truck, or even a chopper!" I shrug and put my arm around him as we both look down. Our crisp black shadows, projected onto the snowy ground below, seem to look back at us like smiling negatives.

The chill picks up but Damon is well padded and the sun keeps us cozy in our chair. I point to the purple mountains and evergreen trees and tell my son to enjoy this spectacle. Eighty feet below us, the simple shadow of Damon and me sitting together on the chair lift with my arm draped across his shoulder resembles a perfect black silhouette of father and son stamped on the snow. I find myself wishing we could hold on to this moment and stay suspended up here indefinitely.

Jon arrives and the two boys hit the slopes. Eventually, they work up to the Roman Candle, a daunting four-hundred-foot vertical drop. At first, they snowplow from side to side and sit down when it gets too scary. But slowly, they overcome their fear and ski down in one run, returning full of pride and achievement.

I watch them from Manny's Run, an intermediate trail, until I'm satisfied they're okay. Once, I'm skiing down the hill when Damon suddenly zips past, sailing by me like a confident pro, knees bent and poles tucked under arms.

"Hi, Dad!" Damon chirps with bright red cheeks as he whooshes past me. I do a few more runs for appearance's sake, but really, I'm so excited I can't wait to get off the slopes and share what I just witnessed with Shealagh.

Our grinning, self-assured son flying right past me on his skis and racing downhill with abandon!

It feels like the blessed advent of the ordinary — it feels like a miracle.

CHAPTER 24

"Damn! His albumin is down from three point seven to three point four," I report to Shealagh in January, after getting Damon's latest lab results from Columbia.

"But that's statistically insignificant — within the margin of error," she notes.

"Yes, but his total protein also fell, from 5.8 to 5.1," I reply. "I know it's a small drop, but the direction is backward. This is *not* good. Heparin was supposed to buy us a year or two, but its effects seem to have peaked after *three months*." I shake my head. "We can't seem to stop this thing!"

"It's too early to know. Let's at least wait for the next test," Shealagh says.

"Sure." I nod. I'm only too happy to defer the bad news, but inside, I know.

I intensify my search for alternative therapies. I continue reading the latest medical and scientific literature and talking to researchers in the United States and abroad.

I check in with the half dozen leading hospitals where I've established connections. I register for an international conference on PLE. I'm open to any angle or approach and even consider enrolling in medical school or auditing targeted classes. I'm on the case 24/7.

Whenever I run into any person anywhere with the slightest expertise — a postdoc on a late-night train from Cambridge to London, a physician at a New Year's Eve party, a former classmate turned scientist at a reunion — I pepper him with questions that might reveal a link between his field and Damon's problem. But I don't explain why.

I'm careful not to breathe a word about Damon to anyone but close friends. My wife's philosophy, Tell Them Nothing, seems prudent. Damon's illness so isolates and dominates our existence, we cannot let it completely overwhelm our lives. We have two other children and many other obligations. I must hold on to my job to support the family and it's easier to maintain things on a professional level and not let our personal crisis bleed into everything. Sympathy is nice but misfortune can also be turned against you.

I violate our rule and broach the subject at work only if I think it might benefit

Damon. One day, the Nobel laureate James Watson, co-discoverer of the double helix, is in my office for one of our brainstorming sessions. We've collaborated on several projects and have a good relationship. Watson is an original, if controversial, thinker, he knows everyone, and he's had ongoing medical issues with his own son, whom I've met.

"Hey, Jim," I ask, "who's the smartest out-of-the-box cardiologist you know?"

Watson squints and gawks through his glasses, still, in his seventies, a precocious spirit. "Oh, well, I know a lot more about cancer because that's what all my friends seem to get. And the Watsons don't have much family history of heart disease. We're lucky —"

"I'm looking for a maverick who works on the human heart."

"One day they'll solve the immune issues and give everyone a pig's heart!" Jim chortles. "Or build artificial hearts and implant them like pacemakers. It's just a pump, for goodness' sake!" He shrugs and flicks his hands to indicate the glaring simplicity.

"Yeah, but meantime, I need help now. It's personal and confidential —"

"Sure. I'll see if I can think of anyone and

let you know."

After enlisting Watson — he never finds the perfect cardiologist but asking him helps me feel I've left no stone unturned — I e-mail a scientist in China. Then I contact an alternative-medicine guru in India.

At home, things seem to go on as before. Our lives are filled with the daily bustle of three children and the steady drumbeat of their never-ending activities, but Damon remains in developmental lockdown.

He's still outgoing and even widens his social circle at Tech. But he hasn't grown and appears paler than ever. When he sits, stork-like, on a tall stool at the kitchen counter, his skinny legs folded on the rungs beneath him resemble toothpicks. His slight lower body seems to be receding, even while above the counter, he remains a strong, active presence.

"Hey, Dad, can I go to Web2Zone for an all-nighter on Friday?"

"One of those LANsomnias?" I say, and Damon smiles. These raucous, dusk-to-dawn video game elimination tournaments have become his favorite hangout. "Yeah, you can go, long as you take an extra half dose of heparin the day before and the day after," I reply. It's good for him to have an injection-free night out with the boys, and

I'm all for it.

"Thanks, Dad. I won't forget to pre-dose. Believe me, shooting a needle into your arm in a room filled with loud music is one sure way to kill a party!"

Damon's wit, always keen, now takes on a more rapier-like quality. He skewers his siblings more mercilessly than before and even, occasionally, turns on his mother. He's a teenager, of course, and still sweet at heart, but there's a dark new edge, barbed with fury that glints though at unguarded moments: "That's stupid, Mom. I'm fourteen and you're treating me like a child. Leave me alone!"

Shealagh worries about Damon constantly. Her own health suffers. She has asthma, rashes, back pain. She's depressed and exhausted. She can't tolerate the stress of her job and wants to stop working so she can be home more for Damon. She wishes to help make his life easier while creating a more nurturing environment for Sam and Miranda.

After reducing her hours and scaling back from three days to two, we agree she should stop working altogether. We'll find a way to adjust. Although Shealagh's salary has never been more than a fraction of our household income, taking it away will leave a shortfall, especially as our medical bills are increasing. I promise to speak to my employers about a raise or to find another source of income. Either way, things have deteriorated to such a point for Shealagh that we don't really have a choice. My wife is tough but our situation is off the charts.

My own state of mind at this juncture is also parlous and I feel under constant, unrelenting pressure. I walk around all day with a knot in my stomach and a clenched tightness in my chest. And there's no escape, not even at night.

I jerk awake well before my normal five A.M. rising time, and I no longer feel refreshed or restored. My brain has grabbed the minimum rest essential for survival and then it forces me back to consciousness, like an interrogation agent slapping my face.

My writing, key to my peace of mind, also takes a hit because I often must work on Damon's case instead. There's no time or space left for the deep dive of imagination. My writer's haven has turned into a business office, full of grim, mounting stacks of medical files and reports. Even when I'm not corresponding with doctors across the country and writing careful e-mails describing Damon's latest symptoms and results, or poring over mounds of new data, or setting up appointments and more tests, my mind is unquiet.

One night, I dream I'm driving a car with Damon and Shealagh sitting beside me. Suddenly we're lurching off the road and careening down a steep mountain, with a dark tunnel at the end. There's a metal railing on one side of the car and nothing on the other. I pump the brakes but they don't work and the automobile, instead of stopping, accelerates and takes on a life of its own. I yank the steering wheel and repeatedly slam the vehicle against the railing, trying to use the guardrail to slow it down. But the car only speeds up and races downhill like a runaway train until I realize there's nothing more I can do to stop it. Just before we hit the tunnel and crash in a fireball, I turn to Shealagh and Damon and cry from the depths of my soul, "I'm sorry!"

Then I wake up, coated in a cold, clammy sweat.

Around this period, while in southern Mexico, I fall into a deep, unmarked construction hole on the elevated terrace of a bar — for real this time.

It's nighttime and I'm striding ahead of colleagues to a table on the balcony when the ground gives way beneath me. I plummet down a blind, bottomless shaft in a state of complete disorientation and increasing alarm for about ten feet — which feels like ten miles, or ten years — before slamming into the rocky ground. I crash in a shattering heap but because I drop for such a long time in the darkness, I'm actually *relieved* when I hit something, since I know I can't survive if it lasts much longer. I break three major bones in my wrist and smash my hand to smithereens, but I'm lucky because my head misses an exposed sewage pipe by inches and I remain conscious.

Once I realize I'm basically okay — my shoulder is dislocated and my face and body bruised, but I can think clearly and I can move the arm — my main concern is not to worry Shealagh and the kids, and not to let this interfere in any way with my duties to my elder son.

Compared to Damon's situation, my reference point for everything, I've already determined this is a relatively trivial problem. Although I'm still in shock and looking at an operation to reconstruct my wrist and permanently insert a metal bar into my flesh followed by a year of painful therapy, I'm already a little bored and impatient with my own mishap. I know I heal well, it's my left wrist and I'm right-handed, and all my major organs are fine.

Someone drives me to the hospital in Cuernavaca, where I'm tempted to let them operate the next day. But I'm alert enough to call my friend Jeff Friedman in New York, and Jeff, who has an MD and a PhD, along with a wry sense of humor, says, "It's your hand, Doron, a complex, delicate organ involved in fine motor coordination and multiple daily tasks, and presumably you want to use it with minimal impairment for many decades, rather than dragging it around like a crooked stump for the rest of your life — so no, I don't think you should have this surgery in a rural Mexican hospital!"

We both laugh and I wind up flying back for the operation, but what strikes me most about this incident is how Damon's condition has completely altered my perspective and how blasé I now feel about any problem short of life and death. I also register how the shock of my near-fatal accident has brought me mysteriously nearer to Damon. As if descending into that dark pit and brushing up against death was a way to embrace my son and take some of his suffering onto myself.

It makes me ponder the nature of accidents. My gravest injury until now was a car accident thirteen years earlier, which closely followed Damon's first open-heart operation. It, too, almost killed me, but it also gave me a personal window onto my son's agony and the ordeal of recovery, which I thus was able to secretly share with him.

CHAPTER 25

Second semester freshman year in the Brooklyn Tech cafeteria, seventh period, a girl named Rebecca introduces Damon to her buddies at the corner table, and before long he is sitting and chatting with them every day.

Rebecca is cute and all the boys have a thing for her, but after a while the guys get to know each other too. Soon Damon makes a new set of friends, and this fledgling entity, "the Group," which extends to over a dozen people and will eventually overlap drama as well, becomes his main high school crowd.

Two boys in particular, Max and Zak, start hanging out with Damon on a regular basis. When I come home, they're often sitting around the computer in Damon's room.

"Hey, guys. What're you playing?" I watch as Damon and Zak battle it out on-screen, blowtorching platoons of squiggly critters across a cartoon landscape.

"Worms." Max grins, taking pity on my ignorance. He has a solid build, glasses, and black wavy hair. "Damon always beats us at this but he's not up to our level on Warcraft yet," Max says. "But he's coming on like a fiend!"

"Damon's not going to win today!" Zak yells over his shoulder. Zak also is broad-framed but he has fair hair, which he dyes in striking pastel hues. "I'm gonna be last worm standing!" Zak declares, launching a Banana Bomb.

They go into "sudden death" but Damon pulls it out with a ninja rope and a drill. "Take that, you wormling!" Damon shouts, giggling to victory.

The three friends engage in many shared activities — concerts, movies, basketball, blogging, practical joking, amateur filmmaking, experimental drinking, sleepovers — but their preferred pastime is computer video games and their preferred venue is Web2Zone, an Internet café and game room in the East Village. This bricks-and-mortar cyber-paradise boasts two floors honeycombed with hundreds of computers, PlayStations, Xboxes, and HDTVs. When I drop Damon off on Cooper Square, he walks into a funhouse of digital fantasy and thrills, a wild, 3-D world apart from reality.

The two-day international symposium on PLE that I attend is a sobering affair, as Dr. Chin warned me. A small group of scientists and physicians describe promising avenues of research and provocative leads — I attend every talk and read every paper — but the world's experts remain fundamentally baffled.

I meet bewildered family members, their faces etched with fear, who hang on every word. They describe heart-rending struggles that sound all too familiar. I note the most bold and advanced among them have taken matters into their own hands. One desperate father has had the entire bacterial floor of his daughter's stomach wiped clean and is trying to control everything that enters her system.

I return with a bleak overview but focus determinedly on the 20 percent of PLE patients who survive and how to navigate Damon through this terrifying illness. In my overnight bag are pages of notes, scientific papers, and references to pursue.

As I step into our house, still digesting what I've seen, Damon comes down the stairs, catching me off guard. "Hey, Dad, how'd the conference go?"

"It was pretty useful." I fumble around. "I learned a lot — there's good research going on — but it's still early days and there's no magic bullet yet. We'll have to keep looking."

Damon frowns. "I thought if I managed to make it past this phase and into my twenties, the PLE would get better on its own," he says in an aggrieved tone. "That once I'm grown-up, I wouldn't need the protein so much."

I wince, torn between wanting Damon to grasp his illness — he's entitled to know what he's up against — and not wishing to undermine his confidence.

"Yes," I reply, "but it's a little more complicated. Because first we have to get you *past* this stage, which we will, once we figure out the best way . . ."

Damon gives me a brooding look, as if I've sown fresh doubts. We go down to the family room, where the TV news is blaring, and I try to explain it better.

"Look, it's a very diabolical enemy, your PLE. Think of it like a murderous tyrant, a Hitler or Stalin or a Saddam Hussein" — the United States has just invaded Iraq, and everyone is baying for Saddam's blood. "We have to stop it in its tracks. We have to vanquish our foe!"

Damon screws up his features. He doesn't think of his situation in such dire terms, and he doesn't want me to either. I've hit the wrong note again.

"Okay, maybe that's going too far," I backtrack, "but you know we got a real fight on our hands, right?" Damon nods. He's okay with this. "That's all I meant."

We hang out on the sofa and watch TV together. A show comes on about the space program and JFK's famous promise to land a man on the moon.

"A new biography of John Kennedy just came out," I tell Damon. "A historian got hold of his medical records and it turns out Kennedy was much sicker than anyone knew."

Damon's eyes stay on the TV screen but his head tilts in my direction.

"From a very young age, the future president had a series of grave ailments," I tell my son, listing them: "Scarlet fever, colitis, back injury, urethritis, Addison's disease, bowel problems, weight loss, sleep disorders . . . In the White House, Kennedy was taking ten to twelve medications a day and getting six daily injections for his back. Sound familiar?"

"Really? But he looks so youthful and

vigorous in photos. And so tan!"

"Yeah, he worked hard on his image." I smile. "But this is a guy who was so sickly as a child that twice they called the priest and read the last rites over him. Twice! They gave him up for a goner. And look what he made of his life."

"That's cool." Damon nods, weighing the information. "I didn't know that."

"Me neither," I admit. "But it's inspiring to see what people can accomplish despite early setbacks. How overcoming illness and adversity builds character . . . Hey, D-man, maybe one day, you'll be president."

Damon gives me a look that shows how absurd he finds this, but I persist. "Maybe that's what all this is about. Forging your character in the crucible of suffering. You're being tested . . . and you'd make a damn good president!"

"Thanks, Dad, I appreciate the vote of confidence," Damon replies tartly, "only I don't want to be president." He shrugs with complete disinterest.

"Oh." I had not expected this. It silences me, but only for a moment. "Maybe I'll be like JFK's father and I'll hector you into it."

"You can't really force someone to run for president," Damon observes. "And even you wouldn't go that far, Dad."

"Hey, didn't you admit it was my prodding that made you realize you could be an A student in middle school?"

Damon pauses. "Yes, but that was something I wanted, I just wasn't sure I had it in me. Being president sounds really boring. Why would I want that job?"

Over Easter break, we visit SeaWorld in San Diego. The most striking creature we see is a giant, glorious, gleaming white polar bear. He stretches out in his lair, with enormous, recumbent strength packed into his long body.

"Cool." Damon stands transfixed by the magnificent creature.

"Think he knows he's trapped and we've just re-created his habitat?" I ask.

"Maybe this is all he knows," Damon says. "Especially if he was born here."

"Or maybe he's biding his time and waiting for a chance to escape."

"Maybe." Damon smiles enigmatically. He pauses. "Hey, Dad, is he male?"

The question, though appropriate for an adolescent boy, catches me by surprise. I peer at the bear's powerful, fur-clad legs but can't be sure. "I wouldn't tangle with it either way. This feels like the top of creation."

Back at the hotel, Damon and Sam play-fight more aggressively than usual. Sam is a half inch taller now, and when they wrestle, Sam threatens to overpower Damon, a potentially seismic shift.

"Okay, Sam, let's start again but away from the TV," Damon says, flushed and panting but still in charge. Sometimes, when they really go at it, it looks like Sam could inadvertently hurt Damon with his wild flailing. Sam still doesn't know his own strength, yet even as he forces Damon back, Sam hesitates because he so reveres his big brother.

Back in New York, we go see Sam perform at the PS 29 All-Star Show. Kyle, in a Mickey Mouse hat, joins Damon in the school auditorium, two seasoned graduates returning to their alma mater for laughs and nostalgia. They can't believe how small it all looks now.

"That's because you're so much bigger," Shealagh tells them.

"Not me!" Damon says dryly. Several parents mistake Damon for Sam, and Damon must awkwardly explain that he is Sam's *older* brother.

Sam is on the gymnastics team and the pep squad. We watch him leap and tumble and do a slithering caterpillar roll with his teammates. At halftime, a teacher reads a poem about a boy with red hair and a strange gift and we're amazed to see a silent, athletic, and self-sufficient Sam step from the wings. He walks on his hands from one end of the stage to the other.

"Wow, I didn't know Sam could do that," Kyle remarks, smiling amid the ovation.

"Nobody knew!" Damon says with a trace of pride. "I caught Sam practicing but he kept it a secret. Our Sam is a man of mystery!"

The next day we watch Miranda march in the St. Patrick's Day parade with her Irish dance class. Normally she wears a black leotard and black skirt as she joins in a mass, synchronized display of pounding legs and clicking feet. But today she's clad in a bright green folk dress with a gold headband and carries the school banner with her friend Caroline. After, we take them for ice cream and the two eight-year-old sirens turn heads with their captivating cheerleader-type routines.

"Hey, Dad, better keep an eye on those girls," Damon warns, both playful and protective. "They were getting some pretty strange looks out on the street!"

Around this time, the Tribeca Film Festival takes place. At a reception I host following a film panel, I introduce Damon and his friends to various well-known figures, including two of the festival cofounders, Jane Rosenthal and Craig Hatkoff. When the third founder, the actor Robert De Niro, walks into the room, there's the usual celebrity buzz. De Niro, a shy, astute, and highly alert man who does not miss much, makes the rounds and greets everyone he knows, including me because of my formal affiliation with the festival. He's followed by a train of publicists and managers and photographers. I try to catch his eye because I want to introduce him to my son. De Niro is a legend, and as a New Yorker, former cabbie, and boxer, I feel a special connection to him, like about a billion other people in the world. But there are too many eager attendees clamoring for his attention, and I can't compete with the crowd.

As he starts to leave the reception, De Niro circles back and comes up to me smiling, as if we're the oldest pals in the world and he's forgotten to tell me something, which is just trembling on the tip of his tongue. "Hey, Doron . . ."

It's a generous gesture and a real star turn, an instinctive reading of the scene meant solely to make me look important in front of my son and his friends.

He *really* is a great actor.

De Niro lingers and I make the introductions. He shakes hands with Damon and his friends. The three teenagers bask in the limelight while Damon talks to De Niro about a variety of subjects until the actor has to leave for his next event.

When I get home that night, there's a message from Dr. Hayes. Damon's total protein has sunk to 4.1 and his albumin is back down to 2.5. He's given up almost all the gains he made from the heparin.

CHAPTER 26

"Why am I so tired all the time?" Damon cries at night to his mother. "Why do I *get* so tired?" He looks frail and sluggish and admits he can't always keep up with his friends. He runs out of energy and goes to bed early, setting his alarm clock so he can rise at dawn and complete his homework before school.

He's also taking on more fluid. We can see it in his puffy face and in the progressively more "pregnant" look of his belly, which he obscures with baggy clothes. One night I give him a massage and feel a hump of flesh between his neck and shoulder.

"Hey, what's this buffalo fat doing here?" I joke, holding the fold of flesh between my fingers. Damon becomes very self-conscious — he's sensitive about the slightest hint of anomaly — until I assure him it's not fat, just his thick neck.

But privately, I worry it's one more sign

of fluid retention.

He's also getting more bouts of nausea. Partly it's the humongous pills and thick protein supplements and greasy liquids he must swallow several times a day. He walks around the house sucking on limes, his mouth a wedge of green, to counteract the sickening fatty oils.

Shealagh and I take him to Children's Hospital of Philadelphia and sit in the waiting room in a state of deep dejection. It feels like we're running in circles, unable to break the PLE chokehold. The endless maze of hospital visits only magnifies our anxiety. Damon, sitting with headphones across from us, notices our downcast expressions.

"Hey." He waves from his armchair, flagging down our attention with a slow, gentle sweep of the arm — "Hi, Mom, hi, Dad!" — and coaxes us out of ourselves with a soft, radiant smile.

We smile back guiltily at our son. His languid hand, arcing up from a pale wrist, describes a modest but grand salute, like a young member of the royal family hailing his subjects. He commands us not to forget him — "I'm right here," his luminous smile says — and promises that everything will be okay.

It's a curious and touching reversal. The

sick child reassuring the anxious parents and reminding them to be thankful for what they have.

Dr. Chin examines Damon with his usual thoroughness and care and notes the textbook deterioration in his condition. Damon's liver is enlarged, with increasing fluid about the belly and face. And a dense patchwork of spidery blue veins crisscrosses his abdomen, chest, and upper arms, giving his skin a dusky, translucent fragility.

"The blue blood is sprouting new venous pathways as it tries to shortcut back to the heart in a desperate bid for oxygen," Dr. Chin tells us, gently tracing the branching veinlets across Damon's torso. "It's a sign of increasing systemic stress," he says softly.

After Damon goes to watch videos in an outer room, we discuss our remaining options, including a Fontan "takedown," followed by an attempted repair of Damon's second ventricle. "It's a long shot but it would restore a normal circulatory system for him," Dr. Chin says. At the Mayo Clinic a year earlier, I asked Dr. Gordon Danielson, a pioneering heart surgeon, about such a procedure, and he admitted it had never been successfully performed, that it would require lots of surgery — much more than a transplant — but in theory, there was no reason it couldn't be done. Now Dr. Chin gives us the name of a surgeon who "might consider" undertaking such a high-risk operation.

We also review fenestration but agree to wait a little longer and pursue other, less invasive approaches first. We call Damon back into the room and Dr. Chin addresses him.

"Well, Damon, heparin isn't helping so we'd like to try something new."

"You mean I still have PLE?" Damon says in his disarming way.

Dr. Chin is tactful but Damon is too sharp, and Dr. Chin too respectful of his intelligence, to obscure the facts. "Yes, that's why you feel so tired and why you're puffy," Dr. Chin says, adding that we have some interesting leads on treatments to modulate PLE but there's no single answer. "We just have to keep searching and find a solution that works for you."

I watch my young son, who grasps what Dr. Chin is saying, take this in. His face pales and his leg twitches, swiping the water bottle behind him, but he hangs in and meets the news head-on, agreeing to try the alternatives.

I feel deeply distressed that I can do nothing to shield my son, even though he's sitting only a few feet from me. Shealagh looks equally helpless and bereft. We're both overwhelmed and stymied but chime in with hopeful asides about the future and console ourselves that we still have many cards to play.

Among my best-informed advisers is Dr. David "Dudu" Bar-Or. A physician, biomedical researcher, and chief scientific officer of a company he founded, Dudu runs a trauma center in the Southwest while developing new drugs and diagnostics for diseases. He's not only a first-rate clinician and bench scientist with dozens of patents to his name, he's also married to my cousin Ohna. Like Dr. Chin, Dudu possesses rare breadth and is critical of received medical wisdom. He also always takes my calls and provides a frank insider's view.

Dudu has devoted much time and research effort to Damon's case and the dread mystery of PLE. From the start, he's felt the mechanism of inflammation, which his lab focuses on for its role in inflammatory and autoimmune diseases, is a key component. Now as I press him with increasing urgency, Dudu hits on a new approach.

"To control the balance of inflammation and anti-inflammation enzyme function, or to defend against any illness, you need a strong immune system," Dudu tells me. "But Damon's T cells and B cells, the key white blood cells for fighting infection, are extremely low. So I suggest we try him on IVIG — intravenous infusion of immuno-globulins."

IVIG is a blood product that supplies antibodies, or an immune boost, for people who have an immune deficiency or an au-toimmune illness. Dudu has also seen it used effectively in the ER for organ failure, another way of looking at what's happening to Damon's heart, liver, and gut. In addi-tion, Dudu believes IVIG possesses an anti-inflammatory component that theoretically could help target Damon's underlying PLE.

A literature search quickly shows others have used IVIG for PLE without harmful effects, and with some benefit. "Ideally, IVIG could reduce inflammation and keep Damon's albumin from leaking out. At the least, it will improve his general immunity and health status," Dudu says.

It sounds like it's worth a try and even Dr. Hayes does not object, though Colum-bia does not administer IVIG at this stage and she's not sure what good it'll do. But to her credit, Dr. Hayes gives me leeway to seek alternatives. She's fundamentally cau-tious but knows the limits of current treatments and shares our concern about Damon.

In early summer, after one week in Martha's Vineyard and a week in Cape Cod, Damon and I fly west for his first IVIG treatment. An immunologist colleague of Dudu's gives us a private room where an IV is started and an IV stand with an infusion bag is wheeled in. Damon reclines on a sofa — a black pillow sets off his red hair — while a clear infusion of immunoglobulins drips down from the tall IV pole and flows into his arm. I imagine healing balm from the Tree of Life but in fact, at one stage, Damon grows dizzy, his pressure drops, and he becomes nauseated. The doctor slows the infusion rate and he doesn't bump it up again until Damon has recovered. But he interprets the reaction as a good sign, an indication the compound is "having an effect."

Damon and I hang out most of the day until his infusion is complete. We watch videos, eat lunch, and banter. I help him wheel his IV pole to the bathroom. A couple of times, Damon dozes off. I watch his thin, IV-encumbered arms hugging the white blanket to his chest, his weary head rolling back as the impassive machine gurgles and clicks away.

He endures this latest trial like a pale stoic, resolute even in slumber.

I track the vital fluid flowing into Damon's veins and pray something fundamental is happening. Is it so much to ask?

Damon gets through the infusion without further incident. The doctor says he should feel better in a week, though sometimes several infusions are needed for an initial response. "Either way," he says, "take it easy for the first twenty-four to forty-eight hours until your body adjusts."

I help a relieved but still shaky Damon climb into a taxi for the airport — he wants to return for rehearsals the next day. At first, he's sensitive to every bump and lurch on the road. At the terminal, he gets a headache and he holds on to me on the automatic walkway. Inside the cabin, the bright lights blind him and he pulls his hoodie over his eyes, moaning. "It hurts . . . I'm dizzy!"

I've had a good feeling about this treatment, but now I start to wonder.

We arrive home at two A.M., exhausted. But Damon rises by eight the next morning for school because parts are being assigned for *Pericles*. I only hope he gets through the day.

He calls me at noon in the office to report he got the part he wanted. I'm very pleased for him and note his chirpiness.

"Aren't you tired from yesterday? I know I am," I say.

"No, I'm good. I think I even feel a slight . . . improvement." Damon pauses, as if digesting this himself. "Is that possible, Dad? So soon, I mean?"

"Why not?" I register a warm glow, as if *I've* just been infused. "First, even if it's a placebo effect, you still *feel* better. And you may be one of the lucky ones who respond fast."

"Yeah, Dad, but this is *really* fast."

Everyone is thrilled with Damon's early response to the treatment. We go for another infusion a few weeks later, and Damon gets another palpable lift. We decide to make the most of this good news by returning to northwest Scotland in August for a family vacation on the Isle of Skye.

Damon's improvement gives us all a boost, but we can't tell if this is the decisive turning point — he seems much peppier — or just another short-lived hope.

I make an appointment to speak to the president of my foundation about a raise. Shealagh has stopped working and Damon's medical bills are escalating. Shealagh's family won't help and mine can't, so we must look elsewhere.

My stock is high at work and I have merit-based grounds for a raise. I also have a good relationship with the president. But what's hard is dropping my professional facade and admitting I have a seriously ill son at home whose care I oversee. I've scrupulously fenced off this part of my life from the office and my larger work environment. Even my assistant doesn't know, and going public has stopped me from requesting help sooner. But now I must break cover because the situation is too dire.

As I wait outside the president's office and review my request, it strikes me that not just this crisis but my entire professional career has been shaped by Damon. It was only after Damon's birth and jolting diagnosis that I sought my first full-time job, in my thirties. Until then I'd been a freelance writer and editor, happily doing my own thing. But I needed health insurance, and would need it forevermore, so I grabbed the first thing I could, paying my dues for a few years until I'd recovered my balance. But I never resented Damon or regretted the decision. It was an honorable duty for a great cause.

My long-deferred meeting with the president goes well, or as well as might be expected. He cannot give me what I ask for but he promises to help, and he does, once he gets the board of trustees' approval. I leave the room feeling more naked and exposed, with my financial problem only partly solved, but with my faith in people — and specifically, in the people I work for — reaffirmed.

Two weeks before Skye, Shealagh takes Sam and Miranda to her sister's place in the Channel Islands. I have work and Damon has theater, so we two remain in New York. When I return from the office, we sit in the backyard, shooting baskets, barbecuing, or just hanging out. The peaches are starting to come in on our big tree but the birds are pecking the downy fruit to pieces.

"Can you believe these goddamned cheeky sparrows and redbirds!" I gripe.

"You'd be cheeky too if you didn't have enough to eat!" Damon chides. He leaves the birds extra seeds in his window feeder.

Saturday morning, I get us ham and egg bagels, then drop Damon at Barnes & Noble while I go to the pharmacy to refill his medications. When I return to the Seventh Avenue bookstore, I find Damon browsing in the theater section.

"Hey, Dad, can you help me find a good play for our fall production?" Damon asks.

He's already taking a leadership role in Drama Club. "We want fun stuff that's not too hard to stage with lots of parts."

"Sure." I confidently select several classic plays and provide brief synopses.

"No, I don't think so!" Damon gives me that killer adolescent shrug, making me feel badly outdated, until I find a modern play he deigns to consider.

That night we go see a French film in Brooklyn Heights, then sit out on a narrow street fragrant with tree blossoms. The shady plane trees in the soft summer air, the muffled streetlights, and the café intimacy remind me of Paris, where I once lived. I drink beer while Damon sips an orange soda. We discuss the film and many other subjects. Damon is good company and we can talk about almost anything. I realize he's becoming a friend.

I want to invite Damon to a matinee of *Long Day's Journey into Night* but I hesitate over the subject matter. The play's mother is a dope fiend, the son a sickly youth expected to die from his illness. But I decide Damon is old enough — he already knows things I never will — and he shouldn't be deprived of great art. I want to share all I can with him.

A few years earlier, overcoming similar

scruples, I took him to see a documentary about Jewish children rescued from Nazi Germany and sent to live with foster families in England. Some of these children, like my mother, who waved good-bye to their parents from the train, would never see Mummy and Daddy again. I had to balance the emotional impact of this material with Damon's need to understand his history and his grandmother's past. He was young but I took him anyway. As we sat in the Lincoln Center theater, we spotted a familiar face in the audience. It was my mother, come in from Queens for the same show!

Thus now, on a bright Sunday, I take Damon with me to see Eugene O'Neill's posthumous masterpiece. The play is long, over four hours, and it unfolds slowly. But it still astonishes with its uncompromising yet sympathetic depiction of tight-knit family members who damage one another grievously, by intent or not, within the bosom of consanguinity.

The play leaves both Damon and me feeling emotionally depleted but filled with the exhilaration of seeing a great work. It forges another strong link in our deepening bond. And by the time we exit the theater, dusk has fallen like a curtain over the city, and the long day has indeed turned into night, making us feel we must hurry home before a dark fog settles in over the spooky metropolis.

CHAPTER 27

In August, the whole family returns to the Isle of Skye for the first time since Damon's diagnosis two years earlier, and in the beginning, everything feels different.

The Red Cuillin and the purple moors and the blue lochs appear like a still-life encased in a glass paperweight, a beautiful but closed-off reminder of the carefree existence we've lost. Suddenly we're aware of all the things Damon *cannot* do. There's no cover or social camouflage here. Damon's small stature and strained pallor stand out against the vivid landscape.

The contrast with his playmates is even more striking. I watch Damon trail his buddies Lachlann and Jamie as they stride through the bracken or lope along the bay. He works overtime just to keep up, arms pumping, hips swiveling, and spindly legs shuffling in outsized wellies. "Let's build a fort on that hill," he says, trying creatively to slow the pace. He's similarly exposed as he runs on the soccer pitch.

"Everyone's bigger than me now," Damon says with a sigh. His friends have all shot up and developed in the two years we've been away, while he looks physically unchanged.

But Damon has changed, and not just because of his health problems. For one, he's a savvy urban teen habituated to the high school hyperactivity and cosmopolitan cacophony of New York. And Skye has little of that social adrenaline and cultural caffeine. After a few days Damon confides he misses the city. "It's okay here but there's not that much going on. I feel like I'm not doing enough."

"You'll get into stuff here, just give it time," I tell him. But privately I wonder if we did the right thing in bringing him back. We celebrate Damon's fifteenth birthday with a big barbecue, hosting a steady stream of villagers who flow from the front garden into the house and back out again. We're staying in the Pillars this time, a three-bedroom bungalow. Shealagh prefers this pebbled modern dwelling to the old croft because it's more convenient and easier to clean, but Damon and his pals feel no such constraints. They pelt the slate roof, the picture windows, and the stucco walls with a variety of glop, which they then trek through the house. I keep Shealagh plied with drink so she won't go in and see the mess.

"Och aye, that's a bull's-eye!" Lachlann gleefully spatters a windowpane.

We herd the kids into the front garden just long enough to bring out the cake and sing "Happy Birthday." The whole glen resounds with our festivities.

After Sam and Miranda have gone to bed, Shealagh and I lounge with Damon in the kitchen as he sits with his pills and a patch of Saran wrap clinging to his side. The clear wrap, with numbing cream for his heparin shot, evokes a racing bib and endows Damon with an oddly athletic aura.

Outside the cottage, all is silent. Shealagh and I belt back shots of our beloved Talisker whiskey, grown and distilled just a few miles away. Its strong, peaty warmth spreads to the solar plexus. Damon drinks ginger ale between his pills and eyes our amber-colored single-malt with multiple levels of curiosity.

"Can I taste it?" he finally asks, pushing the limits of his birthday license.

"Okay." I pour him a shot, foreseeing the outcome but loath to deny my son.

Damon swishes an infinitesimal drop in

his mouth. "Omigod!" He spits it out with a bitter scowl. "You *drink* that?" He returns to his soda and gapes at us.

"Let's show Mom your photos." I scroll through images from the Agricultural Fair in Ord, where I drove Damon and Lachlann Sunday.

"These are great." Shealagh smiles at a picture of the two boys beside an Aberdeen Angus bull. She looks up. "Oh, guess who's running for governor of California? 'Ja, I'll be back — my mission is to protect you!' " Shealagh mimics wickedly.

"Wow, Mom, I didn't know you could do imitations!" Damon chortles.

"Well, there's lots about me you don't know . . ." Shealagh winks.

"I know you can't tell jokes," Damon says. "Or even get them, usually."

"D-man, that's unfair. I've heard Mom be funny once or twice," I say.

"Neither of you two clever boots can change a lightbulb. *That's* funny," Shealagh says, zinging us back.

After Damon goes to bed, Shealagh and I stay in the kitchen and discuss our ongoing concerns about our son, a topic that increasingly dominates our marriage.

"He didn't appear to get quite the same boost from his second IVIG infusion as from the first," I remark. "I'm not certain, but it didn't seem as effective."

"No, and he looks very bloated, especially when he first gets up."

Shealagh sounds very anxious, so I pull back. "But his appetite is better and he no longer gets the same fatigue. So there's some improvement."

Damon suddenly appears in the doorway and approaches me with a targeted urgency I've learned to dread. I brace myself, while Shealagh looks equally concerned, but also relieved it's not her he's singling out.

Damon unfastens the top buttons on his pajama shirt. "Dad, can you please take a look at this?" He reveals a pin-sized, reddish-brown spot on his pale chest. "Is it a tick bite?" Damon says, looking uncharacteristically rattled.

I inspect the broad, tender cavity of his twice-cracked chest and note the dot is on the suture line, below the rib cage. For many years after his last open-heart operation, a tiny wire protruded from that very spot. It was an eyesore but the wire is long gone, and what remains is a tiny pinhole. I don't believe it's serious, perhaps a minor scar irritation, but I never dismiss a complaint of Damon's, because he is his own best clinician.

So now I tap on his abdomen, searching for any other symptoms or anomalies. I note his belly is full and hard, but before I can probe further, Damon cries out because the area I'm palpating is still tender from his recent injection: "Ow, that hurts!"

"Sorry, D-man." I feel mortified by the discomfort he must bear daily and apologize before shifting to the opposite side. But I find nothing there either.

"I can't see any new problem," I say, looking to Shealagh for her view.

"No, it looks pretty much the same to me also," my wife agrees.

I turn to my son. "We'll just keep our eye on this. Okay?"

"Yeah." Damon seems satisfied, even relieved, with this homey diagnosis, as if he needed reassurance above all. Sometimes it's easy to forget how young he is.

"Give us another kiss." We send him back to bed.

We drive south and visit Philip and Catriona in their starkly beautiful coastal retreat. They always come up for August and the Skye Balls. This time, their daughter Caroline, a onetime actress, is visiting with her husband, a sculptor, and their two children. We are fond of one another and enjoy catching up.

"Damon, are you still doing your theatricals?" Caroline queries in her posh, sweet voice. She shares a birthday and a certain leonine flair with Damon.

"I just played Cerimon in *Pericles*," Damon replies.

"What fun. And did you have a colorful costume? I'll bet you did!"

Several of Shealagh's Scottish uncles show, including red-faced Rory, whose salmon fishery scheme has fizzled, so he's exploring windmills on the Isle of Skye.

"Council's offering a bloody fortune just for putting the damn things up, even if you never generate a kilowatt. We'll form a syndicate and sublease."

Damon watches him, rapt, like an actor taking character notes.

Philip offers me a Famous Grouse whiskey and a comfy chair for one of our fireside natters. He is the queen's representative in his county and thus charged with organizing her upcoming eightieth-birthday celebrations there.

"It's a public occasion so the security is quite challenging. We don't want the antibrigades demonstrating." Philip's eyes twinkle. A very decent, dutiful man with a broad English worldview and a wry sensibility, Philip works for a multinational com-

289

pany in the City of London in order to maintain his land and estate in the country.

"Does the queen have a sense of humor?" Damon sidles boldly up to us, tickled that Philip talks to the queen about mundane items like guest lists.

"Yes, rather a good one." Philip nods. "But it's best to wait for her cues, Damon, before showing off one's own."

As the summer progresses, Damon starts hitting his stride, both physically — the daily habit of outdoor life toughens him up — and socially.

"Let's go to the Portree stables," Damon says. He mounts up and resumes lessons, trots and canters in the ring, and goes out on cross-country treks.

He exercises daily on the big trampoline by Lachlann's house. It's the local hangout. Damon places Miranda and Kerry in the center of the ring and bounces them up and down by jumping on the perimeter of the nylon.

He swings on a tree rope, yodeling, "Nee-yah!" He cavorts on the sandy Braes beach and splashes in the icy Varragill River.

"It's really fun but a little nippy!" Damon grins with chattering teeth.

He tries Ben Tianavaig again and despite setbacks, he reaches the summit.

"I wasn't sure I'd make it," he says, smiling, as he stands panting on the peak.

On quieter days, Shealagh sends him down to the bay to collect mussels with Sam and Miranda. Miranda can't reach the shells and Sam can't pry them loose. "Like this!" Damon shows them, yanking a hard shellfish off its slimy perch.

Sam and Miranda soon grow bored but Damon stays until the bucket is full. He carries his catch to the bungalow, leaving it out overnight so the mussels can purge. Then he helps Shealagh scrape the shells and cook a feast in garlic and wine.

My parents come for a visit. "Damon seems so much better up here. He's active all the time!" my mother notes as he climbs the ruins of an ancient castle.

I've invited my parents not just to see Skye but also to take my father to Glasgow for a tour of his childhood. He hasn't been back for sixty years. Damon surprises me when he suddenly asks if he can join us. I hate refusing him anything but I've long dreamed of making this voyage with my father, just as I took my mother back to her hometown in Germany after the Berlin Wall fell. Now my lifelong position as a son, and my effort to honor that role, seems to collide with my obligations as a father. Fortunately, Damon

291

gets distracted by village goings-on and forgets all about us. On our return, I tell Damon that one day, I look forward to having him accompany me on a similar voyage to my roots. "You got it, Dad!"

One afternoon, Miranda and Sam are walking up from the bay when Miranda feels a sharp thistle across her ankle. She looks down and sees she's stepped on a wasp's nest! An angry swarm pours from the ground and chases the screaming children all the way into the house, where Shealagh and I do what we can. I chase the wasps from room to room, smashing them with a rolled-up newspaper, while Shealagh dunks Miranda in the bath, drowning her nemeses. It looks like we're turning back the assault but unbeknownst to us, dozens of secret invaders still lurk inside the kids' clothes and in their hair. As we relax our guard, the waiting wasps dart out with venomous rage, attacking us from every angle in a *second* wave.

Before the carnage is over, everyone in the house is nursing wasp wounds. But Sam and Miranda, riddled with painful stings, are the worst hit, and they remain in mild shock. We put them to bed, soothe their brows, and sit with them.

The only person unharmed in all this

mayhem — the one wasp-allergic person who would have been most endangered — is Damon. He arrives an hour later, sauntering up from Jamie's and eating a peach in the soft, glowing light.

"Hey, guys, wassup?" He beams at us, oblivious of the tornado that's swept through. The peach juice drips down his fingers.

As summer ends, I'm struck by how well Damon is doing. Skye has worked its magic and he flourishes, as if the pristine air and sea and mountains have reinvigorated him. Briefly I consider staying in Skye and not returning.

If that's what it takes, why not?

We could treat the whole island as one big rehabilitation center, our own magic mountain. There's a decent hospital in town with emergency evacuation, the kids can go to school in Portree, I can write or teach or find other work, and Shealagh can be with the kids. We can all lie low until Damon is better. There are worse places in the world to live . . .

It's a nice fantasy but we have too many ties and obligations back home, including the most sophisticated medical care in the world.

And so, with a lump in our throats and a

flutter of remorse in my own heart, we bid farewell to the blessed Isle of Skye and fly back home.

CHAPTER 28

"I can't believe there's no improvement!" I fume after receiving Damon's first test results in the fall. "He seemed so good in Skye, but what was the point?"

"Don't say that, he had a great summer!" Shealagh cries. "That's important."

"Of course. But his albumin is barely above two. We're back to square one."

"At least it hasn't gotten worse," Shealagh says.

"That's true." I nod. "And he's excited about starting growth hormone injections now that he doesn't have a daily heparin shot."

In November, when Damon comes to my office to help with the Rhodes applications, I'm pleased to see a whole new gang of friends from Brooklyn Tech troop in with him. They're bigger, louder, fouler, and funnier than his previous group, but they're all basically good kids. I only have to yell a few times to keep them in line. In between, they file and ask astute questions. I buy them mountains of pizza when they flag, hand out warm cash from the ATM at the end, and take them all to the movies.

"Thanks, Dad, that was cool!" Damon says on our way home. The group invigorates Damon more than any medication the doctors prescribe.

The Brooklyn Tech fall production of *Picasso at the Lapin Agile* — the play Damon and I chose at the bookstore — is a hoot. Damon dons huge red glasses, a flowery shirt, a ridiculous bow tie, and a shiny yellow jacket, sparking laughter even before he speaks. The show is a hit and Damon spends every available minute basking in the post-play glow and sharing the embraces, confidences, and intimacies of his fellow cast and crew members. But as soon as the props and costumes are put away and the group disbands, Damon starts to look poorly again. He appears exhausted and run-down and takes to his bed, missing several days of school. "I'm just a little tired," he says.

We begin to see this pattern recur. Damon limps along, barely managing to get by, but rallies for any activity involving his friends or the theater.

On New Year's Eve, while Shealagh and I go out to celebrate, Damon throws his own bash at our place. He's become quite the party giver, aided by our tolerance and large rambling house. Shealagh cooks a big pot of chili and Damon loads up on junk food and soda, while Sam and Miranda are relegated to the top floor. "You can't come downstairs!" Damon warns his siblings. He greets guests in top hat and tux, clutching an (empty) magnum of champagne. And while he doesn't quite get the crowd he wanted — teens are notoriously unreliable and certain parents strict about New Year's — enough people show to make his party a success. Damon relishes being master of the revelry.

Once again, however, as soon as the party ends, Damon's condition worsens. He gets a bad headache and misses several days of school. The bitter winter doesn't help, but it's more than that. Weakness and fatigue now seem endemic, and Damon needs a spur to become activated. Otherwise he retreats into protective inertia, a kind of semi-hibernation.

I take him to an afternoon hockey game at Madison Square Garden. The New York Rangers face off against the Tampa Bay Lightning. It's an exciting, hard-fought contest that goes into overtime. "Wasn't that an amazing shot!" I exclaim on the car ride back, turning to him in the seat beside me. But Damon is fast asleep. It's only seven P.M.

This is not only unnerving, it's completely out of character, so I know he's ailing.

One night, I'm cooking up steaks for the two of us when Damon walks in.

"It's awfully bright in here!" He blinks and covers his eyes, grimacing.

"Really? I must need the extra light for my middle-aged eyes," I joke.

"No, my headache's back. The bad migraine that made me miss school."

"Why don't you get an ibuprofen?" I send him upstairs but note his fragility. Damon returns and we sit in front of the TV, eating and chatting.

"Feeling better?" I ask.

"A little," Damon says, but it's obvious he is not himself. There's a new, scared look that flits across his face. It doesn't linger but it's still unsettling. "I get more headaches now," he states. His eyes, previously so steady, dart my way.

"Maybe it's that new globulin you're getting? You'll adjust, you always do." I try to stay upbeat, but I don't have answers. "You excited about your first trip to Sundance?"

"Yeah, it'll be cool." Damon plays along but I can feel his uncertainty and sense of siege. I blanch inside at my powerlessness to do more for him.

Our house fills with dread and unspoken tension. Tempers are shorter, bickering erupts more frequently. Doors slam and voices rise to new shrillness.

Shealagh and I have sharper exchanges with one another, we argue more with the kids, and the kids fight more among themselves.

I see exactly what's happening but don't know how to stop it. My self-discipline starts to falter. I can't write, and I don't know where to turn.

Shealagh has stopped working and is on hand to chauffeur Damon and help him in any way she can. But Damon's worsening condition causes his devoted mother acute distress. Her asthma acts up, her back gives her trouble, and she has difficulty sleeping. One day while driving alone, she is rear-ended by a tractor trailer, which flees the scene without a trace. Shealagh is physically unhurt, but our van is totaled, and her nerves are further frayed.

Sam is applying to middle school, a competitive, high-pressure process under normal circumstances. He drafts a short application essay I correct. But when Sam rewrites the essay, the revised version has new errors, which I correct again. He does a third draft but makes more mistakes. They crop up like defiant weeds that I keep yanking out.

"Go and do it over, Sam! We need a clean copy for your application."

Sam sulks but I won't let him quit until he gets it right, and he can't, or won't, turn in a clean copy. I am all the more intransigent because I won't accept that something so under human agency and control, something so easy to fix, can be botched. Sam, seething, takes out his frustration on Miranda. Shealagh tells me to let it go but all I want is for Sam to copy one error-free page. Sam throws a fit and hits Miranda. Miranda cries and hits Sam back. Damon wakes up from the screaming, puffy and upset, and wants to know what's going on.

Around this period, an old, eccentric friend picks a fight with me and inexplicably breaks off a three-decade relationship. Eventually, I learn that my ongoing crisis with Damon proved too much for him. He's dropped out of everything else — school, marriage, career — but I'd always assumed his witty amorality could not possibly apply to our friendship.

It's a betrayal that blindsides me because

it comes from a seemingly safe quarter. Even worse, it's secretly aimed at my son, whose bodily decline makes my squeamish friend squirm.

But this person's readiness to ditch me despite all our history does perversely signal me that my prospects must really look bad from the outside. I could always rely on him for a hyperacute reading of the prevailing winds.

So I gird myself and clutch my firstborn ever more fervently in my arms. I will draw deeper from my own well, rely even less on others, and spare no exertion as I scour the earth in search of a cure for Damon.

PART III

CHAPTER 29

Hey cine-lovers and gawkers, it's Damon
reporting from the Sundance Film Festival
in Park City, Yoot-ah. Just saw this kick-
ass movie about 2 rock n roll bands. The
director and every1 was there 4 the premiere . . . But seriously, what's with the
black? It's like the only color any1 wears!
Guess it stands out in the snow — but
wouldn't any color? lol.
— From Damon's blog, January 2004

"So where are we?" Shealagh enters my
study and looks over my shoulder as I work
at my desk. We both feel increasingly distraught about our son's condition, but while
I turn to the medical literature and the
medical profession, my wife turns to me.

"I talked to Dr. Chin at CHOP and I also
checked in with the Mayo Clinic and Boston
Children's," I tell Shealagh, adding that I
spoke again to Dr. Hayes and contacted

several other hospitals, government health agencies, pharmaceutical companies, and independent experts and even followed up on several alternative-medicine leads. "If there's a solution, we'll know about it."

Among the stacks of folders on Damon's case, I've opened a thin new file I carry with me at all times, labeled "Hope." Tucked inside are the latest reports on the use of stem cells, medical assist devices, and artificial hearts.

One day in December, I spot an online reference to an article in the journal *Pediatrics* about an Australian doctor who reports he has successfully treated a young girl with PLE by patching together or "resecting" a local lesion in her gut.

If PLE is a leakage of protein from the gut, why not isolate the *exit point* of the leak, like a hole in a tire, and plug it?

Apparently, this is what a resourceful physician at Sydney Children's Hospital has done by using a special diagnostic. The test revealed a "localized, surgically correctible lesion" that doctors then repaired. This fourteen-year-old patient, who, like fifteen-year-old Damon, also had a failed Fontan resistant to all interventions, is reported to be "doing well" after more than two years!

This news makes my pulse race. It's the

first *possible* break in a long time. I quickly order a reprint of the original article, pore over every word, and share it with my big-picture medical allies like Dr. Chin, my cousin Dr. Bar-Or, and my friend Dr. Jeffrey Friedman. All agree it looks intriguing and is worthy of follow-up, though Dr. Chin is less enthusiastic, and everyone urges caution as it's only one case and we don't know all the facts.

Undeterred, I start with a radiologist at NYU Medical Center who tells me, "This technique is very rare because it involves the use of radioactive materials. I've never used it myself but I know someone who might know." She gives me the name of another expert at Memorial Sloan-Kettering. He warns me this diagnostic technique has been discontinued in the United States. "You may need to go to Canada if you want to receive this treatment."

"Going to Canada is a nonissue — I would go to the moon!" I explain.

Finally, I track down the author of this paper in his native Australia, where he holds a faculty position. It seems fitting the elusive answer may lie at the other end of the world.

Alas, this researcher has no good news for me and sounds chastened.

"The patient has suffered a relapse. PLE has returned and she is in a critical state. The doctors are keeping her alive with regular infusions of albumin."

The patient apparently had struggled from the beginning, her course never as smooth as the paper implied. I'm crushed and I want to rebuke this man, but he's just a well-intentioned researcher whose idea did not pan out.

In late January, I meet Damon at the airport in Salt Lake City and take him back to Park City for the last two days of the Sundance Film Festival. We find my best friend, David, who's flown in from Seattle, on snow-laden, banner-festooned Main Street. A hale, rugged guy with a big appetite for life, David's Rough Rider greatcoat flaps open as he leans down, tiny gold ear stud agleam, and wraps Damon in a bear hug.

The closing-night awards ceremony, a televised event, is held in the Racquet Club. We run the gauntlet of security and rope lines, are each issued a bracelet with pull-tags for free drinks, and circulate in the vast reception area. The bar and buffet are hopping.

The Sundance senior team — it's a tiny, hardworking core, with a thousand volun-

teers obscuring the shoestring operation —
alerts me to some mysterious "good news."
Ken Brecher, who runs the Sundance Institute for Robert Redford, wanders over and
says, "We have a surprise for you and I think
you'll be very pleased!"

"Great," I reply, mystified. I introduce
Ken to Damon.

"You must be your dad's secret focus
group, right?" Ken smiles. "What's your fee?
I'd pay a lot to get you on my team!"

"Yeah, I taught my dad everything he
knows!" Damon quips.

"Watch for your surprise!" Ken says over
his shoulder as he dashes off.

We go in and take our seats. A forest of
cranes, tripods, and cameras bristles at the
rear while the stage is dark. A senior pro-
grammer warms up the crowd.

"Okay, guys, it's time for the Sun Dance.
Come on, everybody, on your feet!"

The entire audience stands and begins to
sway in freeform boogie to a joyful beat,
including Damon, who leaps to his feet,
shimmying and bopping as if the ceremonial
spirit is calling to him directly.

The stage clears, music and lights come
up, and the actress Zooey Deschanel wends
her way up to the podium as the televised
show begins.

I provide the play-by-play for Damon while David supplies the color commentary.

"*That* guy got the prize? He couldn't get arrested!" David wisecracks. "Stevie Wonder could see through that film . . ."

Our Science in Film Award is early, as we're still outsiders and few films qualify for our category. *Primer,* an obscure, low-budget film by an unknown first-time director named Shane Carruth, wins.

"Cool!" Damon applauds. I just introduced him to Carruth at the buffet.

The ceremony proceeds with some arresting film clips, endless speeches, and a few flashes of true art. When the final award, the Sundance Grand Jury Prize, is announced, the winner is . . . *Primer!* The Best Dramatic Film Award is a shocker, because this cerebral thriller was shot for $7,000 with an unknown cast yet still manages to beat out several popular, multi-million-dollar films with major stars. As we all pose together onstage, I'm happy for Carruth and appreciate that it's a big shot in the arm for our program.

We go to the after-party, flushed with victory, and accept congratulations from all quarters.

The party is in full swing and I'm on a professional high when I notice Damon has disappeared. I search the mobbed rooms to no avail, then find him out on the terrace, standing alone under the open Utah sky with its chill beadwork of stars.

I walk up to my son. The ski slopes are lit up for night skiing and float above us like gleaming white staircases descending from an invisible heaven.

"You okay, D-man?" I place my hand on his shoulder.

"I just needed a little air." Damon sounds subdued. I don't like his color.

"Hey, it's late, we can go," I say. "You've had a long day with the time change and the altitude and all the excitement . . . Let's save something for tomorrow, okay, champ?"

"No, I want to go back in. I just need a minute." He stands with feet apart, hands on hips.

"You sure, D-man?"

"Yeah, Dad. This is cool."

"If that's what you want . . ." I wait until he's ready, and then we both return inside.

The party is still going strong but suddenly it seems very crowded and noisy and has lost its appeal. My job here is done, and I'm not enjoying it anymore.

I watch Damon circulate solo — he's a teenager and needs his own space — but I can tell he's struggling. He wants so badly to be at this event but he's having a very hard time.

I see his chest heave and his eyes blink. He can't find an equilibrium point. Finally, he marches up to me. "Can we please go?"

We walk outside. I can't tell if it's an asthma attack or something else but the cold, bracing air seems to help and his breathing normalizes. But Damon is very upset with himself for walking out on this party. It's one of the reasons he came to Sundance.

I worry that his illness is not just curtailing Damon's activity but is also starting to change *him.*

CHAPTER 30

Yeah well they (doctors and my parents and my consent) decided to start having me do the infusions myself at home. (The infusions is the procedure that I have about every 3 weeks where they hook me up 2 an IV and pump shit through my veins 4 a couple of hours.) Anywayz they want me to do it at home now so I can have them more often *yey* and don't have 2 go into the hospital which actually is sort of better.

— From Damon's blog, April 2004

"Damon is not getting better," Shealagh remarks shortly after the Easter break.

"I know," I say tightly. We've just returned from vacation and seen the fall-off.

"He sleeps all the time, he barely eats, and he has no energy. He's fallen behind in his classes because he's missed so much school. And he looks terrible!" Shealagh cries.

We're in the kitchen and Freddie, startled by the sudden shift in tone, trots over to see what's wrong. "And that belly — I know it's his liver, but it makes him look *pregnant*," Shealagh says with a shudder. "He's struggling every day. I'm really worried about him!"

I tell Shealagh it may be time to roll the dice on fenestration since neither Dudu's anti-inflammatory drug nor Jeff's assist device have panned out. "It could buy us as much as five to ten years, according to Dr. Chin. And fenestration doesn't rule out any other options, so it seems like the safest way to go. If it makes Damon too blue, we can always reverse it and close up the hole —"

I stop as Damon walks into the kitchen and Freddie leaps into his arms. Damon's face is puffy and his eyes buggy — he just woke up — but he beams at his pooch, who wriggles and licks him all over.

"He missed you!" I smile, noting my son's chalky complexion. Even Damon's hair, overgrown, bowl-cut, lacks its usual luster. "How'd you sleep, D-man?"

"Okay," Damon says. "I'm a little cold." He rubs his arms although it's a spring day and he's wearing his bulky gray hooded sweatshirt, which makes him look even frailer.

"You'll warm up, sweetie," Shealagh says. "Can I fix you something to eat?"

"Not yet." Damon shakes his head. At every meal now, we have to convince him to eat. It's a chore or a battle, depending on his mood, but never a pleasure anymore.

"I can make you scrambled eggs on toast," Shealagh offers.

"I said not now, Mom!" Damon snaps. Then he softens. "I just woke up, I need some time." He glances around. It's one P.M. on a Saturday. "Where's Sam and Miranda?"

"Sam's at gymnastics and Miranda's on a play date," I say. "You have any plans?"

"I may go in for a tech rehearsal for *Tommy*," he says. Although we agreed Damon should save his dwindling energy for school, he got roped into helping out with the spring musical, including a tiny non-speaking part, and we don't have the heart to stop him.

"Want me to drive you?" Shealagh says. Sometimes she gets him to eat on the way.

"Yeah, thanks, Mom." As I walk them to the car, Damon shivers in the sun and slips the hood of his sweatshirt over his head. He looks like a wraith as he climbs into the passenger side and disappears behind the high dash.

■ ■ ■ ■

We wait for Dr. Thomas Spray, an internationally renowned surgeon, in a vacant cardiology office at Children's Hospital of Philadelphia. It's after six P.M. and the regular staff has gone home, making the place feel strangely quiet. Dr. Chin, who's brokered this visit, wants us to meet Dr. Spray not only because he's a preeminent cardiothoracic surgeon equal to anyone at Columbia but also because he's a proponent of fenestration.

"You need someone who has experience performing this procedure *and* the conviction that it works because he's seen the results firsthand," Dr. Chin explains.

Dr. Spray, cutting and stitching since seven A.M., emerges from the operating room after twelve hours of surgery. A tall, distinguished figure, he knows the details of our case and impresses us with his measured manner.

"Fenestration is not a cure-all and I can't guarantee the results, but I think it's worth trying for Damon before you go to a heart transplant." Dr. Spray gives us an earnest, sympathetic, and straightforward look. "We've had some good outcomes with it."

"You also do heart transplants, is that right?" Shealagh asks.

"Yes, and I could perform that operation for Damon, after a suitable interval, if the fenestration did not work." Dr. Spray nods. "However, I don't believe we're at that point."

"I have a patient still doing well six years after fenestration!" Dr. Chin volunteers.

"But you want to do this as an open-heart procedure?" I stare at Dr. Spray.

"Yes." The surgeon nods. "Doing it open-heart in the OR gives me better access to precisely configure the right-to-left shunt between the two chambers of the heart. The open approach also lets me put in pacing wires or other modifications as needed."

"Does that mean you'd have to open my chest *a second time* if the fenestration failed and we had to go to a heart transplant?" Damon narrows his eyes.

Everyone pauses because the patient, a young boy in this case, has spoken.

"I have the same concern," I add. "Damon's body has already been through so much . . . Mayo and Boston do it in the cath lab, without cracking the chest."

"That's why they don't get our results! It's less precise," Dr. Chin says.

"But those results haven't been published

317

yet," I say.

"Well, I could do the fenestration in the cath lab, without opening Damon's chest, but I think the odds are better with the open-heart approach," Dr. Spray says evenly.

We leave feeling this is very complex but Dr. Spray is a world-class surgeon in whose capable hands we could entrust our son, knowing he'd perform at the highest level of the achievable. But we remain uncomfortable with the risks of open-heart surgery.

"What do you recommend?" we ask Dr. Hayes at Damon's next exam. Our son waits out in the hall, where he's updating stage directions for *Tommy.*

"I think we just have to continue with the diet and the meds," she says.

"But you agree that Damon is not getting better?" I look directly at her.

"There are increasing signs of stress on his system." Dr. Hayes's voice is strained but professional. "His condition is consistent with what we see in kids with PLE."

Shealagh and I share a look. "Then we're going to try fenestration!" I state.

"We've only seen sporadic benefits. And there's some risk," Dr. Hayes says dourly.

"I know Columbia is not an advocate of fenestration but even the multicenter study *you* gave me cited it as effective," I reply. "CHOP gets good results and has agreed to do it for Damon." I pause. "The only thing I don't like is they do it as an open-heart procedure."

"We don't do it that way here. It's done in the cath lab," Dr. Hayes says.

"So you *would* support fenestration for Damon?" I give her a sharp look.

"Well, if you've decided to go ahead, why don't you speak to Bill Hellenbrand? He's the director who oversees fenestrations here." She hands me a phone number.

I go meet Dr. Hellenbrand on my own, ready to reject him at the first provocation due to Columbia's apparent lack of faith in fenestration and its rare use there. But Hellenbrand, a stocky, fit New Englander with a direct manner, disarms me with his hands-on approach.

"Come, let's take a look at Damon's pictures." He waves me over to the computer as soon as I enter, as if he's read the playbook on me and knows to dispense with the usual blather, zeroing in on Damon's anatomy and how he would perform the fenestration. "See, I would thread the needle *here* and then try and create an opening *there*." A splash of pixilated color spreads across Damon's two upper chambers.

319

"So you do the procedure yourself?" I ask, surprised.

"I'm the cath lab head, I always do the fenestrations," Dr. Hellenbrand says.

"And you do it in the cath lab, and not open-heart?" I press.

"Yes. We can create the fenestration without opening him up. No need to."

"That's a relief," I say. I ask more questions and he answers each one, a clear-eyed pragmatist who's up to date on the latest research but also acknowledges gray areas.

I came ready for an argument and instead I find almost perfect agreement.

"Tell me, do you really *believe* fenestration can be effective?" I probe for weakness.

"I *know* it can be effective because I have several patients who've done well with it," Dr. Hellenbrand replies. "It's not a big number but it seems to buy a couple of years when it works. Results vary but it's one of the few things that works *at all* against PLE."

I shake my head. "I can't understand why I never heard about you or any of these patients before. Dr. Hayes always seemed so skeptical and pessimistic about trying this."

"Oh, that's Connie, she's always grim!" He chuckles. "It's her style."

"I guess so." I nod, pleased to have found

someone at Columbia whose thinking aligns with mine and who believes we have a realistic shot at making this work. I bring Shealagh and Damon to meet Dr. Hellenbrand and they are equally impressed with the straight-shooting medical director. They're also relieved with his less invasive approach.

"He seems very sensible," Shealagh says.

Damon nods. "I like him."

Everyone is on board, but it's still a risky procedure. We decide to wait for Damon to finish with the spring musical.

Damon plays the youngest of three versions of a traumatized Tommy Walker in the school production of *Tommy: The Rock Opera.* Damon has no lines — he's been struck dumb — but his pale face is wonderfully expressive as he's buffeted between incompetent adults. But what I most notice, in mortifying profile, is the engorged liver that now pads his waist and swells against his T-shirt like a taboo, gender-bending pregnancy or a sorrowful gut on a young boy.

As I watch Damon take a final bow with his far taller and more robust fellow actors, I realize we can't wait any longer. My son bends at the waist with panache, draping his belly with one deft arm, while his red locks tumble forward. Temporarily buoyed by the energy on that stage, he's the picture of actorly decorum, yet he's barely holding it together. I know from his friends he's been falling asleep during rehearsals, and even now, I can see him husbanding his meager resources to stand there and look normal.

I've already had to contact the home instruction board because he can no longer keep up with his schoolwork. He's faltering, through no fault of his own. We schedule the fenestration for the first available date after his show.

CHAPTER 31

Saturday was pimpstars bday/cast party/ soft porn orgy lol. That pretty much kicked ass cause we got 2 watch our *Tommy* video and do that dancing thing and somehow randy angel and drummer dude got naked . . . except I was majorly out of it super exhausted 4 no reason which kinda sucked cause I didn't feel like doing anything.

— From Damon's blog, May 2004

"Okay, buddy, now we're going to place this mask over your head — here, feel the padded inside groove — to make it easier for you to go to sleep."

Dr. Hellenbrand turns out to be a skilled medical technician and a first-rate physician.

He explains what he's going to do, then does it.

In Damon's case, this involves fenestration of the lateral tunnel Fontan baffle: opening the conduit previously made to carry Damon's returning blood to the *right* side of the heart and to the lungs, so that it now flows directly to the *left* side of his heart.

"This rerouted blood will not get rid of its carbon dioxide or pick up oxygen at the lungs, as normal blood does, but it will, hopefully, relieve pressure on the right side of Damon's heart — pressure believed to be contributing to, if not directly causing, his PLE," Dr. Hellenbrand tells us. "The trade-off, if it works, is that Damon will have less oxygen but more energy — and no PLE!"

Dr. Hellenbrand creates this fenestration — from the Latin word for window — using a sheath catheter that threads a fine needle through Damon's veins to his heart, where it can be imaged on a screen and manipulated to cut precisely. Once he's fashioned the opening, Dr. Hellenbrand inserts a tiny wire stent to keep the fenestration from closing. Then he checks the hemodynamics, verifies all is okay, and brings Damon to the recovery room.

The whole process takes under three hours, and Damon tolerates it well.

"I talked to Damon the whole time and

explained everything I was doing, in case he could hear me," Dr. Hellenbrand says, mindful of Damon's previous experience in the cath lab. "He was fine and there were no complications."

Given the buildup and our own fears, we feel gratified by the relative smoothness of it all. Damon is still weak and groggy from the anesthesia when we see him but he also looks relieved that it's over.

"Hey, D-man, you did great. How you feeling, big guy?" I squeeze his hand.

"Okay, I guess. I'm a little tired and sore . . ." He has pale eyelids and dry lips.

"You thirsty, sweetie?" Shealagh says. "Let me get you some ice."

As Shealagh feeds him ice chips, I stroke Damon's hair. He's exhausted but otherwise he seems like himself. I even fancy I detect an improvement.

"Does he look less puffy in the face to you?" I whisper to Shealagh.

"Don't say things like that, you'll jinx it!" Shealagh reprimands me. "It's probably his preoperative fasting, or being so worn out . . . It's too soon for any real change."

Damon stays overnight in the hospital and by the next afternoon, he's back home.

What happens over the next week unfolds like a dream.

Day by day, the fluid and all the associated puffiness that has accumulated about Damon's body begins to dissipate. It goes down slowly, so initially we wonder if we're imagining it. Shealagh plays the preemptive skeptic and I too am wary of mirages and will-o'-the-wisps. We've been down this road so many times before . . .

But by day three, it's undeniable, and by day five, we're quietly cheering from the sidelines, afraid to spook the still-unfolding miracle.

Damon can't help but notice it too. There's a lighter load on his body and less resistance when he moves. He has a cautious new spring in his step and a watchful half smile on his lips. "Hey, can you guys see a difference? I feel more like . . . like myself."

After a week, his face is almost back to normal, like an obese actor shedding his fat suit. Damon's clean jawline emerges from a soft, jowly chin, his fine nose clarifies from puffy cheeks, and his blue eyes shine from buggy lids. He's a lean, handsome boy again!

And it's not just Damon's face that returns to its familiar, attractive lineaments. Damon's huge gut also starts to shrink and recede. It diminishes daily. Ten days out, his swollen belly just drops away.

The fluid accumulation around his arms and legs also evaporates, so that we see just what a skinny figure, or a "stick man," as Shealagh dubs him, Damon really is underneath all his puffiness. His essence is revealed in the form of a scrawny but determined body that has shucked off its foreign coils and returned to its boyish core.

It's an astonishing transformation — an exorcism even. I understand the hemodynamics and the medical process that's brought us here, but the whole thing seems more like a sci-fi B movie.

We cannot believe how relatively unscathed our son looks!

Our house fills with rejoicing.

We know this kind of progress can be short-lived and that we must maintain and build on it. But it's still incredible to behold. And it means the dread PLE nemesis can be rolled back, that it has a point of vulnerability, and that we have a point of attack.

The first blood tests confirm what we see. Damon's albumin climbs back over 3.0 for the first time since the initial heparin spike. But unlike the heparin, which had to be injected daily, fenestration involves a one-time fix that should hold for *years*.

Suddenly, we're almost a normal family again. We celebrate and go to Radio City

Music Hall for the premiere of the new Harry Potter film.

We begin with a pre-film Hogwarts meal replete with Snape stew and Dementor cocktails, served at tables wreathed with a witch's mist of dry ice. Then we make our way across the mobbed, cordoned, red-carpeted street to the glittering Showplace of the Nation.

I run into several familiar faces as we head to our seats, which are lined with gift bags. Damon pulls out a Muggles T-shirt and tries it on over his new slenderized belly.

"Hey, Sam, do I look like Dudley Dursley in this?" Damon mugs loutishly.

"No, you look like Harry about to make Marge float away!" Sam giggles.

Miranda holds up a purple Lego kit.

"That's the triple-decker Knight Bus," Damon explains to his clueless sister.

Various celebrities march in with their families and fan out. We also see our Brooklyn neighbors.

There's a great buzz around this big premiere, but my mind is elsewhere. What thrills me is seeing my whole family sitting together in the row beside me: Shealagh and all three of my gorgeous children arrayed one next to the other, smiling and chatting and munching popcorn as if it's the most ordinary thing in the world.

They look like a poster family, and I'm aware of this irony as I introduce them to colleagues and as we just hang out in our seats and wait for the film to start. No one could suspect what struggle lies behind such a wholesome picture or how recently Damon came out of the hospital. Yet somehow we're all here today, still part of this communal event. I'm struck by how convention can take on new meaning to those who risk losing the world.

CHAPTER 32

The surgery might have actually worked, which would be fricken awesome!!! Maybe I've finally beaten this thing, maybe three years struggle will not have been in vain. Maybe this is finally over . . . Well of course not *over*, this is me we're talking about lol but maybe I can just be medically abnormal again without being diseased. Yeah that would be cool. Of course it's too early 2 tell for sure but things are looking up.

— From Damon's blog, May 2004

Memorial Day weekend we drive out to my friend Jeff's place, off the south fork of Long Island. Damon stays behind in the city but agrees to join us in a day or two.

Like any teenager, Damon prefers hanging out with his own friends, but this is especially true now that he gets home instruction and no longer attends classes.

He still goes into Tech for after-school drama, but otherwise he's on official leave and deprived of his regular contact with the Group. And without the daily structure and myriad nourishing interactions of school life, Damon feels isolated. "I never see anyone," he complains.

Blogging and instant messaging, already popular with Damon, become vital modes of staying in touch with friends. A lifeline, and also a forum for expressing a private identity in a public space. And right now Damon is buoyant because the fluid is sluicing off him, and he just got back his first test results:

> In other news: My albumin broke 3, for those of you who that means nothing to, which is probably all of you, just accept that it's a good thing and be happy for me.

In addition to his medical results, Damon has another cause for celebration:

> I was elected vice president of drama club which means I get 2 direct the fall play next year!!!! How fucking kick ass is that?! I hope you all come see it but that may be asking 2 much. Anyway that

331

should be cool, a lot of responsibility and extra work though but at least it is something I really enjoy.

After a concert and a party, Damon takes the train to East Hampton and joins us on Saturday. Shealagh drives the twenty minutes from North Haven to pick him up at the station. She looks for any opportunity to spend time with her son. It's hard for her to accept Damon's male adolescent need to push her away, even if she understands it's age appropriate.

"I know it's a phase but he's rude and treats me like his skivvy!" Shealagh says.

Jeff and I are sitting by the pool Sunday morning when Damon pads out in scraggly red bathing shorts, book in hand. He still carries his stomach like a big barrel, which it no longer is, and black marks still circle his belly, this time from growth hormone injections. But otherwise he looks more spry and ginger, a person quietly but determinedly on the comeback trail. He dips one toe in the pool, checking the water temperature, when Sam and Miranda howl for him.

"Damon, Damon, come into the pool!"

Damon holds up one hand to quell their screeching. He's become very noise sensitive. "I'll come in and play with you later, if you leave me alone now."

"No, no, come in now, Damon!" they clamor. "Play with us now!"

"If you don't stop, I won't come in at all!" Damon frightens them into silence. He settles into a canvas chair near Jeff and me and I see he's got *Romeo and Juliet,* this summer's workshop play.

"What part you trying out for?" I ask.

"I don't even know if I'm accepted into the program," Damon grouses.

"Come on. They adore you. And you've made the cut the past two years."

"Yeah, which means my audition must've really sucked!" Damon can't extract the suntan lotion so I grab the tube and squirt some into his palm. "Alums always get in, but I haven't even heard back!" Damon daubs his brow and cheeks, leaving defiant white smears on his face.

"They're just disorganized." I gesture for him to rub the lotion into his skin. "I'm sure your acceptance letter will be waiting for you when we get back."

"If you say so, Dad!" Damon swipes at his face, making an even bigger mess.

"I do say so!" I lean over and spread the cream across his face, trying to massage it in. He briefly tolerates my intrusion before pulling back.

After Damon leaves, Jeff turns to me, grinning. "He looks pretty good. You must feel relieved."

"Yeah, it's kind of unreal." I smile. "Question is, will it last? Often, you get a quick, short-term effect and then, poof, it all goes, and you're back to square one."

"But the fact that it could resolve like this at all is a positive indicator," Jeff says like the scientist-doctor he is. "Makes me think it's more like a plumbing problem that can be fixed."

"Yes, it worked," I agree. "And so far, so good. Though between us, I already worry his belly looks marginally fuller than last week, but I'm probably hallucinating."

Jeff pauses. "You're bound to get some fluctuation before it settles out."

"Yeah." I nod. "And this means I can probably take him out to Hollywood this summer to be on *Deadwood,* which he really wants to do. He's very serious about acting and my friend Milch, the show's creator, has offered him a small part."

CHAPTER 33

Do you want 2 see my play?
If so please talk 2 me today.
Five dollars is what they say
Everyone will have 2 pay.
(Although I get a few tix free
those must go 2 family.)
But if you think you'd rather hurl
Just know in 1 scene I'm a gurl.
— From Damon's blog, June 2004

The good news is that not only has Damon been accepted into the Looking for Shakespeare summer theater program for the third year running, but he lands the choice role of Mercutio, "kinsman and friend to Romeo." It's his biggest part yet, and he's ecstatic about it. He throws himself into rehearsals and prepares excitedly for the big day.

The bad news is that by mid-June, even before rehearsals start, the positive effects of Damon's fenestration begin to unravel. It doesn't happen overnight, but the signs are unmistakable. Damon's face and belly puff up, and his albumin drops back below 3.0.

We take Damon to see Dr. Hellenbrand, who confirms the palliative effects of the fenestration seem to be wearing off. "I'm sorry. We don't know why." He shakes his head. We assume the opening has closed over, which often accounts for a reversal. But tests show the stent is holding and blood is still flowing through the opening. Instead, Damon's system seems to be reverting to its familiar protein-losing state by deliberately offsetting the positively shifting dynamics through a perverse homeostasis.

The bottom line is that the PLE is back, albeit in milder, stealthier guise, and Damon experiences a resurgent fatigue, made all the worse by his brief improvement.

Nevertheless, despite the apparent reversal, Damon still looks better than before his fenestration. He remains well ahead of where he started and seems to be having an excellent summer. So while we're disappointed the PLE has not been eliminated, we feel heartened by Damon's improved appearance and increased energy. Maybe we've reduced the threat to a manageable level? Even a steady, noncatastrophic state feels like progress.

One afternoon, I introduce Damon to a special visitor, my high school Shakespeare teacher, Irwin Wolfson, who's flown up from Florida.

A brilliant, outrageous, and big-hearted man — his outsized, Falstaffian qualities now span a girth of 265 pounds — Irwin was one of the finest teachers and best teacher friends I had. Now I want him to meet my oldest son, who's the same age I was when Irwin introduced me to *Hamlet, Macbeth, Othello,* and *King Lear.*

Damon and Irwin sit across from one another on the green couch in the family room: my small, pale, and preternaturally wise son with his leonine head and my former teacher, still smooth skinned and sleek haired, if grayer, at seventy, with a vital, pleasant-looking face marked by dark, deep-socketed eyes.

"Your dad tells me you're a Shakespearean actor?" Irwin says in a rich, resonant, and loaded voice. The extra weight makes it awkward for him to sit, but once he's shifted his huge, egg-shaped belly over his thighs, he perches on our couch like a visiting king.

"We do one play each summer," Damon says, nodding. "*Romeo and Juliet* this year."

"One of his greatest hits, a crowd-pleaser!"

Irwin nods. "You agree, Damon?"

"I can see why it's popular," Damon says as Irwin leans forward, a glint in his eye.

"Personally, I always thought *Romeo and Juliet* was much ado about nothing."

Damon grins and cocks an eyebrow, waiting to see where this is going.

"It's an early, pretty, but comparatively immature work, at least when set beside the later, greater plays," Irwin trills. "Even the great Samuel Johnson — the guy penned thirty thousand couplets; he could produce more meaningless shit than any human — found the play's strains 'polluted.' I'm guessing he meant it lacked *tragic necessity;* would you agree, Damon?"

"What about the language, Irwin, the poetry?" I protest while trying not to laugh.

"Oh, well, that's music!" Irwin nods. "Look, the man could turn a phrase. There are twenty-seven thousand words in Shakespeare. The King James Bible uses seven thousand. And I will grant you the play has its glories and riches. For anyone else, I might deign to call it a masterpiece."

Damon and I exchange smiles but Irwin just shrugs.

"It's all relative — didn't Einstein say that? Or was that my uncle Mort? Damon, you should feast on *Romeo and Juliet* as only

a sixteen-year-old can. Because it's all hor-
monal."

"Isn't the Capulet-Montague feud relevant for people your age?" Damon asks.

"Oh, methinks an arrow doth pierce my
wounded breast!" Irwin grabs his chest and
guffaws. "Now you remind me of your dad,
Damon, when he was my student — except
your father had blond hair and it was
shoulder-length. He was very popular with
the ladies, as I'm sure you are . . .

"But to answer your question, young
man!" Irwin switches into a high rhetorical
gear. "You're asking if these two youngsters,
Romeo and Juliet, beautiful and pure as the
snow, are corrupted and besmirched by a
tainted world with its long enmity? And if it
must ever thus be so?"

Damon half-nods as Irwin pauses.

"Alas, dear sweet boy, what can I say that
will neither offend truth nor violate your
father's desire to protect you? The world is
a dung heap and a cesspool, a contamina-
tion and an abomination, and man is aught
but a little bug, a gnat, a pissant! Every once
in a while someone removes the rusty pliers
from our nipple and the pain stops, briefly,
before the charnel house operations resume . . .

"But why take *my* word? As *King Lear*

shows — perhaps the summit, as well as the summation, of human expressive achievement — even if we are fortunate to be nobly born and attain a ripe age, we must lose it all, including those we most love, and be reduced to mad, blind impotence amidst a raging, pitiless storm. Bound upon 'a wheel of fire' and stretched out on the 'tough wrack of this world.' Could Willie have made it any *plainer?*"

"Irwin was never big on free will," I tell Damon. "We argued about it in class."

"Arguing? 'Twas no argument!" Irwin booms, and turns to Damon. "Your dad just hadn't lived or lost and suffered enough to understand that what you *want* the world to be and what the world *is* are two separate things." Irwin gives me a sharp, fond look before returning to Damon. "Your father was just a callow, gifted, moderately conceited kid who thought because he could get A's and get laid, and all the happy horseshit that went with it, the world was his . . . What can I tell you, Damon, except what I tell all my students? We're just not in charge. We want to be but we're not. It is the stars — the stars above govern our condition."

"So you don't believe *anything* we do makes a difference?" Damon pipes up.

"Possibly it can make a difference, at the margins — which is where most of life transpires, so it's not unimportant — but *nothing* can change the final outcome of a single fate," Irwin says. "Eventually we all die, it's just a question of *when.* And the when is part of a larger, cosmic pattern, not vouchsafed us to see in any way, shape, or form. We must simply learn to *accept* it — and I don't care what dumb religion you believe in or how many Higgs bosons you can tie on the end of your string theory."

Irwin starts declaiming:

Not a whit, we defy augury. There's a special providence in the fall of a sparrow. If it be now, 'tis not to come; if it be not to come, it will be now; if it be not now, yet it will come: the readiness is all.

"I like that. That's pretty cool." Damon bops his head. "Where's it from?"

"Well, I didn't write it!" Irwin declares. "I wish I had but I just don't have that kind of talent. Frankly, Damon, in all my years teaching, I never met anyone who did —"

"It's from *Hamlet,*" I tell Damon, recalling that I first read the play thirty years earlier with Irwin.

"Hey, why not fly down to Florida and

341

bring Damon to my *Hamlet* class!" Irwin cries. "I teach every Wednesday to an overflow crowd of old retired folks. Most can hardly move a muscle, but they hobble in every week on crutches and walkers to hear me parse the text. They love everything to do with sex and fucking — some things never change — and you know me, I just read the words . . . Many of my students were distinguished people once. Now all they want to know is, why doesn't Hamlet just stab the sucker? I guess everyone wants the truth in the end, if not before . . . My mother, who didn't have two cents but lots of sense, said to me, 'What's with this Shakespeare?' I said, 'Ma, he never lies to me' . . . So come on down to sunny Florida and let's see if the old fat fuck still has his fastball . . ."

I smile at my incorrigible teacher. "Thanks, Irwin. I'd love to bring Damon to hear you lecture. But summer's not good," I say gently. "Will you still be teaching Hamlet in the fall?"

"You kidding? I take two years over that play. Fall's fine."

"Cool. I've never been to Florida," Damon says.

CHAPTER 34

I'm Mercutio!!! Yeah it's so cool it's such an awesome role!
> — From Damon's blog, June 2004

"Nay, gentle Romeo, we must have you dance," Mercutio declares with a smile.

In *Romeo and Juliet,* I watch my son onstage and for the first time I feel like an admiring theatergoer as much as an indulgent father. Damon burrows into the text and makes the material his own.

It's not just my own biased view. A successful actress friend I've invited turns to me early on and says, "Bloody hell, he can teach *me* about acting Shakespeare!"

Partly, as always, it's the casting. Damon shares many traits with Mercutio and he plays all these qualities to the hilt, stealing every scene with his clever banter and ribaldry. And Shakespeare helps by giving him the best lines.

But Damon also displays growing artistry and maturation. While many of the performers race through their lines like a dutiful catechism, Damon takes his time and savors the words one by one, teasing out their full meaning and never shying away from the Bard's frank sexual innuendo: "If love be rough with you, be rough with love. Prick love for pricking, and you beat love down."

When the notorious showdown with Tybalt begins, I worry about Damon's ability to hold his own. The smallest person on that stage, he's been leaping about and verbally skewering everyone, but now the scene calls for direct physical confrontation. Damon's baseline energy is low and it's hard to see how his dandified, prattling Mercutio will *ever* fight.

But though a head shorter than the taunting Tybalt, Damon's Mercutio steps right up to the enemy Capulet and stares him down. The sight of true fearlessness can only arouse fear in those not so unburdened, and Damon's face is chillingly, defiantly *unafraid.* He draws his sword and forces Tybalt back with a powerful kick and parry, quickly gaining the upper hand.

"Arrghh! Raahh!" Damon's thrusts are accompanied by loud grunts, in case anyone missed that he's winning. But when Romeo

tries to stop the fight, Tybalt, "under Romeo's arm, thrusts Mercutio in." It's an unfair attack, unwittingly abetted by Romeo, but it fatally wounds Mercutio and sends him to the ground.

As he confronts the horrific specter of his unjust, premature demise, Mercutio repeatedly curses both the Capulets and the Montagues. Damon underplays the scene — he sits slumped on the ground, pale, wounded, and caustic, his lolling head cradled by Romeo until detachment gives way to tragic recognition and bitter resentment at his galling fate:

"A plague o' both your houses! Zounds, a dog, a rat, a mouse, a cat, to scratch a man to death! . . . They have made worms' meat of me."

It's an unspeakable moment as Damon lies mortally wounded on the stage at the end of Act II.

"He can audition for us anytime!" my actress friend says, smiling, as we all applaud.

CHAPTER 35

I would just like to say that for having 2 days planning My Party Rocked The Hizouse!!! Yes I said hizouse sue me! Yes yes it did there was much sex (but none of it involving me . . . 😲 what a shocker lol . . . ah self mockery where would I be with out it).
— From Damon's blog, summer 2004

Although Damon continues to socialize with his growing legion of friends from theater and school throughout the summer — and to hold the biggest and coolest sleepover parties at our house, aided by our easygoing attitude (since we want him to have fun with the least exertion) and abetted by the fact he's a chick magnet, on friendly if largely platonic terms with the most beautiful girls, which draws all the guys too — Damon's summer is not all fun and games.

This would-be eleventh grader has several classes and two New York State Regents exams to make up. It's a tall order, but Damon has always kept pace in school until this year, and he's determined to catch up. The fenestration seems to have given him a chance to regain lost ground and to rejoin his cohort for the fall semester.

A tutor, Andre Lawe, comes to our house four days a week to work with Damon. A Columbia University chemistry graduate preparing at twenty-five to be a school principal, Andre is sensitive to Damon's medical ups and downs. Tutor and tutee breeze through the work when Damon is up to it, and when he's not, they set it aside for long heart-to-hearts.

"We chat about everything — life, music, relationships, movies, politics, books," Andre says in his mellow way. "Damon teaches me stuff every day."

Sometimes I come home from work and find Damon and Andre giggling and carrying on in the kitchen like two mischievous schoolboys. They are cooking up science experiments for Damon's chem lab and the whole place stinks. Shealagh has long since fled upstairs, after supplying the two principal investigators with pots and measuring cups, and I can see why. Having burned moth balls to demonstrate conversion principles, they seem to be cultivating mold in the sink and setting off a series of not-so-controlled explosions.

Damon gets through the Math Regents, the chem lab, and global history, leaving only the killer Chemistry Regents, which has a 50 percent fail rate. I plan to fly him to the *Deadwood* film set right after the test, as his reward and, hopefully, his incentive.

Damon is excited about the chance to appear on a major television show. He's been watching the critically acclaimed, X-rated western series on HBO in preparation, with special dispensation from his mother. Above his desk is a handwritten note from the show's creator and head writer, David Milch: "Dear Damon, I've written a part for a 16-year old red headed boy. Come out to Los Angeles and be on *Deadwood*."

It's a rare invitation but *Deadwood* is still a month away and New York is broiling in August, so we drive up to Martha's Vineyard, a summer tradition. Damon signs up for sailing lessons in Edgartown and makes impressive progress, learning technique, maneuvers, points of sail, how to read the water and dock.

"I can see he's serious about it," the instructor, a licensed captain who usually looks askance at his spoiled summer clientele, says approvingly.

Damon's health has worsened since last summer, and any physical activity now seems to stress his system. But he still manages to go clamming and fishing and to swim in the ocean with us, even if Sam challenges him on the Long Bridge and in other small ways. But on the Flying Horses and in the gaming arcade, Damon remains the reigning champion and undisputed leader.

Before leaving the Vineyard, Damon gets to do a solo sail in Edgartown harbor, demonstrating mastery of the basics at the end of class. The instructor rides with the other student but Damon, the star pupil, is allowed to skipper the boat by himself despite the busy harbor traffic.

He wears an orange life jacket and racy dark sunglasses and starts with a steady hand on the tiller. Everything appears smooth until he has to scramble and tack around a tight turn. The big boat wobbles and begins to stall — its wood groans and the sails fluff as if it's lost its headwind and might actually head *backward* — when Damon pushes the tiller toward the sail and heaves himself from the port to the starboard side with textbook timing.

The canvas fills again, and the boat resumes sailing in the right direction.

I watch from the dock as Damon steers the swift-moving vessel along the active harbor, a small, capable boy standing in the stern and piloting his large craft with impressive dexterity. He's checking a hundred details and making constant adjustments but keeping it all on a true course. As he glides past us, I spot the budding pride of a natural helmsman on his keen face.

"Yup, he's got the hang of it," the instructor says, nodding.

CHAPTER 36

Hey hey, it's Damon here giving you all a live update straight from Hollywood. lol. Yeah, so this is my second day here and I've already pulled almost an all nighter (my dad dragged me home) on the set of *Deadwood* which is an awesome set. The town is like life size and you can (and I did a couple of times) get lost. Oh for those of you who I forgot 2 tell (apologies) here is the deal: There is this show called *Deadwood* on HBO which is really cool. It's like this new style western complete with drinking gambling violence and whores lol. So my dad happens 2 be friends with the creator of the show who said he'd put me on. Which is awesome. And I just found out yesterday that I'm probably gonna get a speaking role which is very cool. Yeah.

— From Damon's blog, August 2004

Melody Ranch Studios, where the 1870s

western series *Deadwood* is being shot, sits in Santa Clarita, California, in an arid canyon thirty-five miles northwest of Los Angeles. The location, site of such classic westerns as *High Noon,* was once a ranch owned by the singing cowboy Gene Autry. Now it's been converted by the best set designers and builders in Hollywood into one of the largest working sets, complete with a realistic mining town, a huge interior soundstage, a fifty-person crew with a hundred extras, plus twelve horses, five wagons, three buckboards, and one ox. Not to mention numerous offices, trailers, dining facilities, trucks, cranes, cameras, and all the standard backlot infrastructure.

When Damon and I first arrive — it's a forty-minute drive from Santa Monica — we're amazed you can walk through this town as if it were real. It boasts authentic mining camp streets and period buildings with sides and rears, not just facades, so you can wind your way through the dangerous back alleys and shoot, stab, or fornicate with anyone you meet.

Sheriff Bullock's new house sits atop Main Street while farther down Main is the Gem Saloon, where the notorious Al Swearengen dispenses whiskey, whores, and his own justice. The murderously charismatic

Swearengen is Bullock's chief antagonist and sometime ally, the pair embodying two sides of the same ambivalent need for order that underlies this complex drama and its devil's-bargain vision of American history. (Almost every character is based on a real person, not just Calamity Jane and Wild Bill Hickok.)

A hotel, doctor's office, and one-room newspaper offer temporary relief from more whorehouses, gambling dens, saloons, and shanties. These dwellings are interspersed with crude shops: a dry goods store, bakery, eatery, cooperage, boot maker, and butcher. Everything in this mining camp looks primitive and grubby, the naked sun beats down on the unpaved streets, and bloody animal skins hang everywhere.

David Milch, the man whose darkly moralistic vision has brought this world to life — the show's creator, head writer, and executive producer, as well as the famously profane Emmy-winning writer of such hits as *Hill Street Blues* and *NYPD Blue* — slouches tautly but amiably on a shaded part of Main Street when we first show up. Milch, bantering with the cinematographer James Glennon, stops to answer a question from set, receives fresh pages from a script supervisor, and finishes his story before walking over to give me a hug. He extends a very formal, courtly hand to Damon.

"It's an honor to finally meet you, Damon! Your dad's told me so much about you — only the good stuff is true, right?"

David wears his trademark faded black T-shirt and gold-rimmed glasses. He still looks lanky and oddly boyish as he nears sixty, an impressive, if largely genetic, feat, given the highly publicized abuse he's heaped on his body from decades of various addictions. A brilliant, twitchy, and complex guy, David has a big heart to go with his big talent and is a magnanimous host.

"Damon, that big camera you're staring at is for the day's first setup — can you believe this business? No one works until six P.M.!" David smiles. "But the desert sun is unforgiving, so you be careful, okay?" He sends a PA for sun cream and orders Damon watched. "Keep this boy out of the sun or I'll break your balls and chop 'em up!" David says with a grin.

David introduces Damon to his wife, Rita, and to the lead actor Ian McShane:

"Hey, Ian, say hello to Damon, he's also an actor. We're gonna write him a part . . . And, Damon, these lovely ladies are gonna dress you up."

As the wardrobe ladies fuss over Damon,

I note it's in the nineties, even after five P.M., and the glaring sun, still high and raw, burns like a blowtorch. Damon's face is hot and flushed, even if he's too stimulated to notice.

"Rita, please take them to my trailer to cool down!" David hands us off to his wife, a painter and the mother of their three kids. "Damon, I'll see you later, pal."

Rita leads us to a posh "Rio Suite" from the production vehicle company Movie Movers. I make Damon take a water bottle from the well-stocked fridge. He sips, absorbing all around him, including David's notorious last-minute script "inserts." The room hums with air-conditioning.

"Wow, Damon, you do have amazing red hair!" Rita smiles. Damon's vivid locks have already sparked admiration from many quarters. Now Rita chats with Damon and catches up with me until we hear voices outside.

"That's Dave. He's here!" Rita winks.

David is escorted wherever he goes, and his movements on the lot are closely tracked by headset-wearing staff. But the trailer is private.

"Hi, Damon. Got all you need, pal?" David enters and shuts the door behind him.

"Yeah, it's nice and cool in here." Damon smiles on the sofa. "Very comfortable."

"Better be! Know what they *charge* for these suites . . . ?" David goes to the sink and swishes mouthwash. "So, Damon, you're in eleventh grade now?" David spits and grins. He taught at Yale and still has a touch of the assistant professor, but he's also the head writer and gently probes Damon about the kind of person, and actor, he is.

"I've mostly done Shakespeare and musicals, but also some comedy," Damon says.

"What, no television! And you're sixteen and call yourself an actor?" David deadpans.

"I'm still learning!" Damon retorts, and they share a laugh.

The PA knocks on the trailer door. "It's time, David! Crew call is for six!"

David turns to Damon. "I've been summoned. Want to ride over with me?"

"Sure," Damon says. They descend the trailer and step into a white golf cart.

David pushes the silent starter motor and sits back. "Okay, go ahead."

"But I've never driven anything but a bumper car before!" Damon protests.

"Well, this is the same — forward, reverse, accelerator — just don't bump anything."

Damon, nervous and excited, steps on reverse and almost crashes into a tractor.

"I warned you!" Damon laughs as David

stiffens in the seat beside him.

"Try it again," David says calmly. Damon makes it across the road this time but over-steers, swinging in erratic loops and jolting them both in their seats.

"Sorry!" Damon giggles as David braces against the dash, ignoring his beeper.

A PA trots over with pointed urgency. "Everyone's waiting on set, David!"

David nods but stays put, displaying serene patience as he sits beside Damon. It's a side of David, who is notoriously fidgety and abrupt, I've rarely seen.

Damon finally masters the controls and proudly drops David off on set.

"Thank you, Damon." David salutes him before the waiting crew.

Main Street starts to fill with a colorful hubbub as the costumed cast trickles in for the six P.M. call. Production runs final checks, while the crew mans its stations.

A great sense of playful adventure hangs in the air, tempered only by the ticking of the five-million-dollars-an-episode money clock.

Damon stands rapt and watches as it takes the entire twelve-hour shift to complete a single scene. One actor keeps blowing his lines, and there are technical issues, like keeping all the torches lit and repeatedly hosing down the dusty road so it can reflect this light. Plus actor queries about why a character would do this or say that, followed by Milch's eloquent riffs on motivation and plot with a nod to history, psychology, philosophy, criminology, and modern culture.

It seems slow and drawn out but what Damon is witnessing from his perch near the director — a spiky-haired New Yorker, Ed Bianchi — is the nuts and bolts of film-making.

"It's so different from theater," Damon says. "The actors do it all in short takes!"

Damon loves all the rituals of being on set, including that "lunch" is always served six hours after crew call, even if it's midnight when we all go to the giant tented mess hall.

"Grab a tray and come with me, Damon," David instructs. The cast remains in period costume as we line up for hot food. We carry our trays to cafeteria-style tables filled by hordes of ravenous extras with filthy faces and bevies of statuesque, candy-eyed women in low-cut dresses. Damon is on cloud nine — he sits at David's table with several of the lead actors, talking shop in this carnival atmosphere — and he doesn't want to leave.

Outside time means little in this buzzing,

brightly lit world.

The first night I let my mesmerized son linger on the set until four thirty A.M. before I drag him off to bed. In the next week, we go regularly to Melody Ranch though I try to get him back by midnight so he doesn't exhaust himself. I still rise by six A.M. and get in almost an entire day's work before I wake Damon up around one or two P.M. He rarely wakes by himself.

Sometimes when I watch Damon sleep, he looks so slight and retracted under the big covers, his pale body collapsing in on itself, that I start to worry again. But then I note his belly and face look less bloated, so we've made progress. And his improved appearance bodes well for his acting debut, assuming that happens, which is not a foregone conclusion.

"Will I really get my own part?" Damon asks after that first day, rightly uncertain.

"David assured me you'll have speaking lines, but he hasn't written them yet, and he's got a lot on his plate," I reply. "Plus, nothing is ever easy or certain in this town, no matter who you know . . . So we'll have to play it by ear, okay?"

"Sure, Dad. It's cool just being here."

"Why'd you let me sleep so late?" Damon

asks the moment I wake him. But he knows.

"Don't forget your meds and your shot!" I remind him as goes into the bathroom. Damon now injects growth hormone daily, but he's grown an inch or two, so he's happy to do it.

After his regimen, Damon quickly brushes his teeth, dons shorts and a T-shirt, grabs his cell phone, and stands by the door, all in under five minutes.

"Okay, I'm ready!" he says.

I bring along his sun hat, which he always "forgets," but I let him eat breakfast in the car to save time.

We stick the latest CD in, put down the top, and take off. Damon enjoys my driving and leans forward in his seat as we zoom past one vehicle after another.

The wind picks up in the speeding convertible, blowing Damon's hair like wildfire in the snapping breeze. He's strapped in, but the propeller force of his flapping hair looks like it could catapult him into the sky. He grins at me and his blue eyes dance with the thrill of roaring power. I gun the engine and we rocket forward and experience the rush of pure velocity together. It's a scream!

The instant we reach Melody Ranch, the bond between Damon and me is broken and he can't wait to ditch me and join the cast. I take my laptop and go work in David's trailer.

I make occasional forays onto the set, but early on it's clear that even when Damon and I walk onto the same lot, we go through different doors. I'm oriented toward writing and writers, whereas for Damon, it's about actors and acting.

"You seem to fit right in," I say. "Is there a secret password or handshake?"

"No, Dad, we're just actors. But some of these guys are *really* good."

All the actors in the show welcome Damon. Ian McShane, who plays the fearsome Al Swearengen, reveals to Damon the gentlest disposition, along with a friendly Manchester accent, beneath that hard face and glaring eyes. "And how is young Master Damon today? You keeping that sweet peaches-and-cream out of this bloody awful sun?" McShane smiles and rubs Damon's back.

But it's Paula Malcomson, a gifted Irish firebrand and the show's blond poster whore, who adopts Damon from day one. "Let's get you out of this fuckin' heat, Damon! I got good AC in my trailer and a new copy of Yeats, the later poetry. No sane person should be walkin' out in this shit storm. They don't pay *that* well."

Paula and Damon hang out. They discuss literature, theater, life. They share confidences. One day I see them going into her trailer and realize they even *look* alike: Paula is petite and also has pale skin and luminous blue eyes, while her yellow-blond hair has the same intensity as Damon's coppery thatch.

"You could be brother and sister!" I tease them.

But the male crew members start a different rumor on set about all the time these two spend behind closed doors: "Hear what happened? Trixie got Damon!"

When Damon steps from Paula's trailer, he emerges with a new mystique. He blogs for his pals about it: "The cast is really cool especially the main whore aka Paula (Trixie). She was really nice and sorta showed me around and we also hung out in her trailer . . . NO! You people with your dirty minds you disgust me lol jk."

Another person who connects deeply with Damon is Gary Leffew, a stuntman and a world-champion bull rider. When Milch sought real-life cowboys to give him a flavor of that bygone world, all hands pointed to Gary Leffew, rodeo hall-of-famer and famous hell-raiser, as the nearest modern-day embodiment.

"Hey, amigos, when you only work for eight seconds a day, you got lots of free time for gettin' into mischief," Gary explains to Damon and me.

After we're friends, Gary tells me about the first day he met Damon.

"I seen this young boy standin' on the set in his own bright pool of light. It come off him like a glow!" Gary says. "He had a real powerful life force shinin' out — I tell ya, I never seen one that strong, it was just dazzling! I could watch it move with him whenever he moved . . . Man, I just had to go up and meet Damon!"

Gary takes Damon and me to the L.A. Equestrian Center, where he stables his horses for the cast to practice on. We mount and enter Griffith Park.

Damon and I are used to English riding and must adapt to the Western style. And Gary has no helmets for us. But it's Gary's wild, zippy horses that require the biggest adjustment. They don't just trot or canter but *gallop* up the twisting hillsides, nicking other riders and nearly plunging us over the ravine.

"Whoa! Stop!" we shout as they chase blindly after Gary's horse.

Gary is a great bull rider, the daredevil of rodeo, and can stay upright on any animal.

But Damon and I are amateurs, and when not hanging on for dear life myself, I worry about Damon, who has a listing seat and little apparent strength or control. But Damon has good instincts, and when his horse gallops off unbidden, Damon bounces along in the saddle, tilting crookedly and riding it out like a rag doll until his horse slows down or one of us gives him a hand. Once I have to chase Damon down and grab his reins until his pony, throwing a fit, calms down.

Gary sits atop his horse with his perfect riding posture, chuckling. "Yeah, he'll do that every so often. He gets kinda feisty, but he don't mean nothin' by it."

It's a beautiful, rolling park with peaks and canyons and switchback trails.

A coyote appears and spooks Gary's horse, who rears and bolts, throwing Gary briefly off balance and sending Damon's horse and mine fleeing as well. There's a moment of pure panic until Gary manages to bring his horse back under control about a foot from the edge of a ravine, while I try to box in Damon's pony.

Fortunately, it's only a close call, but it makes me realize that although Gary is the best rider in the world, even he can't protect us. Damon and I must stay on full alert and fend for ourselves. Which may be one reason we wanted to come here with Gary — a paradox Gary, in his cowboy way, has grasped from the start.

As we climb, we see the modern sprawl, from downtown Los Angeles to Burbank with the Hollywood sign above. Yet we're enveloped by deep nature.

"Can we ride up to the sign?" Damon says with a cheeky smile.

"I never done it but I don't see why not," Gary says, impressed. "But we gotta hurry if we want to find our way back before dark."

We twist and wind our way up through the dense brush and watch the city drop away. It grows quiet and windy as we ascend the forested mountain, with steep escarpments and dramatic ravines. Even our horses fall silent as we round the last, dusty curve of the trail and come out over a high, narrow ridge.

There's just enough light as we overlook the valley. Across from us is a summit topped by a transmission tower, while a big range of mountains stretches on the horizon. Between lie sprawling urban centers with tiny, twinkling lights.

The cities of men look like a small thing from here, a glitch in the landscape.

We pat our horses' manes and stroke their damp flanks.

"Rockin' awesome!" Damon beams atop his golden pony, hatless and proud as all get-out.

CHAPTER 37

"It's my life! And I don't want to live forever
. . . I just want to live my life!"
— Some song I can't remember
at the moment
— From Damon's blog, August 2004

We return to the *Deadwood* set and it's still unclear whether Damon will get his part. Time is running out — Damon has to get back for school — but we still face several obstacles.

"You need a work permit," I explain to Damon. "An actor under eighteen must be an enrolled student with a C average but you had home tutoring the previous semester, so we don't have your report card."

"Maybe my tutor could send in my grades?" Damon says.

David Milch is also concerned about Damon's health. Like many people on the set, David has developed a real fondness for

Damon. Unlike them, he knows about his illness.

"You sure he's up to this? We're in a record-setting, ball-shriveling heat wave and Damon's been looking a little pale to me. I don't want to push him —"

"Damon always looks pale," I counter, smiling. "And despite the heat, he can't wait to show his stuff. He really wants to do this, David!"

Finally, there is the business of a major studio production with a tight schedule and money riding on every shot. David has power, but it's not unlimited.

There's a day when it seems we won't make it. The production is behind schedule, and David isn't even on the lot. Our return flight is booked, and it feels like our window may have closed. Paula has no scenes today, so she's away, and Gary also has a day off.

"It's a hundred and one degrees!" the PA informs us at noon. Even the Gem Saloon, where "action" and "going again" echo all day, feels depleted. The snow-cone maker has melted.

At lunch we sit in the wilting mess hall with A. C. Lyles, a dapper eighty-six-year-old man who comes to the set every day dressed in a dark suit and tie, no matter how hot it is. Lyles, who's worked at Paramount for over sixty years and knew everyone, from John Barrymore and James Cagney to Ronald Reagan, is a living link with old Hollywood.

"Don't worry about your part; you're special, I can always tell!" Lyles says to Damon. "And David's a genius. He'll make it happen!"

Sure enough, by evening word comes that David has returned and he and his staff are working on Damon's lines. We know it's real because there's a ripple of excitement from wardrobe and makeup, big fans of Damon. We also hear from production and writing with more precise instructions.

Damon's status changes instantly. He becomes someone to watch.

His actor friends drag him to the popular Friday lottery, held under a big tree with all the cast and crew, from star to gofer, assembled.

The lottery is a weekly tradition, in which David hands out thousands of dollars from his own pocket in cash prizes, ranging from $100 to $500. It's a big, fun morale builder and a welcome weekend bonus to support staff and crew who earn modest scale wages.

"Five hundred dollars goes to — John Vitteli. John, get your ass up here!" David barks. The lottery is vintage Milch, because not only has David become rich from TV writing, but he's also wildly generous, carrying wads of cash and doling out hundred-dollar bills like candy to doormen, waiters, valets. He loves scattering chips from his winnings.

"One hundred dollars goes to" — David reaches into the hat — "Damon Weber!"

Blushing, a surprised Damon walks through the cheering throng to receive his prize.

"Man, some guys get all the luck!" David, who owns racehorses and gambles, grumbles affably as Damon comes up. He pats him warmly on the back.

Damon returns and shows me the $100 bill. "What do I do with this, Dad?"

"Whatever you want," I reply, but Damon isn't satisfied. "Okay, let's use it to buy David a thank-you present," I say. "Word is he wrote you a scene."

When we finally receive the script pages for Damon, we are very pleased.

"I got seven lines of dialogue with Sheriff Bullock's son!" Damon exclaims.

"Yes, it's a small, beautifully crafted scene — a brief idyll amid all that grimness," I remark. "Two young boys who glimpse the rare chance of friendship before it vanishes."

"My character is called *Damon,*" Damon

notes. "And my father, a gold prospector Gary plays, is called *Damon's Dad.* How do you like that, Dad?" Damon grins at me. "I got a real part . . ."

The next twenty-four hours are very exciting as we prepare for Damon's debut.

I feel like an aide entrusted with a young celebrity.

Damon himself is walking on air. He looks taller, more glamorous, more chosen.

He carries the script wherever he goes and studies it. Learning lines is something he knows, and seven lines is a piece of cake. I give him my scene notes and he nods politely.

We get several calls the night before from a diligent PA on the graveyard shift.

"Damon's first up on the call sheet, so we need him by eight thirty A.M.," he says.

"Fine," I reply.

Two hours later, he calls again. "Sorry, but can you bring him to set at seven A.M.?"

"Sure," I say, then hang up and turn to Damon. "That's a five thirty A.M. wake-up call for us!"

Still, it's flattering to be the focus of so much effort and attention. We can feel the gears turning on Damon's behalf as he becomes part of a powerful system.

All evening, I can see him mouthing words

from the script and trying out different angles. He's rehearsing. A few times, I catch him grinning quietly to himself. He's happy and full of purpose, living in a world he cares about.

We go into the small outdoor pool before hitting the sack. Damon has been more active in the water on this trip, a good sign. He dives for plastic rings and swims between my legs. We toss a soggy foam football back and forth under the twinkling stars.

As we exit the pool, I notice how regal he looks in his big white terry bathrobe. When we ride the elevator, it seems other people also stare at Damon like he's someone whose name they should know.

As we get ready for bed, I stick my head out of the bathroom and catch him injecting himself. He's twisting across his trunk to insert the needle into his thigh, and his exposed torso looks very swollen and pasty.

Damon finishes and lets his pajama top cover his flank. Instantly, he's Damon again — the handsome boy they'll shoot. He flashes me a hard, furtive glance, as if to say this is one more insult, but he can manage it. And we agree, without a word, not to discuss it.

I lean over and kiss my star in the making

good night.

"Sweet dreams, D-man."

CHAPTER 38

My dad's friend the executive producer/
unofficial writer/unofficial director (it's basically all his show) is also very interesting.
He gets around the set in a golf cart and
changes the script last minute which some
actors aren't always thrilled about. lol.
— From Damon's blog, August 2004

We're on the freeway by six A.M. and it's
blissfully free of traffic.

The sky is clear and the rugged San Ga-
briel Mountains glisten along the Pacific
Coast Range. I buy Damon fresh strawber-
ries, which he loves, and watch him nibble
on the luscious fruit, smiling dreamily, as
we zip out to Santa Clarita in a red convertible for his screen debut. I don't know if it
gets much better than this.

We arrive on the lot at seven A.M. sharp.
The PA, a stocky kid called Kenny, greets
us. "Thanks so much for coming on time!

Can I get you any food or drink? *Anything?*"

The day of deference has begun. Kenny leads us to a small day trailer with a stepladder, part of a long Star Waggons unit. The name "Damon" is on the door, which makes my son feel rightly special.

Next to Damon's trailer is a trailer with "Damon's Dad" on it. I smile but don't go in. For today, it belongs to Gary Leffew.

Kenny leads us to Sheriff Bullock's new house, which sits on an elevated site dominating Main Street. Damon's scene unfolds here.

The multi-gabled wood house is fronted by steep stairs that wind down to street level. Halfway down the stairs is a dry "creek," which the crew is filling from a hose. Various camera and lighting assistants position large filters and screens to deal with the anticipated glare. The air is still cool but the open desert sky is cloudless, and you can sense the gathering force of the rising sun.

The director Steve Shill has Damon walk through each shot to work out the markers.

David Milch arrives in his ever-present black T-shirt and five o'clock shadow, looking like he's slept on the lot. He's trailed by the usual retinue. David flips through the script pages. "Cut these lines on page six

375

and add this!" David tells Shill. Damon has now been on set long enough to grasp that in television, unlike film or theater, the head writer/executive producer is top dog. David utters a few more instructions before loping over.

"Ready for your big day?" He gives Damon an affectionate pat but we can see he's distracted. There's much to do before shooting commences.

We go to the tent for breakfast and get ham and cheese omelets from the short-order cook. Everyone treats Damon like a VIP, which is what you turn into when you have a scene coming up. Kenny brings forms to sign from the Screen Actors Guild and Department of Justice.

Two women from wardrobe drape Damon in a burlap shirt, filthy blue overalls, and black lace-up boots, topped by a wool cap. The fashionistas have admired my son from day one and beam at his costume. "You rock, Damon!"

Next Damon is led around the corner to makeup, a long, narrow trailer fitted out like a chic hair salon. Four leather-and-chrome chairs swivel opposite four large mirrors, while wigs, brushes, and makeup kits line the counter. Tim Olyphant, the lanky leading man who plays Sheriff Seth Bullock, is sitting in the last chair, being fussed over by a team of makeup artists and enjoying it.

A trimly goateed man in a white shirt meticulously roughs up Damon's hair with his hands and fluffs it up with fine instruments. "You've got great hair — we don't have to do much!" Two female assistants smile and nod while a younger makeup guy in a *Scorpion King* T-shirt systematically begins applying a coat of dirt to Damon's face, his hands, and the back of his neck.

Damon steps out of the makeup trailer looking like a Norman Rockwell illustration from a Mark Twain novel. Tom Sawyer in South Dakota, circa 1870. A staff photographer takes a publicity shot of Damon standing beside a horse.

Main Street is busier now and the sun is already heating things up, though it's not yet nine A.M. Everyone sheds layers. The director, down to shirtsleeves, remarks, "Crikey, it's going to be a bloody scorcher!"

The big 35 millimeter Panavision camera has been mounted on a tripod on Bullock's front porch. The crew positions giant white, black, and silver panels around the camera to try to balance the streaming light. It's a tricky, moving target. They improvise, using ladders to hide auxiliary white lights under the burlap shade of an adjacent house.

Dozens of costumed extras flow through the town and begin to fill the street with the bustle of daily nineteenth-century life. Horses and wagons clop by while weary-looking men sit outside their tents with rifles slung across their laps and chopped wood at their feet.

Damon rehearses climbing into the wagon and Gary, playing Damon's father in a shabby gold-prospector outfit, gives him a practice ride up Main. "Gonna be a long hot day, son!" Gary says. "You best rest up 'fore we light out."

Josh Eriksson, who's playing William opposite Damon, arrives, though he's not in costume yet. His script dangles in one hand. The director introduces the two boys — they quickly size each other up while exchanging polite greetings — and then he rehearses them.

Damon already looks warm and stiff in his heavy costume — the experienced actors wisely wait until the last minute to suit up — and we all know it's going to get much worse.

The forecast is for triple digits, possibly the hottest day yet.

Paula Malcomson arrives and sits on the shaded saloon porch. Paula is not shooting today but has driven out to support Damon.

Her hair is loose and she wears a casual pink top. "Hey, Damon!" She gives a dazzling wave.

"Hey." Damon blushes and smiles at his cheering section.

"D-man, drink!" I hand him a water bottle. His lips are dry and he's dehydrated. He obliges me with a perfunctory swig but he's got more important things on his mind.

The lighting crew continues juggling the angled screens by Bullock's house, trying to keep up with the blazing sun. "Put some Kinos down," the cinematographer, James Glennon, instructs. Glennon, a bulky, shambling figure, employs a first assistant to look through the viewfinder, a second to pull focus, and a third to move the camera on its tracks, but his keen eyes don't miss a mote of dust if it might show on-screen.

David Milch grins with delight at Damon's costume and makeup. "You look fantastic, Damon!" Then his scowl returns. "But it's over ninety degrees and not even ten A.M.! I want you to keep drinking and stay out of the sun as much as possible. I'll have a PA standing by with an umbrella for you at all times . . . Otherwise, just have a good time and try to enjoy yourself. You're a member of the guild now!" David notes.

"What does being a member of the Screen

Actors Guild mean?" Damon asks.

"You get a minimum daily rate and health
—" David starts explaining, then stops. "It
means next year when you come out here,
you'll have an agent and you'll shake me
down for a lot more money!"

Hordes of extras now populate every inch
of Main Street. A PA quickly tops off the
creek. They want it brimming, but the sun
keeps evaporating the water.

Damon and Josh get into position, Josh at
the top of the stairs, where he's just emerged
from Sheriff Bullock's house, and Damon
facing him halfway down the stairs.

Steve Shill checks with David Milch and
yells, "Action!" and the two boys, along with
other actors, run through the whole scene
once as the camera rolls:

Damon: You just move here?
William: Just yesterday.
Damon: I watched the sheriff build this
house.
William: Mr. Bullock is my Pa's brother
that married my Ma after my Pa was
killed, so now he's my Pa and my
uncle.
Damon: Big trout lives in that deep part
down there.

Damon's Dad, a wiry gold prospector

380

*down at the ribbons drives up in a buck-
board.*

Damon's Dad: Damon!
Damon (over his shoulder, to his father):
Comin'. (*to William*) My Pa and me are
going to Oregon to grow apples.
William: Are you coming back?
Damon: Pa says, we ain't never coming
back. *Descends one step.* Keep your
eye on that rainbow. I call him Jumbo.
*Damon climbs into the wagon beside his
father and they begin to ride up Main
Street and out of Deadwood. William and
Damon watch each other.*
Bullock (coming out of his house):
Mornin' William.
William: That boy is going to Oregon.

*Close up on Damon looking back at Wil-
liam as his father drives them away.*

Although the scene will now be broken
down into individual lines, and parts of
lines, and shot many times from multiple
angles, with many takes and retakes, a
spreading murmur can be heard after this
initial run-through. The precipitating cause
is Damon.

The only person other than me who does

not look completely surprised by his performance is Paula, who is already smiling and thinking of the notes she wants to give Damon. Otherwise, there are many open mouths on the set.

Until this moment, everyone, including David himself, had assumed the showrunner was doing a favor for a friend's kid and they'd have to get through this with the least amount of damage or embarrassment. It's not an unheard-of occurrence on a film set.

But now the air is charged.

Damon has them floored.

You can *feel* the buzz. Glennon, a renowned veteran, trudges over to me and says, "Congratulations! You can go into semi-retirement. That boy is really good — he's a natural!" He smiles in his dour way. "Tell your wife your kid will never be out of work in this business."

Glennon's assessment seems to be shared by other observers. They whisper excitedly among themselves. Several walk over to me and quietly express their admiration for this unexpectedly self-possessed young actor.

"He's been acting since he was five," I try to explain. "He knows what he's doing."

David Milch harbors a pensive, dawning half smile. He's been rooting for Damon, but he didn't expect this. I tried to tell him, but I'm the father. David had originally invited me to be on his show — "Come on out and we'll slap a pair of chaps on you and put you up on a horse" — when I suggested substituting my son, a real actor, and David wrote his note to Damon. Now it appears as if Milch knew what he was doing all along — giving a gifted young actor his first major break.

Once Damon's acting bona fides have been established and the pleasant surprise has worn off, there's still a big scene to shoot and lots of hard work to do. It will take a couple of hours, with the temperature rising steeply, in alarming increments, as we approach noon.

By ten thirty A.M. it's 95 degrees and by eleven it's 98 degrees. At eleven twenty we break into triple digits and by eleven forty-five a PA informs me that it's 104 degrees, the hottest day of the summer.

Everyone who's not in the scene or working runs for cover, mopping their brow and guzzling water. We are being cooked on the valley floor, with the mountains sealing in the heat. I wear shorts and a T-shirt but the toxic sweat drips off me, even in the shade.

Damon has to stand on the exposed steps and run through his scene in heavy costume and makeup as the sun reaches its zenith.

After each take, a PA steps up and holds a large blue umbrella over Damon, who looks like Little Lord Fauntleroy in dirty overalls, but the moment he hears "Action!" Damon steps back and replays his scene without flagging or complaining. He takes direction well, and he does not fluff his lines.

Early on, Paula Malcomson asks me if she can give Damon some notes.

"Go for it," I reply.

Paula trots out to the blazing steps, pulling Damon aside to confer between takes. They form a classic tableau, the lithe, studious, blond-tressed actress huddling with her young actor friend, her arms crossed over her soft pink blouse while his capped head tilts down to listen. Two serious students of the craft, sharing and comparing.

After, Paula won't reveal what she said. "It's private but I'll tell you one fuckin' thing, I got as much to learn from him as he does from me!" She studies Damon on the monitor, donning brown eyeglasses and clapping on headphones to catch every nuance.

David Milch sits off to the side and studies the same monitor in a contemplative self-entwined pose. He's happy with what he sees but also worried about Damon, the heat, and existential issues.

David calls a time-out to give everyone a break from the sun. "Let's take five!"

Damon comes over and flops down in a brown canvas chair. He's hot and flushed but dripping with pride. He drinks from a water bottle with lordly gusto.

"How is it out there, Damon?" David checks in with his young actor.

"It's fun!" Damon says.

David nods with a dyspeptic smile. "You're doing great but I want you to take more time with your lines. Let yourself be awkward and try to fill the silences with more longing and disappointment," David says. "These two boys really wanted to be friends and are full of regret that it won't happen."

A makeup person dabs Damon's sweating face, and then David escorts Damon to his mark, walking beside his young actor and giving him more tips.

Under David's vigilant gaze, Damon pushes his part emotionally.

"Excellent!" David's face breaks into a small, appreciative smile.

The hardest part for Damon is the physical strain. It's bad enough to wear heavy overalls; a thick, rough shirt; and high leather boots for hours in the unrelenting heat. But what almost undoes him is the repeated action surrounding his last line of dialogue.

Damon must deliver the line in two parts: walking down the stairs after the first half ("Keep your eye on that rainbow") then stopping for the second part ("I call him Jumbo") before turning and hustling up into the waiting carriage with Gary. This last move demands a big effort as Damon grabs onto the seat rail, heaves himself up from street level, and clambers in. And it all has to look completely natural and fluid in the 104 degree blaze.

I know the enormous effort this seemingly routine action demands from Damon and how hard he's trying not to show it. I worry his cover could be blown if it goes on too long. So far no one, other than David, suspects a thing, but it's pushing Damon to the limit.

He's acting on more than one level.

I watch Damon as he turns and comes down the stairs with dogged determination each time, swiveling his hips, rolling his shoulders, and pumping his arms to gain enough momentum to propel his body into the carriage. I hold my breath every time.

Once, I spot Damon wincing and run up between takes. "You okay, D-man?"

"Yeah, I pulled a leg muscle but I'm fine now." Damon shrugs. He's so full of adrenaline, he doesn't feel a thing. It's 104 degrees and my son is in heaven.

And doesn't want me there, though he's grateful I'm near. I return to the sidelines.

They have to shoot this scene two dozen times. It demands coordination between Damon's and Josh's lines, Damon's descending the stairs and ascending the carriage, then Gary driving them up Main Street while Damon looks back at Josh and Josh looks at Damon. After each take, Gary must turn the carriage and ride it all the way back — even the horse is hot and tired! — and Damon must alight from the wagon and resume his position on the stairs. Meanwhile, fifty extras must take their posts and spring to life again.

Somehow, Damon hangs in until we hear the magic words: "That's a wrap."

David hands me a headset. "You need to see just how good he looks on-screen!" I know all about Damon's acting, of course, but when I view the monitor, I'm impressed by how the presence of other talented actors and *Deadwood*'s enhanced production values add depth and create a truly classical movie look.

David Milch high-fives Damon as he

comes in and praises his fine work.

"That was serious acting! I pushed you and you dug deeper . . . I hope you realize how well you did. You gave an impressive, completely professional performance! Almost no one achieves that the first time."

David sends a PA to get his new star a snow cone. "Now you need to cool down and stay out of the sun the rest of the day. I mean it!"

Steve Shill tells Damon he's a real pro and it was a pleasure directing him.

I'm standing apart and watching as several other crew and cast members come up to congratulate Damon, when David Milch pats me on the shoulder.

"I understand." He nods darkly. "These guys think this is just a kid getting his first shot. But you and I, we know what else is going on. It's a fuckin' mysterious process . . ." David starts to leave. "You know, sometimes you do something nice for someone and it turns out well for everyone. That's a good outcome." David gives a beatific smile. "He's such a fantastic kid!"

He pats me again and walks off.

A sexy actress runs up and tells Damon how great he was and that she looks forward to working with him.

Damon blushes, tips back his handsome

rapscallion cap, and thanks her. He looks tired but triumphant, a novice no more. He loosens his shirt and drapes one cavalier arm over the chair, grinning over a dripping snow cone.

PART IV

CHAPTER 39

So school begins tomorrow and I am in a strange way looking forward to it but at the same time apprehensive. After all, it was only a few months ago that I was missing so much school because of all my medical crap that I dropped out and had to go on home instruction which, although easier, is also very lonely. So the surgery has definitely helped but the question is, is it enough? Although I have been more or less fine over the summer, it is not the same. During the summer, I could pretty much rest whenever I needed/wanted to. But school, as we all know, is relentless. Do I really have enough energy (protein) to get through it? And this is Junior Year, the one that really counts . . . and I plan to direct a play and hopefully be in model UN and actually have a life (way to pace yourself Damon!) In truth, my numbers have not really improved that much, they've just stopped going down, meaning I'm not in danger of wasting away or being confined to my bed 24/7 — whoopeee. And of course I have the lovely infusions every 2 or so weeks now at my house, which is much better but it's still going to be a bitch having to go home for those especially when rehearsal starts. But really it's the same problem it always is, which is very simply my energy. And I won't be able to truly tell how much that's improved till school starts. At least I have the comfort of knowing that my doctor is on the same page as me: sending me back to school is an experiment that could very well fail. Of course, I could always drop all the extra curricular shit, settle for 70s and 80s, and call it me. I could also live someone else's life but, surprise surprise, I don't want to. I suppose (at the risk of being cliched) only time shall tell. So enough of me bitching, it's not helping me and it's certainly not helping you. Sorry for those of you who actually are reading this.

— From Damon's blog,
September 12, 2004
(ten days after returning from *Deadwood*)

Despite a great summer and his early excitement about returning to school, by October of his junior year, Damon starts to falter again.

"His albumin is down to two point one and he looks awfully pale and weak. I don't think he can handle school," Shealagh says. "It's too much for him!"

Damon is under attack all over, only this time, we've exhausted all of the treatment options, except for a heart transplant.

Dr. Hellenbrand admits he has nothing more to offer us — "I'm really sorry we couldn't do more for him with fenestration" — and no other doctor or hospital has a better option.

Dr. Chin sends me a paper on "renovating the heart," the experimental use of stem cells to repair injured hearts. But even Dr. Chin scribbles in the margins, "I'm not sure if any of this really applies in Damon's case since his heart has not been acutely injured."

My cousin Dr. Bar-Or still believes inflammation is the key to Damon's illness but he has no ready solution. "I have some ideas," he says, "but they're still in the experimental stage."

My friend Dr. Jeffrey Friedman thinks a mechanical assist device might help but accepts that it's not feasible for now. "The market isn't there, so no one's developing it."

Shealagh's best friend, Dr. Sonja Kassuba, has faith in alternative medicine but recognizes we need an "immediate intervention" to arrest Damon's steep deterioration.

I do a final search for new papers and check in with doctors at a dozen hospitals all over the world, until I've X-ed out every item but the last on my faded master list.

Only the heart transplant remains. We have to accept it and explore it.

We start with Columbia, Damon's regular hospital and a pioneer in heart transplantation. Shealagh and I go to Dr. Hayes, Damon's longtime cardiologist, who has foreseen this day. "I know how difficult this must be for you, but you're making the right decision for Damon," she tells us.

Dr. Hayes leads us straight to the office of Dr. Amelia Mason,* the medical director of pediatric heart transplants at Columbia. Dr. Hayes's recommendations are invariably reliable and she speaks warmly of Dr. Mason. "Amelia knows all about Damon and is eager to meet you."

Dr. Mason smiles behind round glasses as

---

*I have changed the names of "Dr. Mason" and her colleagues in the pediatric cardiology transplant team — Drs. "Davis," "Becker," and "Sanford." No other names have been changed.

she enthuses about the wonders of heart transplants at Columbia.

"It's almost routine now and people can live for twenty years or more with a first transplant," Dr. Mason says. "Many are still going strong in their third decade, and they can always get a second transplant, if they need it, and start the clock all over again."

"What quality of life can they expect?" I ask, noting her cheeriness.

"Oh, a very good one, just like normal. Transplant patients lead full, active lives. We have patients running marathons, skiing downhill, having babies . . ."

"That's good to hear," I say, encouraged but trying to square this with what I've read. "But doesn't Damon's PLE pose special problems for a heart transplant?"

"No." Dr. Mason doesn't skip a beat. "We've successfully transplanted many patients just like him. In fact, one of Damon's biggest problems post-transplant will likely be the risk of injury from all the excess energy he will have with a new working heart!"

"Are you serious?" I say as Shealagh and I exchange hopeful but skeptical glances.

"Yes! These kids can suddenly run and jump like normal children for the first time in their lives," Dr. Mason explains. "They're so excited, they often get hurt leaping around until they learn how to control their energetic new bodies. So you may actually have to *restrain* Damon at first and teach him to be careful."

"We can live with that!" Shealagh chuckles nervously. We're both very gratified to get such a positive overview from the presiding pediatric transplant expert at Columbia. But as Dr. Mason continues in this vein, I begin to feel uneasy.

"Forgive me, but what are you basing this on?" I ask. "Because this isn't what we've heard." I look at Shealagh. "I mean, if transplants are so great, why have we spent the past three years trying to *avoid* one? Have we been completely misled until now?"

"It really works, trust me! We have the experience and patients to prove it!"

"Okay" — I stare at her — "so how many heart transplants have you performed?" Then I fire off a series of questions: "How many were Fontans? And how many had PLE? For how many years had they had PLE? Did the PLE resolve? And how many years post-transplant did the patients live?"

Dr. Mason stiffens and for the first time, her fixed smile wavers.

She bristles. "I don't have it all at my

fingertips!" She looks put out, as if I'm challenging her authority and spoiling the feel-good air.

I seek to reassure her. "Look, our only interest is Damon's well-being, but we've talked to many doctors and read many papers with a *different* view. What data do you have? We need hard numbers." Despite trying, I can't quite hide my exasperation.

"We have an outstanding pediatric transplant program, one of the best in the country," Dr. Mason declares. She either doesn't have the facts or won't discuss them with us. She looks to Shealagh for female solidarity — *Is he always like this?* — and keeps smiling at us with a beaming, content-free expression that says, "Trust me, it's all good."

But it's not all good. We can't get her to talk about any substantive details or any potential trouble spots.

I begin to worry we are getting a sales pitch. Dr. Mason wants to sell us a *product.* Her language is vague and imparts no real information. I must know a hundred doctors and scientists by now, including dozens of Nobel laureates and scores of world-class medical researchers and practitioners, several of them good friends — they form the core of my daily professional and personal life — and not one of them speaks, let alone thinks, in this way. Nor has any physician at Columbia ever addressed us in such a generic, unforthcoming manner.

"Look, I'm sorry, but that's just not good enough for us," I tell Dr. Mason while Shealagh nods. "We can't be the first parents to ask for real data. We're talking about our son's *life,* and we need more facts and more context to make the best decision for him."

I am polite but resolute and there is a long, uncomfortable stretch until Dr. Mason, who has a determinedly bouncy air and has never stopped smiling, comes to recognize she can't close this deal without producing something concrete.

Suddenly she changes her tune and invites me into her confidence.

"So, although it's not published yet, our group at Columbia has a big paper in press that might interest you! It's a multi-decade, retrospective study that reviews, for the first time, all our patient outcomes for cardiac transplantation after the Fontan, including for PLE patients. And it documents all the case histories I referred to."

News of this instantly alters my frame of mind. I feel a ripple of hope and excitement.

"When's the paper coming out?" I ask. I know no such data has yet appeared — I've been searching for it myself — but if Columbia has peer-reviewed results, and if they're as good as Dr. Mason says, then we're in business. It would mean the outlook for Damon is much more favorable than we imagined and we're at exactly the right hospital.

"I can't recall the exact numbers but I can try and get you a preprint as a personal favor," Dr. Mason says. "It won't be published for three to four months."

"I would really appreciate that!" I reply, full of eager deference now.

"That would be so kind of you," Shealagh chimes in.

Dr. Mason, back in our good graces, smiles. "We could also handle the IVIG infusions for Damon, if you like. He now gets them at home under Mount Sinai's care, is that correct?" She fingers the stethoscope around her neck.

"Yes, but we thought Columbia didn't do IVIG. It's why we went to Sinai."

"Oh no, IVIG is part of our pre-transplant preparation program. We use it all the time to help fortify patients before the surgery," Dr. Mason says.

"Really?" I say, and share a secret smile with Shealagh, since we've long pushed IVIG for Damon but had to go it alone. I lower my voice. "It means we were right and Dudu was right, and we've been strengthening Damon all along!"

"Yes!" Shealagh says sotto voce. "But we should probably let Columbia take over now because it's better to have one place overseeing all his care."

We agree to consider having Columbia administer IVIG and set a meeting for Damon with Dr. Mason, parting from her on an up note. Heading home, Shealagh and I feel buoyed. Even if Dr. Mason is only half-right — I still have my doubts about her unqualified boosterism — we're still ahead of our expectations. Maybe a heart transplant really *is* the answer to our prayers.

Back home, I reach out to my brain trust, check in with several hospitals, and read up on transplants. But I don't dig in and burrow deep the way I did with PLE. Early on, Sonja, a strong physician ally and a support to the family, says to me, "This isn't like PLE, Doron, where they know so little and you had to become the expert and make every decision. They've been performing heart transplants for thirty years and have excellent systems and protocols in place. They know what they're doing, believe me! You don't need to take it all on yourself. You can relax a little and trust them on this."

I'm not relaxed but I am profoundly *exhausted,* so I'm relieved to hear we don't need to gather our own data, find our own experts, formulate our own medical plan, and second-guess every move that doesn't accord with the best current understanding and practice, or with our own instincts and common sense.

Passively relying on the medical establishment and trusting them to manage my son's care in his best interest is not, as Sonja rightly notes, a luxury I have allowed myself ever since I was jolted by Damon's diagnosis and the lack of appropriate treatment. So it's very tempting to indulge a little now and let them carry the ball for a while.

Even after Damon meets Dr. Mason, is examined by her, and reacts much as we did — "If you listen to Dr. Mason, transplants are so fantastic, *everyone* should have one, even healthy people!" Damon says dryly — I decide to trust the experts. Columbia has a world-class reputation and a seemingly outstanding track record with patients like Damon.

CHAPTER 40

Yankees slaughter Red Sox first three games but Red Sox come back to win four consecutive games make the world series and baseball history. Due partly to a player who happens to bear the name of Damon.

Which just goes to show you boys and girls: it ain't over till it's over.
It ain't over till its fuckin over.
— From Damon's blog, fall 2004

"I'm tired. I'll go to bed early and do my homework in the morning," Damon says.

Day to day, he continues to struggle. I can see the strain on his body and in his face. The surrounding atmosphere becomes less hospitable to him, the oxygen too thin. Every step takes something out of him.

"I'm out of breath! Where's my inhaler?" he cries.

As his energy wanes, Damon also becomes

more moody and snappish. His siblings and his mother bear the brunt of it but occasionally, he's short-tempered with me as well.

It's more than male adolescence, though that's part of the mix. Because he needs me more than most teenage sons need their fathers, or because he needs me in a different way, it's trickier for Damon to vent his anger at me. But he does get around to it, especially when he needs to impress his peers.

One day Damon is hanging in his room with Kyle, Keith, and Keith's boyfriend. The rest of the family is at the front door, about to head to the local cinema, when Miranda says, "I have a stomachache. I don't want to go to the movies!" She marches back upstairs.

I pop into Damon's room, where he and his pals are sprawled on the carpet. "Hey, D-man, could you keep an eye on Miranda for us until we get back? We can't leave her alone in the house and Mom really wants to see this film." I pause. "Mom could use a break."

Although Damon need do nothing except stay where he is with his friends for a few more hours — they had no immediate plans to leave — he suddenly gets his back up.

"No, I don't want to babysit Miranda!"

Damon protests. "I'm not doing it!"

"Look, if you don't cover for us, we can't go to the movies," I say.

"Well, that's too bad then!" Damon snarls while his pals look on.

"D-man, that's not very considerate," I remark, taken aback by his insolence. His friends watch to see just how far he will dare push his father.

"I don't care!" Damon taunts, emboldened. "I don't give a shit. It's your problem!"

Now he's crossed the line and I'm ready to discipline him when I spot a heartbreaking, exquisitely pained look on Kyle's face. She knows the score and she's bracing for what is about to happen to her friend. On the spot, I change my mind. I tuck my tail between my legs and walk silently out of the room. We can afford to miss the movie.

Another time Damon is having a late-night party when a bunch of guys and one girl decide to spend the night. Damon wants the girl to sleep in the living room but the rule is that girls need privacy with a closed door. Damon argues vehemently with me, and again I feel his strong need to defy me in front of his friends. But this time I won't cede. "She's sleeping alone in your room while you crash with the other guys, or else she's going home! It's your decision."

Damon challenges me with increasing sharpness, and I must find a middle ground between nurturing his fighting spirit and setting rules. But in private, when it's just the two of us, Damon remains his basic sweet self, albeit broodier. And while his life now revolves around his peers, he remains sensitive about his place in our family and in my affections.

"Hey, D-man, I want to try my first triathlon and there's a short intro race next week in New Jersey," I tell him one day. "It sounds from the website like I need someone to help me. You interested? We could hang out after."

Damon studies his middle-aged father, smiling. "No thanks, I got plans." As I foresaw, carrying my water is hardly his idea of a fun weekend. But I wanted to give him first dibs, as I always do, before going next door to Sam's room, where my prospects are better.

"Yeah, I wanna go!" Sam jumps at the idea of an overnight trip with his dad. For him, it's an adventure and a chance to get me to himself.

As Sam and I prepare to leave on Saturday — I wheel my bike by Sam's room while Sam eagerly grabs his canvas bag and joins me — Damon suddenly steps out of his room.

"Hey, what's up?" Damon rubs sleep from a puffy face. The bustle of activity has caught his attention, especially Sam's animation and high spirits.

"We're driving to that sprint triathlon in Jersey and then a little R and R," I reply.

"Huh?" Damon remains only half-awake and is distracted and irritated by Sam's giddiness. "Sam, could you pipe down please, I'm talking to Dad!"

"Remember that race I invited you to? But you weren't interested?" I prod.

"Oh yeah," Damon recalls. "*That* thing." He still has no real interest in going, but he registers, just as I do, that this is a break in tradition. Until today, this was the special kind of trip that Damon and I would make together, while the rest of the family looked on. But this time, it's Sam and me heading out, with Damon staying behind.

"I packed you guys sandwiches!" Shealagh now appears with Miranda, smiling.

"Does your hotel have a pool?" Miranda asks with keen interest.

"It's a motel, Miranda!" Sam corrects her. His lively face is full of pride at our impending voyage and his designated role as my race assistant.

"Well, good luck, Dad," Damon says, then goes back in his room and closes the door.

Shealagh picks up on Damon's vibe and takes me aside. "This is important for Sam. Damon can't get every outing with you. Look how excited Sam is. He deserves this!"

"I know, I even offered it to Damon first. And I want the time with Sam . . . Still, it feels like Damon is getting bypassed in so many ways now . . ."

"We can't hold the others back," Shealagh says, but I can see she's as upset as I am.

Damon starts to miss school every week, for one, sometimes two, days at a time. He sleeps late and complains of headaches and general weakness and fatigue. When he's not holed up in his overheated room, dozing, playing video games, or hanging out online with friends, he drags around the house with a blanket and wallows in the family room or in our bedroom.

"I'm just resting," he says constantly. I can see him cradling his chest and protecting it. He bends forward and leans on any nearby object — a counter, a chair, a table. As if he feels the heavy weight and mass of his heart, its enlarged physical pendency, and seeks to relieve this burden by transferring it to another, external support.

Occasionally, Damon shakes out his limbs

and snaps his fingers with a sudden burst of bravado, as if trying to rouse himself from his torpor. "Yes!" He jumps to attention, as if a bugle call has just awakened him, and he's raring to go. He wants to be his old, active self, even if it takes a self-administered prod to jolt him to his previous state of alertness. But then, with his manufactured stimulus gone, he sinks back into lethargy.

There are small bursts of fun and excitement. Lachlann comes for a visit from the Isle of Skye and the two boys renew their friendship with parties and computer game rooms and boisterous mischief.

For Halloween, Damon summons his creative flair — with a big craft assist from his resourceful mother — and dresses up as a martini glass. He wears a silver bodysuit as the stem while Shealagh configures a pliable mesh frame from a waste-paper basket to serve as the glass bowl. They sheath the bottom in silver and crown Damon's head. Shealagh adds white foam to represent the liquid and a wedge of yellow for the lemon slice and Damon looks sublime and utterly drinkable.

In late fall, I invite Damon and the family to the Hamptons International Film Festival, where I sponsor a program similar to Sundance. I've gone out a few days early for my events, and one day I get a distressed call from Shealagh. She and Damon had spent an entire day at home sitting and waiting for his biweekly IVIG infusion — Damon even missed his rehearsals — but the nurse never came. Columbia, which had taken over his treatment, had canceled the appointment without notifying them.

Shealagh is distraught, close to tears, and Damon is very upset. Promising to handle it, I call Dr. Mason's office — she's been seeing Damon — but I'm told she's not available. When I explain it's urgent and ask for a home number, I'm tartly informed Dr. Mason does not give out her home number but I can leave a message and she will call me back when she is available. I'm used to such screening methods from Hollywood but not from my son's cardiologists.

Two days later, I finally hear back from Dr. Mason. She professes not to know about the cancellation and says I should speak about it with Dr. Hellenbrand since he's still overseeing Damon's care. I call Dr. Hellenbrand, whose home number I do have because like Dr. Hayes and every *other* doctor who's cared for Damon at Columbia, he gave it to me on our first meeting. Dr. Hellenbrand, who's always been straight with me, swears he knows nothing about

411

this snafu. By now I suspect what happened but it seems so at odds with customary medical behavior that I ask Shealagh to check with the home infusion people. Shealagh calls them and the company confirms it was Dr. Mason's office that canceled the treatments!

Indignant and dismayed, I call Dr. Mason for an explanation. But again, I get her answering service and again, I'm told to leave a message. It's hard to describe my state as I go about my business and wait for another full day until she calls me back.

The call comes as I'm driving, but since Dr. Mason is so elusive, I pull off to the side of the road and ask her to explain her behavior. She says nothing — no denial this time, just silence. Then she asks innocently why I'm upset since the IVIG treatment wasn't doing much good anyway. Irate, I tell her I'm upset because she has committed three major errors, each compounding the previous one.

"First," I tell her, "you made what we believe is a wrong medical decision about stopping IVIG! Not only do we feel IVIG has been helping Damon for over a year, but you professed to support this treatment. Second, even if that decision is medically debatable, you never discussed it with us

412

but went behind our backs and unilaterally canceled a treatment that had become a regular part of our lives! Third, when I confronted you about what happened, you passed the buck and did not accept responsibility!"

I say all this with great heat, and it's clear from her tense silence that Dr. Mason is not used to being addressed in this way. It's also clear she has no defense.

"I don't know who in my office could have canceled the treatment," she says. Then she adds, "But at this point, we don't believe IVIG is helping Damon in a significant way, so I'm not sure what the benefit is anyway."

"Well, we think it's helping him and we're going to continue it!" I respond. I'm on a long flat stretch of Montauk Highway with power lines spooling in either direction and I feel a bitter sadness, even more than anger, that anyone can behave in this fashion. But although I'm appalled by Dr. Mason's conduct, I know to stop short of an irretrievable break because she is part of a powerful system and until or unless I find a better system, Damon's vulnerability may force me to deal with this one. I manage to end the call on a civil note.

Damon comes out to the festival and enjoys the films and the parties. He's now a member of the Screen Actors Guild with a bona fide credit to his name — *Deadwood* will resume broadcast in March, and we've learned he's in the third episode — and he has something to talk about with the other young actors, directors, and producers he meets.

But back home, it's clear Damon is slipping. He sleeps late and misses more days of school. He falls farther behind in his work. He's always trying to catch up and return to normal, but he never quite seems to get there anymore. It's increasingly about what the *next* day or week might bring, but not about the present, which is beset with obstacles.

One night, I come home with Shealagh from a big film premiere and after-party. Shealagh has become more withdrawn as a result of Damon's illness, but tonight my wife agreed to go with me, and despite herself, she had a good time and enjoyed the silly glitter.

As we're about to go up to bed, I notice that Damon's light is still on. I knock on his door and enter. "Hi, D-man. You're up late."

"Yeah, I'm just goofing around." Damon slouches on the low armchair in his overheated room, keyboard on lap, looking chalky pale and exhausted. Dirty cups, half-

414

eaten food, and little balled-up white tissues litter his desk area. All of which I'm used to. What I'm not used to — what, in fact, I have never seen before — is the look of flickering fear and stealthy depression lurking beneath his haggard gaze. It darts across his face like a black cat and quickly hides behind the eyes, where he tries to keep it under wraps.

It tears at my heart and makes me realize how bad things have gotten.

Although I know he wants me to go, I decide I can't leave him alone in such a state. I must find a way to cheer him up, or at least to make that scared look disappear. I start blabbing about the evening's events, dropping names and chattering aimlessly. I don't care what I say, I need to banish the darkness that has settled over him.

Eventually I run out of chatter and exhaust his patience. I'm exhausted myself, and I'm dying to go to bed. I have no more excuses to linger. If I'm lucky, I've diverted him. More likely, I've just pissed him off. But I had to try. I say good night and exit his room.

Only now, I'm too riled myself to go to bed. I step out onto the front porch and look up at the late-fall sky. It's blue-black and chilly, with a pale moon over the park.

A brisk wind brushes the tears in my eyes like shards of glass.

I realize tonight is my third and final warning in a dismal sequence. The first was Damon's falling asleep in the car after the Rangers game, and the second his premature exit from the Sundance party. Each episode was completely out of character and showed his illness starting to change him.

Damon is beginning to fall apart before my eyes and he's crying, silently, for help.

I cannot stand by and watch him decline further.

CHAPTER 41

"Guess I'll die another day, it's not my time to go!"

— Die Another Day
(From the latest James Bond movie)

Hey what's up all, how are you?

I'm kinda in a weird place right now but that's life and this is most certainly not Wallgreens! I feel like the tapestry that is my life is unwinding and all the threads are blowing in different directions threatening to fly away completely. I want to reach out and grab them and secure them again but if I try for one thread, I am forced to loosen my grip on another and I may lose it entirely, so I just have to sit tight and watch the pieces flying off. And then of course there's that one thread whose color I desperately need to change, as it would make the tapestry much more beautiful and worthwhile. But then of course that thread might not be able to change colors and in trying I might turn it an ugly brown (like when you've mixed too many paints) and if that thread became brown, the entire tapestry would become ugly and not worth looking at, and maybe even not worth working on, I'm not sure. And *that* was my bad metaphor 4 the day.

Goin for a cath this Tuesday (that's like an operation thing where they knock you out, have a needle with a camera on it go through your body and take pictures). It was supposed to be short originally, but now it's not gonna be because other doctors who wanted other data got involved. Which means I'm not gonna make it to rehearsal tomorrow: sigh: damn, look at me letting people down. I should've known though, a medical procedure, me, short!, ahahaha shirley you jest! Well I guess that's all. Gonna go to sleep, sooo tired, but that never changes lately, sleep or no.
— From Damon's blog, fall 2004

"Hey, D-man, got a minute to talk?"

When, after consulting with Shealagh, I finally go into Damon's room to tell him it's time to consider a heart transplant — a decision I've been trying to avoid for three years and a moment I've been dreading for almost as long — he seems to take it better than I do.

"Sure, Dad, come in." Damon logs out of Warcraft, making room for me on the armchair footrest. He *wants* to have this talk. We both know it's not going well, and he looks to me, as always, for the game plan. I swallow hard.

"So, we're now looking at the heart transplant as our best shot. It has a lot going for it, more than I at first believed. It could be *the* solution." My eyes mist up. Damon has been counting on me, and I owe him an accounting. "I've tried everything. You know there's nothing I wouldn't do for you, D-man!" I tense my left hand and slice like a guillotine across my right arm.

Damon nods. He knows.

I clear my throat and run through the basics: that we haven't made a final decision on the hospital, but Columbia has very good outcomes with heart transplants for PLE patients like Damon. And while there will be new immune issues with a transplant, they're all manageable and consistent with a full and active life. "The operation carries some risk, but after, you'll have a new, fully functioning heart with new energy, D-man!

And you'll be able to grow!"

Damon, absorbing every word, looks soberly relieved. He nods. "That makes sense, Dad." He knows he's in trouble and glad we have something new to try. He understands better than I do that the present situation cannot continue. "Be nice to put this whole thing behind me!" His face shows new hope and resolve.

We make an appointment with Dr. Mason's office and are assigned to her colleague Dr. Clarice Davis. The pediatric transplant group has four cardiologists, all women, with Dr. Mason and Dr. Davis the senior members — though Dr. Davis, like the others, clearly defers to Dr. Mason, the director.

"Damon, why don't you pull up your shirt so I can listen to your heart?" Dr. Davis smiles in her correct, well-groomed manner. She examines Damon and reviews his medical history, but the purpose of this visit is to go over the heart transplant and what it entails. Heart transplants are big business — half a million dollars a pop — and even the busiest places like Columbia handle only about twenty pediatric cases a year, so each one matters to the bottom line.

"Do you feel tired even after you've slept? Is it hard just to do normal stuff, like walking?" Dr. Davis runs through the standard questions about our son's symptoms and quality of life, nodding each time. Suddenly she looks up from her notes.

"You've tried everything, but sometimes your old heart just isn't up to it anymore, is it?" she coos softly, as if his heart is a beloved, ailing pet on its last legs.

Damon, our stoic, long-suffering son, looks disarmed. He nods. "Yeah."

"I know," Dr. Davis says. "But don't worry. We're going to get you a new heart, and you'll be much better!"

I feel moved by the simplicity and directness of this statement, and by Damon's frank response to it. I realize Dr. Davis has used this language before — it's what she does for a living. Nevertheless, it's a sweet, touching gesture that also shows a rather blunt, replace-the-battery optimism. Apparently, we've come to the right store.

Before getting listed for a transplant, Damon needs a catheterization to confirm his pressures and other heart functions are good enough to make a transplant workable. Donor hearts are in short supply, and Damon must pass the test to get approval as a worthy candidate. Assuming he qualifies, we are told Columbia's leading reputation, its regional primacy as a transplant center, and Damon's lifelong affiliation with the hospital will all help to ensure he has priority and will get a heart within a reasonable time.

Dr. Hellenbrand will do the catheterization himself. Meanwhile, at our request, he has reinstated the IVIG treatments and also doubled Damon's diuretic, helping him shed five pounds. But despite short-term boosts from the IVIG, Damon continues on a downward course. He misses entire weeks of school and often sleeps well into the afternoon, going in only for play rehearsals.

"Why don't we get Andre Lawe back to tutor you at home?" I suggest.

"If I take a leave, they might not let me enter the building to direct the school play!" Damon explains. He's been actively engaged with every aspect of *The Man Who Came to Dinner,* slated for mid-December. Auditions proved tricky because most of the actors were his friends but he's made the tough decisions and has the cast he wants. Now he must rehearse them every day and maintain his own energy.

When Damon arrives with his pals at my office for the annual Rhodes Scholarship filing, I'm struck by his scrunched, pallid appearance. He looks almost ghostly under the bright lights. And he moves in such slow motion that I simply discount his contribution to the folders. But he still manages to join in all the fun and after I buy everyone dinner, he pleads with me to take the remaining group to a midnight movie, *Team America: World Police,* a dirty-minded, howlingly transgressive satire that has the kids rolling in the aisles.

Damon goes in for his catheterization a week later. Inside the chilled operating theater, we must again watch our son laid out on the lone bed like a specimen while giant, C-shaped steel arms twist around his frail body and a half dozen masked faces peer at him with disembodied eyes. He succumbs fast to the anesthesia and then Shealagh and I must leave and go down the hall to wait, the loneliest walk in the world no matter how many times you make it.

My wife and I sit in the waiting room until Dr. Hellenbrand — his presence is the most reassuring thing about this day — comes out to tell us all went well and Damon is awake. He confirms that Damon has a good working fenestration so refenestration does not seem warranted, as Dr. Chin suggested, nor does pacing.

"All in all, Damon appears in better shape than many transplant candidates," Dr. Hellenbrand says with a workmanlike nod. "They'll need to take down his Fontan but his anatomical wiring is all in place and we found nothing problematic. He seems good to go!"

By Friday, Damon's results have been processed, and he's formally approved as a candidate for the transplant list.

Shealagh and I are pleased but we don't list Damon right away because we want to make sure we've given every nontransplant option a chance. And we're still not 100 percent convinced Columbia is the best hospital. Plus we want to wait until after Damon's play.

"It's three weeks away and rehearsals are the one thing that gets him out of bed. Otherwise, he's sleeping later and has even less energy," Shealagh says.

I send Dr. Chin Damon's cath results and he agrees they do not support a refenestration or pacing but he suggests we try digitalis. I talk to Dr. Warnes at the Mayo Clinic and she says we can try fractionated heparin. Even while preparing for a transplant, we explore every possible alternative.

Thanksgiving we spend quietly at home, just the five of us, since my parents and my sister have their own plans, and we're in a muted, defensive posture. Our old oven was on the fritz so we've just purchased a new one, and the big holiday turkey comes out looking golden and gleaming. Shealagh has prepared a handsome feast and everyone enjoys the good eating.

"Let's give thanks." I raise a cider glass. "To the family: Damon, Sam, Miranda, and Mom and Dad. And to Grandma and Granddad and Anat."

"And to Toby and Turpin and Julie and Granny," Damon says with a wink at me.

"And to Freddie!" Sam says as the non-person in question licks his sly chops, sniffing the warm gravy. "How could you forget Freddie!"

"And to Rocky!" Miranda cries as her guinea pig squeaks in the next room.

"Yes, to all." Shealagh lifts a glass. "To health, prosperity, and happiness!"

"Cheers!" I say as we all clink and drink. I look at the assembled gathering.

"A special salute to Damon for directing his first play!" I smile at him.

"Here, here!" Shealagh chimes. "And to Sam, for winning first place in the debate competition!" She shows off Sam's fancy gold medal, a recent triumph. If either Damon or Miranda had won such a trophy, we'd have been pleased, but coming from tight-lipped Sam, it's close to astonishing, a

425

reminder our middle son is full of surprises and trying to pick up the slack in his own way.

"And to Miranda for advancing to the next level in Irish dance!" I add.

"Thank you, Dad!" Miranda beams at me and sticks her tongue out at Sam.

We play Trivial Pursuit after, with sharp sibling bickering and one-upmanship, and then Damon screens the 1930s movie version of *The Man Who Came to Dinner.* We review and analyze it in great detail.

"At least the actors all know their lines," Damon observes.

While the family watches TV, I slip off to my study. Traditionally, I try to do something civic-minded with Damon on this holiday, like helping in soup kitchens, but his current state precludes such activity. So instead, I decide to pick a charity and send a contribution in Damon's name. Part tradition, part superstition, since I'm trying to align all the universe's forces on our side. And I know, despite our unrelieved sense of crisis, that we're not the only ones who are suffering.

Surfing the Net, Have a Heart: Adopt a Soldier catches my attention for obvious reasons. It's an effort to provide our forces fighting in Iraq with personal items to ease their overseas tour. Although the war is unpopular, I've reminded Damon that regardless of one's politics, there are young men and women still fighting and shedding their blood for us every day, just as during Vietnam, and we can't forget them. Damon will be seventeen on his next birthday, the same age as some of these troops, and I've always thought of him as a soldier in his own war.

So now I write a check and follow instructions, which includes sending a photo of Damon, first name only, with a short message. I scroll quickly through my digital camera — Shealagh thinks I'm sneaking off to check e-mail and is yelling for me to come back — when I find a good picture of Damon, standing in front of a horse, with a glorious smile on his face. It's from that memorable day we rode with Gary to the top of Griffith Park. I'm struck now, glancing backward, by how unwell Damon looks in most of the recent photos, but in this shot, I got lucky and caught him in a blessed moment, when the light was just right and fell lovingly across his red hair and radiant smile.

I print out the photo, and on the blank side, in my own hand, I tell my adopted soldier about Damon's long, hard campaign, and how I pray that by next Thanksgiving, the two of them will be back home, safe and sound.

CHAPTER 42

"But there's no need for turning back
'cause all roads lead to where I stand, and
I believe I've walked them all no matter
what I may have planned."
— Don McLean (Crossroads)
— From Damon's blog, December 2004

In seeking the best hospital for Damon's
heart transplant operation, New York-
Presbyterian/Columbia University Medical
Center remains the place to beat. Not so
much because of its reputation or because
Damon has been a patient there all his life
and will thus get priority — though these
factors do carry weight — but primarily due
to Columbia's unparalleled experience with
post-Fontan PLE transplants — with patients just like Damon.

When Dr. Mason first hands me the raw,
pre-publication statistics from her study —
she presents them proudly, as if they vindi-

cate her claims — I am jolted by the numbers.

"Hold on. If I add all this up, it means forty percent of patients who received new hearts died during the operation, or shortly thereafter?" I stare at Dr. Mason with a sick feeling in my stomach. "That doesn't sound like a great cure rate to me!"

"Yes, but look at the dates!" Dr. Mason explains that almost all the deaths occurred in the 1970s and early '80s, when patients were much sicker than Damon before they ever went in for their transplant. Several were on ventilators and could no longer function on their own. Columbia's recent outcomes for post-Fontan PLEs are vastly improved. Virtually all are successful. "We've learned how to do this today and solved the earlier problems!" She smiles.

I look more closely at the numbers and see that Dr. Mason is right. For the earlier and more debilitated patients who died, all the fatalities occurred within twenty-four hours of the transplant or soon after. But for the more recent patients who survived to discharge from the hospital — average length of stay, four weeks — the five-year survival rate was 96 percent and the ten-year survival rate was 92 percent, astonishingly good figures, especially when one considers that Damon generally *beats* the spread.

"And it looks like *all* the PLE patients who made it to discharge saw their PLE resolve *completely,*" I say excitedly because this issue had concerned me.

"Yes, and long-term, these patients even do moderately *better* than general transplant patients, perhaps because they're more compliant about their meds."

"This is great news!" I declare, ready to hug Dr. Mason. "It means our biggest challenge will be to get Damon through the operation and past the monthlong recovery period so he can come home. Based on these numbers, once he's discharged from the hospital post-transplant, Damon's prognosis looks *excellent.*"

"Yes, though the first year is also important," Dr. Mason says. "He has to comply with all his meds and we have to keep a close watch over him."

"Sure" — I nod — "but Damon is a model patient, well schooled in compliance from his years of PLE . . . And Shealagh and I are scrupulous and seasoned patient parents . . . Plus, you guys have a *whole team* that specializes in post-transplant care!"

"Oh yes, we're nationally ranked." Dr. Mason nods. "In the top three."

"Great!" I say. Despite the well-documented dangers, this sounds better than I'd dared hope. Dr. Mason's study — I notice Dr. Davis and Dr. Q are coauthors — will become my key document. I parse every line and pore over every statistic. Since it's not yet in print, I relay its data, with permission, to cardiologists at other hospitals and ask how their numbers and their success rates stack up.

Comparing outcomes and judging relative performance would seem like an obvious basis for making an informed decision about a matter of life and death for our son. Since every hospital I've talked to has volunteered to perform Damon's transplant — the half-million-dollar fee again! — I want to know how well they've done with similar patients and similar operations in the past. A no-brainer, one might assume.

But apparently not, I explain in frustration to my wife.

"No one can answer my most basic questions because there's no central database or any systematic method for tracking the number of operations with these types of patients, nor is there any obligation to report outcomes and success rates to patients and their families. And no hospital wants to divulge its numbers because it's a competitive game, and a rival hospital could have *better* numbers."

"They want to filter the information and have it all their way," Shealagh says, as frustrated as I am. "It's not right."

"No. They're effectively asking us to fly *blind,* and to rely on subjective terms such as 'good name' and 'reputation' and unreliable methods such as self-reporting or 'best hospitals' lists . . . To be fair, Columbia normally would not release its numbers and it's only because they happen to be doing a retrospective study — a study that shows them in a positive light and will be good for their bottom line — that they've agreed, after my badgering, to share their data with me."

"Still, at least we have *something* from them," Shealagh says.

"Yes! We can use it as a yardstick with the other top institutions." I nod.

I call up Dr. Michael Freed at Boston Children's Hospital, a cardiologist who's reviewed Damon's case for me. Like everyone, Dr. Freed cautions there are many factors in choosing the right place and raw numbers don't tell the full story.

"Statistics can be read in many ways; the devil is in the details," he warns me.

"True, and the number and success rate

433

of PLE transplants won't be our sole criterion, but it's *one* hard measure, and without
it we're missing key data."

After more debate, Dr. Freed allows he
has not seen Columbia's study. "But if these
numbers are right, I don't think Boston
Children's can match them."

I phone Dr. Warnes at the Mayo Clinic.
She is surprised both by the number of
post-Fontan PLE transplants Columbia has
done and by their success rate. Because I
admire the Mayo Clinic's approach to
patient care, I invite Dr. Warnes to tell me
why I should take Damon to Minnesota for
his heart transplant. But Dr. Warnes, who
assumed the Mayo Clinic had the largest
transplant population for every category —
she poses a number of astute questions
about Columbia's data — is scrupulous and
balanced, as always.

"I cannot, in good conscience, claim that
Mayo has greater experience or greater success with this specific patient subgroup than
what Columbia is reporting," she tells me.

Finally, I call up Dr. Chin, who's been as
involved in our case and as helpful as
anyone. Yet even Dr. Chin, despite his
proven commitment to us, cannot assist us
here. He sends us to the surgeon Dr. Spray,
who sends us to the transplant program

medical director, Dr. Chrisant. Dr. Chrisant once worked at Columbia and is, in fact, a coauthor on the Mason study — it's a tiny, rarefied world and they all know each other, as I've discovered. But Dr. Chrisant, after trying to recruit us as patients, is unforthcoming. "We don't have aggregate data on our Fontan patients I can send you," she says.

Even at Dr. Chin's institution, I cannot get hard data! Dr. Chrisant's reticence leads me to conclude that CHOP's experience must lag Columbia's.

I continue talking to everyone I can. Perhaps no expert better sums up the reasons for staying with Columbia than Dr. Bruce Gelb, a cardiologist at Mount Sinai. I consulted with Bruce fifteen years earlier, shortly after Damon's birth, when he was starting out and I knew his father. Bruce is my cohort, and he's on the ball, so we quickly plug back in.

Bruce sympathizes with my inability to get good comparative data for Damon's operation and admits each hospital is a fiefdom, a world unto itself in a Balkanized system.

"As for choosing the right hospital, I know Tom Spray and he's one of the best, but at the end of the day, the transplant surgery,

435

even in Damon's case, is not that complex. You and I couldn't do it, but for the top cardiothoracic surgeons, it's just another operation. Any of the leading guys at the major institutions can handle Damon's transplant, including ours, which has a world-class team, in case you're interested . . ."

Bruce smiles when he says this, and we both understand he's just doing his job.

"But with transplants, the aftercare is as important as the surgery, so a hospital's proximity is critical," Bruce says. "You'll have to come in often during the first year after transplant. If Damon is showing any signs of rejection or infection, the two most common problems, you'll need to bring him in right away, night or day. So driving two hours to Philly to check on every sniffle may not be very convenient. Whereas Columbia, much closer to your home, and accessible via subway or car, sounds more practical for you."

"I don't mind the inconvenience if it will give Damon a better chance," I say.

"Sure. But look, I know Amelia Mason and her team, and they're fine, as capable as any of the other groups, so it probably makes sense to stay there. Columbia has been treating Damon all his life and they will have his full medical records as well as a long institutional memory and a sense that he's their patient, which can also help."

Bruce makes a persuasive case, especially when I consider the Mason study shows that if Damon makes it home from his transplant, he has a 100 percent chance of surviving the difficult first year with Columbia. Those are odds *no one* can beat, and even if I don't expect it to be easy, this is Columbia's specialty, and they're apparently very good at it.

Dr. Mason may not have started as my favorite physician but if she can help ensure a good outcome for my son, I'll be her best friend and number one fan. In fact, my highly plastic brain already is embarked on a makeover for the now-essential Mason.

The clincher is Damon. "I want to stay at Columbia for my transplant," he states.

It's not any individual doctor that wins Damon over. In fact, he seems to share our concerns now that the straightforward Dr. Hellenbrand has handed us over to the more nebulous "pediatric transplant group." But Damon does harbor a sense of loyalty and faith in the institution that's treated him from birth. Or perhaps it's just a need for reassurance, a feeling of greater comfort with a place he's known all his life. Whatever it is, I've learned to listen closely to Damon and to trust his instincts and try to honor them when I can.

If I had good evidence to the contrary — for example, if another hospital had a markedly higher success rate — I might have to reconsider. But in the absence of such counterevidence, I work on the assumption that Damon knows things we don't or can't know, and if he feels better, or more secure, he'll do better.

And the data is so strong. It's nice to think we've been at the right place all along.

CHAPTER 43

You see I can't seem to sleep
But fear not it's not cause I weep
I'm tired as hell
but see there's a bell
incessantly ringing
do you know what to do?
can you stop the dingdinging?
a bell in your head?
No no no, you misread
more like a thousand all goin off in my
   mind
and no matter what I can't stop, pause or
   rewind
these thoughts that are flowing
Where the hell am I going?
   — From Damon's blog, December 2004

Damon sleeps longer and longer now that
he's on home tutoring again. Some days it
looks like he'd go on sleeping into the next
night if we didn't wake him up, as he's

asked us to, for after-school rehearsals. The Tech fall production, only two weeks away, has become the focus of his remaining energy and drive.

"I can't miss one rehearsal!" Damon says. "We still have a long way to go!"

He rises around one P.M., instantly alert, and knows exactly what he must do. He showers, dresses, and composes the daily cast sheet, printing copies. Then he jabs a heparin injection into his bruised flesh. "I hardly feel it anymore," he says.

Damon pads down to the family room. "Freddie boy!" he greets the pooch, who rushes excitedly at him. Using an old towel, Damon begins to spin his dog through the air. Freddie's gleeful teeth grab on to the ropy cotton as he swings in a low arc about Damon's rotating trunk, almost *willing* himself off the ground and into orbital compliance as he sails prettily about his paling Svengali. Even now, no one quite possesses Damon's showmanship. But like everything else, this trick is becoming harder for Damon to pull off, and he soon tires.

Damon heads to the kitchen and gathers his stockpile from the cabinet and fridge. "Here we go!" He perches on the high stool and begins to slog through his pills, vitamins, supplements, and oils. The more recalcitrant ingestibles he coats with applesauce.

"Let's see what's playing." He remotely clicks on the small TV above the counter and gloms onto any diversion while swigging, swallowing, and gagging his way through his daily stations of the oral cross.

It's a quick fifteen-minute car ride to school, and Shealagh is eager to drive Damon and spare his diminishing strength. She tries to coax him to eat something solid, an apple or other fruit at home and, if he's up to it, an Egg McMuffin ("hold the cheese") at the drive-through on the way to Tech. Damon usually arrives just as school is letting out, around three P.M., and heads into the South Elliott Place entrance. A resolute, pint-sized figure, he braves the giddy stampede of a thousand bodies pouring from the building, high-fives a few friends, and makes his way inside. He's popular with the security guards at the sign-in desk, which helps, since technically he's no longer enrolled at the school.

"Just gonna rehearse." Damon smiles. He heads for the big auditorium and enters a cavernous, semi-desolate space with a sunken orchestra pit below a vast, remote stage. A scattering of students hang off the railing while factions loiter in wayward aisles and shadowy corners. But Damon's arrival, like the sheriff hitting town, presages the dawn of order and coherence.

"Hey, everyone, Damon's here! Time to get started!"

The director in every sense, Damon knows his audience and comes prepared. "Okay, listen up, here's your daily sheet!" He hands out a typed list with the day's scenes and activities laid out. Damon can count on a few allies: the drama mentor, Mr. Wasserstein; Alexandra, a talented actress and president of the drama club; Josh, the reliable stage manager; and Damon's good buddy Max, his right-hand man. But teen discipline and attention span can still be erratic, so Damon introduces new routines.

"I got a new tape with some great chill-out music!" Grinning, Damon pops the latest New Age tracks into the player and the ambient music instantly alters the mood. He leads the class in exercises, focusing them before they start rehearsing.

But new problems arise, starting with the issue of a life-sized wooden sarcophagus into which a scheming character is enticed. Lifting the tall box with a live body inside is tricky, while the lid keeps sticking, raising claustrophobic alarms and wild banging from within: "Get me outta here!"

Damon also must deal with the anxiety of a young actress worried she won't be able to kiss a fellow actor, as the scene demands, because of his unromantic appearance.

"I know it's hard," Damon says. "Just close your eyes and pretend he's Brad Pitt."

More ominously, Damon loses his lead at the eleventh hour, jeopardizing the entire show. The director must scramble to keep the production from imploding.

"Okay, I need someone who can learn all of Sheridan Whiteside's lines and carry the play with less than two weeks to go!" Damon sighs.

As if things aren't bad enough, the drama club needs extra money for the production. Shealagh and I underwrite some costs, and Damon hawks knickknacks with his friends at school lunch to raise more funds.

For props and costumes, Damon's biggest asset is his mother. When he needs an antique 1930s suitcase, eagle-eyed Shealagh spots a canvas case with leather handles out on the sidewalk. For an old-fashioned feather duster, Shealagh finds a good bamboo-handled facsimile in Chinatown. For period dresses, Shealagh rummages through the racks at the Salvation Army. When she can't improvise, Shealagh drives

Damon and the costume designer, Vlada, to the big costume warehouse in midtown and buys them the right outfits.

It's hard to believe Damon is overseeing every facet of this sprawling production and rehearsing his actors — including the new lead, who doesn't yet know his lines — in the midst of his deteriorating health and the ticking transplant clock. But he is.

We've agreed that right after the play, I'll take Damon to L.A. to see his *Deadwood* pals before we list him for a transplant. Once listed, Damon can't travel, nor will any of us dare to leave home base, until he gets his new heart. The offer could come at any hour — usually from a car accident or sudden trauma — and we have to be ready to move fast.

"They estimate the average wait is three to six months, but I think it could happen sooner given your size, blood type, status, hospital, and other preferential circumstances," I tell Damon. "But we can't count on that, and no one can promise us anything. So we have to prepare to put our lives on hold and be on call around the clock, for an indefinite period."

Given this imminent lockdown, I make a quick business trip to Paris just before Damon's play. During a free afternoon, I

444

take off like a cooped-up kangaroo and hop for miles through the city where I once lived and studied, turned twenty-one, and had one of the great love affairs of my youth. I cover half the metropolis on foot, striding at breakneck speed. Finally, I circle back to Trocadéro, where the old cinematheque served as my second home; shoot past Balzac's house; and descend the rue Raynouard, where the cops would stop and hassle me for driving my girlfriend on the back of my Mobylette.

I'm pleased to find the apartment building where I rented a tiny *chambre de bonne* is still there, with its narrow attic window overlooking the Eiffel Tower. But what most strikes me on my swift walkabout, other than my blistering feet, is how *altered* my life now is. I search in vain for the ambitious, romantic young man who hungered after every intimation of beauty and truth this magical city seemed to offer, and who threw himself headlong into love and art — the two seemed inextricable — believing no higher goal or nobler purpose existed. The notion of marriage and kids never entered *his* consciousness.

Yet now I live for my wife and my children, and Damon has become the center of my existence. It occurs to me *he* is my romance now, or some platonic version thereof, and I love him and fight for him with the same ardor I once reserved for the love of beautiful women and the pursuit of artistic inspiration.

I'm still pondering this back home in Brooklyn, sitting in the kitchen with Damon on Saturday afternoon. Shealagh has taken Sam and Miranda ice-skating in Prospect Park, so it's just the two of us. Damon is downing his pills, slowly, which is how he does everything now, when he turns to me. "So how was Paris, Dad?"

I can't tell whether he's really interested or just passing the time while taking his meds, but soon he's probing boldly and has me saying more than I intended. Under deft interrogation, I tell Damon about falling madly in love the summer of my freshman year in college and cohabiting with a wild spirit.

"Where did you meet her?" Damon asks.

"On the beach in St. Tropez. We were lovers before I knew her name — or how many other guys she was still seeing." I glance at my son, realizing I've passed the point of no return. "She was eighteen and hard to resist. I was nineteen."

"Cool." Damon nods as if I'm showing him a bootleg film, with his unrecognizable father in an unfamiliar role. "Then what happened?"

"She led me on a mad chase, I followed her halfway across France, persevered, but refused to let it be a summer fling. I came back the next year, and we lived together in Paris while I went to university, or tried to . . . It was an exciting roller coaster, but then the ride ended. It's hard to be free of any social rules and live only on the edge of each moment. She was bolder and more out-there than me, but a little unstable too, and it got worse."

"How?" Damon tries to sound casual and downplay his avid interest.

"Well, there were lots of things . . ." I sigh. "I guess the short version is, sometime after me, she spent six years in prison for accidentally killing her lover."

Now I have Damon's complete attention in a different way.

"She didn't intend to," I quickly explain. "I think she wanted to settle down with this guy. But the knife slipped."

"What was she doing with a *knife?*" Damon screws up his features.

"It's complicated . . . She was a purely spontaneous person, always true to her impulses. That can be dangerous but also very alluring, especially when the transgressing person happens to be beautiful. I fell hard for her. I was young."

Damon's lips drift into a secret smile as he processes this information.

"Probably better if we don't let your mother know we discussed this." I wink at him. "And of course, not a word to Sam or Miranda."

"Of course." Damon nods. "Thanks for telling me, Dad."

"Yeah, no problem. You asked, I answered. I don't regret any of it, though we both got hurt. She once asked me, years later, if it was possible to love too much . . . The moral, in my view, is *go for it* — whatever 'it' turns out to be for you."

Damon raises an earnest, pale ginger eyebrow. "How will I know?"

"You'll know, believe me!" I chuckle but Damon isn't satisfied.

"It's easy for you, Dad, because you always got what you wanted."

I laugh, flattered he'd think so. "Not always, D-man, not always! No one ever does. Not if you're playing for real."

Damon studies me, taking this in. "I'm still not sure how I'll be able to tell."

"If you want to break it down," I reply, "when you're willing to lose everything and make any sacrifice, including giving up fiercely held notions of yourself, you'll know."

Damon looks like he's still trying to get a handle on this. I smile.

"You have wonderful surprises and undreamed-of delights in store, but you'll know what's true when it appears. I have total confidence in your abilities."

"If you say so, Dad." Damon gives me a skeptical but intrigued look.

That evening we all go to see *Finding Neverland.* The film explores the life of J. M. Barrie, the author of *Peter Pan,* and reveals that Barrie lost his older brother as a child and created the figure of Peter Pan and the notion of Neverland, a place where no one grows old or dies, in part to try to console his shattered mother.

I thought I was taking my family to a nice holiday movie but I leave the theater feeling as if we've all been ambushed in the dark and forced to confront a taboo subject. It seems there's no escaping our predicament. But as we drink hot chocolate and unwind after, everyone says they liked the film and no one seems upset.

I don't share my feelings with anyone — I don't wish to think about them myself — but the next day, after working at my desk all morning, Damon approaches me in the kitchen. He's been notably warmer since I shared my past.

"How's your novel going, Dad?" He fixes his sparkling eyes on me.

"Okay." In truth, I haven't been able to write for months due to his situation but I continue to jot notes on my plot and characters. So now I mention a major shift given fresh impetus by the film we just saw. "I'm moving away from *Romeo and Juliet* and toward *The Tempest*."

I'm using literary shorthand, but Damon instantly gets what I'm saying. Soon, I'm telling him as much about my novel as I've told anyone, and he's not only nodding as if he understands, he's asking me astute, penetrating questions.

It's an epiphany for me. I'm simply floored that this young man sitting across from me, whose education and development I've helped guide at every stage, is now providing *me* with enlightened feedback on my own creative work.

There aren't more than three or four people in the world I can usefully talk to about my writing — who know enough, and care enough — and suddenly I realize my son has become one of them!

It's like waking up to find an amazing gift under my pillow or a priceless gold coin in my backyard.

The universe has just become that much less vast-seeming and solitary for me.

CHAPTER 44

Damon Weber (Director, Vice President of the Drama Club): *The Man Who Came to Dinner* is a simple comedy about not so simple people. So was the process that led to the production you are about to see. Like Mr. Stanley, I was not the same person by the end. The play before you is the result of two months hard work by a wonderful, charismatic cast and a dedicated and committed crew whom I've been lucky to work with. Although we had our fair share of octopuses, large bills and the occasional cockroach, we somehow managed to pull through. I would like to thank my parents, especially my mom for her much needed assistance with props and costumes. Lastly, I would like to thank everyone who came here tonight because the audience is what brings a play to life.

— From the playbill to the Brooklyn Technical High School production of *The Man Who Came to Dinner,* December 2004

We sit on the floor along the proscenium of the stage with our winter coats on our laps, and a profusion of hats, scarves, Kleenex, and cough drops scattered at our feet. Almost everyone has come to support a friend or relative.

This overstuffed drawing room farce by George S. Kaufman and Moss Hart is a somewhat dated screwball romp, and most of the time Damon has his hands full just keeping the sprawling twenty-nine-person ensemble on their marks and on cue. But the dialogue and action keep flowing at a good pace with no showstopping snafus — the lead relies on youthful cockiness and sheer exuberance when his actual lines elude him — and there are myriad comic turns and hilarious caricatures. Even the upright mummy case is effective.

When it's over, the audience applauds and gathers around the cast but I remain seated, still mulling the subtle shaping intelligence of Damon's direction.

"Did you just see what I saw?" I turn to Krista, a theater teacher.

"Nice job. He improved on the film version in a couple places," she says with a smile.

"Damon, Damon!" The cast clamors for the director to join them onstage.

Damon jogs up and takes a quick, deep bow at the waist, the suave young director in his glory. For the first time, I realize the true depth of his artistry.

Afterward, our proud family congratulates him. "Damon, did you get that girl out of the mummy case yet?" Miranda looks concerned. Then we all wait as he wanders through the auditorium and makes his good-byes one by one.

"Think he has any idea how good he is?" I ask Shealagh.

"It's hard to tell but I think he's just happy he managed to get out of bed and stand here tonight!" Shealagh says with a mix of welling pride and relief.

I continue pondering Damon's craft as we meander up chilly DeKalb Avenue and troop into Applebee's with his pals. It's crowded and noisy on a Saturday night, and we have to wait for several tables so we can all sit together.

Damon is several seats away from me,

ensconced with Kyle and his other buddies, so I cup my hands above the din to get his attention.

"Amazing job, D-man! You really showed me something new tonight!"

The play is already old news and Damon is eager to keep up with his friends and their latest preoccupation, but he still manages a quick, grateful smile my way. "Thanks, Dad."

I try not to think about how pale he looks. For tonight, his accomplishment imbues him with a shining luster, and as I sit back in my molded plastic chair in this packed, voluble, and stupefyingly ordinary chain restaurant, I'm proud to salute an emerging young artist and to place an honorary crown on his head.

With the countdown to transplant ticking loudly, Damon and I fly to L.A. and visit the *Deadwood* set. It's as if outside time has stood still in that remote canyon. We see all our buddies and the cast members as they troop into the dining tent in their 1870s frontier garb and makeup after several hours of shooting.

David Milch tells Damon that every person who's watched his performance was knocked out by it and asks Damon to take a first pass at writing his own expanded part for next season.

"Wow, thanks, that sounds like a cool opportunity," Damon says.

"You bet your ass it is." David grins. "But I know you have good ideas."

The rodeo star Gary Leffew, who didn't know of Damon's illness, is shocked by the news and amazed he still rode with us. "So it's showdown time? He's gonna do great, I ain't seen no man tough as Damon . . . I'll be pullin' for him with all I got! For you too, my friend! Stay strong. Ain't nothin' harder than this."

Although we planned to stay on set till nighttime, Damon runs out of energy — I'm struck by his deteriorations since the summer — and we must leave early. As we make our somber farewells, David Milch approaches Damon very gingerly and asks if he can give him a kiss.

Damon pauses to consider, then slowly nods.

The actress Paula Malcomson meets us for tea the next day and shares the same easy rapport with Damon. "They finished editing your scene and it looks fuckin' great, Damon . . . So how was directing your first play? Aren't actors a pain in the ass?"

Later Damon and I are sitting poolside

when his friend Max calls from New York, frantic because he couldn't reach Damon and feared he'd gone in for his transplant.

After Damon calms Max down, we wade into the pool and toss a rubber ball back and forth. I notice Damon, a tad wobbly, still catches my throw each time. I recall when we spent hours practicing to improve his motor skills but now he can handle anything that comes his way. We toss the ball, ten, twenty, thirty times . . . We pass fifty, then a hundred throws, hooked in the back-and-forth. I watch Damon in red swim trunks as he zeroes in on the flying orb and nabs it with perfect hand-eye coordination each time. How can a boy so ill be this proficient? Can I really let them *rip out and replace* the heart of such a flawless performer?

Our last night, I take Damon to the premiere of *Meet the Fockers* and he has a good giggle over this star-studded comedy. Then we head to the gala reception under a huge tent, where I introduce him to various film people I know.

We spot the actor Dustin Hoffman, surrounded by security and a crush of fans. I sponsored a panel with Hoffman two years earlier, and after I prod him, he recalls the event, claims to remember me, and lets me introduce him to my son.

"So what kind of acting have you done?" Hoffman asks. He wears makeup above his powder blue shirt and actually listens and responds to Damon.

Damon's face lights up as they talk, and not just because Hoffman is a major star, a genuine talent, and an intelligent conversationalist. What also hits Damon — right between the eyes, as it were — is that Hoffman is not much taller than he is!

I watch my son rise on the balls of his feet and lift up his head as he discusses their shared love of the craft with the renowned actor and registers that *this could be him.* It's involuntary and owes as much to other similarities he can sense close-up, but the size is a leveler exposing a deeper truth: *Hey, maybe I could do this.*

Damon is far too modest to utter such a thought, but I see the flash of recognition in his face as he stands and holds his own beside Hoffman.

As I watch the two dapper figures, their heads bent close, bright-eyed and smiling, I'm struck that despite the fifty-year age difference, they have something important in common. And I grasp that if Damon continues on his current path, and if he keeps getting the right breaks, Hoffman represents

one kind of actor route, or a plausible acting context, for such a career direction. It's
a heady thought, but I don't feel grand or
prideful about it. It's just one possible
window into Damon's future, and Damon
might not even choose that path, nor am I
sure it's the best path for him. And of course
he might fail, if he did choose it. But it's a
preview of, and a highly privileged glimpse
into, where, theoretically, Damon could fit
in, if that were the path he followed.

CHAPTER 45

It's a bird, it's a plane, no it's Damon updating! Lol Hey everyone, I'm back. What tis up? So lots has happened but you get none of it. So anyone know a good place to have a New Year's party cause I feel like relaxing this new year aka not hosting the group's New Year's party lol. I still love you all, some more than others . . . Yeah so, if anyone's got an idea 4 a New Years' party that doesn't involve the words "amish country" or "Damon's house" please share . . . Been playin massive amounts of World of Warcraft and it's been much fun. Btw why is everyone saying bueno? Well that's all 4 now, later dudes and dudets.

— From Damon's blog, winter 2004

Having made the General Decision for a heart transplant for Damon, and having selected our return from L.A. as the Decision Period for getting his name on the wait list, we now face the Decision Moment — that precise instant when we make The Listing Call.

That triggering act will unleash a cascade of events culminating, if all goes well, in the surgical removal of Damon's original heart from his chest cavity and its replacement with the fully functioning heart of another, freshly deceased individual.

It's a huge step — a leap of faith, as well as science.

"We've consulted *every* medical expert and exhausted *all* known therapeutic options," I tell my wife. "Not a single practical treatment of any kind remains on my list!" I make a show of crumpling the now-useless piece of yellow paper in front of her and trashing it.

We've had to accept not only that transplantation is the sole remaining option but also that we must act soon if we hope to successfully avail ourselves of it.

"He's getting chills and looking more listless and enervated," Sonja notes on her latest visit. "I wouldn't wait much longer."

We see the warning signs and know she's right. From the start, we've understood there was a fine balance between trying to avoid a transplant altogether and not completely closing off the transplant window, so that this procedure remained a viable alternative if none other could be found. Now the balance has tipped. While Damon's latest tests show he's still in relatively decent shape for this operation, time is running out.

Yet now, with the day of reckoning at hand, it becomes challenging to pinpoint the optimal moment for listing Damon. The hospital has provided little guidance. "You can list him whenever you're ready but we don't need to see him for two months," they tell us. Shealagh and I feel it's far more urgent — a matter of weeks or even days, not months — but my wife leaves the exact timing to me. It's a complex, monumental decision, the biggest I've had to make, and I run every scenario to get it right while grappling with powerful, conflicting emotions.

"It could take six months or longer to find him a new heart and he could decline fast before we do, which is one reason to list him now," I tell Shealagh. "But it could also take twenty-four hours to find him a donor heart, which means we must be ready to let him go into the operating room from the minute we list him!"

Every extra day with Damon is precious

now. He sleeps late and hangs around the house, playing computer games and blogging and IM-ing his pals. He takes his pills and his shots. He watches a lot of TV, wrapped in a sweatshirt and blankets in the family room.

I catch him when I can, especially around the television set. *Scrubs, Family Guy, What's My Line?* and *Sex and the City* are his current favorites, though he also tunes in to endless reruns and just about anything on Comedy Central. "What you watching, D-man?" I sit beside him no matter what's on and share wry commentary or a wordless communion.

I'm so eager to be near Damon I request a tutorial on World of Warcraft, his most consuming pastime, and spend hours battling monsters and undertaking quests in the trippy kingdom of Kalimdor.

We go to my parents' house in Queens for the first night of Hanukkah, a family tradition. Many relatives and friends are there and all are aware of our situation — Damon looks small and hunched in his *Deadwood* sweatshirt and his bowl-cut hair frames a chalky face — but we try to pretend it's just another holiday.

We lay out our presents by the teak cabinet and gather to light the menorah. The silver candelabrum stands on a cloth that Damon painted in kindergarten: it's filled with his bold, brash colors, all unified by a glorious overarching rainbow, once his signature motif. My wife and I share a wistful pang at this pictorial memento of our firstborn's sunny childhood.

Shealagh has cut her hair short and wears an embroidered purple blouse. She puts on a brave front, but the suffering is etched into her face. Sam and Miranda, both vivid in colorful T-shirts, provide a stark contrast with their subdued older brother. Their careless bouncing energy underscores his sluggishness and increasing marginalization.

As my mother prepares to light the first candle on the antique, finely wrought silver candelabrum, she turns to Damon.

"This menorah is from my home in Leipzig. It belonged to my parents and is one of the few things I had from them before they were killed with all my relatives . . . When the time comes, I'm going to give it to *you* to keep in the family!"

My mother's voice trembles and Damon, who's heard this before, bows his head, humbly acknowledging the firstborn honor. "Thanks, Grandma."

My father hands my mother a prayer book from her home in Germany and takes one

464

from his parents' home in Glasgow. My mother recites the blessing and lights the candles on two menorahs and we sing "Rock of Ages." Damon joins in the rousing victory song. He looks pasty by the glow of the hanging lamp, and his oversized sweat-shirt swallows his doughy body, but he's determined to participate in the celebration and adds his conscientious notes to our motley warbling.

"Sammy, what are we celebrating today?" My father dives into his catechism mode as we sit down to eat at the long, resplendent table.

Sam looks at Damon, who shrugs and looks right back at Sam with steely silence. Damon's patience with his siblings has suf-fered, along with everything else, during this period, even if Sam's veneration of Damon is undiminished.

"The miracle of the oil," Sam pipes up, after seeing he's on his own.

"What kind of oil, like at the petrol pump?" My father keeps a poker face.

"Daddy, spare us the history lesson till later, okay?" my sister cuts in, ostensibly on our guests' behalf. "It's a Jewish holiday, they're all the same. They tried to kill us, we survived, now let's eat!" She grins with tart charm.

"Everyone can sit down. I'll put on the first latkes," my mother says.

I bring out my camcorder and start to pan across the table, noting each attendee. But when I get to Damon, he shifts sideways, out of frame. I wait but he uses his glass of hot cider with cinnamon stick to keep my view obstructed. He's become very resistant to being filmed.

"Come on, D-man, I'm shooting everyone. It's a record of the event."

"No," Damon says. I can't determine if it's because he's more self-conscious about his appearance or if he sees my effort to record him as a tacit admission of uncertainty about the future. Or perhaps it's simply because he's a teenager and I'm his father.

But Damon now regards me and my camera as an intrusion, and I must catch him off guard if I want a clean shot. It's a big change because ever since I filmed Damon as a four-year-old sitting on the doorstep of our Adirondacks cabin — a young boy bathed in sunshine and surrounded by green blades of grass, smiling at a slow summer day — my son and I have had a special rapport through the camera and Damon has always *encouraged* me to record his unfolding glory.

Yet now, even after I respect his wishes and put down my camcorder, Damon remains an elusive figure. He eats sparingly, like a bird, and flits off several times, darting to the bathroom or roaming about the house.

"Is Damon okay?" my mother asks once. "He seems to have disappeared."

"I'll get him," I say, and put down my fork. I search the house and find him upstairs in my old room, lying down on my old bed in the dark. I can't see him at first and it's very quiet, but I feel a faint presence enfolded in the gloom.

"That you, D-man?"

"Yeah, I just came up to phone my friends, and I must've drifted off."

I wait for him to wash his face, and we go back downstairs together.

Later, after the orgy of gift-opening and shredded wrapping paper, Sonja walks over to me, her back to Damon. "You know I'm really very impressed by everything you've done for him. No medical expert in the world could have done more than you have for your son, and you should feel good knowing that."

My sister leans over and says, "I couldn't agree more. You're amazing parents!"

These comments, which I hear from

several quarters lately, only increase my anxiety, although I know people mean well. If I'm such a good father, why is my son so sick, and why haven't I been able to make him better? And if the transplant really offers hope, why does everyone sound like they're trying to console me *before* the operation?

My mother walks around and hands out big jelly donuts, pressing the traditional sweets on every guest. Damon politely accepts a donut but lays it aside on the glass table, leans back against a beaded cushion, and closes his eyes. Everyone sees how out-of-it he is.

We wait for a seemly interval and depart, earlier than usual.

We're very close now and it's only a matter of days before we make The Call. Winter break has started and school's out for everyone, not just Damon.

Each morning, we wake up wondering if today is the day, and each evening we find something worth cherishing and holding on to: a small affirmation of what we still have, be it Damon's brief outing to the library or a friend's sleepover, Damon cackling on the phone or plotting a New Year's Eve party. It's surprising what comprises an acceptable quality of life when the alternative is unknown. Never has the status quo looked more appealing and worth hanging on to.

Why give him up, or risk losing him, any sooner than we have to?

There may be some denial and wishful thinking behind our delay. If we just wrap Damon up in our deepest embrace and hunker down, enveloped in the safe cocoon of a love-filled home and its daily routines, surely this will pass?

But there's also a pragmatic, selfish reason for waiting: we don't want to let Damon go one nanosecond before we must, and we feel so connected to him that we trust our own independent monitoring system to signal us when it's time.

The new Columbia study has made us much more optimistic about the risk/benefit ratio for transplants. And there is a strong likelihood of a life-altering *improvement* for Damon. But it's still a dire step.

So we prefer to wait. But I check Damon almost hourly.

One evening, I return to his room to continue our conversation — I left to answer the doorbell — when I find him laid out on the carpet, completely immobile. He's fallen asleep, as if in midsentence, his mouth gaping like a fish's. It's only five P.M. but already dark beyond the curtains. The air inside his overheated room is insufferably close. Sticky spoons and open medicines and white balled-up little tissues litter the ground. I can see the life force ebbing out of my son.

If we wait any longer, we're sealing his fate.

I go upstairs and find Shealagh. "It's time, baby. We gotta do it!"

"I know." She sighs deeply.

I call up Columbia and get Damon listed. It's three days before Christmas.

CHAPTER 46

Anyway, a belated Happy New Year's to all . . . Went 2 Max's for New Year's twas fun. It's ironic all the days over the break where I was just bumming around (except 4 Max's thing) were the most fun and the days when I had plans wound up sucking . . . Oh if I forgot to mention it, which I think I did, there are whispers of putting me in the hospital . . . coincidentally around the same time, there are also whispers that Damon has started carrying his Turkish knife around: . . . hmm . . . . . . coincidence, I think not. Note 2 self: must sharpen that thing. (what Damon you have a Turkish knife! Uh, where? How come none of us has ever seen it or know where it is?? Think about that question 4 a minute and see if you can't answer it yourself lol.) Thank gosh 4 Krista (my neighbor) 4 rescuing me Friday. I went over 2 her house and watched Jaws (which I'm ashamed to admit I had not seen till tonight, it was awesome) If I am going 2 die I hope its cause someone shoves a big pressurized gas can in my mouth and then shoots it. What a way 2 go lol. Though I don't suppose that's the kind of medical malpractice or mistakes 1 usually hears about: lol. (Oh btw, Krista is 23 so don't get any ideas lol I know how your minds work) Thanx Nicole and Nef 4 your comments. Ok goodnight all.

— From Damon's blog, January 2005

From the start, getting Damon listed for a heart transplant is a flawed process.

When the time finally comes, I take a deep breath and call Dr. Davis at Columbia. It's been a long, painful journey, but now that we're there, I'm hoping for a little orientation and support. I expect she'll be very responsive, since we've accepted their assurances that a heart transplant is the right way to go and they are the right people for the job.

However, despite the excruciating struggle that precedes this momentous decision, it turns into a big anticlimax because Dr. Davis is not at the hospital when I call. Nor is Dr. Mason on the premises. And no one can tell me how to reach either of them.

I've phoned to announce our readiness, at long last, to hand over our son into the care of the pediatric cardiac transplant unit at Columbia — the single most agonizing choice we've ever made — but there's no one on the other end to receive the news! Nor is anyone on hand to tell us about next steps or to provide the standard set of instructions.

I'm left hanging on the phone with the solitary, beating echo of my own heart. It's especially frustrating because neither doctor has given me her contact information, so I have no way of getting through to them.

I leave a message for Dr. Davis, saying I need to talk to her about Damon *right away.*

"We've never been shut out like this by physicians managing Damon's care! Not at Columbia, nor at any other hospital!" I complain to my wife, who is equally perturbed.

"And he's never been this sick before! How can they just ignore us?" Shealagh says, fuming.

I wait all day but Dr. Davis does not return my call.

"I don't get it," I tell Shealagh the next night. "Even Columbia, one of the biggest centers in the country, only does about twenty pediatric transplants a year, so *each*

473

one is a big deal, with a whole team assigned to every case. Our call is supposed to initiate an entire protocol, so it's very odd no one has bothered to phone us back."

"I guess it's the Christmas period," Shealagh says. "Harder to find people."

"We're still several days pre-Christmas . . . And patients can be *ignored* if it's inconvenient?" I frown. "They should be prepared for us and on top of this!"

That night, before going to bed, I send Dr. Davis an e-mail saying I fear we're running out of time and I need to talk to her about next steps. I leave more voice messages with her answering service, underscoring the sensitivity of this matter.

The next morning, I check my e-mail but still no response. Nor a voice mail. I phone the hospital again. I feel we're ready to make the biggest leap of our lives, a concession wrung out of us after years of resistance, only no one seems to care. On the third day, increasingly worried about this lack of response, not to mention the lack of responsibility, I call the transplant unit, determined to get through or raise hell.

Dr. Davis and Dr. Mason are still nowhere to be found, but after refusing to leave another message, I am transferred to a Dr. Thea Becker at New York Hospital. Dr.

Becker explains that she is one of the four cardiologists on Columbia's team, the other three being Dr. Mason, Dr. Davis, and a Dr. Sanford. Although Dr. Becker is clearly the junior member — we haven't heard of her until now, she is part-time at Columbia, and her voice has the stiff, by-the-book callowness of a graduate fellow — Dr. Becker assures me that all four cardiologists in the pediatric transplant unit are "interchangeable."

"We pool all our information, so anything you say to one of us is shared with the others . . . So you see, even though I've never met Damon or examined him, I know all about his case and I can help you as well as any of our other cardiologists," Dr. Becker says.

"With all due respect, that's an absurd concept!" I tell Dr. Becker. "Whatever happened to continuity of care and direct, firsthand observation of the patient?"

Although I'm appalled by this notion — it sounds like a fancy excuse for no-shows and lax supervision by senior doctors — and although I don't intend to let a raw novice like Dr. Becker, who's never even taken Damon's blood pressure or listened to his heartbeat, manage my son's transplant care, it occurs to me she might serve as well as anyone for our immediate needs. Getting Damon's name on the national transplant registry is a technicality in a largely bureaucratic process, and no personal knowledge of Damon is required. If Dr. Becker can help us speed up this protocol, we could save valuable time. And the junior Dr. Becker seems eager to prove her utility. At least she's *there*.

"So what do I need to do to get Damon listed?" I ask, softening my tone.

"If his transplant evaluations are completed, you don't need to do anything."

"You sure? That sounds too easy," I say with a laugh.

"That's it, but I can check on his status just to be certain," Dr. Becker says.

Two hours later, Dr. Becker calls back to say Damon has been placed on the transplant wait list. She mentions this so casually it takes a minute to sink in.

"He's listed?"

"Yes. He's on the national registry. His evaluations were all in order."

"Great . . . So from here on, the offer could come at any moment?"

"That's technically correct, yes. Though it usually takes several months."

Dr. Becker sounds very offhand, almost cavalier, which bothers me.

"But it could happen *tomorrow,* right? You can't predict! . . . So what should we do?"

"Haven't you read the booklet?" Dr. Becker asks.

"I skimmed it and my wife's read it about twenty times," I explain. "And I'll memorize it now that I know it's real. But can you please just give me a quick recap?"

Dr. Becker sighs. "The main thing is to have an overnight bag packed and ready to go to the hospital . . . You'll also want someone to look after your other children if both you and your wife plan to stay with Damon . . . He will need to wear a beeper and we'll want a list of all your phone numbers — home, office, cell — so we can reach you the minute we find a donor match . . . The transplant coordinator will contact you with further details."

It takes a moment after I hang up to accept what we've done. I relay these developments to Shealagh, then go and share the news with Damon.

"Cool," he says. "It'll be nice if we can fix my problem for good."

He seems relieved a search is under way and pleased at the possibility of success. Even as we speak, his face and belly are puffy and he exudes a muted, Buddha-like air as he calmly awaits release from his imperfect body.

I run through the broad outlines of the process for him. "Do you understand what's involved, D-man? You have any questions for me, or anything else you'd like to know?"

"I think I got it and if I need to know more, I can always go online," Damon says with a shrug.

I'm surprised he seems to be downplaying this. Then I realize how sensible he is. He trusts me to handle the details, he'll rally when he needs to, but otherwise he just wants to get on with his regular life. What else is there to do? It's a wise strategy and I don't mess with it.

Shealagh and I discuss what to tell Sam and Miranda.

"They know Damon is in trouble and that we're talking to doctors," I say. "And like all kids, they know more than their parents think . . . But now we need to fill in the blanks."

"Yes, I agree. Why don't you go first?" Shealagh says. "I'll give them the soft version after." My wife smiles.

It's not easy to explain to one's children that their brother's failing heart must be replaced with a stranger's heart — a freshly deceased stranger, whose size, age, and blood type must roughly match. But the kids, in their way, grasp the concept about as well as us.

Miranda accepts my words at face value and goes to brood in private — she's either sparing her feelings or mine, probably both — while Sam assails me with questions.

"Why does he have to stay in the hospital so long?" Sam demands.

"A month isn't that long. His body has to heal," I reply.

"But why does he have to keep taking all those medications?" Sam's still upset.

"So he doesn't reject his heart, and so he doesn't get an infection," I explain. "Since it's not his original heart, his body will attack it unless we keep his defense system down. But if his defenses are down, he could catch an infection, so we have to protect against that too."

"But why does he have to take all those medications *for the rest of his life?* It's not fair!" Sam cries as if it is all subject to my control and I could change it.

"Look, Sam," I finally say. "Damon will have more energy, and he can grow with his new heart, and those are *two* great things we can't afford to pass up!"

We talk to my parents, who respond with customary stalwartness.

"We're on standby and ready for duty,"

my father says. "Once Damon enters the hospital, we'll move into your house and camp there for the duration."

"Thanks, you guys! Only one parent is permitted to sleep in Damon's room but both Shealagh and I intend to be on the case twenty-four/seven."

"Call for you, Dad!" Miranda says, and my heart skips a beat. Every time the phone rings, we hold our breath because it could be The Offer. At work, I alert my assistant to my whereabouts constantly, though she still doesn't know why, and I check my cell phone compulsively. Shealagh and I speak several times a day and get nervous if too many hours have elapsed without an update.

Damon continues to have large groups of friends over to our house during the Christmas vacation. I still come downstairs and find teenage flirting, petting, and strutting around, but I notice the kids leave earlier and fewer spend the night. When I remark on this to Damon, he says with an enigmatic sigh, "Well, it's different now."

"I can't tell if it's different because the kids all talk about college and moving on while he's fallen behind," I tell Shealagh, "or because he can't keep up physically with them. Or is it because they feel funny know-

480

ing he's waiting for a heart transplant?"

When an old friend, Daniel, visits, the boys spend all their time on the computer. After Daniel leaves, I ask Damon what Daniel had to say about his upcoming surgery.

"We didn't really talk about it," Damon replies.

"Any reason?" I ask, trying to mask my surprise.

"No, it just didn't come up," Damon says with an ambiguous shrug.

But for our family, it comes up, as text or subtext, in *everything*. For New Year's, Damon has a party at Max's while the rest of us are going to a bash in Manhattan. We'd love to celebrate with Damon but we're happy he has his own plans. Damon promises to keep his cell on and we can get to Max's in no time if The Offer comes.

As we start to drive off, I realize I never wished Damon a happy New Year. He's still in our house with friends, and I won't see him again until 2005! To Shealagh's consternation, I shift into reverse and speed backward along our one-way street before leaping out of the vehicle, charging into the house, and embracing my son — "Have a happy and healthy 2005, D-man!" — before I jump back into the car and tear off again. Shealagh is upset with my driving and we fight all the way into the city until the big party diffuses the tension.

At midnight, as the colorful fireworks explode over Central Park and the glass windowpanes shudder, Shealagh calls Damon on his cell. She speaks to her darling boy from the window seat, then hands him to Sam and Miranda, who eventually pass him over to me.

Damon sounds champagne giddy, with lively party noises in the background. He's riding high. I can still hear a tremulous catch in his larynx but his merry, resonant voice soars with impish delight, reassuring me that our world remains intact for a little longer.

A week later, after returning to work, I become increasingly concerned about the continuing lack of communication from Columbia Presbyterian Hospital.

Dr. Davis still has not answered my e-mail, nor has she or Dr. Mason called me back. Absent my one talk with Dr. Becker — she's never around, and no one seems to know her — it's as if nothing has happened, nothing has changed.

We've had no instructions about the transplant preparations, nor does anyone seem even mildly interested in Damon's condition. Dr. Hayes, our longtime cardiologist, is off the case, and Dr. Hellenbrand, who temporarily took over, has handed us on to the transplant unit. Both Dr. Hayes and Dr. Hellenbrand were highly attentive physicians and responsive caregivers, but neither Dr. Davis nor her boss, Dr. Mason, whom Dr. Hayes entrusted us to, seems to have taken the most basic responsibility for our case.

"No one's examining Damon. They're not even giving us his weekly lab results, which we always got before, so *we* can tell how he's doing," Shealagh says.

"And they're not tracking changes from his new meds or calling to check on him," I add. "They're not even returning our calls. It's as if we've been dropped!"

I decide to send a stronger message to Dr. Davis. This time, I don't just describe my frustrations but I title my e-mail, "Who's in Charge of Damon Weber?"

I've noted Dr. Mason's marketing mindset pervades her entire team, and I surmise Dr. Davis will not want such a telling question visible in her inbox.

Sure enough, within three hours, Dr. Davis calls back and agrees to meet us.

Shealagh, Damon, and I go in to Columbia. Dr. Davis, smilingly polite, examines

Damon and asks how he's doing. She reviews the transplant procedure and preparations, walking Damon through all the steps and describing each stage. She has a bright, cheerful manner and is very thorough and professional.

"How long will it take you to find me a new heart?" Damon asks.

Dr. Davis explains that transplant patients are classified under three categories: status 1A, for those in the most urgent need; status 1B, for those with the second-highest priority; and status 2, for all other "active" patients on the wait list.

"Damon, since you are classified a two, the lowest priority, you'll have a six-to-twelve-month wait, though it could be sooner — being under eighteen years of age may work in your favor — or alternatively, even later. No one can predict." Dr. Davis smiles.

As I hear this, something nags at me. I recall that Dr. Bruce Gelb, in one of his asides, had mentioned Damon could qualify as a 1B due to his small size, under the criterion "failure to thrive." I hadn't fully understood what Bruce meant at the time, but his words come back to me now, and I ask Dr. Davis about them.

"No, that's not true. Damon is a two,"

484

Dr. Davis says. "You're mistaken."

"I'm sure you're right," I reply, "but I'm surprised a leading cardiologist like Bruce Gelb, who's a pretty sharp guy, would make such an error."

"I can't answer for him but I know transplants, which is my specialty!"

"Of course." I let it drop. I don't want to risk further antagonizing Dr. Davis after my e-mail, and it's possible I'm the one who made the error or misremembers.

Dr. Davis continues to instruct Damon about his big day in a clear, cogent manner, but she seems beset by second thoughts and turns to her assistant.

"Erica, could you go get me the big manual on heart transplantation?"

Moments later, Erica returns with a tome. Dr. Davis tears it open and races through the pages, searching with her index finger like an avid medical student.

"I'm not sure" — Dr. Davis finally looks up from the manual — "but you *may* have a point about Damon's status. I'll research it more and get back to you."

I'd already given Dr. Davis the benefit of the doubt, so this fumbling uncertainty unnerves me. We leave feeling uneasy about what's going on, obviously hopeful for a status revision in our favor but also worried about what such a revision might signify.

The next day we get a fax from Columbia informing us that Damon's wait-list status has been officially changed from a 2 to a 1B.

It's the difference between being high priority and low priority, between waiting for a few weeks or up to a year. It could also mean the difference between life and death.

We're naturally pleased Damon has moved up the ranks and now stands a better chance of receiving a new heart in a timely manner. But it also confirms that for the past two and a half weeks, Damon has been erroneously listed.

It's unsettling. My sense that no one was taking charge of our case proved truer than I suspected. Had we not challenged Columbia, Damon could have missed a lifesaving opportunity. And it was only by a fluke, a stray remark from a more knowledgeable physician, that I had any inkling about this snafu.

Around this time, Dr. Chin e-mails to ask me how it's going. I describe the listing error and other flaws, venturing that the transplant surgeons at Columbia may be first-rate, but the transplant cardiologists seem to verge on incompetence.

"Have I made a mistake?" I ask Dr. Chin, giving him a chance to set me straight and also to criticize a rival institution.

"You probably wouldn't do much better at CHOP, since half the cardiologists there were trained at Columbia!" Dr. Chin writes back.

I take it he shares my general view of the cardiologists but does not consider Columbia's listing error as startling or as unusual as I do. It could be my standards are too high and exacting, an occasional weakness of mine.

Eleven days after we correct Damon's listing classification, we get The Offer that a donor heart has been found for him.

CHAPTER 47

"Have you heard it's in the stars, next July we collide with Mars!"
> — Some Cole Porter song
> — From Damon's blog, January 2005

One snowy afternoon in the final days leading up to his transplant — it must have been a weekend but for the life of me, I can't recall exactly when — Damon is hanging out with his friends by the front of our house. I am sitting out on the green metal porch chair in my bulky winter coat, having brushed the fresh white powder off the seat. It's cold but the sun is shining. I'm watching the boys throw snowballs.

Damon is on the top step and he doesn't have much energy but he enjoys flinging down a few loose blobs at his pals on the pavement below or absorbing a shot or two with a soft white splatter on the meat of his coat.

Splat! He opens his arms and twists his torso so the snowball lands smack against his flank. He grins as if he scored the direct hit himself.

While his friends continue pelting each other down at street level, Damon shuffles over to me in my porch chair and innocently, as if it were the most casual act in the world, deposits himself in my lap. He perches chirpily on my knees, like a bird alighting on a statue.

The move catches me completely off guard. It's so at odds with Damon's customary teen behavior — especially when his friends are around!

At first, I assume he's stealing a breather, and I play it cool, so as not to embarrass him. But instead of pulling away and dismissing it as a gag, Damon stays put, showing clear intention. He snuggles up to me and gets more comfortable in my lap. It's a touching overture, as well as a very willful and conscious regression. Damon deliberately makes himself into a child again — into *my* child — and cleaves to me with endearing filial adoration.

I'm totally disarmed, and my heart melts faster than the snow dissolving in the bright sun. Damon doesn't say a word as he sticks to me and ignores his friends, but he doesn't

489

need to. He's aware of everything and is making a clear statement.

It's the most beautiful gesture and the most eloquent tribute I have ever received. Damon salutes our unique history and our deep bond while acknowledging, without any conditions or inhibitions, his great love for me.

I wrap my arms around my son and try to balance him on my knees — even with his illness, he's much bigger and heavier now — and I hungrily respond to his show of affection. I strive to maintain decorum for both our sakes, since we're sitting out on the porch and everyone can see us from the street. But we're not really a part of the world anymore, at least not in the same way.

I hold Damon tight and register his weight and his warmth and his spirit. He leans against me with his baggy coat while I press my face against his neck and shaggy head. We clasp hands. It's the deepest conversation we've ever had, or will have, about what's happening in our lives and how we feel about one another.

Yet not a word passes our lips.

I can't remember how many years it's been since we sat entwined like this, embracing openly. And I can't believe it's my acerbic sixteen-year-old son who has initi-

490

ated this intimate exchange — despite the full-daylight company of his friends. He doesn't seem to care, as if he's taking time out to deal with more important matters.

We hold this position for a blessed interval and I am filled with gratitude. Damon is not only showing me his love but allowing me to reciprocate without restraint or censure.

My cup runneth over, and I never want this moment to end.

CHAPTER 48

Hell, I wouldn't mind a date lol. Well this is the first time I've been home alone on a Friday since forever and it sucks. I'm so lonely. There's nothing to do or at least nothing I can do. Been trying 2 amuse myself by bouncing my empty medicine capsules off the cork board in my room. For those of you who have never tried it (all of you) DON'T! I've also tried 2 use my syringes as darts. Doesn't work too well cause they're too light and if you try throwing them with any force there's a risk of them bouncing back and hitting you in the eye. In fact they've done a lot of interesting things except 4 stick in the cork.

It doesn't help that I've gotten even worse. I have no energy anymore. I often find myself sitting there in this lethargic state doing nothing and I keep falling asleep on my floor. I could right now if I let myself.

My brother had to wake me at 3:30 pm today. I'm fast becoming the one thing I've fought not 2 be: a homeridden weakling. And no, I don't care that many kids who have a single ventricle system and never even got PLE have been on homeschooling their whole lives. I'm not many kids.

But what can I do at this point, just fuckin wait? I can't fuckin stand waiting and I don't know how I'd last more months of this. World of Warcraft is fun but it's not a supplement 4 life . . . Wow that's the most pathetic statement I've ever written. (hehe "wow" anyone see the irony?)

I'm not sure what 2 do with myself. I can't make new friends like I used to cause I'm just too out of it 2 be myself. The only people I can still enjoy hanging out with are my old friends like in small groups or individually. But I'm worried my life is slowly slipping away from me and there's nothing I can do but sit back and watch. And wait.

Well I guess all I can say is I need something . . . and it better fuckin b a heart!
— From Damon's blog, January 14, 2005

Shealagh is folding laundry in the family room around lunchtime when the phone rings and Columbia informs her they have an offer of a heart for Damon.

We've been warned to expect false alarms but since we can't know for sure until we get to the hospital — presumably a donor-organ-harvesting team from Columbia is on its way to the donor site — we must move quickly.

Shealagh wakes Damon, who sleeps late into the afternoon now, and breaks the news in a wavering voice. Damon nods and begins to get dressed, remaining calmer than his mother.

Then Shealagh phones me at the office. I'm in a meeting and have to step out.

My wife tells me about the heart offer. We review our plan and coordinate schedules. Shealagh sounds extremely tense, so I remind her not to panic. This is what we wanted.

I grab my coat and tell my assistant I'm out for the rest of the day on private business. I call my parents and a few friends en route.

Shealagh loads two bags into the car and meets me at Sam's school with Damon and Miranda. She asks me to drive. Damon sits in the back in a sweatshirt and baggy jeans, looking deceptively composed, like a boxer before a championship bout. I ask him how he's doing and he says fine, he was fast asleep but is coming around. He listens to his iPod.

I try to look at him through the rearview mirror or steal a glance over my shoulder. He's so vibrant and alive it's hard to imagine anything bad could befall him. He's just a sweet teenage kid who needs a new heart, like the Tin Man in *The Wizard of Oz,* a film Damon watched so many times as a toddler he wore out the videotape (although he loved the Cowardly Lion most). Now we're going to the Emerald City to get Damon *his* new heart.

We arrive at the hospital quickly, earlier than expected, and they must scramble to accommodate us. We're shown to a lounge-like preadmission room. A TV screen displays a "Hello Damon" crawl. It impresses Sam and Miranda more than Damon.

Dr. Becker, whom we've never met, comes to greet us. She's a young, sober Indian woman, correct and a little stiff, exactly like her voice. She checks Damon's vitals and takes blood but lets him keep his regular clothes. We're so early, having reached Columbia well in advance of the organ procurement team, that the situation remains in flux.

I try to imagine the donor heart being removed, examined, carefully packed in a cold fluid, and loaded onto a helicopter. The logistics have always been fuzzy, and I once upset Damon by joking we had to wait for the right person to croak before he could get his new heart. The idea of anyone suffering for his benefit is intolerable to my son. Now we must remain on standby and stay in the hospital, possibly for hours, until the heart gets here, further tests are conducted, and a final determination is made regarding its viability as a donor organ for Damon.

Dr. Becker reviews the basics and brings us forms to sign. "I do not have specifics, but we must assume it's a go until we are otherwise notified," she says.

It's clear Dr. Becker does not have much experience or authority and is acting as a go-between. When I indicate we'll withhold our final consent until we get more information, she promises the surgeon will come speak to us before anything happens.

"Who's the surgeon today?" I ask. There's Dr. Q, the superstar called in for special cases, and Dr. Mosca, the distinguished head of transplant with the most operations.

"Dr. Jonathan Chen." Dr. Becker mentions the youngest member of the surgical team. "He's brilliant, a rising star recruited after a national search," she says, trying to reassure us.

It's a lottery system, and we've drawn the least familiar card. I console myself they must not consider Damon an especially difficult case.

My parents arrive and swell our group to party size, though the mood is anything but jolly. Sam fiddles in the corner, eyeing his brother and biting his lip; Miranda sticks close to Damon and clings to his every move; Shealagh packs and repacks the overnight bags, trying to keep it together; and I pace and harangue the medical staff with endless queries and commands. Nor can my parents help much. My father, an affable extrovert, is discomfited by stillness and uncertainty, and my mother, a resilient survivor, carries her own historical baggage.

But everyone is there because they love Damon. And this collective warmth and solidarity, the family turnout, does signify. Like the dockside send-off to a perilous solo voyage, our group presence provides the human context and the basic orientation for Damon's journey. We are both the start and the finish line, and Damon knows he just has to get back to us in order to be safe.

Damon slouches in an armchair with a book on his lap, a play called *Kimberly Akimbo*. It's a mordant comedy about a sixteen-year-old girl with an illness that makes her age at four times the normal rate. I'd gotten Damon and my mother tickets and now my mother prevails upon Damon to read aloud from the play.

It's a shrewd distraction because Damon loves to perform, but I'm too focused on unfolding events to heed him. Will the donor heart get here in time, or will we go home empty-handed? I recall reading the human heart can survive only four hours outside the body before it loses the ability to function post-transplant.

But at some point Damon's rich, lively, and dramatic voice, an inexhaustible spigot of words and storytelling verve, reaches me too. My son declaims with relish from the slender volume in his pale hands, and he has his audience, as usual, rapt. The writing is sharp and funny, with a wry, outcast irony. Even the medical staff stops to listen, arrested by this uncommon use of the facilities. And it strikes me, watching my son weave his familiar spell, how Damon is always at home in the realm of art, even in the hospital before a life-threatening operation.

Two physicians in white coats appear, one of them Dr. Chen, who informs us that the donor heart is in good order, and we are moving forward.

My system instantly switches to high alert. So this is *not* a run-through.

Dr. Chen appears a capable sort, youthful and still aspiring, but with enough experience under his belt, and I decide I like him. Not that I have much choice. (I could refuse the offer if he didn't seem up to the task, but it would leave us waiting indefinitely.)

Dr. Chen reviews the procedure, answers our questions — displaying a firm, supple intelligence when I press him — and departs with a confident, provisionally reassuring smile.

Now everything turns more breathless and accelerates.

My parents gather Sam and Miranda, and after heartrending hugs, they go. Damon changes into a gown and slippers. He's wearing a red ribbon from Kyle for good luck. The nurse lets him keep the ribbon on his left ankle but below, she tags him with a white plastic snap-on bearing his name, date of birth, hospital ID number, and admitting cardiologist. She attaches an identical white plastic tag to his right ankle.

They place Damon on a gurney, put in an

IV line, and recheck his vitals.

The anesthesiologists come by and ask their questions. They leave.

Dr. Becker scurries up the hall to tell us they're almost ready in the OR.

Shealagh and I hover near Damon, finding any excuse for physical contact and any premise for small talk. Anything to avoid confronting what's about to happen.

"That soldier we adopted in Iraq wrote back. Her name is Dana," I tell Damon.

"Cool," Damon says, though he looks surprised. "I didn't realize you sent in my picture, Dad . . . I'll write back when I get out of the hospital."

"When can we see that new portrait of you and Max?" Shealagh asks. Only yesterday, Damon posed with Max for a painter friend of Max's parents who became enamored of Damon's "look" when she met him New Year's Eve.

"Ask Max's mom. It's her friend," Damon says. "She has a gallery."

"Think we can buy the painting from her?" I inquire.

"You might want to see it first, Dad!"

A transplant nurse in a moon suit, her face obscured by a mask, traipses over in elastic overshoes. She has come to take Damon to the operating room.

We glance down the long, empty corridor and stiffen. It's time.

Damon, who's sitting upright on his gurney, asks if he can walk to the OR instead of being wheeled in. The nurse, surprised, admits there's no medical reason he can't, if he really wants to and if he feels up to it.

Damon immediately slides off the bed and stands. Even at this stage of his illness, he's proud. And not without capability. He's going to walk in unassisted.

Shealagh and I exchange proud smiles. It's such a Damonesque move, so unintimidated and full of his signature spirit, that it buoys us. Maybe we really *can* beat this thing and turn it into just another station on our journey.

I stroll beside Damon in his blue gown and help push his IV pole. Shealagh walks on Damon's other side, holding his hand while drying her eyes.

The nurse follows behind us, steering the wide, empty gurney down the hall in our wake. *Clickety-clack.* I remind Damon that by the time he wakes up, the worst will be behind him, and he'll already be on the road to recovery. Damon scans my face closely, like a child probing with his fingers, and gives a faint nod.

We've reached the end of the corridor. It's

time to hand Damon off to the surgical team with its scalpels and stainless steel wires and massive, circulating heart-lung machine.

I look at my son. There's so much to say but I decide it's better to keep things as normal as possible, since that's how we want them to end up. He knows what's at stake — we all know — but hasn't he been here before?

There's a positive outcome to this operation, a known path to success, and Damon just has to come out on the right side of it. But we need him to go in with the same confidence and sense of security that's sustained him thus far, and he needs to know we share that confidence.

I recall the first time I had to leave two-year-old Damon alone at preschool. He wouldn't stop clinging to me as he bawled his eyes out on the threshold. I thought my heart would break, but I knew I had to leave him, and I knew it would turn out okay.

Only this time, the outcome is far less clear, and it's not Damon crying.

Shealagh chokes up as she hugs Damon and walks off sobbing.

Then it's my turn. I embrace Damon with open arms, tasting his soft hair. He hews stiffly to me for an instant, but I let him know this is not farewell and we will have time after. I pat his back like a coach before the big game.

"Okay, D-man. This is it, but remember, you know how to do this! You're the toughest person I ever met . . . I want you to go in strong, with good thoughts, and I'll see you in a few hours . . . Love you, big guy!"

As I let go, all too soon, of Damon, I try not to think that I might never hold my son again or get to talk to him and tell him how I feel. Those are just abstract concepts, dark, flitting ghosts, and I simply banish them.

The nurse leads Damon toward the steel doors of the OR, where the faceless surgical squad eagerly awaits him. We watch Damon shuffle forward, a little shaky but still advancing on his own two feet, a small, pale, incredibly brave sixteen-year-old boy with a lion's heart they can never take away, no matter what instruments or drugs they deploy.

The doors swing shut after him.

CHAPTER 49

"I fear no death nor pain."
"What do you fear?"
"A cage."
— The Lord of the Rings
— From Damon's blog, winter 2004–2005

Shealagh and I sit and wait in the lounge of the Cardiothoracic Intensive Care Unit.

This is where Damon will be sent post-transplant.

It's the longest wait in the world.

And the most desolate.

All my research has shown that Damon's time in surgery — the six to eight hours when he lies on the table under anesthesia, his bladder drained by a catheter, his breast-bone cut and parted, with a heart-lung machine circulating his blood, until the surgeon removes his original heart from its connection to the great arteries, sews the donor heart into place, and initiates activity

504

so that the new heart can begin to function, unrejected, on its own, enabling Damon to be untethered from the heart-lung machine — constitutes the single most dangerous period in the entire process.

Damon either comes out alive, or he doesn't.

End of story.

And hopefully, a new beginning.

Though no one wants to give me, or any family member regarding any operation, an actual risk assessment, I piece together my own by combining multiple variables, co-factors, medical history, hospital records, and meta-analyses. Then I take my estimate and get it indirectly confirmed by physicians who tweak it. Doctors can't resist correcting you and showing how much they know, especially if you're on their turf, and I can't tolerate not knowing. So we back into agreement on a ballpark number, even though the doctors would never volunteer or publicly acknowledge an average mortality rate, because it would expose the illusion that they can manage everything.

Numbers tell only part of the story, of course, and I give Columbia the benefit of every doubt concerning their long experience and their improving, self-reported results. But even when I factor all this in,

Damon still has, conservatively, a one in three chance of dying in surgery. It's higher if I look at the raw unscrubbed numbers over time.

One in three is still better than the odds of PLE, except PLE plays out over many years and this will be over in six hours. The verdict will come in very swiftly, and there is no further recourse or court of appeal for us.

In my own heart, I feel that if Damon can make it off the operating table and return to us with his recognizable, fighting self intact, we will persevere. But he has to get out of that room *alive.*

So now we continue to sit and wait in the gray airless lounge. A wall-mounted television flickers with remote, meaningless images, pale reminders of an outside world that once mattered.

A nurse emerges every couple of hours to give us a progress report. We scrutinize her face, her gait, her body language, for any "tells" as she marches across the floor toward us. It's all I can do to stop from running up and shaking the information out of her.

The nurse finally reaches us and starts to speak. The minute she resumes the narrative, I know the story hasn't ended, and I relax. The nurse describes various minor developments and turns in the procedure, all of which I glom on to and store. But there's only one real question I care about, and the answer seems to be "So far, so good."

I pump my fists and yell like a fan after the first quarter. "Yeah, D-man, go, D-man, go!"

Shealagh disapproves of such naked cheer-leading, not to mention premature celebration, but I'm a believer in positively focused energy and momentum.

Or I'm trying to be.

The long day turns into night. I call my friend David in Seattle, the only person I can talk to at a time like this. Shealagh speaks to my parents, who are staying at our house. They report that Sam and Miranda had a nice, big dinner — they both wanted seconds — and went to bed without a peep. All is quiet on the home front.

We get a second positive update but the same letdown ensues once the nurse leaves.

We're getting to the meat of the operation, and there's more to worry about now.

The hospital vigil drags on. And on.

We drift, suspended in a no-man's-land between terror and hope.

We cross the midnight threshold, and then

we're into the wee, dark hours.

Time loses definition and grows amorphous. We float in the void, trying not to disappear down any black holes.

The elevator pings and footsteps approach. My stomach craters and I realize it might be better not to know, because in uncertainty, I can still hang on to faith. I brace myself but in this instance, it's a false alarm. The footsteps aren't for us.

There is comfort in open-endedness but also a point of no return, and as the black hour-hand scythes across the grim clock face, we fast are nearing it.

Damon's operation is taking too long!

Delay can't be good, and Shealagh and I both grow tense. We know the old heart is out and they're trying to put the new one in. But what if the new heart *won't start up?* Damon cannot stay on the heart-lung machine indefinitely. His original heart is toast, and he has no backup if they can't make the new heart work.

As more time passes without a sign, we become even more agitated. What's going on? If Damon isn't out by now, there must be a problem. It's been almost eight hours. Based on their last update, we should have gotten the all-clear over *one hour ago.*

I start paging the transplant nurse when

the figure of Dr. Chen suddenly appears in the lounge, and a ghostly chill passes over us.

He wouldn't show up himself unless he had cause.

I try to avoid despair as I zero in on Dr. Chen from across the lounge. You can tell Damon's surgeon has been through a major battle. He's wearing scrubs like fatigues and resembles a commander returning from the bloody field.

I look him straight in the eye as he reaches us, knowing his first few words will determine the future course of our lives.

"Everything is fine." Dr. Chen cuts to the chase. Neither of us moves. "We put the new heart in and it's functioning well," the surgeon reports from the front lines with evident satisfaction. "Damon did great. They're closing him up and moving him from the OR into the ICU. You'll be able to go in and see him shortly."

It's impossible to describe the impact of his words, unless you've heard angels sing.

We thank Dr. Chen and heap praise upon his magnificent feat. We're so grateful to him! This means everything to us! He's awesome and amazing!

Dr. Chen smiles, sharing our joy and basking in a successful night's work. He looks mightily pleased and lingers to chat, un-winding like an athlete after a great perfor-mance.

"Damon's donor was a very sizable adult with a big heart, so we had to squish things around in order to fit the new heart inside Damon's chest cavity," Dr. Chen says. "It might be a little tight in there until Damon's system adjusts, but it all worked out and I don't anticipate any problems. Damon now has a big, strong heart he can grow into!"

Dr. Chen is also pleased they managed to get supplementary tissue from the donor lungs, because he needed extra pulmonary arteries and veins for his reconstruction.

"I had to fashion a wider connection for the vein between Damon's neck and heart — we refused two previous donors because they didn't have enough extra tissue — but I'm very pleased with the result, and I think you will be too."

Dr. Chen describes several other features of Damon's new anatomy. As I learned from managing Damon's PLE, the structural details of an underlying surgery can have long-term consequences, and it's in our interest to learn all we can. But right now it's the middle of the night and Dr. Chen is exhausted, while we want to go in and see our son. We agree that in a few weeks, we can review all this more calmly if I come by his office for a primer.

When we finally get to see Damon — it always takes longer than they say — it's a shock. But a necessary shock, once we adjust to it, not a grim one.

He lies on his back in the ICU bed, his inert, traumatized body supported by an array of bubbling, suspiring machines and flashing, beeping monitors.

Damon's eyes are puffy and closed, with goop on the stressed lids to keep them from chafing. His trademark red mane bobs above the white hospital pillow, one of his few unchanged features, though it highlights the adjacent deformations. Damon's mouth and nose are mashed by bifurcating respirator tubes taped in harsh X's across his face, while a central IV line enters the right side of his neck in a bloody, Frankenstein-like tangle.

Encumbered with a thicket of inflowing and outflowing ventilator hoses, three chest drainage lines, a urine catheter, IV tubes, pacing wires with silver foil, a green arm board, a black pressure cuff, blue EKG sensors, and a red pulsing probe — all exposed under extra-bright lights — Damon's supine figure is lit up and wired like a Christmas tree!

But perhaps what's most striking, amid all this damage, is how *good* Damon's color already looks. His skin, perfused as never before, *glows* with a warm, rosy sheen. He's flush with pulsing blood, while all traces of blueness, from his face down to his extremities, have been erased.

We've never seen Damon with such a ruddy, healthy-looking circulation!

The source of all this pumping vitality and excitement, the fantastic, throbbing object in question, is visible on the left side of Damon's chest. We can see it moving just below the surface, a creature in its own right, alive and hopping like a jackrabbit. It jitters and flutters and jerks, creating a big stir underneath its translucent envelope of skin. This new, beating *thing* is so large and so frantically active, it looks like it could escape its fragile subdermal lair and leap straight from Damon's chest onto the bed.

Shealagh and I stand in awe before this marvel of human engineering. Damon has a big new heart transplanted into his old body. We can feel its raw, surging power, like an outsized new engine revving up inside a compact car.

Meanwhile, Damon remains in critical

care and many of his functions still require intensive support. His body must make its peace with the donor heart while each of his systems recuperates. Any failure anywhere could lead to massive breakdown everywhere.

Even before Damon wakes up that first day, we have things to worry about.

His blood pressure is too low, as is the urine output from the kidneys.

His CO_2 level is too high, which means he's not breathing enough. The giant ventilator that breathes for him by pneumatically compressing air several times a minute — it emits a deep, steady suspiration, as if the whole room were inhaling and exhaling — has to have its rate adjusted.

And while Damon needs diuretics to chase out excess fluid, he also needs more blood volume because he lost blood during the operation. Even now, he continues to bleed sporadically through three long, spotty drainage lines that exit his body into a clearly marked collection chamber. So the doctors must push more albumin into his body — it comes in big, clear fluid sacs — to increase his blood volume.

By early afternoon, Damon's eyes open and he comes to. Shealagh and I stand on either side of our son, holding his hands, stroking his hair, and trying to comfort him. We fill him in on what's happened and congratulate him effusively.

"You made it with flying colors! Everything's going to be okay!"

Damon nods, his eyes rheumy and bloodshot. He's very weak but cognizant. We watch him check his surroundings and register his new state of mute captivity. He seems most discomfited by the choking respirator tube. The fentanyl and morphine help with the pain, the dobutamine and epinephrine keep his heart pumping strong, but nothing can deflect the apparatus jammed down his mouth, nose, and throat. It forces oxygen into his lungs every ten seconds. He's like a fish who can only stay in the water — who can only stay alive — if it keeps the hook in its mouth. Reluctantly, Damon swallows and accepts his fate.

Shealagh cools Damon's brow with a white towel while I dab the one available corner of his parched lips with wet foam on a stick. We keep him apprised of how well he's doing and what still needs to be done. We can't tell how much he's absorbing, but we can feel him finding a new equilibrium. The fresh incision line where they split his chest looks as if it's already healed, and his whole body radiates with a glowing new epidermis. We even spot Kyle's flimsy red ribbon clinging to his ankle, a small bright emblem of inextinguishable love.

All the surgeons, Dr. Davis admits, say the transplant went "better than expected."

Shealagh and I beam. We knew if they gave Damon a chance, he'd beat the spread.

CHAPTER 50

"Guess who's back
Back again
Damon's back
Tell a friend"

Yes, it's really me and as I'm sure you've all heard already from numerous sources, I'm alive and well. Still in the hospital but out of the ICU and that's all 2 be expected. Hopefully be comin home sometime next week but it's still up in the air.

Soooo what is up everybody?! How did you survive without me? lol. I heard Irena managed 2 get the group together 4 a party which is mucho cool. Sorry I couldn't make it dear, I was slightly preoccupied but perhaps next time.

Twill probably be a while before I can have the group at my house en masse (just because of all the immune suppressant medication I'm on and I don't particularly feel like hangin out with you guys with a mask on the entire time (nothing personal) lol And no Jano, Zak it's not a monster or Zorro mask or anything like that so don't get excited lol jk. But I will figure out a way 2 see all of you as soon as I can and in the meantime I'm sure the group is resourceful enough 2 find a new base for a while.

My room's pretty cool. It's spacious and there's a bed where 1 of my parents can sleep and a tv, a phone and a computer which I'm updating from now. Unfortunately though you have 2 be an admissions user 2 install anything which means no games (and the computer in the "learning center" has a grand total of 0MB of space, now I don't know much about computers but that's not a lot of space so no Warcraft or anything else 4 me). I have internet access (obviously) so if anyone knows some good online games or coolsites or anything, please let me know. In other words people, *entertain me,* I don't care how. Tell me what's been going on with you, what's been happening at Tech, a joke, no matter how bad I assure you it will be better than a blood test. I'm bored as hell in this hospital and there's nothing 2 do but read and pop pills . . . and not the fun kind.

Btw thanx 2 the group and everyone 4 all your support during this. You guys have been awesome! Damn this entry took me a really long time proving that I'm not yet 100% but I knew that, well later all.
— From Damon's blog, February 10, 2005

Damon makes good progress in the hospital following his heart transplant operation but a hail of errors, gaffes, and setbacks threaten to undo all the benefits of his surgery.

Hospitals turn out, paradoxically, to be very dangerous places, and the longer one stays on the premises, the more dangerous they seem to grow.

Even when the doctors and nurses are first-rate, as scores are, the system often conspires against them. And when they are less than first-rate, as far too many turn out to be, they can pose a threat to the patient, which must be defended against at all times.

For the first days following his transplant, Damon shows steady, even remarkable improvement. By day two, he's fully aware and communicating with us via pen and paper, using his left hand because the right is immobilized with the IV line and the arm board. He's weak and sore and very thirsty but he doesn't complain. He even has his sense of humor. When Shealagh and I bicker over who stays overnight, he scribbles *stop arguing!*

Dr. Davis comes by and reiterates the prevailing sense of satisfaction with Damon's operation. But now that the surgeons have done their job, she explains in her mellifluous hierarchical manner, the pediatric transplant group will take over.

"So Dr. Mason is *in charge,*" Dr. Davis trills, needling me ever-so-subtly for my earlier e-mail ("Who's in Charge of Damon Weber?"), which she obviously hasn't forgotten.

But I just smile back and beam at her. Damon is doing well, and I'm ready to hug them all. If Dr. Mason, a stocky woman who bustles into our ICU room with an unmistakable air of self-importance and her own entourage, wants to claim ownership for a successful patient, then God bless her. I just want to get my son home, and I'll help elect her president of the AMA if it will assist in that process.

We bond now, Dr. Mason and I, in the aftermath of a good transplant, and reach a happy accommodation of mutually shared goals. I find new, unseen virtues in her and she's happy to play the wise, experienced overseer, which sits squarely in her comfort zone.

Dr. Mason confers with the surgeons and consults with the specialists, coordinating the various expert inputs, before she presents the daily plan of action.

"We want to try and extubate Damon today!" she announces early on.

It's only the second day, but Damon's blood pressure has reached its target, his urine output has improved, and they don't want his body growing dependent on the ventilator, which can occur after traumatic surgery. Also, Damon's X-ray shows extra fluid around the lungs, which is easier to resolve once he's using his own muscles to breathe.

Weaning an ICU patient off the respirator is always a critical step toward recovery. Can the postoperative patient breathe on his or her own without mechanical assistance? But it's especially significant for Damon because following his first open-heart surgery as an infant, Damon required a full month to come off the respirator. Many attempts were made to wean him, and all ended in failure because he was too weak. Neither Shealagh nor I has ever forgotten that nightmarish month in the ICU, which felt like years, when our son was held captive to a machine and it looked like he'd never come off it.

We know what a big deal this is, and we're apprehensive about it.

Damon also seems worried and shows uncharacteristic anxiety when they ask us to leave the room before extubating him. He starts to cry, the first time we've seen panic from our son during the whole transplant process. It's like having his umbilical cord cut, and he's frightened about losing the external support and being able to make it on his own.

The pulmonologist, familiar with this reaction, tells Damon he can have one parent stay in the room if it will make him feel better. Damon calms down, glances about, and points straight to me. Since he has only two parents and I'm more assertive, it's hardly a surprise pick. Nevertheless, I feel strangely touched that Damon would need *me* in this way, because I've become so accustomed to thinking of *him* as strong and self-sufficient.

It's so easy to forget he's just a kid!

Watching Damon being weaned off the respirator — Shealagh peeks in too, from behind the curtain — is like watching our son be reborn. I stand beside Damon and urge him on while Shealagh roots silently from the ICU corridor. Damon gags and chokes and sputters, and his floundering body jerks and flails as they pull out the endotracheal tube. Ejected into a harsh new environment, he claws and scrabbles forward until he emerges among us, a fledgling, wobbly, self-breathing young creature. *Ecce homo.*

"Bravo, D-man, bravo!" I cheer lustily.

Now we wait to see if Damon can *maintain* this independent state. His chest heaves and all his monitors flash. He shivers and gasps and blinks. It looks like we may have to hook him back up . . . But slowly, he manages to take in oxygen and expel carbon dioxide, and his body finds a precarious new balance.

Like a newborn infant one minute after birth, Damon passes his first Apgar. He's ready to meet the world and breathe on his own.

It's a tremendous milestone, and a cause for great relief and celebration.

Damon runs into his first setback on the Saturday after surgery. I have weekend duty, giving Shealagh a much-deserved rest, and I find Damon with his upper arms and face dramatically swollen. "How you feeling,

D-man?" I frown.

"I'm a little uncomfortable and my arm is pretty tender," Damon admits.

Alarmed — my son is taking on the puffy air of the Pillsbury Doughboy! — I look for a doctor. But it's the weekend shift and no physician or nurse is around. I page the ICU attending and wait over an hour until he shows up.

The doctor says Damon could have inflammation in the neck caused by a clot that must be dissolved right away. They prescribed a drug for it earlier.

"What time did he get it?" I ask, surprised at the absence of any effect.

He checks the chart. "Looks like he didn't get it yet. But I'm sure he will."

"What's the holdup?" I snap. "Didn't *you* just tell me it was urgent?"

I wait with Damon for several more hours, then page the ICU resident, a high-strung young woman with the air of a somnolent undergraduate. I show her that Damon's face is still swelling up. "We need to do something *now!*"

"Yes. Timeliness is key. I'm on it," she says before she runs off.

After lunch — it's now five hours since the order! — I page the resident but she does not respond. No one knows where she is. I head down the ICU corridor and check every room, but she's not there. I start getting desperate when I spot her immured in a small alcove, lost in a pile of reference books. She jumps up guiltily.

"Where have you been?" I cry. "My son is *still* waiting for his medication!"

"I-I'm sorry," she stammers, her face reddening. "I was going to do it."

I storm out, buttonhole the new ICU attending, and read her the riot act. She stays calm, and within twenty minutes, Damon gets his medication.

I watch the drug go in and pray it's not too late. Damon is so bloated he looks like he's ready to *explode,* and I'm not far behind. The new ICU attending tries to mollify me. "We're one of the fastest ICUs in the country," she says.

I stare at her, openmouthed. "You had this order since eight this morning!"

She pauses. "You're right. I don't know why this wasn't done earlier."

I'm struck by her honesty — I'm used to a policy of constant denial — but I remain worried. Damon resembles a blimp. I sit by him, hoping the drug works.

A new resident arrives. "Hi, I'm Jim, I'm here to help in any way."

I explain what's happened, but Jim doesn't

react. He just lingers. So I ask a series of medical questions, but Jim offers nothing but the blandest platitudes.

It's clear Jim knows very little and has no medical task to perform.

"I'm here if you need anything," he keeps saying, although the only thing we now need is for him to go away. "I'll be here all night if you need me."

I'm trying not to be rude when Jim finally goes. As he exits, I hear a small, wry voice pipe up from the bed with perfect timing: "Well *that* was pointless!"

I smile, greatly relieved that Damon, who seemed so out of it, remains alert. It's the best indicator I get that despite his puffiness, he's not slipping away.

That night, as I curl up on the cramped armchair-cot beside Damon's ICU bed, a thin sheet covering my T-shirt-clad body, I feel like an exhausted bodyguard unable to switch to off-duty. I worry about Damon's swelling and about every flashing screen and pinging indicator.

Fluid tends to pool overnight, so I'm on the alert for that. Damon's heart rate is down to 100 — they've weaned him off the epinephrine and dobutamine — which is okay if it holds, but not if it drops. But his oxygen saturation, whose fluctuations send my own heart fluttering, sporadically dips to the mid-80s while he sleeps. Since a higher saturation is better for wound healing, and for just about everything else, I prompt the night nurse — a big improvement over the day nurse — to place an oxygen cannula by Damon's nose.

I monitor all the machines plus the stream of doctors, nurses, and staff who flow in and out of this dimly lit circle. Nothing gets past me. Occasionally, I open one eye to check on Damon's saturation, or the arterial or venous pressure, or the nutrient IV bags, or a new technician. Mostly, I can track them with my eyes shut. Eventually, I drop off for a spell.

Sometime in the dead of night, I am awakened by a shattering sound and terrible screams, followed by frantic footsteps. Once I verify that it doesn't concern Damon, I recall that earlier in the lounge, I saw a group of Hasidic Jews praying. One man has a very sick baby in the ICU, and I heard a nurse say the infant was unlikely to survive. Now, based on the shrieking lamentation and the mournful chanting that fills the halls, the baby has apparently died.

It is a tragedy, and although I don't know any of the parties, I register the loss of a human life in my dim, sleep-fogged brain.

But then, as I console myself that Damon, *my* charge, is safe, a dastardly thought glints: if the angel of death was sent to take one life on this ward, then let this anonymous stranger be that sacrifice, and let my son be left alone!

By morning, things look better. Damon has begun to reverse the fluid overload in his upper arms, neck, and face. He's still swollen, but the Pillsbury Doughboy is deflating.

Damon also gets a great nurse, Angela, who removes his mattress pad since the new beds don't require pads, a fact seemingly unknown to several previous ICU nurses that has resulted in a bedsore. Angela changes all Damon's sheets, gives him a clean new diaper, and refreshes all his dressings, IV lines, and tubes, bringing order and harmony to a sorry mess. She's a godsend, like her name.

Damon's X-ray still shows a hazy wet patch on his lungs, so it's imperative we keep him sitting upright and moving about to help the fluid disperse.

"We gotta get you out of bed, champ!" I unclip his chest sensors and gather his central and peripheral IV lines in my hand. Then I carefully shift him to the edge of the mattress and let his feet find the floor before

I help him stand.

"That's it, good!" I say. Damon leans his light, frail body against mine. I lay a sheet and pillow on the armchair, ease him into it, then cover him with a blanket and drape his IV lines and tubes over it. I turn on the TV.

"There you go, all the comforts of home!"

Damon remains sitting semi-upright for several hours, an excellent development. I divert him, and intermittently, I even coax my son to eat in his birdlike way. He consumes two crackers, half a chicken nugget, about ten French fries, a couple of Fritos, part of my Twix chocolate bar, and one orange segment. He also takes applesauce with his pills and drinks water and lemonade.

I have Sunday football on and Damon, not a fan, starts to take an interest, the first time he's engaged with the TV. Once he stretches and yawns luxuriously, and I feel he's *almost* himself. Problems persist but they seem more manageable.

"My back's sore," Damon complains several times.

"It may be displaced pressure from your big new heart," I say. "Here, let me give you a massage." I work around his tender neck, shifting the filigree of IV lines. His scapula feels bony and frail and I have to be very gentle. But the massage seems to help, at least while I'm giving it, because soon as I finish, he asks apologetically for "more, please!"

We unwind and chat. Damon jolts me when he reveals that he awoke during the last part of his heart transplant operation.

"I could hear the nurses gossiping and trying to move me. They turned me right on my *eye*, which was open against this cold metal slab! My brain wanted to speak, but I couldn't move my mouth . . . I had to wait while they shoved me around until they finally got my body into position. Then it felt like they were sewing up my chest with stitches!"

I grit my teeth and silently curse the anesthesiologists — this is the second time it appeared that they failed to properly sedate my son! — but I let Damon talk it out because it was clearly a traumatic experience whose enormity he's still trying to comprehend.

Damon drifts off, dozing, with good numbers. I make calls. Shealagh and Sam ask me a thousand questions, while my parents are happy to hear Damon is improving. My friend and mentor Art Singer offers to call up Nobelist Eric Kandel, a Columbia star, and have him put in a word for Damon.

Sunday night, Shealagh comes in to relieve me and brings a Big Mac with her. The doctors have warned Damon to consume more calories or they'll have to force-feed him.

"Here, sweetie, I got you something you like!" Shealagh says. Damon sits up in his bed and tries to take on the overstuffed burger. At first, it seems too much, but he manages a small bite and then another, and soon, as his digestive system cranks up, he displays flashes of real appetite, with juicy dribblings down his chin and a fortified gleam in his eye.

"It's good!" Damon nods as if he's just discovered eating. Shealagh and I smile. Damon doesn't finish the burger — he's still a ways from that — but things are looking up.

After ten days, Damon leaves the ICU and goes down to the sixth floor. He still has several more weeks in the hospital under a best-case scenario, but he's judged to be out of immediate danger. It's another major milestone.

Damon's recovery room is spacious, with a TV, telephone, computer, and guest bed. It's like a halfway house, and it puts us one step closer to our dream of returning home.

Everyone now feels sanguine about Damon's prospects. Dr. Hayes visits, beaming with palpable joy and relief. She's known Damon since he was three days old and couldn't be happier for us, especially after all we've been through.

"He looks so good!" she says with a grin.

Dr. Chen, the surgeon, stops by to check in on his patient. He's very pleased with Damon's progress and seems fond of our son. They banter. A *Deadwood* fan, he discusses Damon's upcoming debut. "I can't wait to see your episode, Damon!"

One day, Dr. Chen brings Dr. Eric Rose, the illustrious chief of cardiology renowned for performing the first pediatric heart transplant in the country. Dr. Rose visits us at the behest of Eric Kandel, and his arrival sets tongues wagging.

"Now you're going to meet a real VIP!" Dr. Chen grins at Damon and Shealagh. I'm at work so I miss the walk-through, but Dr. Mason, among others, is all agog about what drew the august figure to Damon's bedside. "How do you know him?" she asks.

Dr. Rose chats with Damon and Shealagh. He describes his first transplant patient, just celebrating his twenty-second anniversary. That patient had to be retransplanted, always an option, but today they know so much more about the immune issues —

"they have it under control now" — that Damon is in a far better position.

Although Damon continues to recover, he hits several snags along the way. He gets a first biopsy revealing no sign of rejection, which is wonderful news, but the cath also shows a narrowing between his old SVC — his superior vena cava — and the donor veins, which will need to be widened with a balloon or a stent.

"I'd wait about six weeks till he's stronger to fix it," Dr. Hellenbrand advises.

Damon also continues to have issues such as high pressures and low saturation, requiring daily monitoring. As he heals, he's weaned off medications and faces new imbalances, such as low potassium. His chest X-ray still shows too much wetness around the lungs. And his chest drainage tube, the last major support system, continues to collect too much blood and pus, delaying its removal.

But Damon's biggest problem, we learn, is that once out of the ICU, he's no longer a priority and we must be even more active in managing his recovery. We do all the obvious things, like pushing him to stand and then walk inside the room. He leans on us and totters forward. Later we get him to take his first tentative steps out in the hallway. He dons a mask and pads slowly as we help wheel his IV pole. He's very weak and doddery and must take frequent breaks, but it's still very exciting for us.

"You're walking on your own, champ!" I cheer. We practice with him daily.

Unfortunately, Damon still has serious medical issues that we can't manage and that no one is attending to. We track all his medications and monitor all his readings and we report all his symptoms. But no one seems to be monitoring *us*. The doctors are unreliable or absent, and the nursing is erratic.

Two weeks after Damon's transplant, we seem to have fallen through the cracks.

Dr. Mason makes fewer visits and is harder to reach. Often she doesn't appear until the evening, when it's too late to do anything, and sometimes she doesn't appear for *several days* despite repeated paging. I refrain from any criticism — I cling to my honeymoon with Dr. Mason — and I ignore her prolonged absences so long as Damon's overall trajectory remains positive. But my wife grows increasingly dissatisfied. One night, after paging Dr. Mason for the third day without a callback — Shealagh is told she's away — my wife spots Damon's missing doctor on TV, standing in the very hospital we're at and smiling for all she's worth in the background of a well-publicized case!

Shealagh is furious and ready to file a complaint. "Damon has serious issues and Dr. Mason *still* hasn't seen him!" she cries.

Dr. Sanford, the third cardiologist on Dr. Mason's team, is supposedly helping to care for Damon. But Dr. Sanford does not make regular appearances. At one point we don't see her, or any doctor, for *four days.* I protest loudly and threaten to report this dereliction of duty until Dr. Sanford finally appears.

"No one's been in to examine Damon for four days!" I thunder.

"Well, we try to limit his exposure to other people," Dr. Sanford replies.

"To *doctors?*" I cry. "Isn't that why he's in the hospital — *to see doctors?*"

"It's not like no one has seen him," Dr. Sanford says defensively. "We have doctors and nurses who watch him when he walks out in the hallway."

"Please! You're doing *drive-by exams* now?" I can't believe my ears. "This is your idea of *world-class* care?"

"And Damon wears a *mask* in the hallway, so how much can you really *see?*" Shealagh points out, more measured than me but

534

equally indignant.

Dr. Sanford, a big, stately, and somewhat academic young woman, gives a tight sigh, realizing we're not buying any of it. "Look, it's been pretty busy around here. I'm pulling double duty. I'm the transplant cardiologist but I'm also the attending doctor on the floor. So I may have been a little overextended."

I'm mortified by such a pathetic excuse but I try to focus on results, not recriminations. "Well, our son needs *a doctor* to look in on him *daily.* He's a heart transplant patient, remember? If you can't do it, we'll request a replacement."

"I can do it."

But even when Dr. Sanford comes to see Damon, her physical examination leaves much to be desired. First, like an increasing number of hospital doctors, she seems as interested in looking at the computer as in examining the patient. Second, her observational skills are poor. When Shealagh warns her about an incipient white growth in Damon's throat, Dr. Sanford examines him and says, "It's nothing." Now, several days later, Damon has a case of oral thrush, a well-known fungal infection that requires immediate attention.

We ask Dr. Sanford how she could miss

such a common complication after we'd pointed it out to her. She replies that it was too *dark* in the room to see properly.

After three roller-coaster weeks, as we begin to focus on leaving the hospital, Damon's chest drainage tube becomes a big issue. He continues to put out too much fluid, a mixture of air, pus, and blood, and we can't remove the tube, and all its appurtenances, until the discharge has abated. We check his output every day and wait for it to subside.

One morning Dr. Sanford enters, glances at the computer, the chart, and my son, and says Damon's drainage is low enough to pull the tube. She leaves.

Shealagh, Damon, and I are thrilled. We've all been waiting to liberate Damon from the chest drainage paraphernalia, which emits an incessant aquarium-like bubbling and gurgling. The noisy contraption follows him everywhere, like an underwater ball and chain.

As we wait, I start to fret about Dr. Sanford's numbers because they sound too low. I bend down to the floor and inspect the collection chamber. I do a double take, because I see *three times* her estimate in the cylinders. And that's just for the overnight drainage, since the chamber was emptied the previous evening.

It's the difference between a safe and a dangerous environment for pulling the tube.

I can't believe it. If Dr. Sanford had bothered to bend down and look with her own eyes, she'd have known her assessment was an impossible number!

Riled up, I complain to the nurse and have her check the computer. Sure enough, the data is wrong. But she just enters the new figures onto the old ones, as if they never existed. Outraged, I tell her she has no right to cover this up.

Just as unsettling, this mistake means we must wait for Damon's chest drainage to *truly* subside, and we can't even *think* about going home until his outflow has abated.

Three days later, I'm on weekend duty again, and Damon and I go on an extended stroll. It's his longest walk yet. As we near our ward on the return, I hear a sudden whistling sound emanating from Damon.

I look down and see his chest tube has separated from its insertion point, and air coming from a tiny exposed hole in his pleural space is hissing like a kettle. It sounds bad, so we flag a nurse, who quickly covers the hole and summons a doctor.

The doctor, a prim-looking woman with glasses, removes the chest tube.

"We need to prepare for an emergency re-implantation in the ICU," she says, and orders a chest X-ray. While we wait, I talk to her and see she's on the ball, a genuine, thinking physician. When the X-ray arrives, she studies it and says, "We could reimplant the tube or try leaving it out and see what happens."

"That sounds interesting," I say. "What do you mean exactly?"

"It's a calculated gamble," she explains. "Worst case, the fluid migrates behind the lungs, making it a little harder to extract. But his body also might adjust to the change and find its own equilibrium *without* the chest drainage tube."

"Go for it!" I tell her, knowing we might not get another chance like this.

Damon lets me convince him because he *hates* the gurgling tube and would do anything to ditch it.

It takes a few days — with one bad night when it looks like we might have to reinsert the tube — but Damon does finally find his own tube-free equilibrium. I silently bless this fine young doctor.

New issues crop up at the last minute. "I'm having a little trouble with words when I read," Damon says one day. Doctors give him a visual field test and note he has difficulty with one section of it. When we ask how serious this is, the senior neurologist replies, "It usually resolves, but sometimes they go blind. It's hard to predict."

Shealagh and I try not to think about this dire specter or the cavalier way it's conveyed. Fortunately, we are assigned a neurology fellow who works with Damon every day and helps him get a handle on this problem. She's just starting out but already has the gift. Once again, a young, talented, and motivated woman doctor does her job and helps Damon over a potentially debilitating hurdle.

We're biding our time now and praying that no more mishaps occur. One morning, the nurse brings Damon a 1,200 mg pill of ibuprofen instead of magnesium — after everyone has warned him that he must *not* take any ibuprofen. This time it's Damon, more alert now, who catches the mix-up and sends the toxic pill back. He talks to me about it repeatedly.

"Dad, she gave me the wrong pill! If I hadn't noticed, I'd have been in big trouble . . . We have to watch *everything,* it's just like you said!" He's shocked and looks at me with new understanding. I'm known as the barking dog by my family, and God

539

knows what else by the hospital staff, and now Damon sees firsthand how critical our vigilance is.

As Damon improves, he seeks diversion and focuses more on the future. He chats on the phone, blogs on the computer, and listens to his iPod. Shealagh orders films for him to screen on our DVD player and reads aloud to him. They devour Laurence Olivier's *Confessions of an Actor.* Damon works out with a physiotherapist and starts to train his body. And he has his mother get an application for his learner's permit. He plans to get his driver's license on his seventeenth birthday and buy a secondhand school bus with his friends for a cross-country trek.

Now that he's better, Damon also receives more visitors in the hospital. Sam and Miranda and my parents and my sister come, and so do several of Damon's friends. Kyle visits several times. Once when I drive her home from the hospital, Kyle turns to me and says, "I have to admit, he looked much better than I expected!"

Trekking up to a big hospital to visit a sick friend who's just had a heart transplant is a brave act for teenagers, and everyone who makes the effort impresses us.

Near the end of Damon's ordeal, my own body starts to recoil against the hospital.

For a whole month, all my days and nights have either started or ended in this grim location, often both, and my life has narrowed to one tiny repetitive loop.

I'm sick of the dank 168th Street subway station, of every greasy fast food joint and takeout place in the area, of the guarded entrance with the string of ambulances outside, of the vendor with his stale peanuts, of the twenty-four-hour crush of desperate people in various stages of distress, of the security guards and the endless winding corridors and tiled floors and fluorescent walls, the insipid cafeteria, the slow elevators, the hollow vending machines, more endless corridors, and then the dusty floor and the weary, white-coated nurses and doctors and technicians and cleaning staff, and the inescapable sour hospital room itself with its tired bed and musty monitors and limp equipment, and my bag of dirty clothes and bare toiletries waiting in a forlorn corner between the cot and the sink.

We finally get the word on a Friday afternoon when my mother and Sam are visiting. Shealagh and I are both in the hospital room with Damon.

Dr. Mason comes by to say that Damon will be discharged tomorrow.

Although we've been anticipating this, it's

still an astonishing moment of liberation.

We all cheer and applaud. It's hard to believe. We've been here thirty-two days!

I go over and give Damon a big hug, then offer a formal handshake to my hero. Everyone pays equally heartfelt and personal tribute.

Damon sits on his hospital bed, quietly glowing.

CHAPTER 51

"I'm Free! . . . I'm Free! . . . and freedom tastes of reality!"

— *I'm Free,* The Who

That's right, I am. After 4 weeks and 4 days I am finally out of the hospital and back at home. What a frickin relief. The computer in my room at the hospital broke down so I couldn't update every other day like I'd figured I would, apologies. Got back on Saturday and have just been recovering and discovering what I've been missing all these years.

Went to play some WC3. I love you guys. I'm not sure how I would have got through all this without you. Thanx to Will, Zak and Max.

— From Damon's blog, February 22, 2005

I can't believe it.

We're back home.

With Damon.

Who has a strong new heart and is doing really well!

He's back in his room, sleeping in his own bed, and eating meals with us.

He's back on his own computer, blogging and IM-ing and Warcrafting.

He's back on the phone with his pals, lolling on his chair and gabbing for hours.

He's back in the family room, building things with Sam and Miranda and playing board games and watching TV and hanging out with all of us.

Damon is also back with his beloved Freddie. He takes the mini-pin for short walks around the block. The energetic dog does not leap at the front door, as usual, but meekly offers up his long neck as Damon slips his red collar on and snaps the buckle. Freddie lingers patiently inside until Damon, still weak, has donned his winter coat and white face mask and signaled it's time to go.

"Come on, Fred." The two companions step outside. Damon holds the leash and pauses to survey things from the porch, once again master of his dominion. He smiles softly. Freddie has enough play on the sixteen-foot lead to run ahead and explore. When the dog gets too frisky, Damon yanks on the Flexi leash and Freddie looks up guiltily, recalibrating his pace so as not to strain Damon.

They return, invigorated, and cuddle together on the sofa.

On his first day back from the hospital, Damon sits down at the piano. He hasn't touched it for years but now he picks out the popular spiritual "He's Got the Whole World in His Hands" and begins to play. He's a little rusty and the piano is a little out of tune, but soon the uplifting gospel strains fill the house.

It's an extraordinary new situation we find ourselves in back home.

The worst is behind us, and while we must continue to monitor the situation closely, the odds now favor us for the first time in a very long time.

It seems too good to be true, so I hunt for flaws and weaknesses. On Damon's last day in the hospital, for his last blood test before discharge, I ask the nurse to check his albumin and total protein, even though it isn't indicated on the order. In all our anxiety about Damon's recovery, I have not forgotten that the underlying reason for the transplant — the cause for such a radical operation in the first place — was Damon's PLE. And I need to see how we're doing on that score, even if the doctors insist it's too early to tell and the test won't mean anything at this stage. But I remain haunted by studies showing PLE may not resolve, *even after a heart transplant,* and I need to verify we've avoided that particularly vicious fate. So I cajole the nurse to check the appropriate box on the blood test form.

That night, after Damon has jettisoned his ID tags and exchanged his hospital gown and slippers like prison garb for his own clothes, and after he's marched out of the hospital on a sunny but cold February afternoon with a cautiously triumphant smile beneath his white face mask, and after he has arrived home to a Winnie-the-Pooh-style hero party with a welcome banner, ribbons, and balloons, and after my kind parents, living in our house and minding our kids for a month, have left with our boundless thanks and everyone else has retreated upstairs, I get a call from Dr. Mason's office. Her nurse informs us, with breathless pride — I note they're always prompter with good news than bad, per the marketing mentality — that Damon's albumin has jumped to a PLE-busting 3.0!

It's not just icing on the cake, it's the whole cake!

Even the pediatric cardiology transplant team, which was opposed to measuring the protein so soon, concedes this is very exciting news.

I thank them for telling us and I hang up, profoundly grateful and relieved.

Now it's definitive, and I can really believe it myself and celebrate wholeheartedly.

A week later, our joy runneth over, as Damon's albumin hits 3.5, which is like mine and yours and that of everyone else who is healthy, normal, and fully functional.

Damon has an efficient new heart and a brand-new lease on life!

Nevertheless, for many days, even weeks, following Damon's triumphant return, I cannot completely process this information. For the past nearly four years, my entire existence has been dominated by this battle for survival and the ceaseless deployment of all available resources toward one overriding goal. And now that the goal has been attained — Damon's illness is cured, and he's recovering — I don't quite know how to let my guard back down or what to do with myself in the freed-up space.

I begin by thanking all the doctors who

helped us, from Columbia and from all the other hospitals, including my dedicated private brain trust. But because old habits die hard, and because I don't wish to be lulled into complacency — even if we've bought Damon fifteen to twenty years, what happens *after that?* — I prod my advisers about future therapies. I'm interested in artificial hearts, xenotransplantation, and stem cell therapy.

Everyone tells me they expect a new era of advances, but I should just kick back and enjoy Damon's success for now.

"I'm very optimistic about Damon's outlook," Dr. Rose e-mails me after I thank him for his help. And everyone seems to share this confidence. So I start to let go and relax. I accept that the nightmare is over, that Damon has been released from his captivity, and that I, too, am liberated.

I'm six weeks from my fiftieth birthday and aware of diverted plans and unmet goals — though it all seems worth it now that Damon is home, safe and sound.

I draw up a list of new goals and plans, including expanding my professional opportunities. I accept several travel and speaking invitations I'd deferred. I apply to a college writing program that requires only a short summer residency. I also register for

548

my first Olympic triathlon. It's only six months away and I've done no training, but it's a spur to both action and imagination.

After the initial euphoria of Damon's homecoming, there is the day-to-day reality of recovery. Yet albeit slower and shakier, that reality is in many ways even *more* thrilling, because now it's all about Damon adjusting and growing into his new capabilities and learning to do things he could never do before.

Damon remains weak from his surgery, with much ground to make up, but even the nature of his weakness has changed for the better. Now when he climbs the stairs from the family room to his bedroom on the main floor, or from his room to our second-story bedroom, he doesn't get out of breath as he used to. His big, new heart keeps his blood pumping vigorously. Instead, it's his muscles that feel the strain, lagging behind his new cardiovascular prowess. "My legs feel sore," Damon says with a wondrous half smile.

But building up his muscles is a workable proposition, and Damon now embarks on a daily exercise program. He stretches and does calisthenics. He performs modified sit-ups, squats, and push-ups. He takes bracing walks with Freddie. And he works out with hand weights, lifting small dumbbells and relentlessly toning his body around the clock.

Now that he's lost all his excess fluid from the PLE — except in the face, where the steroids puff him up — Damon is down to eighty-six pounds. His arms, in particular, look thin. But his appetite is back, and he's diligent about his regimen, eating regularly and exercising several times a day with fierce concentration. He makes steady, impressive progress.

"If you keep this up, we'll be able to run triathlons together!" I tell Damon, and knowing his disciplined determination, it's not as farfetched as it sounds.

It's not just his body but also Damon's mental attitude that bounces back strong. He's full of schemes and plans, and none takes any post-transplant limitation into account. He will catch up on his course work over the summer and apply to college with everyone else during the fall semester of his senior year.

"You may want to stick close to New York for the first year or two, when hospital visits are the norm," I suggest during one college discussion.

Damon bristles. "No! Why would I do that?"

"Hey, New York's not a backwater. You got Columbia, NYU, many goo—"

"No!" Damon repeats. He gives me the baleful teenage eye for daring to hem him in or daring even to *contemplate* such a possibility.

This reaction is mild, however, compared to the resentment I elicit during another discussion of Damon's future. Though he still plans to return to *Deadwood* over the summer, he worries that acting, which he loves, is not serious or public-spirited enough for a full-time career. He's long been interested in diplomacy, and we've talked about the State Department after college. Although such a decision is years away, I incur Damon's wrath when I suggest he might wish to reconsider such a path in light of his heart transplant.

"In the State Department, you must take any assignment they give you," I say. "And most new recruits get sent to the Third World. Now you'll be on immune suppressants your whole life, making you that much more vulnerable to any infection but especially to rare or exotic pathogens, so I'm just saying *maybe* this is not the *ideal career* for you."

"No, I don't agree!" Damon cries. "There's no reason I can't do it."

"True, though your medical history is part of the application . . . But why take the *added* risk? I have friends with normal immune systems who picked up nasty bugs in Asia and Africa . . . There's so many *other* things you can do, D-man."

"But not if this is what I want!" He's so adamant and irate, I decide to let it go. Why have a major dust-up over such a distant possibility? And I don't want to crush Damon's dreams, or even more importantly, to crush his *spirit*.

He even convinces his mother, who then prevails upon me, to let him go to Tech and meet the Group for a first post-transplant get-together. They congregate after school by the park, and Damon promises to wear his mask and to exclude anyone with a cold if we'll let him go. We're supposed to limit his contact with other people but Dr. Mason thinks it's okay if he doesn't overdo it and Shealagh promises to supervise.

The outing is a big success with a large, spirited turnout.

"What happened to your original heart, Damon?" Max asks in his high-spirited, analytic way. "Don't throw it out. You should keep it in a jar and give it to the woman you marry!"

"I don't know, Max." Damon grins behind his mask. "Maybe a little ghoulish?"

"No, it would be so cool and so romantic!" Max insists. "You should do it!"

"Hey, Damon, you ever get your donor's dreams and memories?" Zak asks.

"Hmmm, not as far as I can recall, Zak." Damon smiles.

Damon has checkups at Columbia several times a week. I'm back at work, so Shealagh handles the visits, which take place in Dr. Mason's office. All seems good but Shealagh wants to know about a stubborn, thrush-like growth in Damon's mouth.

"He needs to do a better job of swishing with his disinfectant," Dr. Mason says.

"But he rinses meticulously and very thoroughly, several times a day as directed, and I watch him, so I know!" Damon's vigilant mother replies.

Dr. Mason shrugs. "If he keeps using the disinfectant, it will all work out."

Shealagh still finds Dr. Mason a touch high-handed and too dismissive of her concerns. "She's so bloody sure about everything — *It's all routine* — even when she doesn't seem to have a clue!"

But Shealagh is a worrier, Dr. Mason has treated many transplant patients, and Damon is doing well, so we're not about to complain.

Damon quickly resumes his independent teenage existence. Beyond daily pills and regular doctor's visits, there are only minor nods to his physical recovery.

Every few days, I must help with his Duo-DERM skin dressing. His pressure sore has still not healed, and it's in a sensitive spot near his tush, so I must bend down and find the tiny target. "Okay, you're good, D-man," I say as I stand back up. It's like a last vestige of intimacy, a throwback to all the time we spent together in the hospital.

Otherwise Damon has only a few minor scars near the incision line, and his skin tone is magnificent, with rosy face and pink body.

"I think you're actually growing!" I remark.

Damon tries to repay me with his usual sweetness. On Oscar night, the family is sitting around the TV when he comes up and starts to rub my shoulders. I relish Damon's massages but am worried about the strain on him post-surgery. But Damon digs in with both hands, and using his whole body as leverage, he manages to exert surprising force. He stops after about ten minutes.

"Sorry, Dad, I'll do better next time. I'm still not a hundred percent."

"You kidding? That was great, D-man. Thanks!"

Shealagh and Miranda go up to bed at the halfway mark but the boys and I wait until midnight to see Clint Eastwood's *Million Dollar Baby* win the Oscar. The next day Damon asks me if we can go see the movie. The small theater in our multiplex is almost empty — the film's been playing for months — so Damon doesn't even have to keep his face mask on. It's a thrill to buy popcorn and soda and sit in reclining seats in a dark theater with my son after all he's been through.

When the film's over, we hit a local joint for dinner. Damon was more moved than me by this Hollywood film about a female boxer who's paralyzed after an unfair fight.

"I liked that the main character decided life wasn't worth living on a respirator," he says. "Her dreams were crushed and she wanted to go with dignity. And I liked how her trainer, who loved her, still decided to give her what she wanted by helping her die."

It's a charged subject for Damon, who's just come out of the hospital after a long ordeal, including total maintenance on life support. He's okay now, but he must have experienced many dark, desperate moments. It dawns on me he knows this material far better than I do, and I listen closely to what he says.

It's a great evening for the two of us. We're doing all these routine things together — going to a neighborhood movie, eating dinner at a local restaurant, having a real talk — that we could only dream of doing while Damon was so sick.

Damon polishes off his food in record time, then glances up at me with a mixture of blushing pride and sheepish apology.

"I'm still hungry, Dad. Could I have another burger?"

I grin at my embarrassed teenage son. "D-man, you can have ten burgers — a hundred burgers — have *anything* you want!"

I call the waiter over and order another burger and fries. I've never seen Damon eat like this, and it's exhilarating to watch. He has that sleek, ravenous look in the eye, as if he needs to make up for all those years of frugal eating and meager calories. As if he intends to *consume* his way back to full strength and health.

CHAPTER 52

"No one ever said it was easy."
— Coldplay, *The Scientist*
— From Damon's blog, March 9, 2005

Sometime in early March, I notice Damon's albumin level has dropped to 3.3. A reading of 3.3 is within the margin of error of 3.5, Damon's previous level, but I still don't like the direction. When the next reading comes in at 3.0, I start to grow concerned. I note also that Damon has a slight cough and that he looks droopier. But maybe I'm just being overzealous and have unrealistic expectations for a magical transformation.

I query Dr. Mason about this trend, but as expected, she brushes it off.

"These values jump all over the place in the first months, you shouldn't even be *looking* at them!" she tells me. I e-mail Dr. Chin and Dr. Rose, inquiring from each, "Is this drop within the normal range of fluctuation for a post-transplant patient?"

Dr. Chin replies we'd need to graph more values and study the overall pattern; Dr. Rose suggests I ask Damon's cardiologists, because anything he says would be pure conjecture.

These responses do not allay my concerns, but neither do they induce panic. I just heighten my alert level and watch Damon more closely.

The next day, a Friday, Shealagh takes Damon to see Dr. Mason for his regular visit — he goes three times a week — and Dr. Mason continues with her breezy dismissal of any concerns. She says our son is doing well and there's nothing to worry about. But that same night, around eleven P.M., when we're at home, Damon comes up to our bedroom.

"I just got this kinda *shivery* feeling," he reports, frowning. His breathing is shallow and rapid, he has the chills, and he looks pale. Our son is no hypochondriac, so we take his temperature. It's 100.8, indicating fever, a warning sign of possible rejection or infection.

"All the manuals state that the slightest indication of fever in an immune-compromised patient is significant and should be followed up," Shealagh says.

We don't like this at all and quickly call the hospital, reaching Dr. Davis. We assume we must bring Damon in right away but Dr. Davis says she doesn't think it's necessary.

"A temperature of a hundred is borderline. You can keep an eye on him and call back in the morning. If he doesn't get worse, you could wait until Monday for his regular biopsy."

Shealagh and I are surprised — we've been told that transplant patients must come in immediately for any hint of a symptom — but we're not looking to make extra hospital trips, and Dr. Davis has more experience than us, so we accept her advice and stay home.

By Saturday, Damon's fever is under 100 and he seems calmer. But he still doesn't look quite right to us, though we can't tell if this is normal for the post-transplant period.

We take him in Monday morning but the hospital is slow and doesn't process his biopsy order for an entire day. We will have to wait until Tuesday for the test. We're upset about this but the doctors say they want to keep him in the hospital regardless, so they can start him on a three-day anti-rejection course.

"Isn't that premature, since you haven't even tested for rejection yet?" I ask.

But Dr. Becker — neither Dr. Mason nor Dr. Davis is there to see us — says no. "It's most likely rejection — I heard a gallop when I listened to his heart. Even if the biopsy is negative, it could still be rejection in a different part of the heart."

I scowl. "Doesn't that render the test effectively *meaningless,* since you've prejudged the outcome regardless of the test result?"

Shealagh nods with me, equally confused by this tortured-seeming logic.

"No, this is standard procedure for a patient in Damon's situation," Dr. Becker says. "I assume you don't want to risk a major rejection episode, do you?"

Shealagh and I huddle. We're upset that Dr. Mason is not there and that no biopsy was done all day. Shealagh points out that the junior Dr. Becker has never listened to Damon's heart before, so she has no baseline for diagnosing a "gallop." But we both feel we can't risk *not* giving the course, just in case she's right.

Once we've convinced ourselves, we still have to convince Damon.

"No, why should I take all this new medication *before* we do the test?" Damon protests. "I don't have rejection, believe me! I know my own body."

Shealagh and I feel like shills as we explain the hospital's convoluted rationale to our son. "Sometimes we just have to trust their expertise," we tell him with a deep sigh.

Damon begins the anti-rejection course that evening, and the next morning he goes for his biopsy. The result comes back in the afternoon, and it's negative — there is *absolutely no sign* of rejection. Damon registers 0 on a scale of 4.0!

Damon flashes a sharp "I told you so" look. Shealagh and I feel greatly relieved but remain wary given the conflicting information we're getting.

The doctors not only maintain they did the right thing by *starting* Damon on the anti-rejection course, they now want him to *finish* it too. Dr. Mason shows up the next day, self-assured as ever, and confirms this is her recommendation.

"A biopsy is taken from only one section of the heart, so Damon could test negative and *still* have rejection in a *different* part of his heart." She smiles. "We've seen it before!"

Shealagh and I shake our heads but we don't have enough knowledge or experience to risk ignoring this advice. We're unhappy but at loose ends.

"Why don't you go back to the office? I'll

take it from here," Shealagh offers. "It's just waiting around at this point. At least Damon will be home soon. This is our lot now."

Damon stays in the hospital for several days and blogs to his friends about it:

Yep I'm back at the hospital. Just for 3 days though so I should be leaving tomorrow morning. Actually pretty standard especially in the first 3 months they all warned me that this was something that frequently happens but it's annoying none the less. Came in Monday 4 the usual check-up and the biopsy (that's when they go in with a needle and take out a small piece of your heart). Hadn't been great the past few days I thought it was a cold, *they* thought it was rejection. So they decided they were gonna keep me for the 3 days to give me the IV steroids (standard rejection treatment). I said how bout waiting 4 the biopsy results cause everyone I asked including the doc who said it was rejection said that a cold or other mild infection aka flu fever could and would cause the same symptoms. But better safe than sorry and all that jazz so Monday finds me in a hospital bed. Tuesday afternoon finds the biopsy results. Guess what boys and girls — no rejection. 😲 But of course they'd already started the steroids and its possible so might as well finish the job so I'm here till tomorrow morning. Yippee.☺

Realized and been realizing many things. Can't possibly explain them all don't quite understand them all myself yet. But one thing I'm slowly beginning 2 understand is just how weak I really was before (the heart transplant for those who are confused). Honestly I'll never understand how I got through the last 3 years as well as I did. And now when I think of what I might have been able to do with those 3 years had it not been for PLE it makes me kinda sad. I guess I never really accepted it or admitted it before but now it's suddenly sort of hit me; I had a disease and a bad one, one that could and did kill people and one that no one really knew anything definitive about and who could blame them. About 10,000 people in America have had my operation (the original 1) and 10% of those get PLE that's not exactly much of a data base. And one that could have eventually killed me and was weakening me day by day.

Strange I never really thought of myself

that way until now looking back on it all. But it's not quite over. When I first got out of the hospital I felt great and I still do but the past week and especially being brought back 2 the hospital has made me realize that recovery will not be quick or easy. It's going 2 take time and work and patience. I only mind the time. How much more time is this all gonna take/waste and what am I going 2 lose or miss in the process? But as long as I am moving forward though minor setbacks are inevitable life is very good and I've got a lot of make up 2 do.☺☺☺😁

After three days, Damon leaves the hospital and returns home. He seems okay and there are no more acute episodes. We're all relieved. But he still has a cough and a peckish aspect. And the steroids have given him a distorted moon face and a swollen neck, which, when he first appears in my study in the morning, makes me start. It's painful to see my beautiful boy with such grotesque features.

We go downstairs, where I help him take his morning meds and make him breakfast. We sit and talk, but everything feels off-kilter. Damon looks like he's wearing a troll mask. He describes strange hallucinations in ghoulish detail.

"This fiendish figure was standing behind the door, ready to attack me!"

I ask Dr. Mason about these visions. "Oh, that's not unusual with the strong doses he's on, it'll stop once he tapers off," she replies.

Shealagh also is unhappy with Damon's condition but relieved he's coming off the steroids. She keeps taking Damon to Columbia and reporting various cold-like symptoms: headaches, sniffles, fatigue, swollen glands, breathing problems, and stomach pain. She is especially concerned about the fact that Damon is losing weight — he should be gaining — and that he's experiencing mental confusion. But Dr. Mason says the confusion is typical as patients adjust to cyclosporine, the weight loss is from ascites decrease, and the puffiness is from the anti-rejection course. "There is nothing to worry about," she tells Shealagh.

Shealagh takes Damon to Columbia on a Friday afternoon and despite the all-clear, the next morning he gets the chills and a fever again. This time his temperature is 101 but we're less panicked about it. We call up the hospital and Dr. Sanford, who's on duty, says to bring him in to the emergency room and she'll meet us there. Since it's a Saturday, and Shealagh has already taken Damon to the hospital several times this week, I drive him in.

"I'm sorry you guys have to shuttle me back and forth all the time," Damon says.

"Come on, D-man, this is normal during the first year and we're prepared for it. It's why Mom's home full-time and I'm happy to do it when I'm here . . . The only thing you need to worry about is getting better!" I smile at my son, who looks frail and bowed.

When we reach the hospital, I ask Damon if he wants to wait by the entrance while I park. It's chilly outside and there's a steep hill down to the parking lot, which he'd have to climb. Damon nods, and I drop him by a bench out front before driving down to the lot.

When I return, I see Damon on a far corner of the bench, sitting in a narrow patch of bright sunlight. He's found the *one* blessed spot, and his red-crested head peeps out of his bulky anorak, craning upward to extract maximum warmth, light, and air before he must enter the hospital confines.

I sit on the bench by Damon and steal an extra few minutes in the slanting sun beside him, seizing the same glorious moment and briefly contemplating the same subversive thought.

What if we just stayed here and *refused* to go inside?

I recall Damon reading Melville's *Bartleby the Scrivener* on the plane back from L.A. and its famous words now echo for me in front of the hospital: "I would prefer not."

But then Damon starts to cough, and I know we have no choice. I make him put on his face mask before we walk inside, pass security, and run the gauntlet of chronically and acutely ailing patients that fills the emergency room. I raise my voice at the desk, explaining Damon is an immune-compromised patient and I need to get him out of this pathogen-teeming area. I get a few jaded, gimme-a-break scowls, but someone heeds me because we are soon ushered out of the waiting area and into a small cubicle inside.

To my dismay, Dr. Sanford, who promised she'd meet us, is nowhere to be found. I soon learn there are only two doctors for the whole ER, and they're both besieged. We have a long wait until one finally shows.

Our ER doctor is harried but sharp. She quickly grasps our case and leads us to a small private area where Damon can lie down. I tell her we need a regular room, away from the ER, and she nods. "Yes, but it would be easier if your son's cardiologist was here. I'll do what I can but I must run to my next patient now."

I get Damon comfortable, then go buy us food. We eat by his bed, then Damon tries to nap. But he's too restless, so he asks me about the paper I'm reading and we have a discussion about current events.

At some point, Damon falls asleep. He looks peaceful and settled, and I start to feel better about his condition.

The doctor comes by with Damon's blood results, circling two items. "Your son's liver enzymes are abnormal and his platelet count is very low. His team must deal with this." Then she runs off again. Since none of Damon's cardiologists is present, and I don't know exactly what these values mean — are they abnormal for a transplant patient or just for an average patient? — I focus on Damon's comfort and getting us onto the main floor.

A cardiologist drops by. She examines Damon but tells us nothing. She leaves.

By four P.M. — we arrived at noon — I begin to grow anxious about Damon. The ER is a dangerous place for my immune-compromised son, and I'm eager to get him out of here. But there's clearly a holdup with our room. After many calls and persistent pagings, by five P.M. I learn that the patient currently occupying the room meant for Damon refuses to leave.

He's a low-priority case, he's been cleared for discharge, but he simply *won't go.*

I explain to the nurse how urgent it is to get my son out of the ER. "Yes," she says, nodding.

Nevertheless, for the next five hours, I tussle with a series of inept hospital administrators and bureaucrats to get Damon into his own room. Everyone agrees he needs the bed and should have it. But no one knows how to get the other patient *out.*

I'm amazed the hospital cannot enforce its own rules due to the whim of one patient. But instead of ejecting *him,* they start pressuring *me* to accept an overnight bed in the ER for Damon. "It's out of the question!" I tell them. When they tell me the ER has its advantages, I demand to speak to the supervisor. I leave several messages until he finally calls me back. But to my astonishment, he *too* tries to get us to stay in the ER!

"I'm sorry, but we can't get the other patient to leave," the supervisor says.

"Are you serious? You expect me to endanger my son's life because you can't do your job? Get us a room or I'll file a complaint against you and your whole team!"

"The ER is not so bad and I'll make sure

he gets a nice bed," he wheedles.

"My son is a *transplant* patient and he's *sick!*" I cry.

By nine P.M., after several hours more of this, I finally lose my patience and head for the ward. If they can't do it, I'll get the other patient out myself. It's bad enough none of his cardiologists has seen Damon all day, knowing we had an *emergency,* but I won't let my son spend the night in the ER, a known incubator for infection. I'm furious and it's noted.

I storm up in the elevator, but there's a new supervisor who meets me as I step off. He apologizes hat in hand, admits the error, and promises to have the patient out forthwith.

It's eleven P.M. before Damon finally gets his own room on a regular ward. But perhaps because we had to work so hard to get here, once we arrive, everything quickly normalizes.

Damon is feeling better and the hospital room setup is so familiar, we make ourselves right at home. I check the phone and TV, unpack clothes, open up the armchair.

Damon is chirpy and seems more like himself. Maybe he's already recovered from whatever little problem he had.

The only bummer is that tomorrow night

is his *Deadwood* debut, and I suspect he won't be discharged in time to watch it. Even if everything looks fine, the doctors will likely want to keep him under observation for at least another day.

CHAPTER 53

So for those who are interested, I will be on "Deadwood" this Sunday the 20th at 9:00 on HBO (channel 32 for most I think). The show is an hour and I don't know when exactly I'll be on but probably some point in the middle.

Now a word or two on Deadwood; it's not for everyone. It's very coarse and very vulgar and very violent. It takes a little getting used 2. When I watched the first episode, I was quite daunted but after you watch a couple and get into it you start 2 realize what a great show it really is . . . but maybe I'm biased. Either way this is not me trying 2 convince you or any1 to become a regular watcher of the show (though you're more than welcome 2), this just me keeping you all informed and giving you a little warning. And no I wasn't traumatized nor abused in any way when I

went up 2 the set. Just 4 the record. I must say it was pretty cool watching the 2nd season and knowing all the people and seeing the scenes that I watched them shoot, it makes it a totally different experience.
— From Damon's blog, March 14, 2005

Damon has a decent night in the hospital and the next day, a Sunday, all seems to calm down. During morning rounds, the consensus is he has some kind of a cold and this is not a serious matter. Shealagh comes in the afternoon to relieve me and says Damon looks pretty good.

I'm scheduled to fly to Japan on Tuesday and have a talk to prepare, but with Damon in the hospital, I'm not sure I should bother. Shealagh suggests I draft my presentation. She's glad I'm ready to cancel, but for now she feels the situation is under control. "And you should definitely go if we don't need you here."

That night after I get home, Damon makes his national TV debut on *Deadwood*. Sadly, he can't watch it at a party with his friends, because he's in the hospital, and he can't watch it in the hospital because the place doesn't have HBO. I watch the show alone; it's too X-rated for Sam and Miranda.

Happily, Damon's little scene is a gem and I get many compliments for him. I call Damon on his cell — even in the hospital, he answers reliably — and relay the tributes. Paula Malcomson calls to congratulate Damon, validating his professional bona fides. Gary Leffew also calls, but Gary only gets through to me. "Tell him we gonna ride to the mountaintop again, soon as he come outta there!"

The next day, a Monday, I head straight to the hospital after work. Damon sits up in bed, looking sharp and alert, while Dr. Mason, back on the case, beavers about. She has various people from infectious disease coming in to see Damon and trying to pinpoint what's causing his coldlike symptoms. By this stage, none of us has too many illusions about Dr. Mason — I even catch Damon frowning at one of her explanations — but we've gotten this far with her, and she's the only game in town, so we make the best of it.

I tell Dr. Mason that I'm scheduled to fly to Japan the following day, but I can easily cancel the trip if she thinks there's any reason, *any reason at all,* I should stay.

"No, make your trip — go, go!" Dr. Mason waves her arm breezily. "There's nothing to worry about here. We wouldn't even keep Damon in the hospital if he wasn't so close to his transplant. We're just being extra-cautious."

Dr. Mason tugs on her stethoscope, which she wears like a gym teacher's whistle. "It's always like this for the first year. We'll have Damon in whenever we suspect anything, and you can't put your entire lives on hold. Mostly it doesn't concern you, anyway . . . So go give your talk in Japan, and don't mind any of this. Everything's *fine* here."

"Yeah, Dad, I want you to go!" Damon pipes up.

"We *all* want you to go!" Shealagh chimes in, smiling.

"Can you bring me back some sushi?" Damon asks, fingering bland applesauce.

"You got it," I say. When Damon gets a call, I take Dr. Mason aside.

"What do you think is really going on?" I ask.

"He has something like a mild cold," Dr. Mason tells me, "and we think it's from a viral agent. We're just keeping him until we can determine exactly what it is, to be on the safe side. But it's a routine thing, and we have it totally under control. No worries."

I stay with Damon and Shealagh until the evening. As I gather my overnight bag and see Shealagh's bag in its place, I realize the hospital has turned into our second home.

Sensing the slightest sniffle, I refrain from hugging Damon good-bye because we're still scrupulous about his immune-compromised status. Instead, I just wave warmly to my son and blow him a kiss. "See you, D-man!"

"Bye, Dad," Damon says, waving back.

Shealagh steps out and walks me to the elevator. She gives me a big hug. "It's important for all of us — for Sam and Miranda and for me, as well as for Damon — that you keep plowing forward and not let our lives grind to a complete halt. We need you out there."

The next day, as we're sitting on the runway, I call the hospital for a final Damon check, half-expecting I'll never get off the ground because some impediment may yet crop up at the last minute. But when I reach Shealagh, she reports Damon is sleeping comfortably. "Everything is fine here," she informs me.

I smile and remind myself that we have entered a new, more positive phase.

We take off without incident but some-where above the Bering Sea, our plane runs into serious turbulence, and we go into a sudden nosedive. It's more than the usual air bump, and we drop with alarming speed. In the brief, jolting seconds when we seem to be plunging to certain death, two thoughts flash before me: first, that I really would prefer to live; and second, if I am about to die, it means Damon, that durable son of mine, has survived me after all.

While the first thought induces terror and regret, the second is profoundly soothing and consoling, and actually brings a small smile to my lips.

I sacrifice an entire day and then some on the flight over, and by the time I get to my hotel, meet one of my hosts for a drink, and do e-mail, it's bedtime. I get up early the next morning and speak to Shealagh and Damon for over an hour. Damon had a rough night, spiking a fever, but now he feels better, as if the fever actually improved things.

I sign off and head to the National Institute of Science and Technology Policy to give my talk, "The Image of Scientists and Engineers." Later I meet with a member of the Japanese parliament and have dinner near Tokyo University.

On my way back to the hotel, I begin to fret about Damon. Although I'm not aware of any new problems, worrying about him is my default, and since we haven't spoken all day, I start to troubleshoot in my head, recalling that when I noted it sounded like he was improving, Damon said he wasn't improving, he was deteriorating. I pressed him to explain but he played it down, admitting he felt better today and was just letting off steam. But his remark returns to me now since Damon doesn't usually indulge in that kind of self-pity.

Alas, when I reach Shealagh on the phone, she is in a near-panic and informs me things have gotten very bad, very fast. "The doctors now believe Damon's *liver* may be infected. His liver enzyme levels are elevated, and he's broken out in these red spots everywhere. His platelet count is extremely low, and his body keeps chewing up the new platelets they're giving him. He's feverish, he looks shaky, and he seems *very* weak!"

Shealagh says the doctors have offered to move Damon to the ICU because he can get better care there, and she agreed, because she's worried. "They believe it could be a viral or bacterial infection, but they're still not sure what's going on!"

This news makes my heart shudder and turns everything around me to dust.

It's clear I have to return immediately. I don't know exactly what's going on, but I know I need to be there. I have little doubt we can fix this — isn't the worst behind us now? — but it's going to demand a full-court press.

"I hate to break up your trip but Damon always does better when you're around," Shealagh says. "He draws strength from you . . . And I need you too," she adds.

"Don't worry, it's only a question of how fast I can find a flight at this hour!" I check my watch. "It's now eleven P.M., so I probably won't get out until morning. But please let me have a word with Damon before I start calling around."

Shealagh puts Damon on, and at first he groggily objects to my cutting my trip short for him. "No, you don't need to!" It's an admission things are really bad if they need to call in the cavalry from Japan. But I can tell Damon is not himself and that he's in trouble.

"I'm on my way, D-man, and I will see you very shortly!" I tell him.

Shealagh starts to relax and even Damon quickly accepts the change in plans. By one thirty A.M., I book a seat on the first available flight out of Tokyo. My plane departs Japan on time and to my great relief, there are no delays. We land at JFK after fourteen hours, and I jump into a taxi and head straight to the hospital. I flash ID at the entrance, shoot up the elevator, and race down the hall and corridors, until I find Damon's room at the very end of the Cardiothoracic Unit ICU.

It's ten A.M. Friday morning, an hour *before* I left Japan on the same day.

I embrace Shealagh, who's amazed I made it so fast, and sling my suitcase in a corner before hurrying over to see my son.

Damon lies on the ICU bed with an IV in his arm, looking marginally bigger and older — he's been growing with his new heart. But he's pale, with a clipped, diminished look. A red pulsimeter on his fingertip indicates his oxygen saturation has dropped significantly, while his breathing is rapid and shallow. He's clearly in distress.

It hurts me to see my son looking so weak and beleaguered, especially after all the progress we've made. But Damon's face lights up when he spots me, and he flashes a beautiful smile, edged with embarrassment that he's in this state. "Hi, Dad."

I throw my arms around Damon, and we sit together on his bed. He is coherent, if slower and vaguer than usual. I show him the few trinkets I got him at the airport: a T-shirt stamped with sushi dishes, and a deck of royal Japanese playing cards. Damon, who's been asking for sushi, grins appreciatively at the T-shirt — nothing wrong with his sense of humor! I start unpacking the cards but he says, as if reminding me he still has homework to finish, "We can do that later, Dad, there's other stuff they want me to deal with right now."

"Sure." I step back and let the ICU team do its thing. There's a nurse with spiky brown hair, Hugh, who seems friendly and efficient, and an earnest young cardiology fellow, Dr. October. The ICU attending is a correct, compact Ghanaian, Dr. Ofuri.

I'm told Dr. Mason has not shown up at all and that Dr. Sanford, who's on the premises, is busy in the cath lab — she's supposed to arrive any minute. We're in the hands of the ICU staff, generalists who have no history with Damon. They seem diligent enough but operate perforce on an assembly-line system, with interchangeable patients.

Right now, the ICU team is focused on Damon's low oxygen level. After an oxygen hose fails to help him, the doctors try an oxygen mask over Damon's face. But Damon *hates* the claustrophobic mask. "No!" he kicks against it. It's a delicate matter because we respect his feelings, but he *must* get more oxygen. We try to work out a

581

compromise where Damon holds the mask over his own face. But it's a half measure, and Damon's saturation remains problematic.

Damon also struggles with his cyclosporine, the immune suppressant that comes in a big horse pill. Cardiology is still prescribing it, but Damon, who's having trouble swallowing, gags and resists. Shealagh finally gets him to take it, but it's a trial, and Damon looks ready to vomit, or cry, or both.

By eleven A.M., Dr. Sanford has still not shown up, which starts to rankle.

"I can't understand why cardiology has not yet taken charge of Damon's case, even after it's turned *critical!*" I protest to my wife. "What are they waiting for?"

Only last night, Shealagh was told Damon *urgently* needed to have a central line put in to receive the support he required, but it's eleven A.M. the next day and they still haven't taken him to the cath lab to do it. They're waiting for Dr. Sanford, who is in the cath lab doing a *routine biopsy.*

When I demand to see someone in charge, I get into an altercation with the cardiology fellow Dr. October. She's taking a blood sample from Damon, who squirms and asks me to please hold off.

"Sorry, D-man!" I apologize, mortified I might have *added* to his distress. But once Dr. October leaves, Damon tells me to go ahead and push the hospital.

"I just didn't want you to upset her when she had a needle in my vein!"

I hang back and stay with Damon, torn between my growing anger at the hospital and my tender feelings for him. Shealagh and I surround Damon and try to cordon him off. For a time, it's just the three of us again.

But then I notice that even safely ensconced between us, Damon looks increasingly stressed. His voice is shaky and quavering, and he doesn't seem like himself. He appears to be wandering mentally, and once or twice he completely loses his train of thought. He starts hallucinating, spying his sister on the staircase. Shealagh had warned me Damon was experiencing bouts of mental confusion, but seeing it for myself is devastating. Damon has always been an exemplar of lucidity. Now he begins muttering like a demented old man and speaking gibberish. Then, aware he's not making sense, Damon gets very frustrated and struggles to correct himself. Which is almost *more* painful to behold, because now he keeps cutting in, determined to set things straight, but then he forgets what he wanted to say and starts wandering again.

When the nurse comes by, I slip out with Shealagh and share my dismay at what I've just witnessed. "How could Mason let this occur? Everything was fine when I left on Tuesday! What the hell happened?"

Meanwhile, it's almost *noon* and Dr. Sanford has still not shown up.

"I can fly across two continents and an ocean, and race through two major cities, but she can't come up to see my son *from the fourth floor!*" I tell my wife. "And where-oh-where is Dr. Mason?" I cry, beseeching the heavens as much as Shealagh. "How can Damon's doctor in chief *not* come in to see her patient after such a setback? How much *sicker* does she need him to get?"

We're told it's Dr. Mason's day off.

I'm astonished because no physician assigned to us at Columbia in over sixteen years has ever acted like this. Desperate, I step forward and announce to the ICU staff that this situation is *totally unacceptable.*

"Where is Dr. Mason? Where is Dr. Sanford? Who is in charge, and what the hell is going on with my son?"

Dr. October snaps that she's already answered all my questions, and we must wait for Dr. Sanford before proceeding. I

584

tell her my son can't afford to wait — he's going into a free fall while they're all standing around wringing their hands. "It's obscene!" I say sharply.

"Don't speak to me like that!" Dr. October says.

"My son is not getting adequate care and until he does, I'll speak to you any way that's necessary!" I retort.

Dr. October goes to complain about me to the ICU attending. Dr. Ofuri approaches and tries to be diplomatic but he just repeats the protocol, as if it is all out of his hands. I reject his do-nothing approach and clash with Dr. Ofuri as I did with Dr. October.

The nurse manager overhears the ruckus and comes over to try to resolve it. "Why don't you tell me what the problem is?" she says.

I review everything that's happened and explain my frustration and alarm.

"I've rushed back from Japan after learning my son had taken a sudden turn for the worse, yet there's still no one to explain how he could have deteriorated so fast, or what they're going to do about it! *Where is his doctor?* No one is taking responsibility for Damon's care! They still haven't put in a central access line, after telling us it was *urgent,* and they still don't have a treatment plan. Everyone is waiting for the cardiology transplant team to arrive, while my son is getting *sicker!* And they call this the ICU!" I exclaim.

The manager, who seemed interested in my views, tells me, "Don't raise your voice." I stare at her, realizing she has not heard a word I've said. I tell her I'll raise my voice until someone takes responsibility for this case and my son gets the care he needs.

Now the manager, nakedly harsh, says, "And don't point your finger!"

"What?" I cry. "My son is going into a spiral as we speak, his doctor *still* hasn't shown up and no one knows what to do, and you're concerned that I'm *pointing my finger?* You're lucky I'm staying this calm and collected!" I declare.

"You have no right to raise your voice *or* point your finger and if you don't stop *instantly,* I'll call security and have you removed from the premises!" the manager snarls.

I'm astonished she's turned herself into the injured party while my son lies in the ICU deteriorating. "Don't you feel any obligation for *the patient's* well-being?" I frown.

By now we have a crowd around us and

we're in a nasty face-off. "I've called security and I'll have you *arrested* if you don't behave!" the manager says.

"You can call anyone you want," I reply, furious and pumped with adrenaline. "But Damon is not getting appropriate treatment and until he does, you'll have to deal with me!"

"Are you *threatening* me?" the manager asks with a glint in her eye.

"You're the only one making threats, I'm making a *promise,*" I shoot back.

"You better watch yourself!" she warns as the crowd looks on.

A pale, wild figure suddenly appears in the doorway, standing buck naked except for a tangle of lines and wires. He looks like an escaped marionette on a mission.

"I have to help Dad get rid of the bad people!" Damon announces in a half-crazed but defiant way, small fists clenched in angry solidarity. His red hair blazes, his face is fiery with indignation, and his arterial line looks in danger of popping out. "These people are saying bad things about you, Dad!"

I can't believe my eyes. My young lion has leapt from his sick bed and charged out of the room to defend *me!*

He stands there, the fiercest warrior-ally

I've ever had, with a catheter threaded through his penis and big incision scar running down his chest. His mind flickers in and out, but his sense of justice, and his courage, burns pure.

I walk over and put my arms around Damon, patting his shoulders and reassuring him that everything is okay. *My amazing son.* I lead him back to the room, briefly checking his development — his big new heart has improved his circulation everywhere — before I help him back into bed.

Meanwhile, security has arrived in the form of two oversized, slouching cops. I step out and quickly determine what I must do if they try to put a hand on me. Fortunately, Shealagh intervenes with her mother's privileged position and her posh accent.

"My husband is just trying to get proper treatment for our son, who's very sick. Why don't you help find his doctor, if you want to be useful!" Shealagh says. "Doesn't anyone in this hospital care about *the patient?* What's the matter with everybody here!"

The cops look to the manager, who admits they're still waiting for the doctor. "But that's no reason to become *aggressive,*" she says, albeit more sheepishly now.

One cop, who's been assessing the situation, turns to the nurse manager with a weary but dutiful sigh. "So whaddaya want us to do here?"

Hugh suddenly pops his head out of Damon's room. "His saturation is dropping!"

Shealagh and I rush inside.

A cop follows and peers in, as if we might escape through the window.

Damon's oxygen saturation has fallen to a dangerous level. Hugh tries holding a mask over Damon's face — it's better than strapping it on — but Damon pushes against it.

"If his numbers don't improve, we will have to intubate him," Dr. Ofuri states.

Shealagh and I try to soothe Damon, who's restive and uneasy. He mumbles.

By the time Damon is sufficiently stable so that I can step back into the hallway, the cops look very uncomfortable. They give me a pro forma warning and retreat.

"Well, I'm glad we straightened *that* out," the manager says before scurrying off.

I'm appalled but I don't know what to do. Time is running out and we're marooned here in the very last ICU room. I dig out my BlackBerry, check I have a signal, and go into overdrive, sending several SOSes. I've already contacted Dr. Chin but now I write Eric Rose, cc-ing Eric Kandel in the hopes of spurring Dr. Rose to respond, and plead for assistance, pulling out all the stops:

> Damon is deteriorating very rapidly and I am concerned that not enough is being done and people are dragging their feet in usual bureaucratic mode. His electrolytes are all over the place, platelets in single digits, oxygen so low they're about to intubate, shaking and gibbering like an old man with paranoid hallucinations — I left 3 days ago and he's not the same person! If there is anyone you can contact on our behalf to make sure they treat this with the urgency it deserves, I appeal to you now. Dr. Mason, the chief transplant cardiologist, is not here, and Dr. Sanford in my view is not doing all she can and should. I'm scared for my son and believe time is of the essence.

I also phone Dr. Hellenbrand, Damon's last doctor in this hospital before Dr. Mason. Dr. Hellenbrand has always been helpful, with a sense of moral, as well as medical, responsibility. He's also the head of the cath lab, where Damon needs to be.

Dr. Hellenbrand is in the OR, but his assistant promises to let him know about our situation ASAP.

"I'll get word to him the minute he finishes, I promise!" she says.

I go back to the ICU bed and stay with Damon. He is in visible distress and continues having trouble with his oxygen level and with his concentration. He mumbles something strange about a unicorn, until we realize he's drolly alluding to Hugh, the nurse whose loftily spiked hair could make him pass for a mythical horse with a single horn.

It's the last flash of Damon's whimsical, theatrical imagination before his breathing grows shallower and the ICU attending announces they must intubate him.

I feel like my son has just slipped one more step away from us but there's nothing we can do. He's in very bad shape.

By one thirty P.M., three and a half hours after my own fourteen-hour flight from Japan, Dr. Sanford shows up. She informs us that Damon has contracted an acute infection from the Epstein-Barr virus (EBV), and this infection has led to the dreaded "post-transplant lymphoproliferative disorder," or PTLD.

PTLD is a very serious condition in which the lymphocytes, white blood cells normally involved in the body's defense system, multiply rapidly and attack the vital organs. It's one of the three major threats for heart transplant patients, ranking just behind rejection and infection, and its consequences can be severe.

Damon's body is under attack, Dr. Sanford explains, and they will have to give him extensive support while trying to beat back this invasion. The doctors don't yet know whether Damon's lymphocytes have turned into cancerous cells that can reproduce by themselves or whether they're less advanced. But they have various tools in their arsenal, and now that they know what they're up against, they can take more careful, targeted aim.

"We're hopeful we can bring this under control, but we'll have to move *fast!*"

I try to ignore the brazen irony of the long-missing Dr. Sanford suddenly urging speed. Instead, I focus on her tone and body language. She seems to take a bookish satisfaction in imparting this information. Having just learned many of these facts herself, the results freshly arrived from a California lab, she's proud and flush with her new knowledge.

I don't ask Dr. Sanford why they couldn't figure this out *sooner,* since apparently it's a well-known complication. No one has mentioned the word "EBV" to us before, a term I know from previous research. Nor do I ask why they had to send out a standard PCR test from New York, a high-tech medical capital, all the way to California for an *urgent* result. And I don't even scream when Dr. Sanford tells us, as if she's just discovered the fact, that Damon must go to the cath lab *right away* so they can put in a central access line.

We must move forward, and Dr. Sanford is the only doctor we have right now. At least they know why Damon is sick. And we don't have another minute to lose.

Dr. Sanford says they're prepping Damon for the cath lab now, because they'll need full access for his supportive care. But they have good antivirals and other medications, as well as several experimental therapies to try. She also tells us we must *decrease* Damon's immune suppression because lowered immunity acts as *spur* for PTLD: "No more cyclosporine."

"But I just made him take his daily dose!" Shealagh cries. "You and Dr. Mason have been telling us to take it every day!"

"Look, some immune suppression is still necessary," Dr. Sanford backtracks. "We don't want Damon to have *rejection* amid these other issues, do we?"

My wife and I exchange sharp glances but we don't pursue this obvious screwup. "How do you think Damon contracted this infection?" we ask.

Dr. Sanford smiles like a well-rehearsed teacher. "EBV is very common. Damon probably picked it up from his siblings or his parents or even a friend . . . If anyone in the house had a slight cold or a cough, they could have infected him."

We go back to the ICU room, where Damon is being readied for the cath lab. There's a new sense of urgency now that we have the official diagnosis, and everyone is on full alert. I hear Dr. Hellenbrand will handle the procedure, which is a relief. But knowing that Damon has been harboring a secret, cancerlike infection is deeply unsettling.

Hugh asks me to help with the gurney. I grab one end when Glenda, Damon's first ICU nurse from infancy — she's a supervisor now — emerges from nowhere to give us a hand. So I know it's serious. Every second suddenly counts.

We swing Damon out of the ICU and run up the corridor. The gurney just fits into the elevator. We hop off and begin racing across the fourth floor with Damon balanced on the stretcher like a fragile package. We round several tight corners and sprint into the cath lab.

Someone hands me a consent form as Dr. Hellenbrand, a reassuring figure in his scrubs, shuffles over. Shealagh arrives, and we all briefly confer. But there's no time for lingering because Dr. Hellenbrand must perform what is by now an emergency procedure.

Shealagh and I vacate the premises and go into wait mode by a corridor bench.

It's a long, nerve-wracking wait. Damon's anatomy is tricky and his condition fragile. Yet they *must* find another access point into his bloodstream so they can deliver the requisite medication. Failure is not an option. As we sit in limbo, waiting to see if Dr. Hellenbrand can pull this off, I am amazed to find a live reply to my BlackBerry SOS! Only it's not from Dr. Rose, but from Eric Kandel, who's followed up on his own and, in just over an hour, tracked down the elusive, no-show Dr. Mason for me. Kandel writes:

I just spoke to Dr. Mason, who would be pleased to take a call from you if you were to try and get a hold of her. She has the weekend off and will be in on Monday. However, she's been in touch with Damon and his condition and feels that even though he is very, very sick, she is hopeful they will get him through this successfully. As you probably know he has acute EBV which can be very serious. My prayers are with you.

I show the e-mail to Shealagh and we both shake our heads over Dr. Mason's behavior. Suddenly she's in the loop and pretending to be on top of things. Yet she's still taking *a three-day weekend* on the day her patient is rushed to the ICU, fighting for his life!

I feel my blood seethe. Only three days ago, Dr. Mason assured me Damon's symptoms were completely "routine" and all was "under control." Yet now that it clearly is *not* routine *nor* under control, she feels no sense of responsibility. Not only doesn't she come in to see her critically ill patient, she can't be bothered to call us and explain what went wrong. And for a final twist, she claims she'd "be pleased to take a call *from*" us — a call *we cannot make* because Dr. Mason has never given us any contact information!

Dr. Hellenbrand comes out of the cath lab and ambles toward us. At least we have one decent doctor on our side. Just seeing him restores my faith, even before he speaks.

The cath lab chief, still in scrubs, reports our son is fine. "I couldn't get in through Damon's neck but I managed to insert two access lines. They're both in Damon's groin area and though neither reaches the heart, both can deliver adequate doses of medication into the bloodstream. So we're okay on that score."

We thank Dr. Hellenbrand. He tips his head. It's what he does. But he tells us he thinks he's accomplished all he can for Damon. If we need him over the weekend, we have his number, but he's not sure what else he can offer.

"It's in other people's hands now," he says.

We nod grimly, wishing it were not so. Dr. Hellenbrand gives us a blunt, searching look. I watch him closely, because I know he cares about us but he won't bullshit.

"You're in for a very rough weekend. Call if you want. Good luck." He leaves.

Back on the ICU floor, there is open marveling at Dr. Hellenbrand's handiwork. Damon's groin now bristles like a bionic porcupine, boasting two erect clusters of quill-like IV tubes ready for medication delivery.

As the ICU team swings into action, I make a point of going over and apologizing to Dr. October and Dr. Ofuri for any earlier friction. "We really appreciate what you're doing. Thanks so much." They accept my apology, and we reengage in a congenial manner.

A technician rolls in a hemodialysis machine, "a kidney with a brain" geared for ICU patients. The contraption, known as a CVVH, consists of four pumps and filters that control all fluids into and out of Damon's body. We watch the rotary pumps whir quietly, like spools of film, and create a steady shushing sound as Damon's blood is filtered and waste matter removed into yellow bags. We take solace from the low, murmuring rhythm and the continuous nurturing action of the unit as we hover anxiously by Damon's bedside.

He dozes, flitting in and out of awareness.

Around seven P.M., there's a shift change and a new ICU attending replaces Dr. Ofuri, while Dr. October stays on. Dr. Sanford also departs but tries to reassure us, or perhaps to reassure herself, that they'll watch Damon all night and make every effort to stabilize him.

An hour later, Damon's blood pressure starts to drop and it becomes harder to keep it steady. The medical staff has been giving him intermittent infusions of red blood cells to maintain his pressure, but now he begins to seesaw and they have trouble stabilizing him.

"Up the epi one notch!" the doctor barks. Shealagh and I resign ourselves to a long, stomach-churning night as the ICU team battles back and forth.

We've been glued to the bedside for hours, talking to Damon and encouraging him even though we don't know how much he grasps. Shealagh has only left for the bathroom, and I haven't even done that in my fixation. But at one point, my jet lag, the raw fish I ate in Japan, and the unrelieved stress all get to me, and I make a beeline for the toilet.

As soon as I close the bathroom door, I become aware of a terrible pounding in my chest and a raw hammering in my skull, like the worked-over feeling when I sat in my corner between brutal rounds of my first boxing match against the Royal Military Academy Sandhurst. Only now it's worse, because I can't see my opponent and I don't know how to fight back. I shut my eyes and try to still the awful drilling pain, drifting to a calmer, more detached state, when a sharp knocking barges into my consciousness. At first, I think someone else wants to use the facilities, and I try to ignore them and regain quietude. But the banging persists, louder and fiercer, and then I realize it's Shealagh, and the banging is meant for me.

"Come quick! He's dying!" my wife shrieks through the closed door as I charge out in utter disbelief.

A long throng of medical personnel has crammed into the ICU room and crowded around Damon's bed. In the center, mounted above my son like the lightest, most acrobatic member of the team, squats the petite Dr. October, who's thumping Damon's chest and administering CPR with precise, vigorous strokes.

My son has gone into cardiac arrest!

The doctors are feverishly pushing in bagfuls of red blood while the cool ICU head instructs the nurse to administer doses of epinephrine. Everyone is watching the telltale monitor, which shows a long, flat, *totally inert* line.

I feel stunned and dazed but I refuse to believe this is the end. I approach the bed and grab Damon's leg, the closest I can get to him. All is happening in slow, crushing motion.

"Come on, D-man!" I push against heavy atmospheric resistance, like a diver at the bottom of the sea, and seek to reclaim my son, defiantly yanking him back from the underworld by his leg. "Come on, D-man, snap out of it, you're not going anywhere!"

I tug repeatedly at Damon's ankle, hearing the increasingly hollow, stubborn echo of my own small voice, when the line on the monitor suddenly *jumps.* The doctors all stare.

Shealagh yells at me to move closer to Damon; she's convinced he's responding to me. I edge nearer and continue urging Damon on, though I suspect it's the albumin or the extra shot of epinephrine that's galvanizing his body.

But whatever it is, Damon is reviving, and the terrible gloom starts to lift.

Damon's blood pressure rises, and all his vital signs perk up.

He's back on the big board, all lit up and posting solid numbers.

There's a deep, collective sigh in the ICU room. Everyone exhales, and then normal life returns almost as quickly as it was suspended.

The ICU reinforcements clear out and go back to their stations.

Damon's doctors quickly run an echocardiogram and determine that Damon's heart function still looks good. The ICU attending, a sinewy, unflappable type, estimates Damon arrested for one minute, ninety seconds tops.

"Since someone was pushing blood into his brain the whole time, I don't expect any lasting damage. But we won't know for sure until he regains consciousness. For now, we just need to keep him stable and let him rest."

Shealagh and I compose ourselves and try to assess the damage. Damon's face is very puffy, especially around the thick, goiter-like neck, while ventilator tubes snake out of his bloated lips and raw nostrils. A rash of tiny red pustules stipples his body. Most distressing, his vacant eyes swivel erratically in their sockets. We are told this is typical after an arrest, and it will subside once he snaps back, but it's still a worrisome sight.

We try not to lose heart and remind ourselves this is *Damon*. We've seen him come through so much — we've come through so much together — we'll get through this too.

"He's so naturally resilient. If we just let him get some rest and provide adequate support, his survival instincts will kick in," I tell Shealagh. "No one can stop Damon!"

"Yes, he's such a fighter, I'm sure he'll rally after a good night's sleep."

Hugh, our friendly nurse, overhears this and warns us not to underestimate what's happened. "He's had a sepsis, a life-threatening shock to the entire body where the blood cells spill out of the vessels. It's going to be a dicey few days, like walking on eggshells."

Near midnight, after Damon has stayed stable for a few hours, I call Dr. Bar-Or in Denver, two hours behind us. I tell my cousin about Damon's dramatic deterioration these past days, his sudden arrest, and all the support he's now on.

"It sounds like total organ failure — the leading cause of death in the ICU."

I wince. "What kind of numbers are we looking at?"

"About fifty percent of ICU deaths result from total organ failure," Dudu says.

I phone my parents, late-nighters, and explain we've had a setback. I don't go into details because they also need to be protected. My parents are due to fly the next day on a package vacation, a thank-you present from us for staying with our kids during Damon's transplant. They immediately offer to cancel their trip but I insist I still want them to go.

"There's nothing you can do for us here. Sam and Miranda are skiing in Vermont, and it will ease my mind and give me one *less* thing to worry about if you make the trip."

My parents are unhappy about leaving but reluctantly accede. I promise updates.

Shealagh and I spend the rest of the night in the ICU, sharing the single mattress on the window seat. We lie head to toe, twisting and writhing. Each of us rises often to check on Damon and to talk to the night nurse, who constantly struggles to adjust the machine and keep Damon stable.

I lie awake, exhausted but agonizing as I summon all the known data and review every detail and every twist and turn in my head. I conclude that Damon's current malaise actually began *three weeks earlier,* the night he told us of his shivery feeling. And I now see that this first crisis, when they insisted on treating him for rejection, never solved his problem but only *masked* it.

In retrospect, I grasp that as soon as he finished his course of immune-suppressant medication a week ago, Damon's underlying illness *returned.*

But instead of despairing, I take solace in this hypothesis. Because it means that Damon does not have a mysterious new illness, but only a continuation of his initial complaint. And so, as soon as we properly treat this original ailment, we should be able to bring everything back under control.

As I lie awake by the window, which I now notice for the first time offers a sweeping Renaissance-like vista of the city's rooftops and of the Hudson River, I realize this forty-hour day, which began for me in Tokyo and has been one of the longest and most shattering days of my life, has fallen on Good Friday.

If today was Damon's crucifixion, my hard-pressed imagination hazards, then shouldn't he soon rise up and return to us on Easter Sunday, or thereabouts?

I'm unsure of the exact resurrection sequence — do I recall a Bright Monday? — but I'm prepared to cut a lot of liturgical slack. I vow that if this miracle were to, in fact, materialize, I'd be perfectly willing to convert to Christianity by way of gratitude — or to Islam or Buddhism or to *any* religion or organized movement that could help Damon.

Anyone can have me, so long as they *give me back my son.*

CHAPTER 54

The next day, Saturday, is a busy day in the ICU, with many ups and downs, but grounds for hope.

Damon seems to stabilize, though he's still unconscious, and we all focus on the best treatment for his PTLD.

Dr. Mason finally appears in the late morning. Even *she* must respond to a cardiac arrest, not to mention a Nobel laureate's inquiries.

She bustles about Damon, listening to his chest and checking his bedside monitors. "It's very unusual to get an EBV infection and develop PTLD so *soon* post-transplant. I've never seen it this early and rarely even heard of it," Dr. Mason tells us with a show of confounded expertise. "The good news is that the early form of this illness is easiest to treat and has the best long-term prognosis. So you can take comfort from *that.*"

An oncologist comes to discuss an experimental protocol involving a monoclonal antibody and a chemo agent. He gives me literature to read, but I've already discussed this approach with Dudu, and I know it's probably our best shot. I review it briefly with Shealagh before signing the consent.

"We've called in someone very special, one of the world's leading authorities on PTLD, to consult on Damon's case," the oncologist says with a touch of celebrity awe. And when the "famous" Dr. Manuela Orjuela arrives, she commands immediate attention with her striking appearance and dramatic manner. But she also displays a keen scientific mind and sharp diagnostic skills.

Dr. Orjuela believes Damon has an acute or "fulminant" case of PTLD, and she urges a very aggressive treatment. "I cannot fathom why Columbia waited *so long* to call me in!" she says. "But at this advanced stage, I recommend hitting your son with the combination therapy several times, so we really *zap* his lymphocytes."

But Dr. Mason, whose back may be up because a more high-powered woman doctor is in the room, takes issue with this approach. "I'm concerned Damon may not be strong enough to withstand a double dose of chemo in his current state. We need to find a balance between neutralizing the

PTLD and keeping Damon stable."

Despite my growing disenchantment with her, I share Dr. Mason's concern. "What data do you have on comparable cases?" I ask Dr. Orjuela.

"The data pool for this illness is tiny, and one has to speak of individual cases," Dr. Orjuela replies. "But in my judgment and based on my experience, we need to go all-out to rescue Damon from this attack. All his organs, especially his liver and kidneys, suffered a big hit, and we must do everything to stem the assault. It's a risk, but I would take it."

"We can try one course of treatment and see how Damon responds," Dr. Mason says. "We could always bump it up after an interval if he does well. But I do not want to destabilize Damon, especially after what happened last night!"

Shealagh and I feel torn between these rival views, because like Dr. Mason, we also worry about Damon's fragile state. And it's possible Dr. Orjuela is too invested in this protocol. On the other hand, Dr. Orjuela specializes in PTLD and has seen more cases than Dr. Mason. She may be right that the risks of holding back outweigh the benefits.

In the end, the two women cannot agree

and come to sharp words. But Dr. Mason, as the physician in charge of Damon's case, exercises the ultimate authority, and she makes the final call.

Dr. Orjuela storms off, insulted that her advice goes unheeded.

Damon gets one round of the combination therapy, and we await the results. He's having a marginally better day and shows small signs of improvement, though he remains asleep. But he seems to be stabilizing, and we derive a measure of relief from this.

While Dr. Mason checks Damon's lines and drips — like a fireman arriving one day late, she makes a big show of tidying up the after-blaze — I share my new theory with her. I'm determined to remain congenial and to extract any benefit I still can from her.

"I believe Damon may still be suffering from the original illness that brought him to the hospital three weeks earlier," I tell her. "And if it's really the same illness, this would be positive news, because it means Damon didn't just get hit with a sudden shock to the entire system from an EBV infection."

It's taken me painstaking work to solve this epidemiological puzzle in my head, and

I'm pleased at how the pieces seem to fit together. But Dr. Mason is not impressed.

"Oh, of course, his donor was EBV positive!" she says with an insider's shrug, dismissing my entire reconstruction, not because it's wrong, but because it's so *obvious*.

His donor was EBV positive! These words, tossed out so casually, send me reeling. So she's known this all along? How could she not tell us? And why couldn't she *protect* Damon, if she knew? I want to scream but I suppress my anger so I can learn more while trying to process this shocking information.

If they gave Damon a donor heart with EBV, why didn't they look for an EBV infection *right away* when Damon first got sick, instead of waiting *three weeks* for his illness to rage unchecked? And don't they have standard precautions to take even earlier, from the first day of his transplant, if they knew he had such a ticking bomb? EBV is widespread in the population — I remember that from my own reading — but an immune-compromised, EBV-negative patient like Damon would have been especially susceptible and would merit extra protection if they knew they were giving him an EBV-positive heart!

And why didn't they ever breathe one

word to us about the donor heart before now?

Only yesterday, Dr. Sanford said Damon probably got his EBV infection from one of us at home who had a cold. Is it possible Dr. Mason did not communicate such vital information to her colleague? Or that Dr. Sanford didn't see this on Damon's chart?

Unless Dr. Mason, despite her customary facade of all-knowingness, did not know this *herself* until today? Which would be just as unsettling, because she should have known it, and she should have acted on her knowledge.

These thoughts rush through my mind and leave me feeling even more sickened and angry. Could this entire crisis have been averted? What have they done to my son!

But it's all moot now. We're in this hole, and we must dig ourselves out.

Damon's cardiac arrest, however brief, is considered a signal event, and all day a parade of experts comes in to look at him. But it seems our best hope is still the experimental protocol. Shealagh and I spend the night on the same narrow window bed, entwined in the same uneasy state. We doze to the heaving rhythm of ICU machines while the nurses do impressive, night-long battle with the CVVH, juggling everything to keep Damon stable.

In the morning, I am buoyed because I think I detect an improvement in Damon's appearance. But it's Easter Sunday and I don't trust the possible influence of wishful thinking.

"What do you think?" I ask my wife, with her superior visual acuity.

"I also feel he definitely looks better today!" Shealagh replies. "I noticed it as soon as I woke up, but I didn't want to say anything and jinx it."

We stand quietly by Damon's bed and tick off the improvements we see.

Damon's facial swelling appears diminished. He no longer looks like a troll with an engorged neck, especially on the right side, where a big lump has subsided. Damon's arms don't look quite as puffy or swollen either. And the red pustules that had broken out all over Damon's body, while still visible, no longer look as vivid or virulent.

Damon remains unconscious, but even in slumber, his face looks more tranquil. He appears less under siege and more like his familiar, calmly contained and focused self.

Our hearts soar with reinvigorated hope.

"I keep inspecting him from different

angles, to make sure it's real!" Shealagh says.

"The protocol must be taking effect. His body appears to have responded to the very first treatment," I say in grateful amazement.

We stay on this high all morning and throughout the early afternoon. But around two P.M., I notice that Damon's blood pressure is starting to slip again.

Maintaining his pressure is a constant juggling act: pushing in blood products and albumin as needed, with a bump in the epinephrine when there's no other recourse. Against this, one must balance the fact that he's retaining too much fluid and only essential items should be added to avoid overloading him.

Nonetheless, there are priorities, and the top one is to avoid another crisis and keep Damon stable. I've watched three ICU nurses in a row handle this ably, but now we get a new nurse who does not appear to know what she's doing.

As this nurse fumbles around, Damon's numbers continue heading south. It's like a bad dream on replay, and there's nothing I can do to stop it.

Soon we have another full-blown crisis on our hands as the alarm goes off, and several doctors charge into the room. Gradually, they bring his pressure under control but the entire episode could have been avoided and sets him farther back.

We continue seesawing over the next twenty-four hours. By Monday, Damon's face looks more swollen, and I wonder if we should have listened to Dr. Orjuela's advocacy of a more aggressive course.

On the positive side, Damon finally regains consciousness. He presses our hands to show he understands what we're saying. We're immensely relieved that he's aware and functioning mentally. He's still very weak and groggy, and his eyes still wander at times, but he's clearly responding to our words, and we're overjoyed to have him back.

Dr. Lubritto, the liver specialist, comes by every day to visit. He is very concerned about Damon and mumbles that Damon's cardiologist, not he, should have caught this sooner.

"But as long as Damon stays stable," Dr. Lubritto says, "as long as he doesn't go *backward,* he's doing okay." The key is to keep him from further harm and to let his body recover. "There's nothing *irreversible* here!" Dr. Lubritto repeats in his high staccato.

By Tuesday, we seem to be in a good phase again. Damon had a peaceful night and seems stable. Sonja, a very devoted friend, has flown in to help with Sam and Miranda. In the morning, while the kids are in school, Sonja visits us in the ICU. She's had twenty years' experience as a hospital physician, and she says Damon does not look as bad as she feared. I don't know what she feared, but I take heart from this.

Sonja gives Shealagh a much-needed break and takes her out for a meal and a walk in the hospital garden. Shealagh gets some air and smells the trees and the river. We've been completely shut in for five days, and Shealagh stayed alone with Damon for three days before that.

By early afternoon, we're standing around Damon's bed and feeling more hopeful than we have since his cardiac arrest. The farther we get away from that precipitating event, and the more we can resume our lives and revert to a semblance of normalcy, the better our prospects seem.

Even the ICU head appears more sanguine than usual, telling us, "Damon is still poised on a very narrow beam. But as long as he doesn't tumble off, he's making progress, and the longer he manages to stay on, the better his chances. Every day that he doesn't fall off is a good day."

It seems like we're having a good day.

After Sonja leaves, Shealagh and I take turns going to the lounge and making calls. Once, we steal a break together and share coffee and a pastry.

"Our first child doesn't want to make it too easy on his parents!" Shealagh says dryly.

"No, he really likes to keep us on our toes," I reply. "But he's such a fighter and he's survived so much, he'll get through this."

"He has his special Damon powers!" Shealagh says, and I nod.

We stay in this cautiously optimistic groove till evening, when, just as the sun dips into the river, Damon's blood pressure falls. The nurse does not react but watches passively despite my urging, so I rush out to get the head nurse. But she's not there. Nor is anyone from our ICU team around. Frantic, I race up the hallway and spot a doctor sitting at a terminal. I plead for her help but she is apathetic. When I yell that it's *urgent* and shame her into responding, she goes to find a supervisor instead of coming herself, costing us more precious minutes.

By the time the ICU head and all the doctors have crowded around Damon, we have another crisis on our hands. They have to hit Damon with every weapon in their arsenal and overload him with more fluid — blood products, albumin, epinephrine — before they manage to bring his pressure back under control.

Deeply distressed and bristling at what I perceive to be another totally preventable setback, I demand a joint meeting with Dr. Mason and the ICU head Dr. Ofuri. They're both back on the case today. We go for privacy into the adjoining room, now empty.

I explain to the two supervising doctors what's happened *several times* now, and I ask if they can please instruct the nurses not to let the pressure drop so low before they bump up the dosage, because it creates a vicious cycle.

To my surprise, both physicians agree instantly with my analysis. Dr. Ofuri explains he's just come up with a new algorithm for intervention, and he will make sure everyone on Damon's ICU team understands the stricter standard we're advocating. Dr. Mason nods and concurs with everything. I've never had such a frictionless meeting with them, nor have they listened to me with such apparent deference. It's flattering but makes me wonder what I'm missing. Why would they treat me so nicely all of a sudden?

That night, per my request, the doctors establish a lower threshold for going up on the epi. But we never seem to fully recover from the previous setback.

We get a good nurse again, but even she can't get Damon back to sea level. The kidney machines are going at full tilt and being replaced regularly but Damon continues struggling. The staff is doing all the right things, but it's a terrible night, as we keep getting farther and farther away from the safety zone.

I can do all the calculations in my head — it's all I can do; my brain crunches nonstop — and I begin to despair when I realize we're near the point of no return.

Sleep is impossible. I get up and pace like an inmate on the eve of his own execution.

Daylight brings no relief. Damon now is so overloaded with fluid and so unstable that when the nurse tries to shift his *pillow,* his blood pressure plummets and we have a minicrisis to deal with. He seems to be hanging on by a thread.

Another parade of specialists troops in. But no one has a workable suggestion. They're just running down their checklist, and we're running out of time.

I scour my brain for any lead we might have overlooked. Our current problem is the kidneys, yet we haven't heard from anyone in that field. I know a renal expert at the University of Pennsylvania, and I've started composing an e-mail to him when the new ICU head, a crisp, self-assured brunette named Dr. Verani, asks me what I'm doing. I explain there might still be a kidney angle we haven't thought of, and I'm contacting a specialist I know. Or maybe we could get a pulmonologist to weigh in on the respirator issue . . . But Dr. Verani just gives a quick, condescending shake of the head and tells me not to bother. "I know as much about the kidneys and the lungs as any specialist, and you won't learn anything new."

I feel deflated and sense the last, lingering breeze ebb from my sails.

"But if that's the case," I counter Dr. Verani, "then what's *your* plan?"

"Our plan is to continue what we're doing," she says. "We're providing every form of support we can, and there's nothing else we can do."

"With all due respect, that's just not good enough!" I tell Dr. Verani. "Because what you're doing *isn't working,* and Damon is *going downhill.*" I shake my head. "If you don't have any new ideas, why not ask your colleagues at other hospitals? We're not just going to *give up* and resign ourselves to failure, or is that what you had in mind?"

Dr. Verani looks taken aback but I just roll on.

"I'm sure there's *one doctor* in *one ICU somewhere* who's been in a similar spot and who's found a solution for his patient. I know there's a way out of this, even if we can't think of it ourselves. We just need to find the right expert!"

Dr. Verani mulls my strong conviction. "That may not be a bad thing to try," she says. "I can send out an alert on my ICU Listserv, which links my colleagues across the country, and see if anyone responds. It's an excellent network, I check mine all the time."

I commend Dr. Verani for this suggestion, wondering why she hasn't thought of it before, and ask if she could please send out the alert ASAP, because I'm really worried.

"I'll get on it right away," Dr. Verani promises.

All day long, things continue to unravel. We're only moving in one direction now.

An air of unreality grips us. Time slows down, and people tiptoe around us. Everyone is solicitous and wary.

A psychologist appears and we send him flying. We're a little more polite to the pastor, but we have no time for him either. Someone offers me a cup of tea and though I understand what they're doing, I reluctantly accept because I can feel my strength ebbing.

By evening, the situation around Damon's bedside is turning grave. His numbers keep dipping and no one knows how to stop the slide. We have no more safety net — it lies in tatters — and the doctors are at a loss.

Damon's blood pressure continues to drop for the next hour, and all the machines and medicines and backup systems have been exhausted.

He's going down.

A hush has fallen over the room and there's a physical sense of emptiness and hopelessness. Of terminality.

All unnecessary staff have retreated. It's dark outside the window.

I don't believe this is happening.

Dr. Verani, who normally roves from room to room, comes in to supervise us. It's not a good sign. I ask her if she received any responses to her ICU alert regarding Damon. It's been eight hours. Dr. Verani says she's sorry, but she never got around to sending it.

Dr. Mason is summoned as a matter of protocol. She sweeps into the room and makes a show of putting her stethoscope to Damon's chest, even though his new heart is the one organ that's stayed strong throughout. We all stand by for several awkward minutes while she listens with exaggerated, detective-like concentration to Damon's heartbeat and his breathing, as if they could tell her anything useful at this stage.

Finally, Dr. Mason straightens up and remarks that Damon sounds a little "clearer" on the left side. Dr. Verani and the ICU nurses look away, clearly embarrassed. I get a sudden, queasy sensation — I've never seen Dr. Mason so transparent — and I wonder what else these past few days has been pure show.

But I quickly dismiss all such concerns. I have no more time for Dr. Mason or Dr. Verani. They're completely beside the point now.

Shealagh and I surround our son. He's regained consciousness and is aware of everything. Shealagh is reading to him from *The Picture of Dorian Gray,* the book he brought with him to the hospital. She's pouring all her tenderness into the reading, and Damon is absorbing every word, like a lullaby to the soul.

It's a brave, beautiful, loving act, braver than anything I can do. Mother and son share the deep, gorgeous consolation of art, which I, in a bitter irony of my misguided artisthood, cannot accept. I still want to save my son in the here and now, and I reject any move toward transcendence or sublimation as a form of surrender.

I'm focusing on vasopressin and dopamine and dobutamine. I'm still trying to figure out a way to raise Damon's blood pressure. I can't let him go, and I won't accept that it's over.

But he's fading, and everyone sees it. He lies there in a tangle of IV lines and tubes, his face grossly swollen with a crooked mouth jammed with a respirator and blubbery lips that fuse together at one end. His inert body, its organs ravaged by the untreated infection that has turned into a fulminant cancer, is puffed up from all the fluid he's retaining. And his eyes still swivel erratically.

Dr. Verani, feigning empathy, asks if we want to give Damon a sedative and let him drift away. Shealagh and I stare at one another in mutual horror. Damon is completely aware, and he's still with us! He keeps pressing our hands and responding to things we say.

There is no way in hell we're going to put our son to sleep and deprive our family of this time together!

I suddenly realize these ICU doctors are protecting *themselves.* They're afraid to look death in the face, even though it's their daily business, because they're fearful of confronting their own limitations.

And it's *not over,* as far as I'm concerned.

Damon is on a respirator and dialysis machine and every other form of critical life support, his body is grotesquely swollen and his face busted up, and his hold on existence is slipping away before our eyes. But he is still with us. Shealagh and I grab on to whatever part of him we can reach — anything untethered to tubes, lines, and machines, and not covered up with tape or other impediments.

Shealagh is on Damon's left, bent very low over her son and cooing into his ear as she trembles and tries not to fall apart. She holds on, a fierce, heartbroken lioness who won't stop tending her cub. I'm on Damon's right, my knees shaking, my throat constricting, and my eyes scalding. Even now, I don't want Damon to see me crying, and I keep turning away, ostensibly to reach for a glass of water on the cabinet, but really to try to blot my tears, which won't stop coursing. I fear if Damon sees me crying, he'll know the game is up. But my efforts are futile — it's like holding back my torrential love for him — and I resign myself to the stinging flow. We're beyond such pretense now.

We're all shedding our earthly roles and reverting to elemental cores.

I hold Damon's hand and look into his eyes. From some unknown place, I hear myself begin to tell him things I've never consciously formulated but now emerge with their own stamp of authority and their own momentum.

I tell Damon how much I love him and how proud I am of him. How proud he has always made me feel and what a privilege it is to have a son like him. That he is a magnificent, extraordinary human being, and that no parent could have wished for a more perfect child. That he is perfection itself, in every possible way, and that I cannot even imagine a finer young man or a more exquisite flower of humanity.

These words spill out in a hyperbolic-sounding gush, but there is not one ounce of embellishment in them. I am speaking plain truth, from a place where there is nothing but truth. The purity of love for a pure being, compounded by all the attachments and devotions of paternity and fatherhood. I need only reach into my inmost heart and show my son what's there, what's been there all along. And Damon, who can't speak because of the tube in his mouth and because of the illness raging in his blood, shows me he understands every word I'm saying. He nods with his tender eyes and flashes deep recognition. My praise meets with his profound approval because he knows it's all true, and that he's *earned* it.

There's no time left for false modesty. I'm only giving Damon his due.

Aware of the fleeting minutes, I'm desperate to let Damon know just how special he is and how much he means to me. To compress my boundless love into a nutshell. I tell Damon what a close and wonderful friend he has become. How I can talk to him about everything under the sun, including the most intimate and complex matters, and what a rare thing this is with anyone. To share such an affinity with one's own son is truly remarkable. I lean forward and whisper that if he promises not to tell my buddy David, I think he's turning into my best friend. Damon's eyes bat wildly, showing I've hit a sweet spot.

Meanwhile, Shealagh is cradling Damon's

body and telling him what a brave boy he is, how proud she is of him. He's so full of courage. He is so strong and magnificent. She admires him and loves him with all her heart. He's her wonderful, amazing, fantastic boy.

Damon's courage never falters but his body is buckling.

We watch our son being dragged away from this world, his light slowly extinguishing.

The ICU staff presses in on us, encircling Damon. They're waiting to turn off his life support!

They've written him off already, and their impatience is palpable. And *shameless*.

I block them with my body, using my shoulder as both an impassive shield and a ready spear but unwilling to pay them any heed. They're too inconsequential to bother with. And they'd have to risk their own lives to get past me.

But Shealagh is *enraged* by their close, hovering presence and their unseemly eagerness to shut things down. She screams that they should back off and get away from our son.

It's a mother's piercing cry, and its irate fury carries unmistakable authority.

The forwardmost nurse retreats, and the

entire ICU staff takes a step back. We focus back on our son.

Damon's cell phone suddenly goes off on the bedside table. It's an absurd intrusion, but it involuntarily stirs hope because of its mundane connection to Damon's world — a world that is still going on outside these walls.

No one answers, but we can see from the display screen the caller is Kyle.

Damon's dearest friend and soul mate somehow apprehends what's happening and reaches out to Damon at this precise moment. Kyle's name flashes several times across the screen as the cell phone groans and vibrates on the counter.

Briefly, Kyle is in the room with us, sharing her warmth and vitality and love.

Then the ringing stops, and the phone ceases its uncanny protest.

We lose the connection and are forced back to our grim scene.

Shealagh is still kneeling by Damon, wedged into a tight corner between his head, the IV pole, and various life support machines. It's hard for her to keep twisting and bending low to avoid the mass of equipment, so she tries to come out of her corner. But she quickly becomes enmeshed in a thicket of lines and wires, dropping to the

628

ground to extricate herself and temporarily disappearing from sight. Almost immediately, Damon — as if to show the ICU staff he's not just alive but fully cognizant — notes his mother's absence, and he goes *ballistic.*

Damon thinks he's losing his mommy, and his face crumples. Invisible tears slash his eyes, and silent cries choke his respirator-clogged throat. His immobilized body writhes, and all his monitors go haywire.

You would not have thought Damon could look much worse, but he can. Because now he's not just suffering, he's *bereft.*

I alert Shealagh to what's happening and she rushes back, almost upending the IV pole and several monitors. She squeezes back into her corner and takes Damon's arm, placing her face directly alongside his. She whispers tenderly in her son's ear, until he's "calm" again.

Damon now has both his parents by his side, and there's a sense of completion. As if the outer ring of electrons has been filled, and he's stable again.

Except that Damon's *whole life* is decaying at an accelerated rate.

His blood pressure has dropped below 50, and he's crashing.

I start to kiss him over every available part

of his face — his eyes, forehead, hair, cheek, nose — as I again tell him how perfect and beautiful he is. I'd been frustrated over the past week because I could not truly hug my son for fear of infecting him. But now all that has been mooted, if not mocked, and I just empty out my love and shower Damon with pent-up kisses.

I clasp as much of him as is claspable. His face is all busted up and taped over, but I can still see his beauty.

Shealagh is weeping as she sings softly into Damon's ear. She's had a terrible time these past years and been overwhelmed in so many ways, but in the end, she is strong for her son.

I've never felt weaker or more ineffectual. My son is dying before my eyes, and I don't know how to save him. There is no action in the entire universe I would not undertake on his behalf, but I have no action left to take.

I squeeze his hand and tell him how the two of us are going to go pick apples in Oregon. Damon's pupils flash wanly and he gives me a feeble squeeze back, or so I imagine.

Then he continues to fade.

His blood pressure has dropped below 40.

There's not a single life support system or

drug that can help him any longer.

His body is completely inert, and his eyes are hollowing out.

Damon is collapsing, and the ICU vultures are buzzing again. They've stopped even pretending to sustain him and have turned off the CVVH machine.

They're just standing around, waiting for him to die.

It's effectively over, except that Damon is *still* with us. He's *still* hanging on, and I *still* can't accept the situation or give up on him.

"D-man, listen to me!" I lift my voice and appeal to him as if we're fellow soldiers fighting in the trenches and we could still win this war. "I want you to forget all these goddamn machines and this whole ridiculous setup here! Forget this silly hospital and all these silly doctors. Just go deep *inside.* I know you have the strength — it's time to use it. Okay?" I pump my fists, as I have so often for him, and urge Damon on with every fiber of my fraught being. "Come on, D-man, let's bust out of this joint and just go *home!*"

During Damon's first open-heart surgery, when he was six months old and weighed eleven pounds and things looked very bleak, I would shadowbox ferociously around his ICU bed — while his mobile played "Send in the Clowns" — and try to infuse my firstborn with the fighting spirit. So now I repeat my desperate exhortation, louder and fiercer each time — "Let's just blow this joint, D-man!" — while the impatient doctors smile and try to mask their disdain. They can't wait to shut everything off, including me, the ridiculous, pathetic father who's clearly in denial.

But my son hears me. From some region deep inside his stricken body — a place of love, and courage, and pride, and transcendent will — he starts responding.

The nurses and technicians stop in their tracks. Everyone looks stupefied. Damon's blood pressure has stopped dropping, and it begins to *rise!*

His numbers suddenly start to go up instead of down.

They climb out of their hole and keep climbing.

It's like a fantasy, a wish fulfillment, except it's measurably, verifiably real.

Damon's pressure reaches all the way to 90/70, which is viable. As if he's suddenly sprouted wings and lifted himself above certain disaster.

It has no physiological basis. It contradicts all the numbers and indicators. It's screwy. How can he reverse death?

I yell out my encouragement and applaud Damon's tour de force, a father overwhelmed by a command performance he asked for but never fully expected.

"Go, D-man, go! You're doing it, guy! Yes! We're almost home!"

Damon keeps it up, like a magician or a levitator confounding all the laws of gravity.

Who in the end can say what's possible?

The red digits on his blood pressure monitor stay in the safety zone, despite every sign to the contrary. There's absolutely *nothing* holding them up, save for pure will and determination. And maybe an act of grace.

"See, Dad, I can do it!" Damon tells me in the only language he has left. "I can do anything!"

"Yes, you can, that's my amazing boy!" I squeeze his hand and kiss him ardently.

My son is giving me a beautiful, awe-inspiring farewell gift.

Or possibly rewriting the future for us all.

We stand bolted to the floor and pray he can somehow find a way to sustain this.

He does.

Damon persists, despite all the forces against him. He maintains his pressure and keeps it above the danger line. He holds on.

But no one, not even Damon, can perform miracles forever.

Slowly, he starts to sink again.

Then he *plummets.*

And now there's nothing and no one to catch Damon, because he takes the whole world with him.

It's terrible.

Damon is dying.

My son is disintegrating before my eyes.

He is passing away.

The light in his eyes is receding but it's still there, and I hang on to it and keep talking to him. I again tell him how much I love him. The light gets dimmer and dimmer, like the faint glow from a star that died out billions of years ago. But the dimness remains visible, like a flickering shadow, even as it continues fading and receding. I track it to the most distant, infinitesimal lair in his pupil and I keep groping for single particles of him, like a man just struck blind, who still remembers the light and "sees" it as an afterimage even when it's gone.

Then there is true and total darkness.

Damon's indomitable spirit flies off, leaving only his body.

I hold my son, weeping, and kiss him all over his face.

The blood pressure monitor goes to zero, and they shut it off.

Dr. Mason puts on her condolence face, the shocked bystander, as Dr. Verani steps briskly forward and moves to separate me from my son, whom I'm still clasping. She takes possession of his body, wresting it away from me with cool efficiency, as if I no longer have the right to hold what's left of him and it belongs to her.

"I'm so sorry, Damon is *dead.*"

EPILOGUE

Damon Daniel Weber died on March 30, 2005 — three days before my fiftieth birthday.

That's a misleading statement, since no one you love dies once.

Especially not a sixteen-year-old boy who was your first child.

They die for you repeatedly, over and over. You are condemned to relive their death, and to try to prevent it, and to fail, every time.

And how do you go on?

Your choices are despair, self-termination, numbness, violence, the law (socially sanctioned revenge), letting go (forgetting), starting over (razing the past), and the consolations of nature, society, philosophy, religion, fantasy, or art.

But nothing can change what happened, or bring back what's gone.

The hospital wanted us to leave the room

right after Damon died, so they could make him look "like himself" again. We couldn't grasp what they meant — they seemed unnaturally excited, as if they could undo what we'd just witnessed.

We ignored them — they had zero credibility with us by this point — but eventually we had to leave the room for air, and when we came back, we were horrified at what they so proudly unveiled for our approval. They had removed all of Damon's tubes and IV lines and covered up his bloated, bruised arms. They had combed his hair and wiped his face and cleaned up his swollen features, even spreading shiny Vaseline across his cracked lips. But this transparent makeover made him look far *less* like himself and more like a hollow, tidied-up corpse.

He was truly gone now.

The hospital wanted to know, delicately and without pushing us, but as soon as we could possibly tell them, because they couldn't hold it forever, what our plans were for *the body.*

I drew a total blank, since the thought that Damon might not walk out of that hospital alive had never crossed my mind. Shealagh suggested calling Rabbi Kloner, who was responsive and helpful, proving, if proof be needed, that religion still has a role to play in modern life.

Sonja came to pick us up from the hospital. We drove home in a state of shock but realized that despite the late hour and our desire to grant our two remaining children even one more night of peace, we had to wake them up and break the news immediately. The tragedy would alter their lives regardless of when we told them about it, but they'd never forgive us if we held back the information for even one hour. We could no longer pretend we had any control.

We woke Sam up in his room and told him, then we went upstairs into Miranda's room and told her, and then the four of us huddled together on the king-size mattress in our bedroom, sobbing and clinging to one another like shipwrecked survivors on a raft.

The following day we had to take care of funeral business and suffer through the unspeakable agony of picking out a casket for Damon.

I had to write an obituary for my son, an unnatural act. I ignored the steep per-word charge — the obituary wound up costing us as much as the funeral, but words matter to me, and I had many different kinds of debt to repay — and then I begged *The New York*

Times to include a photograph, because I knew Damon's face would have a bigger impact than all my words.

Sitting around our kitchen table that first stunned morning, Shealagh, Sam, Miranda, and I decided that in lieu of flowers, we would ask that any contributions be sent to an award established in Damon's name. Since theater had been his first love and since Brooklyn Tech had been his final theater home, on the spot we created the Damon Weber Theater Prize at Brooklyn Technical High School. The annual award would recognize a promising student at Damon's school who excelled in acting, directing, or writing for the theater.

The New York Times obituary with Damon's photo was published on April 4. There was also a prominent story in the *New York Post,* accompanied by the same photo, only bigger, and headlined "Tragic Teen Star." The *Post* article began:

Grieving family members are working to boost a Brooklyn high school's theater program in memory of their son — a teen actor who died a little more than a week after making his breakthrough television debut.

639

The story quoted the heartbroken father, the Brooklyn Tech principal, and the television writer David Milch, whose comments were reported thus:

David Milch, the creator and executive producer of *Deadwood,* who worked with Damon in Santa Clarita, Calif., for two weeks over the summer, said, "He was wonderful . . . In his moment, and in the work that he was doing with us, he was perfect."

The *New York Times* obituary and the *New York Post* article, as well as the wide nexus of people we knew, generated hundreds of condolence cards and e-mails. A surprising number of actors, many who did not know Damon, wrote out of solidarity with one of their own. Among the many affecting notes we received, Shealagh and I were struck by a letter from Andre Lawe, Damon's Jamaican-born home instructor who spent many hours with Damon during his last year — when not preparing for exams, the two were often up to their eyeballs in mischief:

I never believed in an angel, that is until I met Damon. How could one continue to doubt when his presence spoke such kindness?

We often talked about different things, movies, music, school and life. Yet he was never uncomfortable to speak about the battles he was facing. I often remarked about his strength and determination: added to that he never showed a sign of fear. Through his reflection, I saw myself and how much I fell short. For I could never become the kind of human being he was. But then no human could ever be like him because he was above us. It was clear that heaven had loaned us an angel.

We held the funeral service at Temple Beth Emeth in Brooklyn, the same synagogue where Damon had his Bar Mitzvah. The place was packed — Rabbi Kloner could not recall seeing it so full, except during the High Holy Days.

Perhaps the most unexpected and strangely gratifying sight was watching over a hundred students and teenagers filling the front pews. It turned out Damon was known by far more than his own circle of friends and was something of a local legend at Brooklyn Tech. The small, smiling red-headed boy who could, and did, talk to everyone, displaying easy confidence, natural empathy, and an engaging wit, had been dubbed by many, anomalously, as "the coolest kid in the school." And even those who did not subscribe to this view knew who Damon was. Most of these kids had never confronted death, certainly not of a peer, and they showed up in force, with shocked, uncomprehending, and grief-struck faces.

Their vital, teeming presence, with tender hearts on sleeves, helped us get through.

The worst moment for me came just before we started, when the funeral home director took me aside and explained that as a matter of procedure, someone had to identify Damon's body. We agreed to spare the rest of the family, so the two of us went to the front of the stage, where the wooden coffin rested on a stand. The director lifted the lid of the casket. I saw a wax dummy of Damon, a compact, bloated figure with a puffy face and a big, coarse coif of red hair that was the empty outline of my son. I nodded, and the director closed the lid.

I still haven't shaken that image.

Several people spoke about Damon. Keith came up with WWDD, for "What Would Damon Do?" describing Damon's wise judgment and resourcefulness as a guide for life. Max and Zak recalled Damon's utterly fearless, grinning stage dive into the crowd during a rock concert, and how they envied his sublime confidence that someone would catch him. Kyle's love and heartbreak over the loss of her lifelong friend and confidante shone through every word she uttered. Andre Lawe, who was so late I thought we'd need to scrub him, emerged at the last moment from the shadows like a spectral figure or a heavenly messenger himself and imparted his deep, mellow spirituality with rueful aplomb. Krista talked about Damon as a serious and selfless student of theater, and announced that a second prize honoring him, the Damon Weber Award for Artistry and Citizenship, was being established by the NYU Looking for Shakespeare program. And Paula Malcomson, in a gesture of pure loving kindness, flew in from Los Angeles to speak about working with Damon on the set of *Deadwood.* Paula's dazzling blondness added a touch of glamour and evoked Damon's own shining radiance.

Sonja gave a physician's perspective on Damon's illness and praised his heroism, as well as that of his parents in battling a flawed system. My mother, Helga, was terse and eloquent about the loss of her beloved grandson, and Sam, normally shy in public, was brave in standing up before the entire assembly, his voice shaking, and expressing his enormous love and admiration for his older brother and his undying gratitude for all Damon had taught him. "He didn't just tell me, he showed me!" It was Sam's twelfth birthday, and though he would stand in the same spot a year later for his own Bar Mitzvah, he had just stepped out in a big way for the first time.

Shealagh and Miranda stood with Sam and me but were too distraught to speak.

I provided a brief narrative of Damon's life and a context for his death, since many people had no idea what had happened beyond the brute fact of his demise. I also thanked all the people who helped us along the way. Among the myriad scenes from Damon's rich but truncated life, I recalled the day in Truro, Massachusetts, when Damon and I built a sand castle on Ballston Beach and then spent four frantic hours battling the incoming tide, furiously retreating, redigging, and rebuilding our original structure and refusing to let our drenched mud mound be swept away, until, exhausted and sweaty, with our muscles and fingernails aching and the light fading, we finally declared sweet victory as the tide peaked and our puny flag was still flying.

There were many other scenes and memories but what most concerned me as I spoke was hewing to the high road and not letting my carefully contained wrath spill out. I had a bitter, trembling sense of fury and outrage locked up in my heart along with my grief, and I knew with a certainty, just as the sun rises every morning, that as soon as this was over, I would have to strap on my armor and go to war in an all-out hunt for justice if it was the last thing I did.

But that was for later, and though it had to be done, I knew it wouldn't bring Damon back. Right now, I could not let any of those feelings mar the beauty that was Damon's life, nor detract from our obligation to mourn my extraordinary son with full rites and honors.

We drove from the synagogue in Brooklyn to the cemetery in the Bronx. David had flown in from Seattle and, along with Sonja, helped us manage the carpool logistics. My parents sat with us in the first limo.

We had been at Woodlawn Cemetery a decade earlier for the funeral of Peggy Day, Shealagh's maternal great-aunt, but this was an altogether different affair. The Days had been a prominent New York family — Ben Day, who gave his name to a form of engraving, owned the New York *Sun,* the main city paper in the nineteenth century, and his relations were prosperous bankers and inventors, while Peggy's celebrated husband, Clarence Day, authored *Life with Father,* the Broadway hit of its decade, which became a classic Hollywood film. Damon had spent many great summers with us at Peggy's house in Truro and enjoyed extended heart-to-hearts with the sharp, vivacious blue-stocking who remained the life of any party into her nineties. Now Damon would be laid to rest beside Peggy, whose lifespan had exceeded his by a multiple of six.

We were directed to the tranquil, tree-shaded family plot with the successive generations laid out in simple granite markers. The site was dominated by a high stone sculpture depicting a handsome Victorian mother reading from an open book to her tousle-haired son, who sits on her lap in his plus fours and gazes up with adoration and wonder. The rough approximation of Shealagh and Damon, and of the scene I had just witnessed in the hospital, was almost unbearable.

We stood in a wide, forlorn circle around the open gravesite. Shealagh's cousin Rory spoke briefly about the Days and their openness to all comers, welcoming the

Webers. My father, his voice quavering, read a melancholic poem from Sir Walter Scott, "Coronach," and I read a defiant dirge from Dylan Thomas, "And Death Shall Have No Dominion." (I had asked my friend John Farrell, a literature professor, for any relevant father-son passages from Shakespeare or the classics, and he had consulted several colleagues, but to our surprise there seemed to be very little.)

We sang two songs: "He's Got the Whole World in His Hands," which Damon had played on the piano when he first got home from his transplant — the songbook on our living room piano was still open to this page when we returned from the hospital for the last time — and "The World's Greatest" by R. Kelly, an R & B favorite of Damon's that Sam had astutely suggested. The mood was very grim and somber and when the singing started to falter, Kyle's musician father, Andre, stepped in with his strong, melodious voice and helped lift and carry us over the hump.

By the time Rabbi Kloner recited the Burial Kaddish and they started lowering the coffin into the ground, there was a hush, followed by quiet sobbing. A few teenagers broke down and wept openly. Shealagh had her arms around Sam and Miranda, all propping each other up and crying quietly, while I stood closest to the grave, almost on top of it, on my own. No one could come near me now because I was completely focused on Damon. I watched a wooden box bearing his remains knock against the sides of the freshly dug pit as it was hoisted down unevenly by creaky pulleys. I made Damon a last promise about setting things right, and I gave him a last kiss. I knew that what was being buried was not just the body of my sixteen-years-and-eight-months-old son, or a big part of me and of my family, but also a normal vision of life.

We sat shiva for the requisite seven days and kept an open house, thanks to very kind neighbors who pitched in. They formed shifts and took turns helping in the kitchen with food and drink and cleaning up at night. For "shiva furniture" — plain wooden benches — the funeral home dropped off two flimsy cardboard boxes, so absurd and useless they made Sam and Miranda giggle hysterically. Mostly we sat out on patio furniture in our backyard by the peach tree and the fig tree that Damon had only recently helped me prune.

For the first days we were surrounded by relatives and good friends from high school and college and beyond, and it was almost like a reunion. But then this group started to leave, and we felt raw and exposed again. Shealagh withdrew to her bed, and I had to greet the remaining visitors on behalf of the family. Many kind people, including professional colleagues and strangers who'd known Damon, or whose children had known Damon, continued to come and pay their respects. Sonja manned the phone and answered the door in the best English butler tradition, until she needed to return home. David, who gave me a personal outlet, had to go back to his family. And then, bereft of these two best friends and buffers, we felt the full chill again.

On the last day of shiva, I received a rejection letter from the writing program I'd applied to. I'd completely forgotten about my application and had been warned I was taking a step back by returning to school, but it was still a rejection in an area that mattered to me — or would have mattered to me if I could have felt anything. I was so numb by this point, I couldn't register any sensation, like a frozen man who must look down to grasp that he's been shot in the stomach. I knew the bullet holes couldn't be a good sign, even if I didn't feel any pain, and that they meant something else I cared deeply about had just been taken from me.

I tried resigning myself with a fatalistic shrug — maybe it was for the best, since I was losing *everything* at the same time — when I heard a dim, defiant voice, like the guardian of my own soul, react angrily on my behalf to this attempted double burial. *Not only do you kill my boy, but now you want to kill the boy in me!*

We decided we needed a complete getaway, so after the shiva, Shealagh, Sam, Miranda, and I flew to Newfoundland, Canada, where we'd never been before, nor did we know a soul. It had the advantage of being stark and beautiful and situated on the very edge of the continent.

We stayed in a modest hotel overlooking the harbor in St. John's, ate in family restaurants, and hiked and explored the area, involuntarily reconstituting ourselves as a family of four. Everywhere we went, we saw and felt Damon's presence — in the close, smiling face of the chalky moon on Signal Hill and in the wild, wind-whipped promontory of Cape Spear. We kept active during the day, and at night we all bedded down in the same room and cried ourselves quietly to sleep.

We returned to New York. I went back to work and Sam and Miranda went back to school. Shealagh stayed home.

My wife and I repeatedly discussed the unsettling events leading to our son's death. He'd had a successful heart transplant and was doing well, and we were both convinced he need not have died if the hospital had only followed the standard treatment protocol. But we needed to be sure we hadn't missed something or overreacted emotionally.

We did a cold chronology and ran it backward and forward. We searched for alternative explanations. Shealagh became obsessed with researching everything known about the infection that had killed Damon. She spent hundreds of hours online, staying up all night to track down arcane studies and references. I conducted less research, though I read Shealagh's material, because I had done the deepest dive possible in the hospital the night before Damon died, and I knew what had happened. But part of me still wanted to discover we were wrong and it was all inevitable, so we could absolve ourselves, as well as the hospital, of responsibility and not have to deal with dredging it all up, reliving the horror, and accusing such a formidable, renowned institution.

In the end, the evidence was even more overwhelming than we'd understood. EBV infection was not some rare event but appeared in all the literature, underlined and in bold, as one of the most common and dangerous — if not *the* most common and dangerous — of all threats for patients like Damon. It was routinely described as "the bugaboo of heart transplants." Yet Dr. Mason and her team of four, who provided little continuity of care but instead rotated shifts so no one was ever fully responsible — "the person responsible is the person on call," Mason would state at her deposition, denying that even as *medical director* she had any ongoing responsibility — never treated Damon for EBV-driven PTLD until the battle was already lost.

Why hadn't the hospital treated Damon for EBV infection at the time he first presented as a high-risk patient with every symptom of this notorious, well-documented killer, and with no sign of rejection? Dr. Mason would later admit under oath that once the hospital knew Damon's donor was positive for EBV, they should have been on the lookout for any indications of EBV infection, and that infection was as common a complication as rejection. Yet she and her team persistently ignored every symptom of EBV infection and kept treating Damon for rejection — the opposite treatment!

But Dr. Mason knew what treatment she *should* have administered because, as we soon learned, in 2004, over a year *before* Damon's death, she coauthored, with Dr. Sanford, a chapter on pediatric heart transplantation in a Columbia textbook. Writing as an acknowledged expert, Dr. Mason advised practitioners that when a patient develops PTLD from an EBV infection, as Damon had, "treatment for the disease includes reduction or temporary cessation of immunosuppression. This approach is effective in the majority of cases."

Yet she never followed her own advice and gave Damon a chance.

Why had Dr. Mason *increased* Damon's immune suppression instead of *decreasing* it and letting his body use its normal defenses to fight off this infection in its earlier stages, as she told fellow professionals was the standard of care?

Damon was the toughest fighter I ever knew but it turned out the hospital not only didn't help him, they actually *prevented* him from fighting back with his own strength. When they upped his immune suppression, they disabled his natural defense system and left him exposed to EBV and then PTLD, choking off his ability to defend himself and rendering him effectively powerless.

Outraged and sickened, Shealagh and I agreed we had no choice but to try to initiate legal action against Dr. Mason, her fellow physicians, and Columbia for Damon's death. We didn't have the resources to hire a team of lawyers to take on the powerful hospital and the well-heeled doctors, so we sought representation on a contingency basis. We knew it would be costly for any attorneys to challenge this hospital and these doctors, so it wasn't easy. But Shealagh and I felt we owed it to Damon to demand accountability for what had happened and to fight for him even after he was gone. We also owed it to our children, Samuel and Miranda, and to ourselves. And we owed it to other children and other parents we did not know because we believed we might prevent future disasters by exposing the responsible parties and their misguided practices.

On Father's Day weekend, I drove Sam to northern Vermont to begin a summer session of circus camp. He'd seen a performance of Circus Smirkus in Oak Bluffs, Massachusetts, and decided it would be cool to join a youth circus. We took a leisurely two days for the drive and wallowed in the motel pool, played basketball, and went to the movies on the way up. It was gratifying to just hang out and be together.

But by Sunday afternoon, our first Father's Day without Damon, Sam and I were both relieved when I dropped him off with his new peers at the camp. In the car driving back on my own, a cascade of emotions suddenly poured out, and I found myself crying and screaming at the top of my lungs, during which time I flew past every vehicle on the road, including a Dodge Charger driven by a Vermont state trooper, who was not too pleased about being overtaken. After the angry trooper warned me to keep my hands on the steering wheel, and after he ran my license and registration through his computer, he seemed to ease up, as if he knew I was not a threat and could smell the tang of sadness and tears suffusing the interior of my car.

"Lots on your mind, huh?" the trooper said. He was a tall, rangy young man.

"Buried my son a little while ago."

He'd heard a lot of lines but he knew this wasn't one. The trooper shook his head. "I couldn't imagine that . . . But you don't want to hurt your family any more, do you? You need to drive more carefully." He handed back my license and let me go.

Miranda insisted on celebrating Father's

Day the next day, a Monday, so as soon I got home from the office, she blindfolded me and led me downstairs to the kitchen, where she had strung a big HAPPY FATHER'S DAY! banner and wrapped lots of tiny presents in pretty paper. There was a handsome table and wineglasses with flower petals on the rims. Miranda gave me a bronze quill pen with a long feather, a tub of ink, and a bound leather notebook.

"Everyone buys you books to read, Dad, but I want you to write one!" She gave me a sweet kiss, then lingered near my face to discover my various imperfections.

Miranda didn't want to go to sleepaway camp like Sam but she took horseback riding lessons daily. She did well, training hard and advancing in dressage and cross-country and jumping. She also mucked out the stables and took younger kids on rides.

Shealagh donated a ton of psychology textbooks to the Salvation Army and washed her hands of her former profession. A gifted craftsperson, she decided to take up furniture restoration, a longtime interest — Damon, among others, had encouraged her to pursue this — and the following year, she decamped to Wales for a renowned summer course in furniture making, specializing in chairs. We converted our garage into a state-

656

of-the-art workshop for her.

In August of that first summer, we settled for several weeks in our country place in the Catskill Park. Sam and Miranda didn't want to sleep alone in the low upstairs bedroom where all three children had stayed for so many years, playing games and listening to Damon's bedtime stories, so their devoted mother became an honorary sibling and slept beside them in Damon's bed.

On Monday, August 8, I was sitting in the one-room writing shack, where Damon would bring me a mug of morning coffee from the main house and signal brunch was imminent — I could hear his high rubber boots scraping across the grass and then the slow creak of the screen door as he knocked politely before he pushed into my lair and his golden smile lit up the whole place as he handed me the steaming coffee, his bright eyes settling on my computer screen or a book on my shelf that he'd ask me about with his warm, inquisitive bird's gaze. On that day, which would've been Damon's seventeenth birthday, I found myself starting to write this memoir about Damon.

It was the one gift I could still give him, and give to the rest of my family. And it was the only place I had left to go for myself, since I could not abide living in a Damon-less world.

I entered my first Olympic triathlon a month later. I knew I was ill prepared but the race had become linked for me with Damon, so there was no backing down. And I had the advantage of knowing I could suffer through anything. The man in the transition area beside me was an Israeli who'd lost his leg in the Lebanon war and competed with a prosthetic limb, which he took off for the swim and strapped back on for the bike and the run.

Our family attended weekly sessions at the Healing Center, a modest Brooklyn facility focused on helping children cope with loss. Sam and Miranda enjoyed going to the Volcano Room to whale away at padded objects. They kept diaries and read from them. Shealagh and I also found solace in our tiny parents' group, no more than four people at one time. We met another woman who'd lost her child after a heart transplant at Columbia under Dr. Mason's care. We did not know the details of her case, but even the Healing Center staff commented on this remarkable coincidence.

In the fall, we found a law firm who felt our case had merit, and in the spring of 2006, a week before the first anniversary of Damon's death — and a month before the first Damon Weber Theater Prize was awarded at Brooklyn Tech in an emotional ceremony attended by a hundred and fifty people — we filed suit against Dr. Mason and New York-Presbyterian Hospital/ Columbia University Medical Center, alleging carelessness, negligence, and malpractice in Damon's death. We also registered a complaint against Dr. Mason with the New York State Department of Health Office of Professional Medical Conduct. I felt, along with the memoir I had started writing about Damon, that I was keeping my promise to my son.

On the first anniversary of Damon's death, we visited his gravesite in Woodlawn Cemetery. My parents, my sister, and several of Damon's friends had paid their respects earlier and left poems and other mementos. Shealagh, Sam, Miranda, and I spent a few heartbreaking hours at the site, planting bright yellow daffodils and arranging colorful marbles on top of his grave, then going off separately to be alone, until none of us could take it anymore, and we left.

We did the same thing the next year, and the year after.

In August 2009, five days before Damon would have turned twenty-one, Amelia Mason, after failing for three years to produce Damon's medical records, testified at her deposition that all of Damon's pre-operative and postoperative clinical records had been shipped to an off-site storage facility and "could not be located despite multiple best efforts." New York-Presbyterian Hospital/Columbia University Medical Center, one of the foremost medical centers in the country, if not in the world, had apparently lost all the most critical medical information pertaining to Damon's heart transplant and the post-transplant infection that killed him.

On Damon's twenty-first birthday, we all visited the cemetery once again.

What do people mean when they talk about a mourning period, or any fixed limit on sorrow and loss, as if it had an expiration date, after which it is no longer valid?

Damon Daniel Weber officially died on March 30, 2005, except no one that you love dies once or ever stops not being alive, and nothing you do can change what happened or bring back what's gone.

Nevertheless, you can still fight — for truth, justice, beauty, memory, love, and the fiercely evolving human future . . .

Damon, three years old and smiling on a wintry January evening, is buttoned up in a snug navy blue and bottle green anorak and a

Thomas the Tank Engine wool hat to match. We're strolling along the southwest perimeter of Prospect Park when a light snow starts to fall. The redheaded child glances up at the sky with his bright blue eyes and puts out his hands to touch the twinkling white confetti. The crystalline particles dissolve in his palms, delicate and wet and vaporous. Delighted, he yanks off his cap so he can feel the glistening snow drops on his hair and his face, raising his beaming gaze skyward. He lets the vanilla fractals tickle his nose.

We're about to tell him to put the cap back on so he won't catch cold, but he's having too much fun, running in circles and chasing the scurrying flakes like elusive white butterflies in a rain forest. Besides, the air is pleasant, almost balmy. And Damon's excitement is contagious. Shealagh and I feel inspired by this sudden burst of animation from our exuberant only child.

Damon is beguiled and transfixed by the miracle of snow. He marvels as the clustering, diamond-shaped flakes settle over the ground and the trees, transforming all around him into an enchanted white playground. He pumps his arms in the air and stamps his feet and begins to dash through the carpeted streets in an ecstatic rampage. He runs and yelps and cavorts, shaking his fists at the sky in a blizzard of joy, a madcap snow dance before the gods of the upper air.

Shealagh and I chase after our son, sprinting to catch up with this dervish, who's whooping and hollering as if there is no tomorrow.

The heavenly firmament is raining down its glittering alabaster treasure, and Damon can't believe this bounty. He wants to touch it and smell it and taste it, but most of all, to celebrate it. He keeps dashing through the streets with giddy, outstretched arms, pounding the snowy asphalt with his little legs and reaching for the fertile sky, as if he could grasp and salute all nature's glory in one great, grinning embrace.

He's the happiest little boy in the world, and his face is filled with wonder at the unfolding and eternal splendor of life.

Grahamsville, NY 8/8/05 — Windsor Terrace, Brooklyn — Isle of Skye, Scotland — The Writers Room, New York City — Truro, Massachusetts — Vegas Diner, Bay Ridge — Delta Airlines — Oak Bluffs, Martha's Vineyard — F train, IRT Line — Grahamsville, NY 8/8/09

AUTHOR'S NOTE

On more than one occasion, Damon — who knew me as well as anyone ever has, and who was rarely off point — would walk up and say, "You should write a children's book, Dad." I always felt vaguely flattered but also a little guilty as, unlike many writers, I'd never even *considered* writing a children's book. Even within our family, my father Robert was the real storyteller and my wife Shealagh the most engaging story reader. So I wasn't sure what to make of my son's idea, which he seemed to repeat with increasing conviction over the years, going so far as to wag his finger and smile at me with his bright-eyed, preternatural wisdom.

"*You* — you should write a children's book, Dad!"

Baffled but intrigued, I resolved that if ever I *did* write a children's book, it would be about Damon in some way.

So now, as I approach my acknowledgments, it strikes me that perhaps *Immortal Bird* is the book Damon meant. It is not a children's book in the traditional sense, but it is about a child and his growth to the verge of young adulthood. It is a book about Damon's life, tragically cut short, and although I labored over it for several years, in one sense it is the most involuntary thing I've ever written. While the material was dauntingly painful and I found myself taking frequent emotional breaks — literally lying down to catch my breath as I waited for the paralyzing anguish to pass — I never experienced a whiff of writer's block or the hesitation or uncertainty that comes from creative impasse. This book *always* had momentum and a sure sense of purpose, and it *always* had Damon's bright spirit and his palpable presence behind it. I knew what I had to do from the start and my son guided and kept me company while I did it, staying with me to the very end.

The son is father to the man, and in this instance, perhaps the real author of the book.

ACKNOWLEDGMENTS

As I stumbled in the darkness following Damon's death, two friends encouraged me to write a book about him. As obvious as that may now seem, then it came to me as a revelation and a lifeline. I wish to thank David Milch, the writer and television producer, and Nancy Milford, the biographer and teacher, for their personal advice during that difficult period.

My first reader was the journalist and author Katherine Eban and she played a key role in steering me to a first-person account. Katherine was an excellent sounding board throughout and revealed herself to be a first-rate editor as well as a kind friend.

Kathy Robbins, the first and only agent I approached with this manuscript, agreed to represent me after reading sixty pages, which changed the whole course of this book. I've never had a literary agent in my corner before — I've published three books and written several others — and it really makes a difference. And no one does it better than Kathy, a dedicated, morally centered professional with an incisive grasp of the creative process and the marketplace. Kathy and two of her agency associates, Rachelle Bergstein and Michael Gillespie, gave me excellent notes and feedback throughout. I thank Rachelle and Mike and predict a great future for them both, and I salute Kathy for her generous spirit, sharp acumen, and tenacious, tough-minded engagement. She is a great agent and a good friend to have.

Among readers of the first draft, I wish to thank my wife Shealagh, my partner in all things Damon, for whom getting through these intensely personal pages took enormous courage; my parents Robert and Helga, who suffered their own deep loss but persevered; my longtime friend David Brumer, always there in every way; Arthur Singer Jr., the Joe DiMaggio of philanthropy, a barometer of intelligence, wise judgment, and good taste; the writer Richard Rhodes, a unique talent, and the psychologist Ginger Rhodes, his sympathetic wife; and Jason Epstein, an early champion, preparer of great feasts, and a legend, who seems either to have been involved in or present at the birth of virtually every important book and publishing development of the last half century.

I also sent the early ms to a dear college friend, the critic and editor Robert Tashman, who was dying at the time from pancreatic cancer. I didn't expect Bob to read it — I'm not sure I wanted him to, it was more a gesture of love — but he took time in his final months to peruse the first section. Bob was unusually positive and complimentary and then added, in that inimitable way dreaded by many well-known writers from his days at *Granta* and *The New York Review of Books:* "But I have some issues." Bob died before he could enumerate them but I know he's up in heaven, waiting to tell me, and I look forward, if I ever get there, to hashing them out with him.

Dr. Paul Marantz and Dr. Joseph Feldschuh, two outstanding physicians with broad knowledge and experience, reviewed the manuscript from a medical perspective. I thank them for their close and careful reading.

Michael Rudell, my literary lawyer, is one of the best-kept secrets around — those of us fortunate enough to work with him all know this — so I'm ambivalent about outing him. In the field of entertainment law, he is, truly, supreme. Michael was an early believer in me, long before this book, and he has provided wise counsel on multiple fronts over many years. I'm grateful to him and pleased to count him among my friends. Neil Rosini, a top attorney who works with Michael, reviewed my manuscript with impressive thoroughness and care.

Jonathan Karp, executive vice president and publisher at Simon & Schuster, responded swiftly to the draft manuscript with an immediate offer, always heartening to an author. A truly gifted and sensitive editor as well as a smart, savvy publisher, he oversees every aspect of production and marketing with a deft hand. Jon still has the look of a boy wonder, but he is a wise and accomplished man with real depth of feeling, and I am grateful for his unstinting support and consideration.

Among Jon's talented and committed team at Simon & Schuster, I'd also like to thank Nicholas Greene, editorial assistant; Loretta Denner, production editor; George Turianski, production manager; Christopher Lin, jacket designer; Jackie Seow, art director; Ruth Lee-Mui, interior designer; Alexis Welby, associate director of publicity; Jessica Abell, marketing coordinator; Marie

Florio, rights manager; and Elisa Rivlin, general counsel.

My thanks also to Louise Quayle, foreign rights director for The Robbins Office.

I wish to salute and thank Judith Donnel, Joseph Miklos, and Joseph Awad of Silberstein, Awad and Miklos for representing us in our lawsuit against New York-Presbyterian/Columbia University Medical Center. For those who question the value of trial lawyers, they give ordinary people without a voice a chance to seek justice and accountability from powerful institutions that might otherwise commit harm with impunity.

I must also acknowledge The Writers Room in New York City, the nation's oldest and largest urban writer's colony, where I've been a member since Damon's birth. I wrote my first books in The Writers Room and although I only managed to slip in for short stints on this manuscript, The Writers Room is a gift to all writers and my spiritual home. Its existence sustains me even when I'm not there, and its light burns 24/7, thanks in no small measure to its dedicated Board and its exceptional executive director, Donna Brodie.

Most of all, I could never have undertaken such a project without the explicit encouragement and support of my family. Shealagh, Sam, and Miranda each agreed they wanted me to tell Damon's story and all generously shared their recollections as best they could. I especially wish to thank Shealagh, for whom reliving these events was unspeakably painful. I incorporated every memory or scene she shared, and I changed anything she asked. Nevertheless, this is a father's memoir, constrained by my experience and perspective, and as such it cannot possibly do justice to Shealagh's extraordinary love for Damon or her unique and amazingly close bond with her son. Rarely has a mother poured so much of herself and so much love into a child, or met with such reciprocal love and adoration. Nor can this memoir fully honor Sam and Miranda's love for their brother and their remarkably deep connection with him. It can only hint at what they all had, and lost.

My wife and children honored the long hours of work and seclusion this book demanded and stood with me in wanting to resurrect Damon for the world. Each, in his or her own way, made sacrifices to help bring this book into being. For all that and more, I am deeply and eternally grateful to my immortal family.

ABOUT THE AUTHOR

Doron Weber was born in Israel, grew up in New York, and was educated at Brown University, the Sorbonne, and Oxford, where he was a Rhodes Scholar. He has worked as a newspaper boy, busboy, waiter, and taxi driver and is the coauthor of three published nonfiction books and various articles. For fifteen years he has directed programs at the Alfred P. Sloan Foundation, a nonprofit institution that supports science, education, and the arts.

The employees of Thorndike Press hope you have enjoyed this Large Print book. All our Thorndike, Wheeler, and Kennebec Large Print titles are designed for easy reading, and all our books are made to last. Other Thorndike Press Large Print books are available at your library, through selected bookstores, or directly from us.

For information about titles, please call:
(800) 223-1244

or visit our Web site at:
http://gale.cengage.com/thorndike

To share your comments, please write:
Publisher
Thorndike Press
10 Water St., Suite 310
Waterville, ME 04901